Mill Level 1 Training Tutorial

To order more books:

Call 1-800-529-5517 or

Visit www.emastercam.com or

Contact your Mastercam dealer

Mastercam X^7 Mill Level 1 Training Tutorial

Software: Mastercam X^7

Author: Mariana Lendel

ISBN: 978-1-926955-76-6

Date: November 1, 2013

Notice

In-House Solutions Inc. reserves the right to make improvements to this manual at any time and without notice.

Disclaimer Of All Warranties And Liability

Copyrights

Trademarks

Table of Contents

MASTERCAM SHORTCUTS

Icon	Function	Keyboard Shortcut	Icon	Function	Keyboard Shortcut
	Analyze entities	F4		Mastercam version, SIM serial number	Alt+V
	AutoSave	Alt+A		Motion controller rotation point	Alt+F12
	C-Hook or user app	Alt+C		Pan	Arrow keys
	Configure Mastercam	Alt+F8		Paste from clipboard	Ctrl+V
	Copy to clipboard	Ctrl+C		Redo an event that has been undone	Ctrl+Y
	Cut to clipboard	Ctrl+X		Regenerate display list	Shift+Ctrl+R
	Delete entities	F5		Repaint	F3
	Drafting global options	Alt+D		Rotate	Alt+Arrow keys
	Exit Mastercam	Alt+F4		Select all	Ctrl+A
	Fit geometry to screen	Alt+F1		Selection grid options	Alt+G
	Gview–Back	Alt+3		Shading on/off	Alt+S
	Gview–Bottom	Alt+4		Show/hide all axes (WCS, Cplane, Tplane)	Alt+F9
	Gview–Front	Alt+2		Show/hide coordinate axes	F9
	Gview–Isometric	Alt+7		Show/hide displayed toolpaths	Alt+T
	Gview–Left	Alt+6		Show/hide Operations Manager pane	Alt+O
	Gview–Previous	Alt+P		Undo the last creation or event	Ctrl+U, Ctrl+Z
	Gview–Right	Alt+5		Unzoom to 80% of original	Alt+F2
	Gview–Top	Alt+1		Unzoom to previous or 50% of original	F2
	Help	Alt+H		Zoom around target point	Ctrl+F1
	Hide entities	Alt+E		Zoom with window selection	F1
	Level Manager	Alt+Z		Zoom/unzoom by 5%	Page Up/Page Down
	Main attributes, set from entity	Alt+X			

Mill Level 1 Training Tutorial

CUSTOMIZE MASTERCAM

Create Your Own Keyboard Shortcuts

+ **Choose Settings > Key Mapping.**

+ Save sets of shortcuts to different key map files (.KMP).

+ Open .kmp files in any text editor.

Change Toolbar Layouts

+ **Choose Settings > Customize.**

+ Name sets of toolbars and save them to different toolbar files (.MTB).

+ Choose **Toolbar States** to hide or display toolbars.

Customize the right-click menu

+ **Choose Settings > Customize > Drop downs/Right mouse button to add your own functions (.MTB file).**

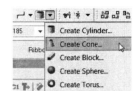

Use drop-down menus

Choose Settings >Customize > Drop downs tab to add dropdown menus to toolbars.

WAYS TO GET THE MOST FROM MASTERCAM

Mastercam Training

In-House Solutions offers unsurpassed industrial training for Mastercam and Robotmaster. We have training facilities in a number of cities across Canada and some of our courses can also be offered onsite, depending on trainer availability. Learn more at **eMastercam.com/store**.

Our library of **Mastercam Training Solutions** consists of several product lines that cater to any learning style. Learn Mastercam at your own pace with our **Training Tutorials**, teach your students with the help of our **Instructor Kits**, learn the theory behind Mastercam with our **Handbooks**, get projects à-la-carte with our **Single Projects**, let our instructors show you best practices with our **Video Training** or go digital with our **eBooks**.

Mastercam Community

eMastercam is the one-stop web resource for Mastercam users. People from all over the world visit the site whether they are teaching, learning or working with Mastercam daily. Members can post questions, comments or share projects and success stories. Visit eMastercam.com and sign up for your free account today!

For downloaded pdf please visit

www.emastercam.com/qrc

Tutorial	Geometry Functions	Surface and Toolpath Creation
#1	Create Rectangle. Create Parallel Lines. Create Circle Center Point. Xform Translate.	Open Contour Toolpath. Drill Toolpath.
#2	Create Rectangle. Create Chamfer. Create Circle Center Point. Create Polar Arc Xform Mirror. Join Entities.	Facing Toolpath. Circle Mill Toolpath. Contour Toolpath. Spot Drill Toolpath. Drill Toolpath. 2D Contour (Chamfer Toolpath).
#3	Create Rectangle. Create two Polygon. Create Fillets. Create Circle Center Point. Create Line Endpoint- Vertical Edit Trim Divide. Create Rectangular Shapes.	Setup 1 Slot Mill Toolpath. 2D HS Dynamic Core Mill Toolpath. Contour Toolpath. 2D HS Dynamic Contour Toolpath. Setup 2 Facing Toolpaths.
#4	Create Polar Arcs. Create Circle Center Point. Create Line Tangent. Create Fillet. Xform Mirror. Create Arc Tangent to Two Entities. Edit Trim 3 Entities. Create Ellipse. Xform Offset. Create Letters. Create Boundig Box. Xform Translate.	2D High Speed Core Mill Toolpath. 2D High Speed Dynamic Core. Pocket with Island Toolpath. Pocket Remachine Toolpath.

Tutorial	Geometry Functions	Surface and Toolpath Creation
#5	Create Circle Center Points. Create Line Tangent. Xform Mirror. Create Arc Tangent. Create Arc Polar. Edit Trim. Create Fillets. Xform Rotate. Xform Translate.	Setup 1 2D High Speed Area Mill Toolpath. 2D High Speed Dynamic Area Mill Toolpath. Transform Toolpath. Drill Toolpath. Circle Mill Toolpath. Contour (Chamfer Toolpath). Setup 2 2D High Speed Dynamic Area Mill Toolpath.
#6	Top Construction Plane. Create Rectangle. Create Rectangular Shapes. Create Line Parallel. Create Arc Tangent. Create Arc Endpoints. Xform Translate. Create Circle Center Point. Front Construction Plane. Create Circle Center Point. Left Construction Plane. Create Rectangulat Shape.	Setup 1- Top Tool Planes. 2D HS Area Mill toolpath. 2D High Speed Rest toolpath. Setup 2 - Front Tool Plane. Drill Toolpath. Setup 3 - Left Tool Plane. Slot Mill Toolpath.
#7	Create Rectangle. Create Circle Center Point. Create arc Tangent to 1 Entity. Create Line Parallel. Create Chamfer. Create Line Polar. Edit Trim.	2D HS Dynamic Core Mill Toolpath. 2D HS Core Mill Toolpath. 2D HS Blend Mill Toolpath. 2D HS Peel Mill Toolpath.
#8	Download a SolidWorks file from www.emastercam.com. Open the file keeping the associativity to SolidWorks.	Feature Based Drilling (FBD) toolpath.

Tutorial	Geometry Functions	Surface and Toolpath Creation
#9	Create wireframe geometry: Create Circle Center Point. Create Line Tangent. Create Line Parallel. Create Rectangular Shapes. Create Fillet Chain. Create a solid geometry: Solids Extrude.	Feature Based Milling toolpath. Feature Based Drilling Toolpath.
#10	Download the file from www.emastercam.com. Create a New View. Xform Translate 3D. Delete Duplicates. Edit Trim Two Entities.	Setup 1 2D HS Dynamic Area Mill Toolpath. 2D HS Dynamic Rest Mill Toolpath. Setup 2 2D HS Dynamic Core Mill Toolpath. 2D HS Dynamic Contour Toolpath.

GETTING STARTED

Objectives:

✓ Starting Mastercam
✓ The Student will learn about the Graphical User Interface.
✓ The Student will learn how to navigate through Mastercam.
✓ How to use the Status Bar to set the attributes.
✓ Set the Toolbar States.
✓ Setting the Grid.

STEP 1: STARTING MASTERCAM

1.1 Enable the Unified Backplot/Verify System

> **NOTE:** To be able to follow this tutorial you will need to enable the Unified Backplot /Verify System. The change has to be done in Mastercam Advanced Configuration as shown in this step.

- Select the **Start** button.
- Select **All Programs** and click on **Mastercam X7** as shown.
- Select **Utilities** as shown.

- Select **Advanced Configuration** as shown.

> **NOTE:** If you are running **Windows 8**, from the **Start** page, right mouse click and in the lower right corner click on the **All Aps** icon. Under **Mastercam X7** select **Advanced Configuration**.

◆ Make sure that **Mastercam X7** version is selected as shown.
◆ Select **Backplot** from the list and set the **Classic Backplot** to **Disable**.

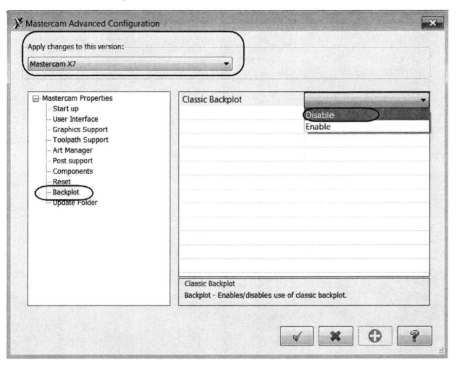

◆ Select the **Apply** button to apply the changes.
◆ Select the **OK** button to exit. ✔

1.2 Start Mastercam X7

◆ To start the software, from Desktop, click on the shortcut icon as shown.

STEP 2: GUI - GRAPHICAL USER INTERFACE

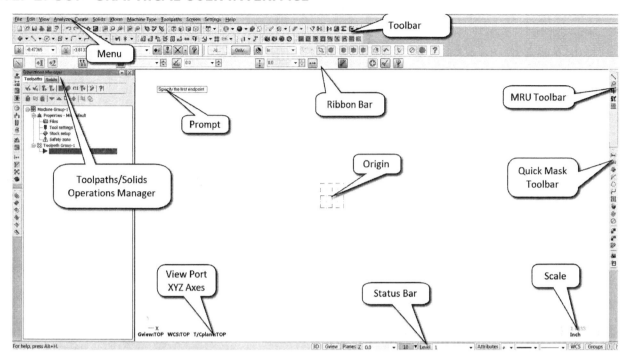

Menu	Allows you to select all the functions in Mastercam to create geometry and toolpaths.
Toolbars	Can be used instead of the menu to create geometry and toolpaths.
Ribbon Bar	Allows you to enter the values and settings that define the entities that you are currently creating or modifying.
Function prompt	Prompts the user for info.
Status Bar	Allows you to set the attributes (color, level, style, and width) and the View/Plane and Z depth currently used.
Toolpaths/Solid Manager	Lists the history of the toolpath operations and solids.
Origin	Geometry origin from which the system measures the point coordinates in X,Y and Z axes in the current plane.
Graphic Area	Workspace area in Mastercam where the geometry displays.
MRU Toolbar	Lists the most recently used functions.
Quick Mask Toolbar	Lets you select all entities of a specific type.
Scale	Shows you a scale of the object on the screen.
View Port XYZ Axes	Inform you which Graphics view, WCS and Toolplane/Construction plane you are working in.

STEP 3: NAVIGATE THROUGH MASTERCAM

In this step you will learn how to use the menu functions in Mastercam to create geometry.

3.1 Using the Menu to select the command Create Line Endpoint

- Left click on **Create.**
- Move the cursor on the drop-down menu to the **Line** function. This will open a flyout menu with all the commands related to create lines.
- Left-click on the desired command Endpoint as shown in <u>Figure: 3.1.1</u>.

Figure: 3.1.1

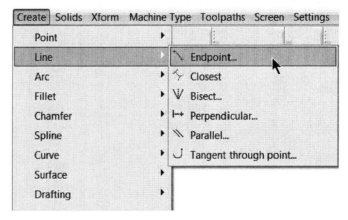

3.2 Using the Toolbars to select the command Create Line Endpoint

- Left Click on the **Create Line Endpoint** command icon as shown in <u>Figure: 3.2.1</u>.

Figure: 3.2.1

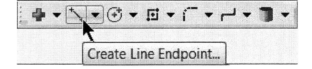

◆ To see the commands which are found under Create Line, in the menu bar choose the drop down arrow to the right of the icon as shown.

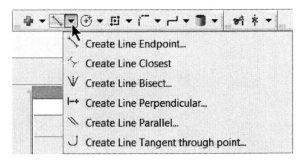

3.3 Reorganizing the Toolbars

NOTE: Mastercam is fully customizable meaning you can move the toolbars anywhere you desire allowing you to work more efficiently.

◆ To move a toolbar select the left vertical line in front of the toolbar and drag it to the desired location on the screen as shown in <u>Figure: 3.3.1</u>.

Figure: 3.3.1

NOTE: To customize the toolbars please see the General Notes.

3.4 Create Line Endpoint Ribbon Bar example

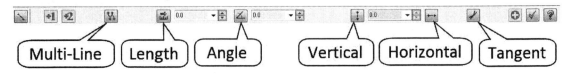

◆ To create a line left click on the screen. Then enter the distance and angle if necessary.

◆ To continue making lines choose the **Apply** ⊕ button from the ribbon bar or press enter. To exit the current command select the **OK** ✔ button or press the **Esc** button.

◆ To undo the last command use the **Undo** button. ↺ The Undo button can be used to go back to the beginning of geometry creation or to the last point of the saved file. Mastercam also has a **Redo** button ↻ for your convenience.

3.5 Function Prompt

- Prompts the user to execute a command.
- For example this prompt is used in the **Create Line Endpoint** command as shown in <u>Figure: 3.5.1</u>.

Figure: 3.5.1

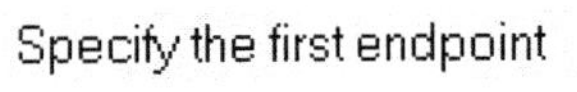

Specify the first endpoint

3.6 Status Bar

- The Status bar seen in <u>Figure: 3.6.1</u> is used to set the drawing attributes, view, plane, Z depth and construction mode.

Figure: 3.6.1

| 3D | Gview | Planes | Z | 0.0 | ▼ | 10 | ▼ | Level | 1 | ▼ | Attributes | + | ▼ | —— | ▼ | —— | ▼ | WCS | Groups | ! | ? |

2D / 3D Construction	Toggles between 2D and 3D construction modes. In 2D mode all geometry is created parallel to the current Cplane at the current system Z depth. In 3D mode you can work freely in various Z depths, unconstrained by the current system Z depth and Cplane setting.
Gview	Sets the graphics view which you will view your geometry from. You can choose a different standard Gview, an existing named view, create a new named view or set the Gview to the current Cplane.
Planes	Sets the construction plane in which you create and manipulate your geometry. You can change the current plane by selecting a different standard plane, selecting an existing named view, creating a new named view and by setting the plane to equal the current Gview.
Z Depth	Sets the current construction depth. To set this click the drop down arrow and pick one from the most recently used list or click the **Z:** label and pick a point in the graphics window to use the Z depth values based on the selected entity.
Color	Assigns the current color. To change the current color click in the color field and select a colour from the colour pallet.
Level	Sets the main level you want to work with in the graphics window. To change the current working level type the level number in the box or select the level using one of the following methods.
Attributes	Lets you change one or more drawing attributes.
Point Style	Displays and sets the systems point style.
Line Style	Shows and sets the system line style.
Line Width	Displays and sets the current system line width.

Work Coordinate System (WCS)	Allows you to redefine the WCS. You can choose from a list of stand views, specify origin coordinates, access the view manager or use the named function to access the view selection dialog box.
Groups	Defines a collection of entities or operations that can be manipulated as a single entity.

3.7 Change the Current System Colour

◆ Left Click on **System Color** as shown.

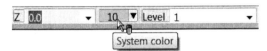

◆ Select the desired color from the dialog box as shown in Figure: 3.7.1.

Figure: 3.7.1

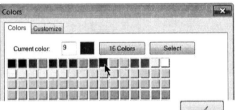

◆ Select the **OK** button to exit the command and begin creating geometry in the color of your choice.

NOTE: Any geometry on your screen will remain in the previous system colour. This change will only affect the geometry you create going forward.

3.8 The Toolpath Manager

- The **Toolpath Manger** displays all the operations for the current part.
- You can sort, edit, regenerate, verify and post any operations.
- For more information on the **Toolpath Manager**, please refer to **General Notes**.
- The Manger can be hidden to gain more space in the graphics area for creating geometry. Press **Alt + O** to hide the manager and **Alt + O** to reopen the manager as shown in Figure: 3.8.1.

Figure: 3.8.1

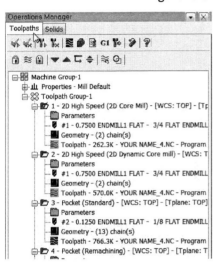

STEP 4: SETTING THE TOOLBAR STATES

♦ Before starting the geometry creation we should customize the toolbars to see the toolbars required to create the geometry and machine a 2D part.

Settings

♦ Toolbar States as shown.

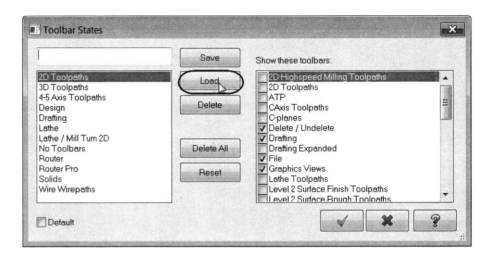

Mill Level 1 Training Tutorial

Mastercam. X⁷

- From the left column select **2D Toolpaths**.
- Choose the **Load** button as shown in Figure: 4.0.1.

Figure: 4.0.1

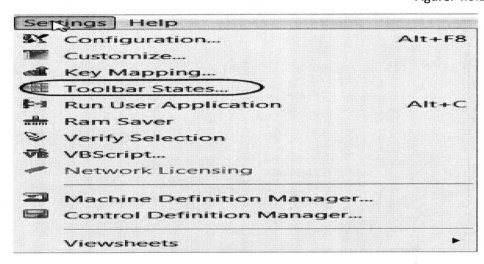

- Select the **OK** button to accept the toolbar states.
- The 2D Toolpaths icons will be displayed to the left of the **Operations Manager** as shown in Figure: 4.0.2.

Figure: 4.0.2

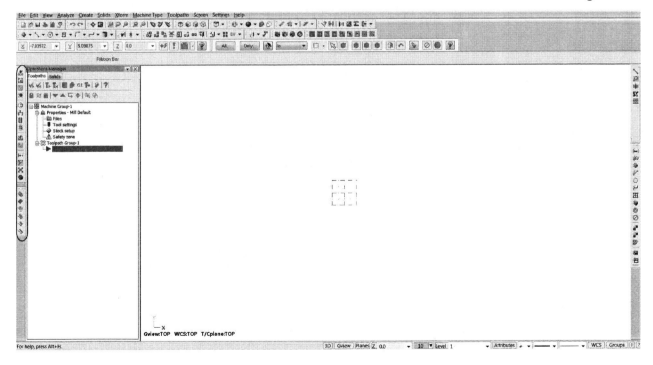

STEP 5: SETTING THE GRID

* Before beginning to create geometry you will enable the **Grid**. This will show you where the origin is.

Settings
* X Configuration.
* Select **Screen** from the configuration **Topics.**
* Select the plus sign (+) beside screen as shown in <u>Figure: 5.0.1</u>.

Figure: 5.0.1

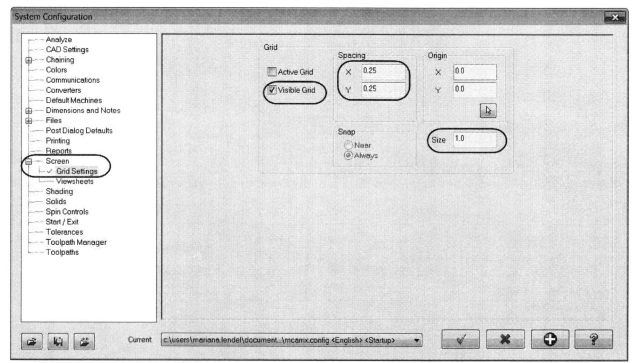

* In **Grid Settings** enable **Visible Grid** and change the **Spacing** to **X = 0.25** and **Y = 0.25**.
* Set the **Size** to **1.0**.

* Choose the **OK** button to exit.
* Select **Yes** to save the setting as shown.

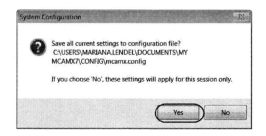

Mill Level 1 Training Tutorial *Mastercam.* X⁷

♦ The grid will appear on your screen as shown in <u>Figure: 5.0.2</u>.

Figure: 5.0.2

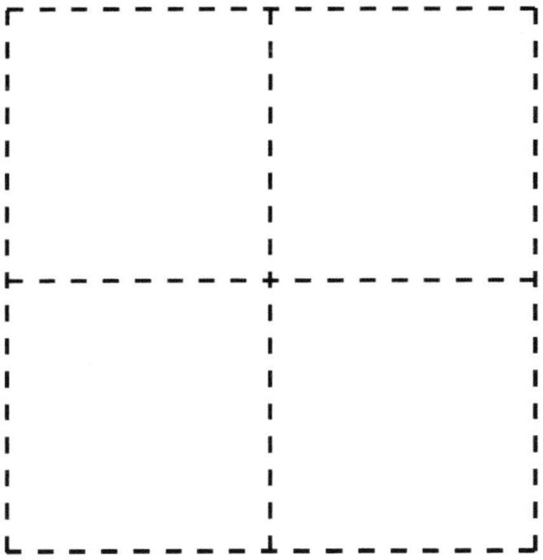

Mill Level 1 Training Tutorial

TUTORIAL #1

OVERVIEW OF THE STEPS TAKEN TO CREATE THE FINAL PART:

From Drawing to CAD Model:
- The student should examine the drawing on the following page to understand what part is being created in the tutorial.
- From the drawing we can decide how to go about creating the geometry in Mastercam.

Create the 2D CAD Model used to generate Toolpaths from:
- The student will create the Top 2D geometry needed to create the toolpaths.
- Geometry creation commands such as create rectangle, line parallel, circle center point and translate will be used.

Create the necessary Toolpaths to machine the part:
- The student will set up the stock size to be used and the clamping method used.
- An Open Contour toolpath will be created to remove the material on the both steps.
- A Drilling toolpath will be created to machine the through holes.

Backplot and Verify the file:
- The Backplot will be used to simulate a step by step process of the tool's movements.
- The Verify will be used to watch a tool machine the part out of a solid model.

Post Process the file to generate the G-code:
- The Student will then post process the file to obtain an NC file containing the necessary code for the machine.

 This tutorial takes approximately one hour to complete.

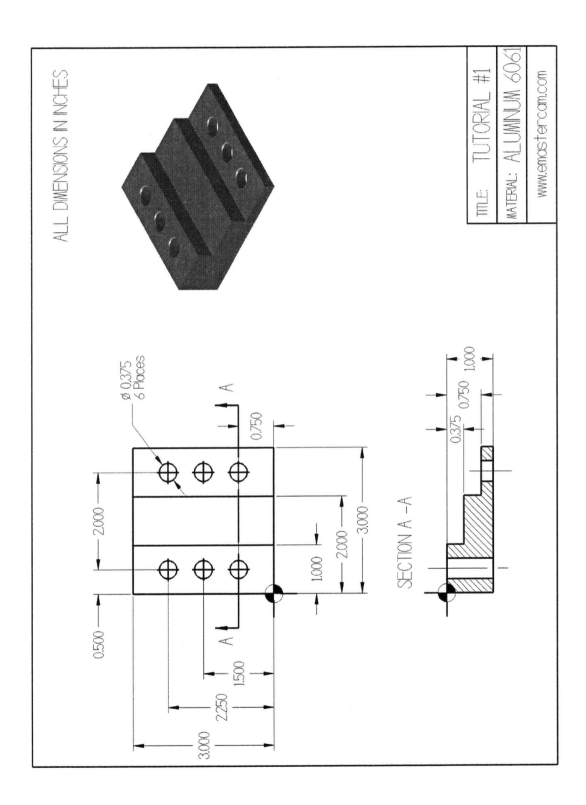

ALL DIMENSIONS IN INCHES

TITLE: TUTORIAL #1

MATERIAL: ALUMINUM 6061

www.emastercam.com

Ø 0.375
6 Places

0.750

2.000

3.000

2.000

1.000

0.500

1.500

2.250

3.000

A

A

SECTION A – A

0.375
0.750
1.000

GEOMETRY CREATION

STEP 1: SETTING UP THE GRAPHIC USER INTERFACE

Please refer to the **Getting Started** section to set up the graphics user interface.

STEP 2: CREATE A RECTANGLE

In this step you will learn how to create a rectangle knowing the width, the height and the anchor position.

Step Preview:

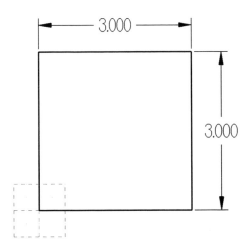

2.1 Create a 3.0" by 3.0" Rectangle

Create

♦  **Rectangle.**

♦ Enter the **Width** ⬚ and **Height** ⬚ as shown.

| | 3.0 | ▼ ⬚ | | 3.0 | ▼ ⬚ | ⊞ | ⊞ | ⊕ | ✓ | ? |

♦ Press **Enter** after typing the values to see a preview of the rectangle.

Mastercam. X⁷

◆ [Select position of first corner]: Select the **Origin** as shown in <u>Figure: 2.1.1</u>.

Figure: 2.1.1

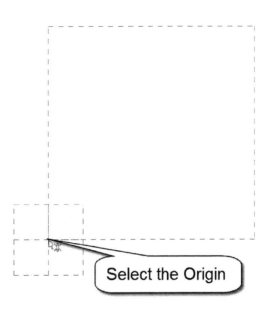

Select the Origin

◆ Make sure that when selecting the origin, the visual cue of the cursor changes as shown.

◆ Select the **OK** button to exit the **Rectangle** command.

◆ Use the **Fit** icon to fit the drawing to the screen.

NOTE: During the geometry creation of this tutorial, if you make a mistake you can undo the last step using the **Undo** icon. You can undo as many steps as needed. If you delete or undo a step by mistake, just use the **Redo** icon. To delete unwanted geometry, select it first and then press **Delete** from the keyboard.

STEP 3: CREATE THE PARALLEL LINES

In this step you will learn how to create parallel lines knowing the distance between them.

Step Preview:

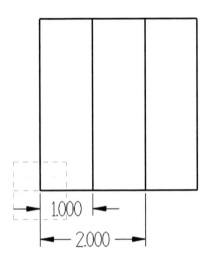

Create
* **Line.**
* 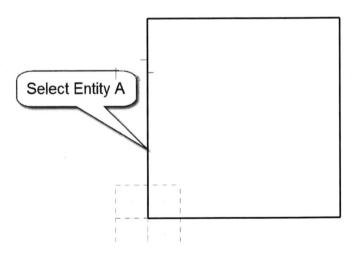 **Parallel.**
* [Select a line]: Select **Entity A** as shown in Figure: 3.0.1.

Figure: 3.0.1

◆ [Select the point to place a parallel line through]: Pick a point to the right at the selected line.

NOTE: The color of the geometry is cyan which means that the entity is "live" and you can still change the line parameters if needed.

◆ Enter the **Distance** ⊬ **1.0"** (press **Enter**).

NOTE: To continue using the same command you can either select the **Apply** button ⊕ or press **Enter**. To exit the command you can either start a new command or select the **OK** button. ☑

◆ Press **Enter** again to continue in the same command.
◆ [Select a line]: Select **Entity A** as shown in Figure: 3.0.2.

Figure: 3.0.2

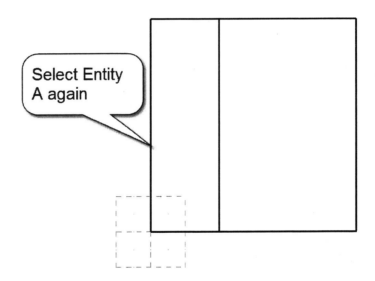

Select Entity A again

◆ [Select the point to place a parallel line through]: Pick a point to the right at the selected line.

◆ Enter the **Distance** ⊬ **2.0"** (press **Enter**).

◆ Select the **OK** button to exit the command. ☑

◆ The part will appear as shown in <u>Figure: 3.0.3</u>.

Figure: 3.0.3

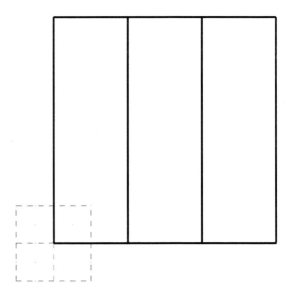

Mastercam. X⁷

STEP 4: CREATE CIRCLES

In this step you will create circles which will later be used to drill holes in the part.

Step Preview:

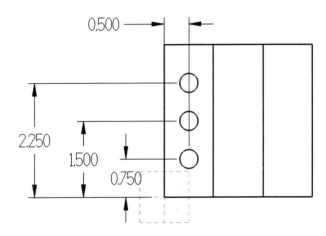

Create

* **Arc.**

*  **Circle Center Point.**

* Input a **Diameter** of **0.375** in the ribbon bar and then select the icon to lock the value.

* Select the **Fast Point** icon from the **AutoCursor Ribbon Bar.**
* Enter the dimensions **0.5, 0.75**as shown, then hit **Enter** on your keyboard.

* Select the **Fast Point** again.
* Enter the dimensions **0.5, 1.5** and hit **Enter** on the keyboard once again.

* Select the **Fast Point** again.
* Enter the dimensions **0.5, 2.25** and hit **Enter** on your keyboard once again.

* Once complete choose the **OK** button to exit the command.

STEP 5: TRANSLATE/COPY THE CIRCLES

In this step you will learn how to use Translate command to copy the circles knowing the distance along X axis.

Step Preview:

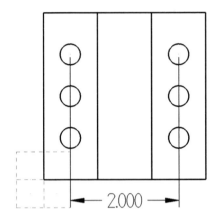

Xform

♦ **Translate.**

♦ Translate: select entities to translate]: Select the three circles as shown in <u>Figure: 5.0.1</u>.

Figure: 5.0.1

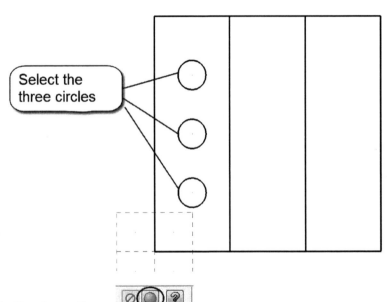

♦ Press **Enter** or select the **End Selection** button to continue.

• In the **Translate** dialog box, make sure that **Copy** is enabled and enter **2.0** in the **Delta X** as shown in Figure: 5.0.2.

Figure: 5.0.2

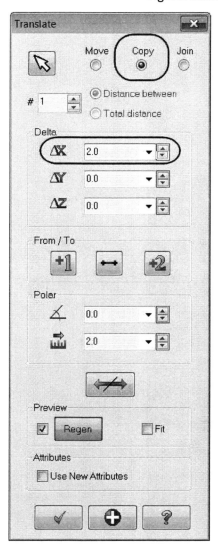

The geometry should look as shown.

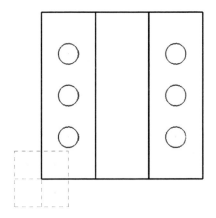

• Select the **OK** button to exit **Translate** dialog box.

NOTE: When performing a transform function (**Xform**), Mastercam creates a temporary group from the originals (red) and a result (purple) from the transformed entities. However, they stay in effect only until you use the **Screen**, **Clear Colors** function or perform another transform function.

Screen

• Clear Color.

STEP 6: SAVE THE FILE

File

• Save As.
• File name: "Your Name_1".

TOOLPATH CREATION

SUGGESTED FIXTURE:

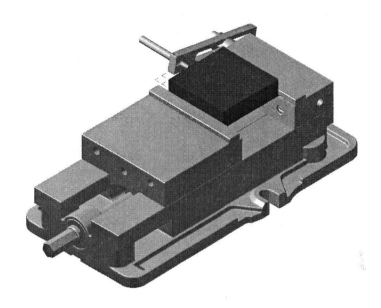

SETUP SHEET:

TOOL LIST

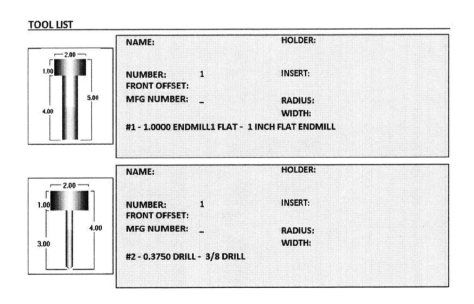

NAME:	HOLDER:
NUMBER: 1	INSERT:
FRONT OFFSET:	
MFG NUMBER: _	RADIUS:
	WIDTH:

#1 - 1.0000 ENDMILL1 FLAT - 1 INCH FLAT ENDMILL

NAME:	HOLDER:
NUMBER: 1	INSERT:
FRONT OFFSET:	
MFG NUMBER: _	RADIUS:
	WIDTH:

#2 - 0.3750 DRILL - 3/8 DRILL

STEP 7: SELECT THE MACHINE AND SET UP THE STOCK

In Mastercam, you select a **Machine Definition** before creating any toolpaths. The **Machine Definition** is a model of your machines capabilities and features. It acts like a template for setting up your machine. The machine definition ties together three main components: The schematic model of your machines components, the control definition that models your control capabilities, and the post processor that will generate the required machine code (G-code). For a Mill Level 1 exercise (2D toolpaths) we need just a basic machine definition.

> **NOTE:** For the purpose of this tutorial, we will be using the **Default mill** machine.

* To display the **Operations Manager** press **Alt + O**.

* Use the **Fit** icon to fit the drawing to the screen.

Machine type
* **Mill.**
* **Default.**

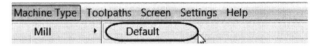

* Select the **OK** button to exit **Machine Definition Menu Management.**
* Select the plus sign in front of **Properties** in the **Toolpaths Manager** to expand the **Toolpaths Group Properties.**

Select the Plus sign

* Select the **Tool Settings** to set the tool parameters.

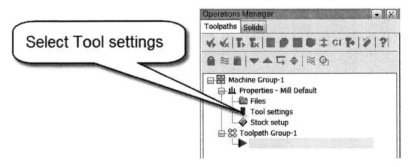

Select Tool settings

• Change the parameters to match <u>Figure: 7.0.1</u>.

Figure: 7.0.1

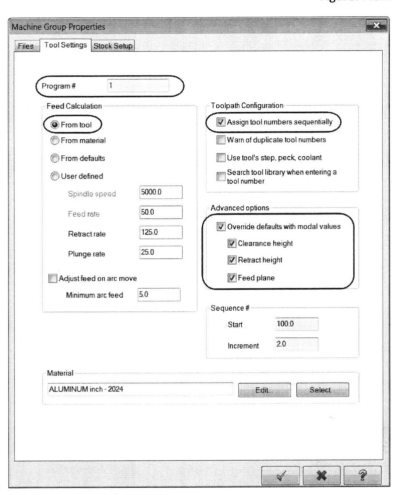

Program # is used to enter a number if your machine tool requires a number for a program name.

Assign tool numbers sequentially allows you to overwrite the tool number from the library with the next available tool number. (First operation   tool number 1; Second operation tool number 2, etc.)

Warn of duplicate tool numbers allows you to get a warning if you enter two tools with the same number.

Override defaults with modal values enables the system to keep the values that you enter.

Feed Calculation set **From tool** uses feed rate, plunge rate, retract rate and spindle speed from the tool definition.

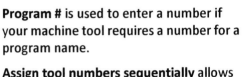

- Select the **Stock setup** tab to define the stock.
- Set the stock shape to **Rectangular** if needed and enter the stock dimensions as shown in <u>Figure: 7.0.2</u>.

Figure: 7.0.2

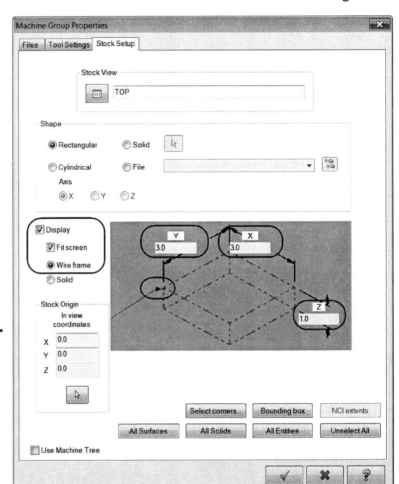

The **Stock Origin** values adjust the positioning of the stock, ensuring that you have equal amount of extra stock around the finished part.

Display options allow you to set the stock as **Wireframe** and to fit the stock to the screen. (Fit Screen)

NOTE: The **stock** model that you create can be displayed with the part geometry when viewing the file or the toolpaths, during backplot, or while verifying toolpaths. In the graphics, the arrow shows you where the stock origin is. The default position is the middle of the stock. Click on the corner of the part to set it as the stock origin.

- Select the **OK** button to exit **Machine Group Properties**.
- Select the **Isometric** view from the graphics view toolbar to see the stock.
- Use the **Fit** icon to fit the drawing to the screen.

◆ The stock model will appear as shown.

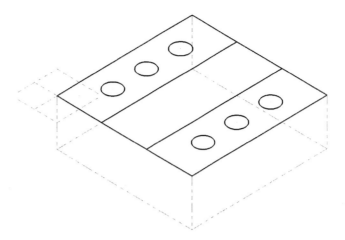

> **NOTE:** The stock is not geometry and can not be selected.

◆ Select the **Top** view from the view toolbar to see the part from the top.

STEP 8: MACHINE THE 0.375"STEP USING OPEN CONTOUR TOOLPATH

Contour toolpaths remove the material along a path defined by a chain of curves. Contour toolpaths only follows a chain; they do not clean out an enclosed area.

Toolpath Preview:

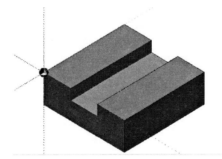

8.1 Chain Selection

A **Chain Of Entities** consists of one or more entities linked together in order and direction. The distance between the endpoints of two consecutive entities of the chain has to be equal or less than the chaining tolerance (0.0001"). In an open chain, the start point is placed at the end of the chain closest to the selection point and the chain direction points to the opposite end of the chain. See the **User Notes** chapter for more information on chaining.

Toolpaths

- **Contour.**

- If a prompt appears to **Enter new NC name**, select the **OK** button to accept the default.

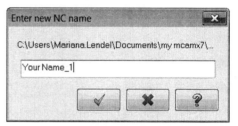

- Make sure that the **Chain** button in the **Chaining** dialog box is enabled as shown to be able to select the contour.

• Select the first chain as shown in <u>Figure: 8.1.1</u>.

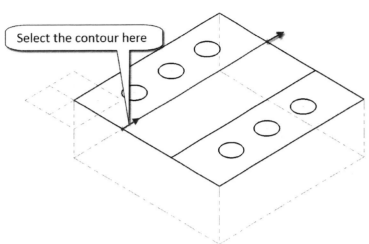

Select the contour here

NOTE: The direction of the chain determines the cutter compensation side (Left or Right) to orient the tool on the proper side of the geometry. For our example be sure to chain the contour in a **CW** direction. Otherwise, select the **Reverse** button.

• Select the **OK** button to exit **Chaining**.
• In the **Toolpath Type** page, the **Contour** icon will be selected.

Contour   Pocket   Facing   Slot Mill

NOTE: Mastercam updates the pages as you modify them and then marks them, in the **Tree view list,** with a green check mark. Pages that are not changed are marked with a red circle and slash.

8.2 Select a 1.0" Flat Endmill from the library and set the Tool Parameters

♦ Select **Tool** from the **Tree view list**.

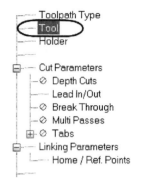

♦ Click on the **Select library tool** button.
♦ To be able to see all the tools from the library disable **Filter Active**.

♦ Scroll down and select the **1.0" Flat Endmill** (# 243) as shown.

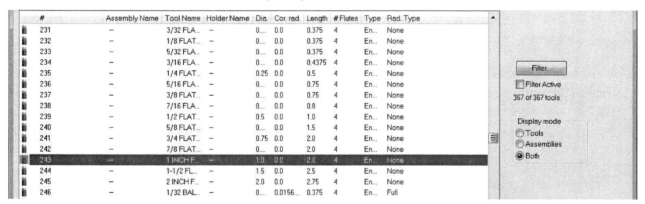

#	Assembly Name	Tool Name	Holder Name	Dia.	Cor. rad.	Length	# Flutes	Type	Rad. Type
231	–	3/32 FLA...	–	0...	0.0	0.375	4	En...	None
232	–	1/8 FLAT...	–	0...	0.0	0.375	4	En...	None
233	–	5/32 FLA...	–	0...	0.0	0.375	4	En...	None
234	–	3/16 FLA...	–	0...	0.0	0.4375	4	En...	None
235	–	1/4 FLAT...	–	0.25	0.0	0.5	4	En...	None
236	–	5/16 FLA...	–	0...	0.0	0.75	4	En...	None
237	–	3/8 FLAT...	–	0...	0.0	0.75	4	En...	None
238	–	7/16 FLA...	–	0...	0.0	0.8	4	En...	None
239	–	1/2 FLAT...	–	0.5	0.0	1.0	4	En...	None
240	–	5/8 FLA...	–	0...	0.0	1.5	4	En...	None
241	–	3/4 FLAT...	–	0.75	0.0	2.0	4	En...	None
242	–	7/8 FLAT...	–	0...	0.0	2.0	4	En...	None
243	–	1 INCH F...	–	1.0	0.0	2.0	4	En...	None
244	–	1-1/2 FL...	–	1.5	0.0	2.5	4	En...	None
245	–	2 INCH F...	–	2.0	0.0	2.75	4	En...	None
246	–	1/32 BAL...	–	0...	0.0156...	0.375	4	En...	Full

♦ Select the tool in the **Tool Selection** page and then select the **OK** button to exit.

♦ Make all the necessary changes as shown in <u>Figure: 8.2.1</u>.

Figure: 8.2.1

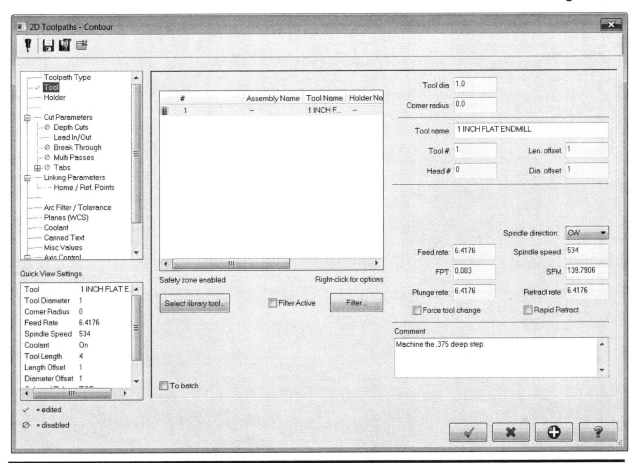

The **Feed rate**, **Plunge rate**, **Retract rate** and **Spindle speed** are selected from tool definition. You may change these values as per your part material and tools.

In the **Comment** field enter a comment to help identify the toolpath in the **Toolpaths/Operations Manager** such as the one shown above.

8.3 Set the Cut Parameters

• From the **Tree view list**, select **Cut Parameters** and make the changes as shown in <u>Figure: 8.3.1</u>.

Figure: 8.3.1

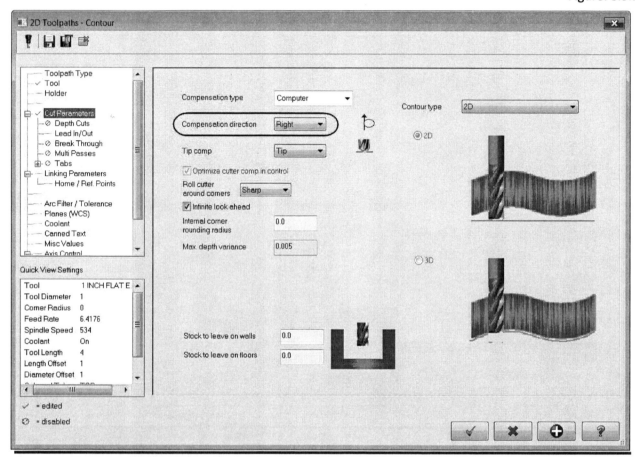

Compensation type set to **Computer** allows Mastercam to compensate the toolpath based on the tool diameter and does not output G41/G42 in the code.

Compensation direction set to **Right** compensates the toolpath to the right of the chain based on the chaining direction. See the<u>Figure: 8.3.2</u>.

Roll cutter around corners set to **Sharp** inserts arc moves around corners in the toolpath. The radius of the arc moves is equal with the radius of the tool.

Infinite look ahead prevents the toolpath from crossing itself (fish tail).

Figure: 8.3.2

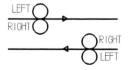

8.4 Set the Lead In/Out

- From the **Tree view list**, select **Lead in/out** and change the parameters as shown.
- Make sure that you disable the **Entry** and the **Exit** options and enable **Adjust start/end of contour** as shown in Figure: 8.4.1.

Figure: 8.4.1

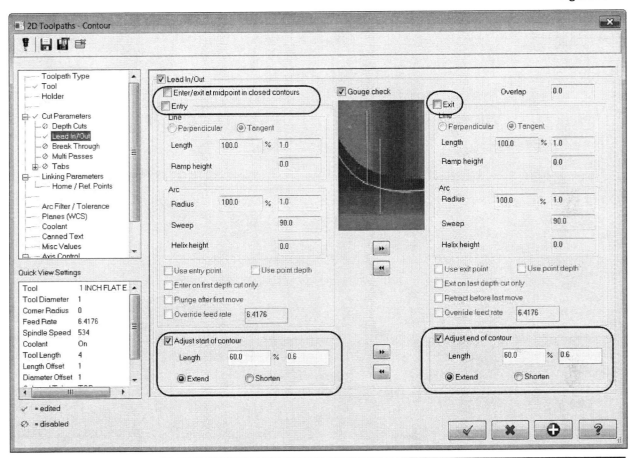

Lead In/Out allows you to select a combination of a **Line** and an **Arc** at the beginning and/or end of the contour toolpath for a smooth entry/exit while cutting the part.

Adjust start/end of contour moves the starting/ending position in open contours by adding (Extend) or removing (Shorten) the specified length.

8.5 Set the Linking Parameters

♦ From the **Tree view list**, select **Linking Parameters** and change the parameters as shown <u>Figure: 8.5.1</u>.

Figure: 8.5.1

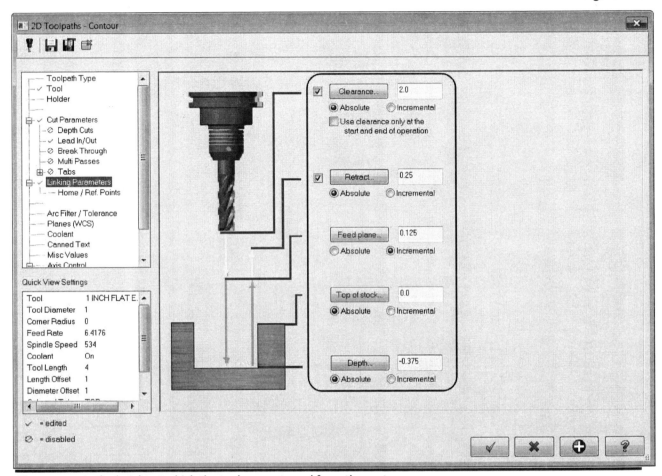

Clearance sets the height at which the tool moves to and from the part.

Retract sets the height that the tool moves up to before the next tool pass.

Feed Plane sets the height that the tool rapids to before changing to the plunge rate to enter the part.

Top of stock sets the height of the material in the Z axis.

Depth determines the final machining depth that the tool descends into the stock.

♦ Select the **OK** button to exit the contour parameters.

Mill Level 1 Training Tutorial   *Mastercam.* X^7

STEP 9: BACKPLOT THE TOOLPATHS

Backplotting shows the path the tools take to cut the part. This display lets you spot errors in the program before you machine the part. As you backplot toolpaths, Mastercam displays additional information such as the X, Y, and Z coordinates, the path length , the minimum and maximum coordinates and the cycle time. It also shows any collisions between the workpiece and the tool.

◆ From **Toolpaths Operations Manager**, select the **Backplot/Verify Options** buttton as shown.

◆ To use the stock information from the **Job Setup,** click on the **Stock Setup** to enabled it as shown.

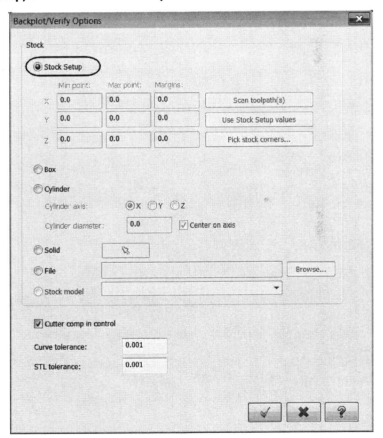

◆ Select the **OK** button to exit **Backplot/Verify Options**.

- From **Toolpaths Operations Manager**, make sure that the toolpath is selected (signified by the green check mark on the folder icon).
- Select the **Backplot** selected operations button.

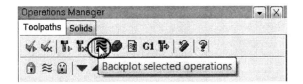

> NOTE: Mastercam launches a new window that allows you to check the part using **Backplot** or **Verify**.

- Select the **Backplot** tab and have the following settings enabled as shown.

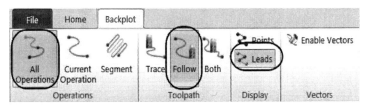

- Select the **Home** tab and make sure that you have the following settings on as shown.

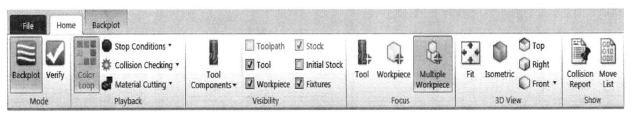

- To see the part from an **Isometric** view select the **Isometric** icon. Isometric

- To fit the workpiece to the screen, select the **Fit** icon.   Fit

- You can step through the **Backplot** by using the **Step forward** ▶▶ or **Step back** ◀◀ buttons.

- You can adjust the speed of the backplot.   Speed: ▬▬▬

◆ Select the **Play** button in the **VCR** bar to run **Backplot**.

◆ The toolpath should look as shown <u>Figure: 9.0.1</u>.

Figure: 9.0.1

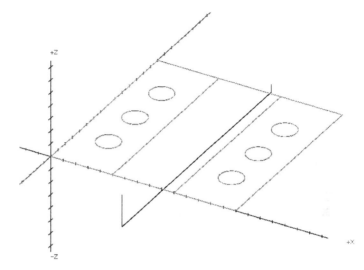

STEP 10: SIMULATE THE TOOLPATH IN VERIFY

Verify Mode shows the path the tools take to cut the part with material removal. This display lets you spot errors in the program before you machine the part. As you verify toolpaths, Mastercam displays additional information such as the X, Y, and Z coordinates, the path length , the minimum and maximum coordinates and the cycle time. It also shows any collisions between the workpiece and the tool.

♦ From **Mastercam Backplot Home** tab, switch to **Verify** and change the settings for the **Visibility** and **Focus** as shown in Figure: 10.0.1.

Figure: 10.0.1

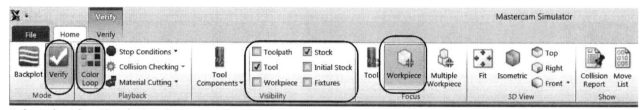

♦ Select the **Play Simulation** button in the **VCR** bar to run **Verify**.

♦ The part should look as shown in Figure: 10.0.2.

Figure: 10.0.2

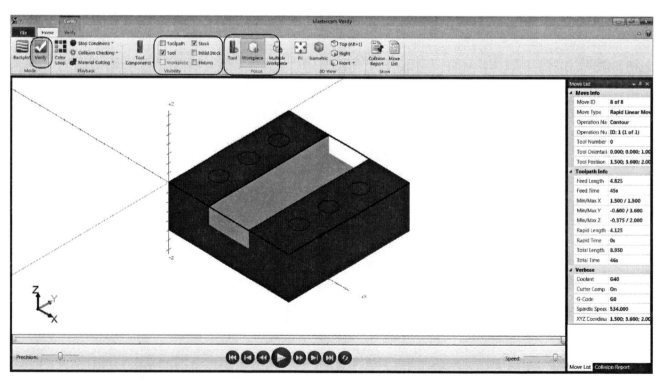

Mastercam. X⁷

NOTE: To rotate the part, move the cursor to the center of the part and click and hold the mouse wheel and slowly move it in one direction.

To **Zoom In** or **Out** hold down the mouse wheel and scroll up or down as needed.

• Click on the **Isometric** icon  and then the **Fit** icon to see the part in the original position if needed.

• To check the part step by step, click first on the **Start** icon.

• Click on the **Step Forward** to see the tool moving one step at a time.

• The part should look as shown after several steps.

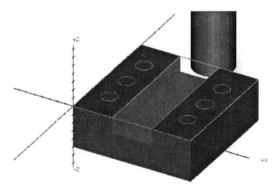

• Click on the **Step Forward** until the toolpath is completed.
• To go back to Mastercam window, minimize **Verify** window as shown.

STEP 11: ADD MULTI PASSES

Multi Passes lets you define multiple cutting passes. The tool approaches the part geometry at the cutting depth in steps instead of cutting right to the part geometry.

Toolpath Preview:

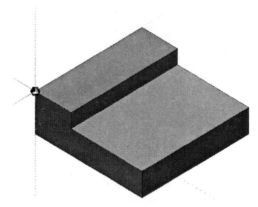

• To modify the parameters, from the **Toolpaths Operations Manager**, in the contour toolpath, select **Parameters** as shown.

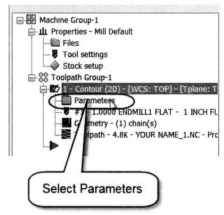

• From the **Tree view list** select **Multi Passes** and make the necessary changes as shown in <u>Figure: 11.0.1</u>.

Figure: 11.0.1

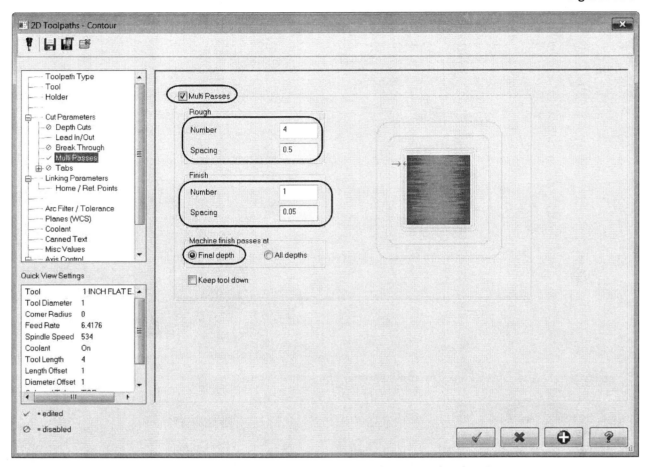

• Once the changes have been made select the **OK** button to exit the **2D Toolpaths- Contour** parameters.

> **NOTE:** We made a change to the Contour parameters, this toolpath is now marked as a dirty toolpath/ operation. A dirty toolpath or operation occurs anytime you make changes to the toolpath parameters.

• From the **Toolpaths Operations Manager,** select the **Regenerate all dirty operations** button to recalculate the changes made to the toolpath.

11.1 Verify the toolpath

◆ Click on the **Verify selected operation** icon.

◆ For information on how to set the verify parameters and to simulate the toolpath, please check page 42.
◆ The part will appear as shown in <u>Figure: 11.1.1</u>.

Figure: 11.1.1

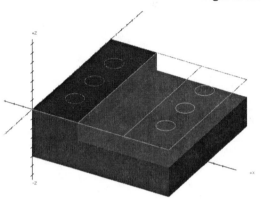

◆ To go back to Mastercam window, minimize **Verify** window as shown.

◆ In Mastercam, the toolpath will be still displayed in the graphics window as shown.

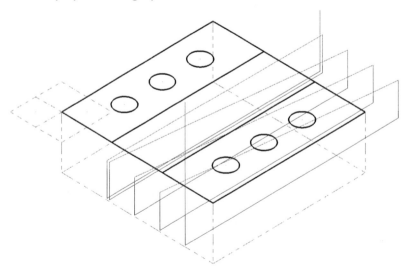

Mastercam. X[7]

◆ To remove the toolpath display press **Alt** + **T** or click on the **Toggle display on selected operations**.

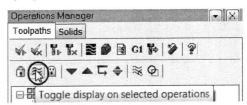

STEP 12: MACHINE THE 0.750" STEP USING OPEN CONTOUR TOOLPATH

Toolpath Preview:

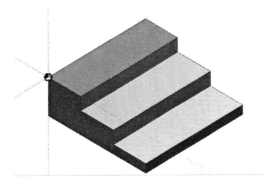

12.1 Chain Selection

Toolpaths

◆  **Contour.**
◆ Make sure that the **Chain** button in the **Chaining** dialog box is enabled as shown to be able to select the contour.

◆ Select the first chain as shown in <u>Figure: 12.1.1</u>.

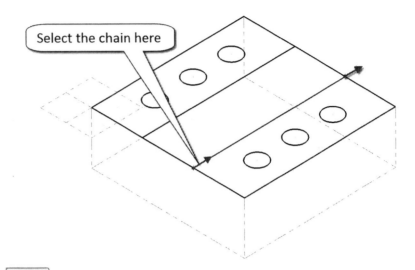

Select the chain here

◆ Select the **OK** button to exit **Chaining**.
◆ In the **Toolpath Type** page, the **Contour** icon will be selected.

Contour   Pocket   Facing   Slot Mill

Mastercam. X⁷

12.2 Set the Tool parameters

◆ Make all the necessary changes as shown in <u>Figure: 12.2.1</u>.

Figure: 12.2.1

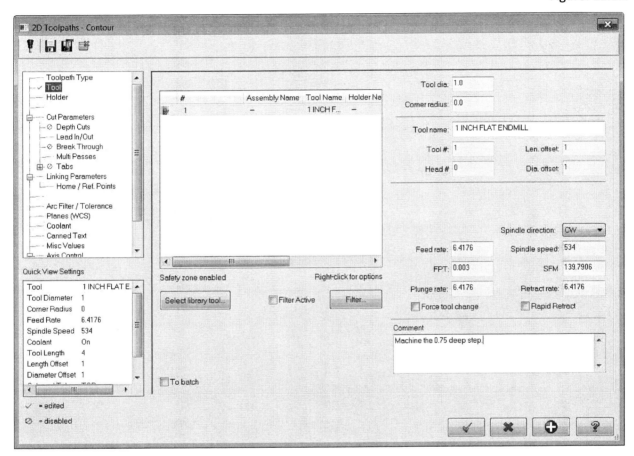

NOTE: The Cut Parameters and the Lead In/Out are mentained from the previous operation.

12.3 Set the Multi Passes

♦ From the Tree view list, select **Multi Passes** and change the **Number of the roughing passes** as shown in <u>Figure: 12.3.1</u>.

Figure: 12.3.1

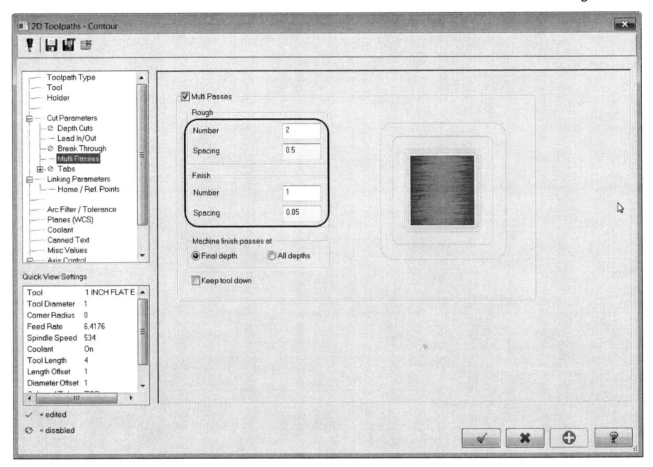

12.4 Set the Linking Parameters

◆ From the **Tree view list**, select **Linking Parameters** and change the **Depth** as shown <u>Figure: 12.4.1</u>.

Figure: 12.4.1

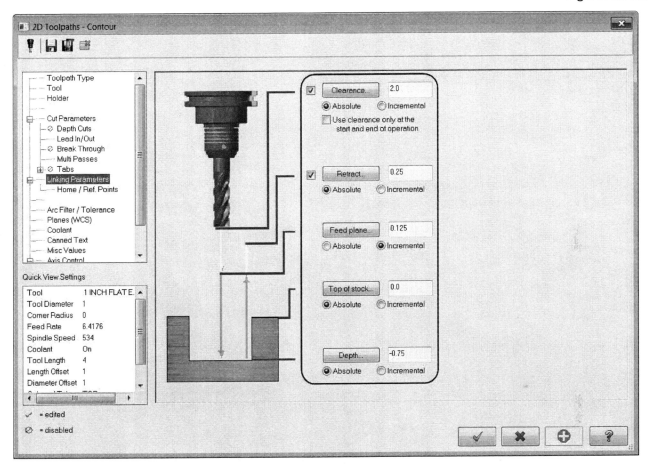

◆ Select the **OK** button to exit the contour parameters.

12.5 Verify the toolpath

• From **Toolpaths Operations Manager**, select both operations by clicking on the **Select all operations** icon.

• Select **Verify selected operations** icon as shown.

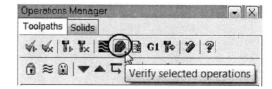

• Set the **Verify** simulation as shown on page 42.
• The part will appear as shown in <u>Figure: 12.5.1</u>.

Figure: 12.5.1

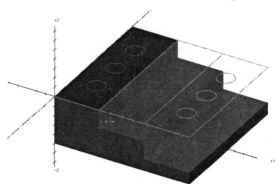

• To go back to Mastercam window, minimize **Verify** window as shown.

• To remove the toolpath display press **Alt** + **T**.

STEP 13: DRILL THE 6 HOLES

A drill toolpath is used for cutting holes in material.

Toolpath Preview:

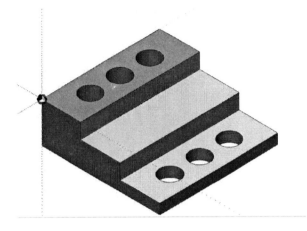

Toolpaths

- ◆ 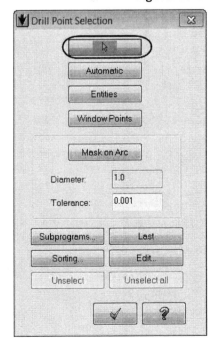 **Drill.**
- ◆ The **Drill point Selection** dialog box will appear as shown in <u>Figure: 13.0.1</u>.

Figure: 13.0.1

• Select the arc center points as shown in <u>Figure: 13.0.2</u>.

Figure: 13.0.2

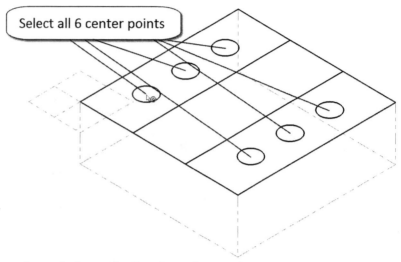

Select all 6 center points

• Ensure the **Auto Cursor** icon appears as shown before selecting the points as shown.

• Once the 6 center points have been selected choose the **OK** button to exit the **Drill Point Selection** dialog box.

• In the **Toolpath Type** page, the **Drill** icon will be selected.

Drill   Circle Mill   Point   Helix Bore   Thread Mill

13.1 Select a 3/8" Drill from the library and set the Tool Parameters

• Select **Tool** from the **Tree view list**.

• Click on the **Select library tool** button.

• To be able to see all the tools from the library disable **Filter Active**.

* Scroll down and select the **3/8" Drill** (#128) as shown in Figure: 13.1.1.

Figure: 13.1.1

#	Assembly Name	Tool Name	Holder Name	Dia.	Cor. rad.	Length	# Flutes	Type	Rad. Type
125	–	LTR. T D...	–	0....	0.0	2.0	2	Drill	None
126	–	23/64 D...	–	0....	0.0	2.0	2	Drill	None
127	–	LTR. U D...	–	0....	0.0	2.0	2	Drill	None
128	–	3/8 DRILL	–	0....	0.0	2.0	2	Drill	None
129	–	LTR. V D...	–	0....	0.0	2.0	2	Drill	None
130	–	LTR. W ...	–	0....	0.0	2.0	2	Drill	None
131	–	25/64 D...	–	0....	0.0	2.0	2	Drill	None
132	–	LTR. X D...	–	0....	0.0	2.0	2	Drill	None

* Select the tool in the **Tool Selection** page and then select the **OK** button.
* Make the necessary changes as shown in Figure: 13.1.2.

Figure: 13.1.2

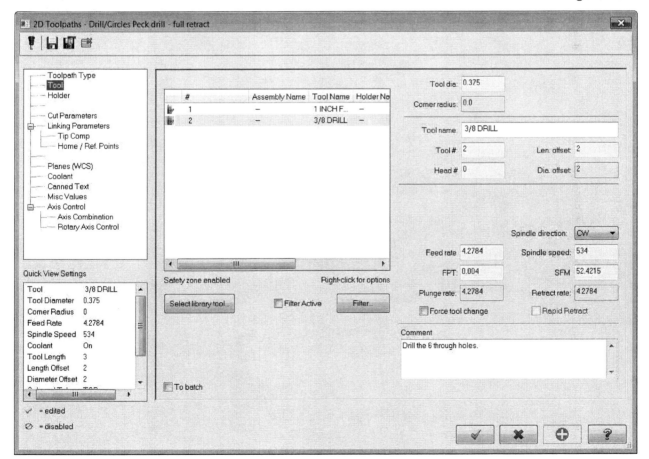

13.2 Set the Cut Parameters

♦ Select the **Cut Parameters** page and change the **Cycle** to **Peck Drill** as shown in Figure: 13.2.1.

Figure: 13.2.1

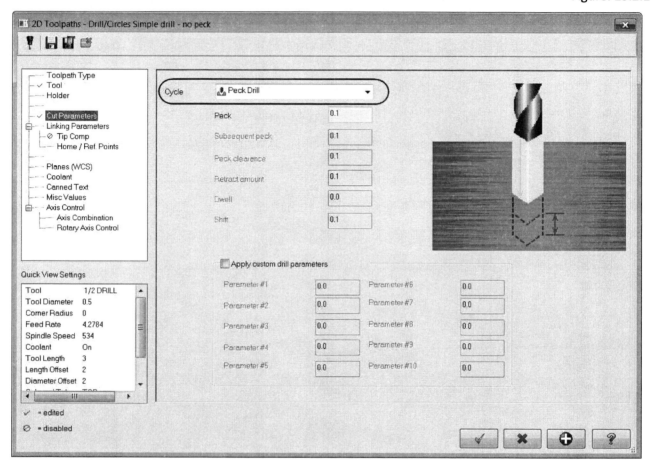

♦ Choose **Linking parameters**, enable **Clearance** and set the **Depth** to **-1.0"** as shown in <u>Figure: 13.2.2</u>.

Figure: 13.2.2

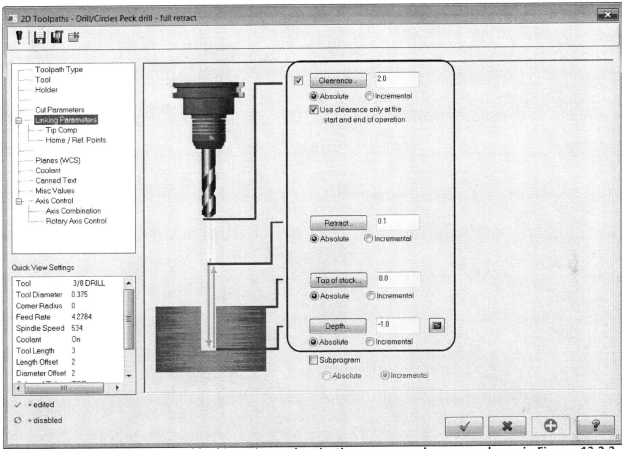

♦ Choose the option **Tip Comp,** enable this option and make the necessary changes as shown in <u>Figure: 13.2.3</u>.

Figure: 13.2.3

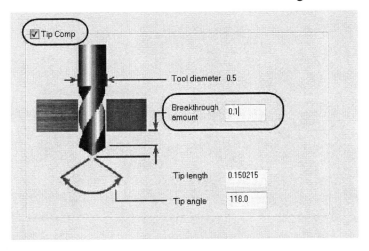

♦ Select the **OK** button to generate the toolpath.

13.3 Verify the toolpath in the Material Mode

• From **Toolpaths Operations Manager**, select all operations by clicking on the **Select all operations** icon.

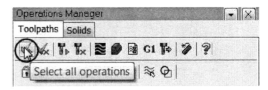

• Set the **Verify** options as shown on page 42.
• The finished part will appear as shown in Figure: 13.3.1.

Figure: 13.3.1

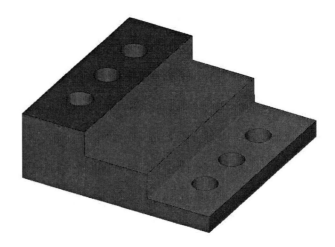

• To exit **Verify** click on the **Close** icon.

STEP 14: POST THE FILE

Posting refers to a process where the toolpaths in Mastercam are converted to a format that can be understood by the machines control, specifically the G-codes. In most cases every machine will require its own post processor; customized to produce code formatted to meet the machines exact requirements.

♦ Ensure all operations are selected, if they are not use the button **Select all operations** in the **Operations Manager.**

♦ Select the **Post selected operations** button from the **Operations Manager.** G1

♦ In the **Post processing** window make the necessary changes as shown in Figure: 14.0.1.

Figure: 14.0.1

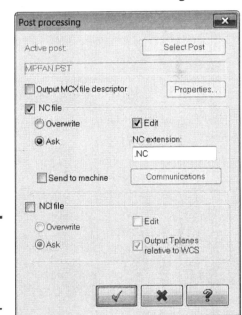

NC File enabled allows you to keep the NC file and to assign the same name as the MCX file.

Edit enabled allows you to automatically launch the default editor.

♦ Select the **OK** button to continue.

♦ Save the NC file.

• A window with Mastercam Code Expert will be lunched and the NC program will appear as shown.

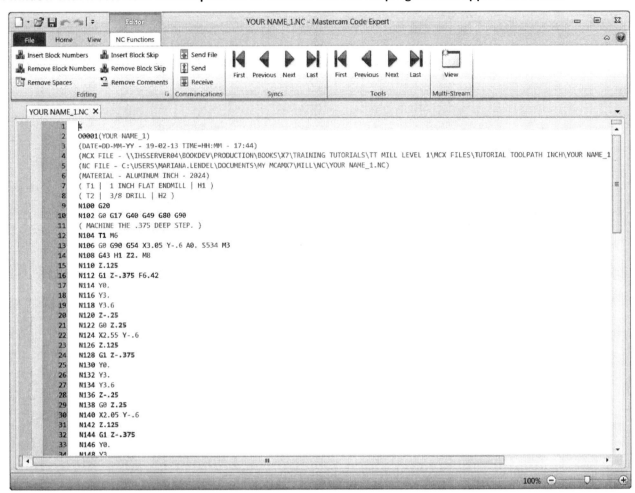

• Select the red **"X"** box at the upper right corner to exit the editor.

STEP 15: SAVE THE UPDATED MCX FILE

REVIEW EXERCISE - STUDENT PRACTICE

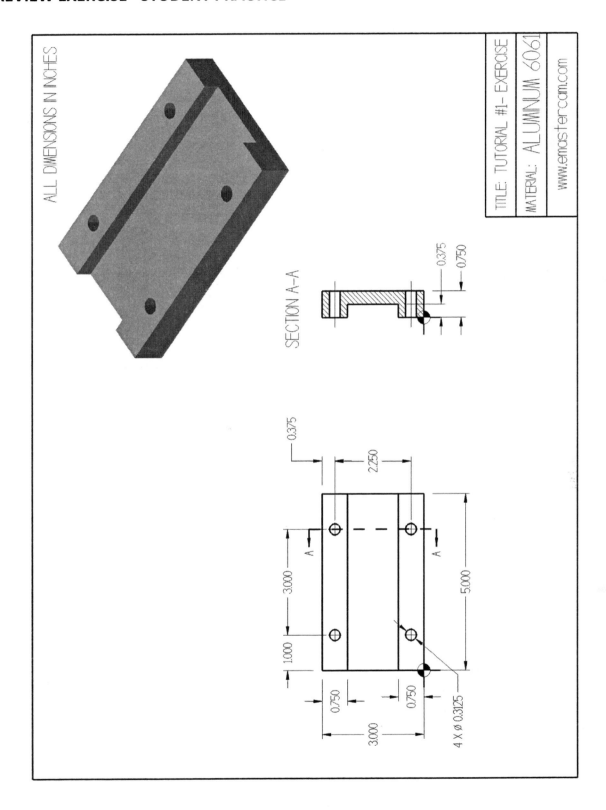

ALL DIMENSIONS IN INCHES

SECTION A-A

0.375
0.750

0.375

2.250

A

A

3.000

1.000

5.000

0.750

0.750

3.000

4 X Ø 0.3125

TITLE: TUTORIAL #1- EXERCISE

MATERIAL: ALUMINUM 6061

www.emastercam.com

CREATE THE GEOMETRY FOR TUTORIAL #1 EXERCISE

Use these commands to create the geometry.
- Create a Rectangle.
- Create Line Parallel.
- Create Circle Center Point (position using Fast Point).
- Xform Translate.

CREATE THE TOOLPATHS FOR TUTORIAL #1 EXERCISE

Create the Toolpaths for Tutorial #1 Exercise as per the instructions below.

Set the machine properties including the stock.
Remove the material in the center of the part Contour (2D).
• Chain the two lines that define the pocket in the same direction as shown.

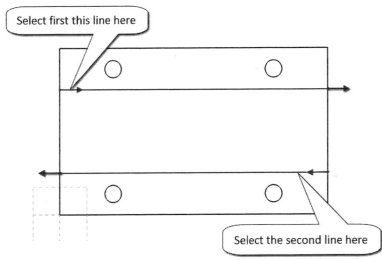

Select first this line here

Select the second line here

• Use a **7/8"**Flat Endmill.
• Based on your chaining direction ensure the Compensation direction is set correct.
• No **Depth Cuts**.
• **Lead In/Out** ensure the arc radius is set to zero.
• No **Break Through**, no **Multi Passes**.
• Set the depth according to the drawing.

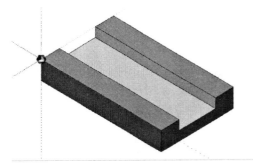

Drill the holes through the part.
• Use a **5/16"** Drill.
• Choose the **Drill/Counterbore cycle**.
• Depth set according to the drawing.
• Enable **Tip Comp** and input a **Breakthrough amount**.

NOTES:

TUTORIAL #1 QUIZ

◆ What is a Contour Toolpath used for?

◆ What does Backplot do?

◆ When would you use Multi Passes?

◆ When would you use the drill cycle Peck Drill?

TUTORIAL #2

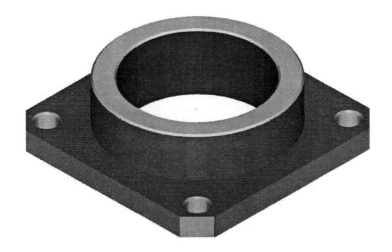

OVERVIEW OF STEPS TAKEN TO CREATE THE FINAL PART:

From Drawing to CAD Model:
* The student should examine the drawing on the following page to understand what part is being created in the tutorial.
* From the drawing we can decide how to go about creating the geometry in Mastercam.

Create the 2D CAD Model used to generate Toolpaths from:
* The student will create the Top 2D geometry needed to create the toolpaths.
* Geometry creation commands such as create rectangle, chamfer, arc polar, circle center point, mirror and join will be used.

Create the necessary Toolpaths to machine the part:
* The student will set up the stock size to be used and the clamping method used.
* A Facing toolpath will be created to machine the top of the part.
* A Circle mill toolpath will remove the material inside of the large hole.
* A Contour toolpath will be created to remove the material ouside the boss shape.
* A Drilling toolpath will be created to spot drill the four holes.
* A Drilling toolpath will be created to machine the through holes.
* A Contour toolpath with 2D chamfer option will be created to chamfer the top of the boss.

Backplot and Verify the file:
* The Backplot will be used to simulate a step by step process of the tool's movements.
* The Verify will be used to watch a tool machine the part out of a solid model.

Post Process the file to generate the G-code:
* The Student will then post process the file to obtain an NC file containing the necessary code for the machine.

 This tutorial takes approximately one hour and half to complete.

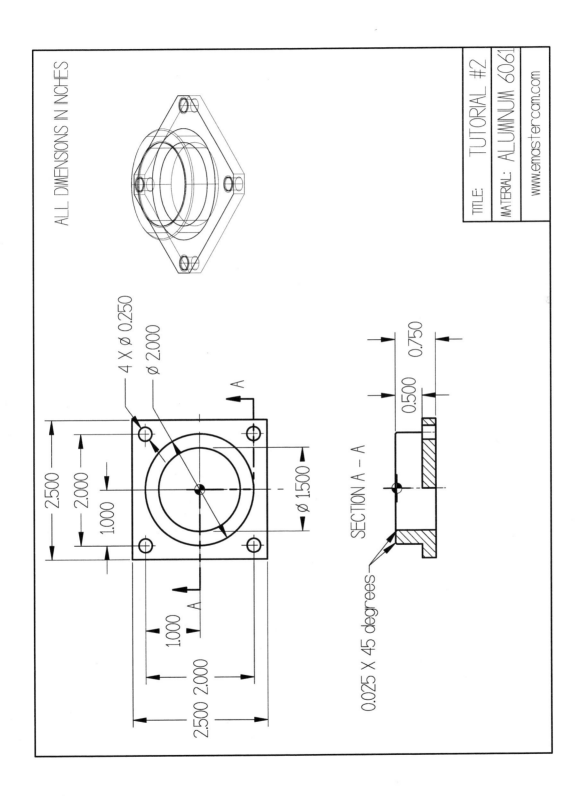

ALL DIMENSIONS IN INCHES

TITLE: TUTORIAL #2

MATERIAL: ALUMINUM 6061

www.emastercam.com

4 X Ø 0.250

Ø 2.000

2.500

2.000

1.000

Ø 1.500

1.000

A

2.500 2.000

SECTION A – A

0.750

0.500

0.025 X 45 degrees

GEOMETRY CREATION

STEP 1: SETTING UP THE GRAPHIC USER INTERFACE

Please refer to the **Getting Started** section to set up the graphics user interface.

STEP 2: CREATE RECTANGLE

NOTE: The drawing is symmetric about both X and Y axis. You will create only a quarter of the geometry and then use **Mirror** command to complete it.

In this step you will learn how to create a rectangle knowing the width, the height and the anchor position.

Step Preview:

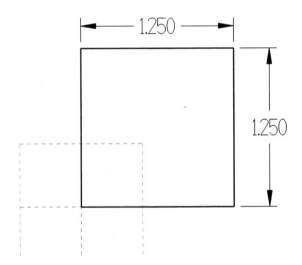

2.1 Create a 1.250" by 1.25" Rectangle

Create

+  **Rectangle.**

+ Enter the **Width** and **Height** as shown.
+ Press **Enter** after typing the values to see a preview of the rectangle as shown.

* [Select position for first corner]: Select the **Origin** as shown in Figure: 2.1.1.

Figure: 2.1.1

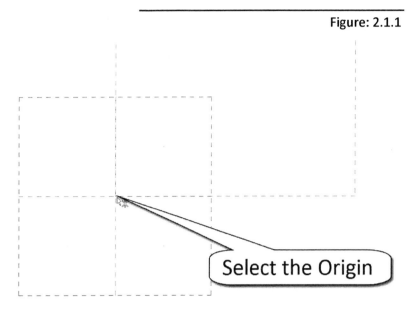

Select the Origin

* Make sure that when selecting the origin, the visual cue of the cursor changes as shown.
* Select the **OK** button to exit the **Rectangle** command.
* Use the **Fit** icon to fit the drawing to the screen.

NOTE: During the geometry creation of this tutorial, if you make a mistake you can undo the last step using the **Undo** icon. You can undo as many steps as needed. If you delete or undo a step by mistake, just use the **Redo** icon. To delete unwanted geometry, select it first and then press **Delete** from the keyboard.

STEP 3: CREATE A CHAMFER

In this step you will create the 0.25 X 45 degrees chamfer.

Step Preview:

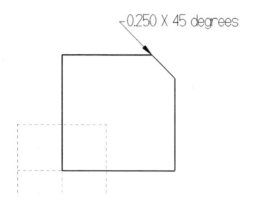

Create
* **Chamfer.**
*  **Entities.**
* Enter the distance **0.25** in the ribbon bar and ensure the chamfer style is set to **1 Distance** and **Trim** is enabled.

* Select the two lines to create the chamfer as shown in Figure: 3.0.1.

Figure: 3.0.1

Select first line here

Select the second line here

> **NOTE:** A preview of the chamfer will appear when you select the second line.

♦ Select the **OK** button to exit the command.

STEP 4: CREATE THE CIRCLE

In this step you will create a circle knowing the diameter and location.

Step Preview:

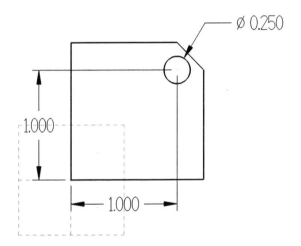

Create
♦ **Arc.**

♦  **Circle Center Point.**
♦ Enter the **Diameter 0.25** in the ribbon bar.

♦ Select the **Fast point** command.
♦ [Enter the co-ordinate]: **1.0, 1.0** and hit **Enter**.

♦ Once complete choose the **OK** button to exit the command.

STEP 5: CREATE POLAR ARCS

In this step you will create two polar arcs knowing the radius, the center point, the start angle and the end angle.

Step Preview:

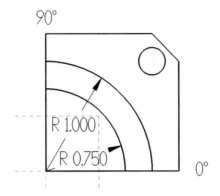

Create
* **Arc.**

* **Arc Polar.**

* Enter the values in the **Ribbon Bar** as shown and press **Enter** after all values are entered.

* [Enter the center point]: Select the **Origin**.

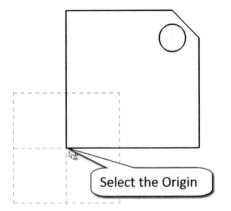

Select the Origin

* Select the **Apply** button to continue in the same command.

Mill Level 1 Training Tutorial

Mastercam. X⁷

• The part will appear as shown once complete.

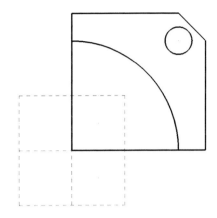

• Enter the values in the **Ribbon Bar** as shown and press **Enter** after all values are entered.

NOTE: To enter the values in the Ribbon Bar, type the radius and then to move to the next field press tab. The diameter will be automatically updated. To move to the next field press again tab.

• [Enter the center point]: Select the **Origin**.

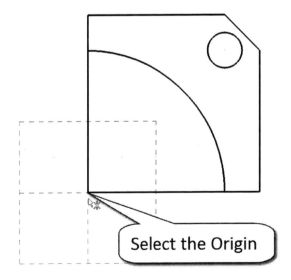

Select the Origin

• Once complete choose the **OK** button to exit the command.

• The geometry should look as shown.

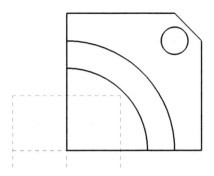

STEP 6: DELETE THE CONSTRUCTION LINES

In this step you will delete the center lines that are going throug the origin.

Step Preview:

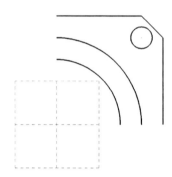

• Select the two lines as shown in Figure: 6.0.1.

Figure: 6.0.1

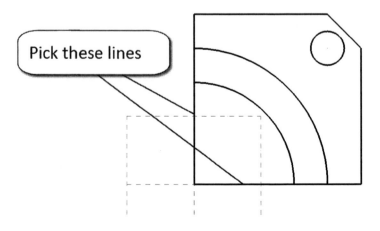

Pick these lines

• Click on the **Delete** key from the keyboard.

Mastercam. X⁷

STEP 7: MIRROR THE GEOMETRY

The **Mirror** command allows you to complete the geometry. You will mirror the geometry about both X and Y axis.

Step Preview:

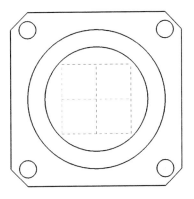

Xform

♦    **Mirror.**

♦ [Mirror: select entities to mirror]: From the **General Selection** toolbar, select the **All** button.

♦ Make sure that **All Entities** is enabled to select all entities as shown.

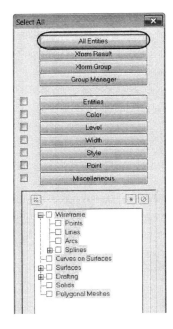

♦ Select the **OK** button.
♦ Press **Enter** to finish the selection.

• In the **Mirror** dialog box, make sure that **Copy** is enabled, the radio button in front of the **X axis** is enabled and **Fit** is enabled as shown in Figure: 7.0.1.

Figure: 7.0.1

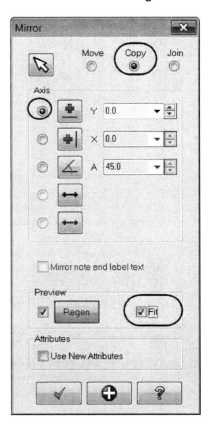

• The preview of the mirror will look as shown.

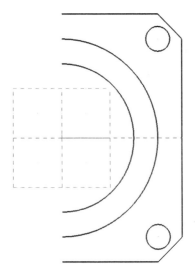

• Select the **Apply** button to continue in the same command.

* [Mirror: select entities to mirror]: From the **General Selection** toolbar, select the **All** button.

* Make sure that **All Entities** is enabled to select all entities as shown.

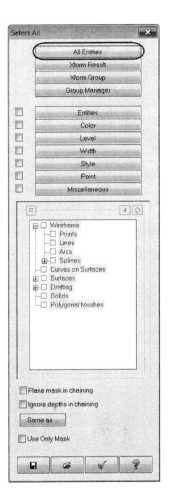

* Select the **OK** button.
* Press **Enter** to finish the selection.

- In the **Mirror** dialog box, make sure that **Copy** is enabled, the radio button in front of the **Y axis** is enabled and **Fit** is enabled as shown in <u>Figure: 7.0.2</u>.

Figure: 7.0.2

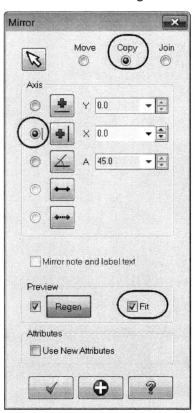

- The preview of the resulting geometry should look as shown.

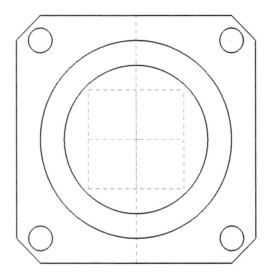

- Select the **OK** button to exit the command.

NOTE: When performing a transform function (**Xform**), Mastercam creates a temporary group from the originals (red) and a result (purple) from the transformed entities. However, they stay in effect only until you use the **Screen, Clear Colors** function or perform another transform function.

Screen

♦  **Clear Color.**
♦ The geometry should look as shown.

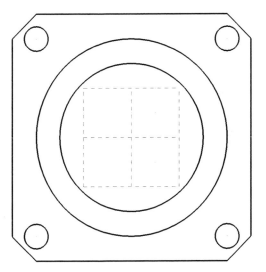

NOTE: The lines and the two big circles are broken in 2 and 4 segments due to the mirror command. To be able to select the circle for the circle mill toolpath you will have to join the arcs.

STEP 8: JOIN THE ENTITIES

Join function allows you to join collinear lines, arcs that have the same center and radius, or splines that were originally created as the same entity.

Edit

+ 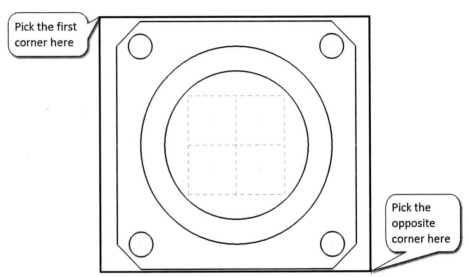 **Join entities.**
+ [Select entities to join]: Make a window around all entities as shown in Figure: 8.0.1.

Figure: 8.0.1

Pick the first corner here

Pick the opposite corner here

NOTE: To make a window, pick a point to the upper left corner and drag the cursor to the opposite corner and click. All the entities inside of the window should be selected (color yellow).

+ Press **Enter** to finish the selection.

NOTE: The entities are automatically joined.

STEP 9: SAVE THE FILE

File

+  **Save As.**
+ File name: "Your Name_2".

TOOLPATH CREATION

SUGGESTED FIXTURE:

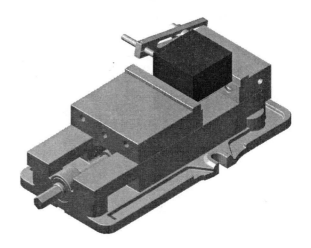

SETUP SHEET:

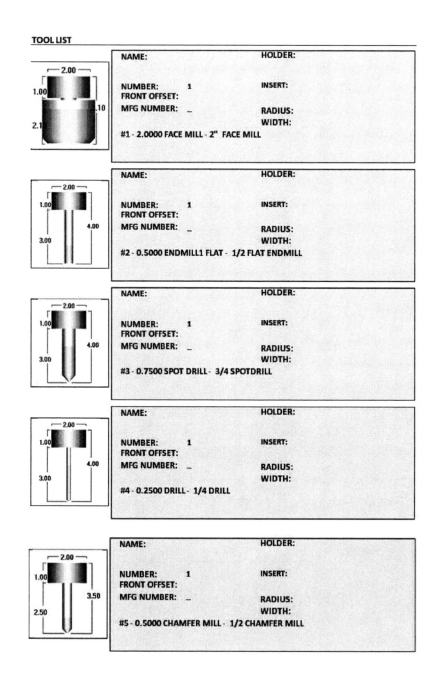

STEP 10: SELECT THE MACHINE AND SET UP THE STOCK

In Mastercam, you select a **Machine Definition** before creating any toolpaths. The **Machine Definition** is a model of your machine's capabilities and features. It acts like a template for setting up your machine. The machine definition ties together three main components. The schematic model of your machines components. The control definition that models your control capabilities and the post processor that will generate the required machine code (G-code). For a Mill Level 1 exercise (2D toolpaths) we need just a basic machine definition.

> **NOTE:** For the purpose of this tutorial, we will be using the **Default mill** machine.

- To display the **Operations Manager** press **Alt + O**.

- Use the **Fit** icon to fit the drawing to the screen.
Machine type
- **Mill.**
- **Default.**

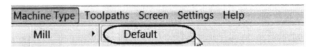

- Select the plus sign in front of **Properties** in the **Toolpaths Manager** to expand the **Toolpaths Group Properties.**

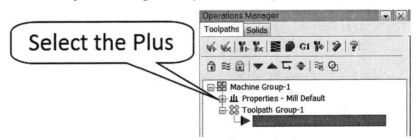

- Select **Tool settings** to set the tool parameters.

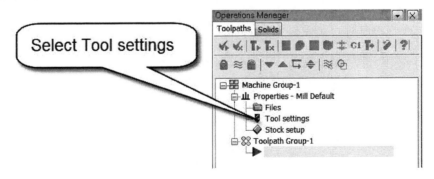

• Change the parameters to match the screen shot as shown in <u>Figure: 10.0.1</u>.

Figure: 10.0.1

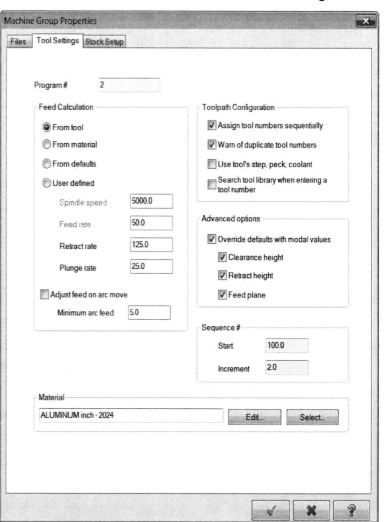

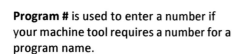

Program # is used to enter a number if your machine tool requires a number for a program name.

Assign tool numbers sequentially allows you to overwrite the tool number from the library with the next available tool number. (First operation tool number 1; Second operation tool number 2, etc.)

Warn of duplicate tool numbers allows you to get a warning if you enter two tools with the same number.

Override defaults with modal values enables the system to keep the values that you enter.

Feed Calculation set **From tool** uses feed rate, plunge rate, retract rate and spindle speed from the tool definition.

• Select the **Stock Setup** tab to define the stock.
• Select the **All Entities** button near the bottom of the **Stock setup** page as shown.

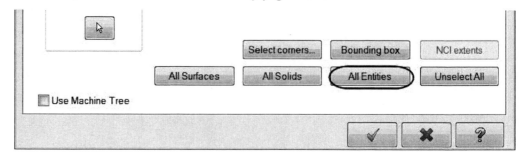

- Select the **Yes** button if the **Bounding box** warning appears as shown.

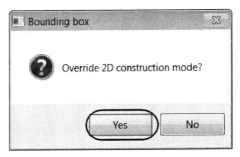

- In the **Stock Setup**, enter in the **Z** field **0.85** and the **Z Stock Origin 0.1** make sure that the rest of the parameters are as shown in Figure: 10.0.2.

Figure: 10.0.2

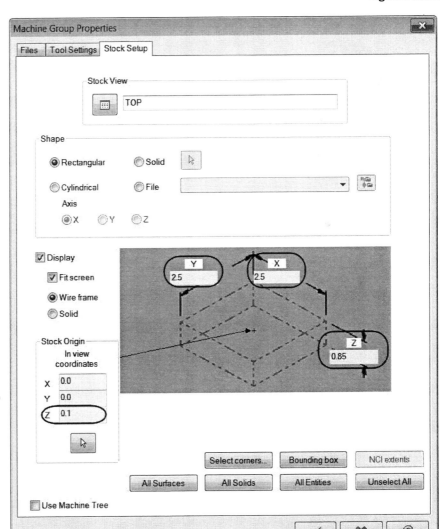

The **Stock Origin** values adjust the positioning of the stock, ensuring that you have equal amount of extra stock around the finished part.

Display options allow you to set the stock as **Wireframe** and to fit the stock to the screen. (Fit Screen)

NOTE: The **stock** model that you create can be displayed with the part geometry when viewing the file or the toolpaths, during backplot, or while verifying toolpaths. In the graphics, the plus shows you where the stock origin is. The default position is the middle of the stock.

• Select the **OK** button to exit **Machine Group Properties**.

• Select the **Isometric** view from the graphics view toolbar to see the stock.

• Use the **Fit** icon to fit the drawing to the screen.

• The stock model will appear as shown.

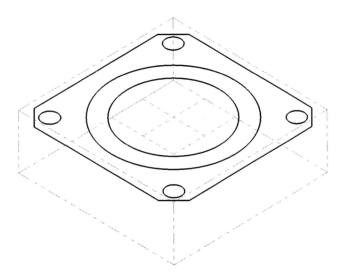

NOTE: The stock is not geometry and can not be selected.

• Select the **Top** view from the view toolbar to see the part from the top.

Mastercam. X^7

STEP 11: FACE THE PART

A **Facing** toolpath quickly removes material from the top of the part to create an even surface for future operations.

Toolpath Preview:

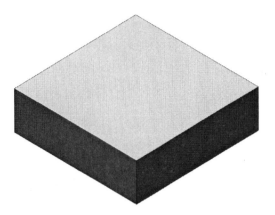

Toolpaths

* **Face.**

* If a prompt appears, **Enter new NC name**, select the **OK** button to accept the default.

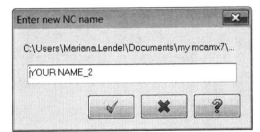

• When the chaining dialog box appears choose the **OK** button to use defined stock and exit the **Chaining** dialog box.

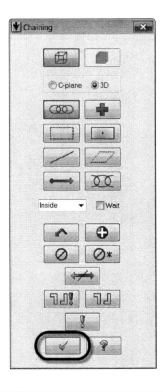

NOTE: Mastercam will create the Facing toolpath defined from the stock setup.

• In the **Toolpath Type** page, the **Facing** icon will be automatically selected.

Contour   Pocket   Facing   Slot Mill

NOTE: Mastercam updates the pages as you modify them and then marks them, in the **Tree view list,** with a green check mark. Pages that are not enabled are marked with a red circle and slash.

11.1 Select a 2.0" Face Mill from the library and set the Tool parameters

◆ Select **Tool** from the **Tree view list.**

◆ Click on the **Select library tool** button.

◆ To be able to see all the tools from the library disable **Filter Active**.

◆ Pick the **2" Face Mill (#316)** as shown.

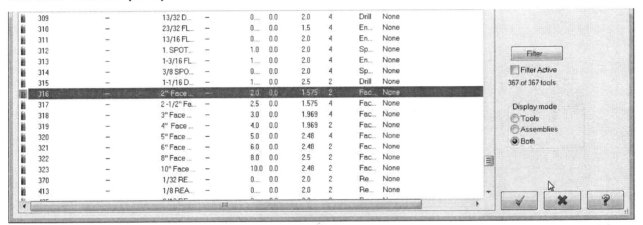

◆ Select the tool in the **Tool Selection** page and then select the **OK** button to exit.

◆ Make all the necessary changes as shown in Figure: 11.1.1.

Figure: 11.1.1

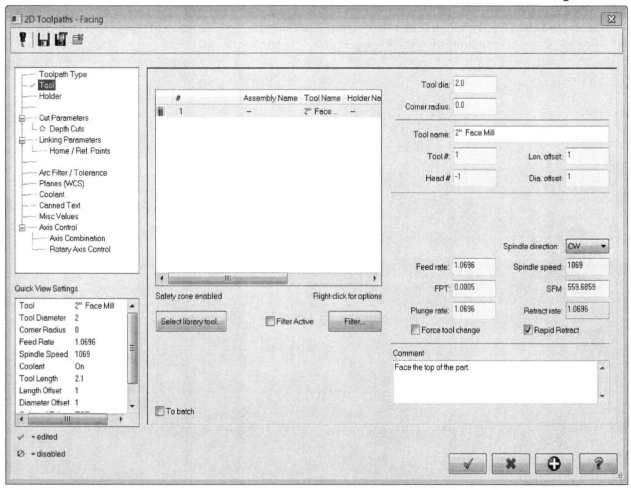

The **Feed rate**, **Plunge rate**, **Retract rate** and **Spindle speed** are based on the tool definition as set in the **Tool Settings**. You may change these values as per your part material and tools.

In the **Comment** field enter a comment to help identify the toolpath in the **Toolpaths/Operations Manager** such as the one shown above.

• Select **Cut Parameters** and make the necessary changes as shown in Figure: 11.1.2.

Figure: 11.1.2

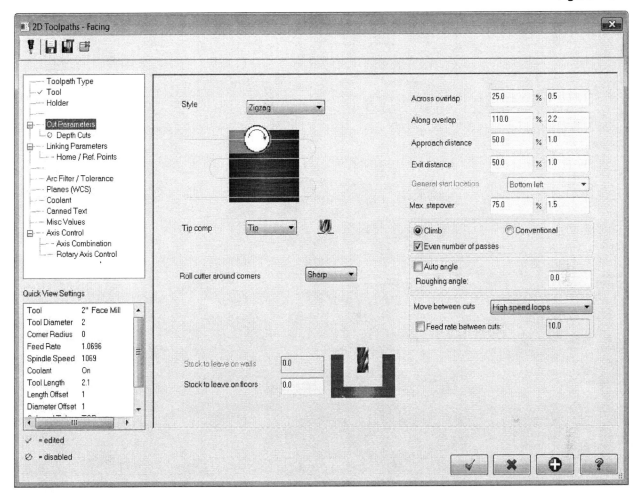

The **Style** (facing cutting method) **Zigzag** creates a back and forth cutting motion.

Move between cuts determines how the tool moves between each cut. This is only available if you select the zigzag cutting method.

High speed loops to create 180 degrees arcs between each cut.

● Select the **Linking Parameters** page and make the necessary changes as shown in Figure: 11.1.3.

Figure: 11.1.3

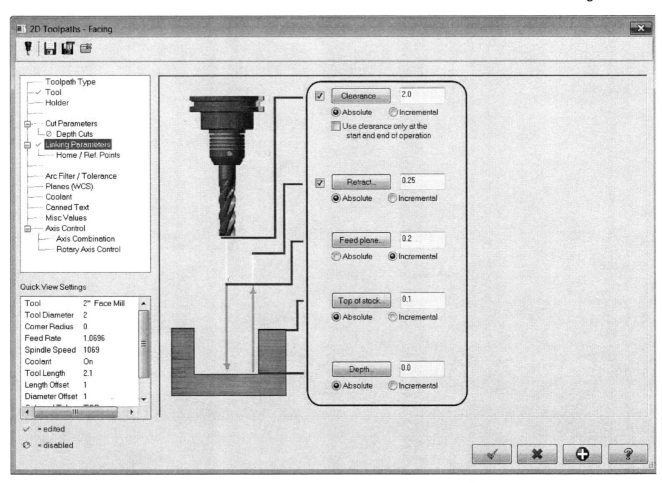

Clearance sets the height at which the tool moves to and from the part.

Retract sets the height that the tool moves up to before the next tool pass.

Feed Plane sets the height that the tool rapids to before changing to the plunge rate to enter the part.

Top of stock sets the height of the material in the Z axis.

Depth determines the final machining depth that the tool descends into the stock.

● Select the **OK** button to exit the **Facing Parameters**.

> **NOTE:** The top of stock is set to **0.1"** because in our **Stock Origin** we have this set **0.1"** above the origin. The depth is set to **0.0"** because this is the depth we want the tool to go to.

STEP 12: CIRCLE MILL THE INSIDE HOLE

Circle Mill Toolpaths remove circular pockets based on a single point. You can select either point entities, center points of arcs. Mastercam will then pocket out a circular area of the diameter and to the depth that you specify.

Toolpath Preview:

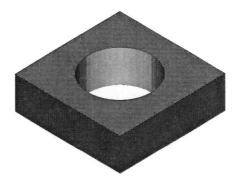

12.1 Drill Point Selection

• Press **Alt +T** to remove the toolpath display.

Toolpaths
Circle Paths.

• ⊖ **Circmill.**
• From the **Drill Point Selection**, click on **Entities.**

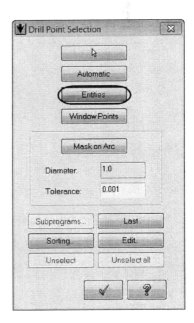

• Select the **1.5"** diameter circle as shown.

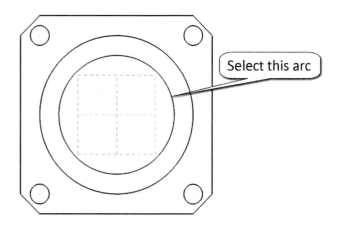

Select this arc

• Select the **OK** button to exit **Drill Point Selection**.
• In the **Toolpath Type** page, the **Circle Mill** icon will be selected.

Drill   Circle Mill   Point   Helix Bore   Thread Mill

12.2 Select a 1/2" Flat endmill from the library and set the Tool parameters

• Select **Tool** from the **Tree view list**.

• Click on **Select library tool** button. | Select library tool... |
• To be able to see all the tools from the library disable **Filter Active**.

• Scroll down and select the **1/2" Flat Endmill (# 239)** as shown.

231	–	3/32 FLA...	–	0...	0.0	0.375	4	En...	None
232	–	1/8 FLAT...	–	0...	0.0	0.375	4	En...	None
233	–	5/32 FLA...	–	0...	0.0	0.375	4	En...	None
234	–	3/16 FLA...	–	0...	0.0	0.4375	4	En...	None
235	–	1/4 FLAT...	–	0.25	0.0	0.5	4	En...	None
236	–	5/16 FLA...	–	0...	0.0	0.75	4	En...	None
237	–	3/8 FLAT...	–	0...	0.0	0.75	4	En...	None
238	–	7/16 FLA...	–	0...	0.0	0.8	4	En...	None
239	–	1/2 FLAT...	–	0.5	0.0	1.0	4	En...	None
240	–	5/8 FLAT...	–	0...	0.0	1.5	4	En...	None
241	–	3/4 FLAT...	–	0.75	0.0	2.0	4	En...	None
242	–	7/8 FLAT...	–	0...	0.0	2.0	4	En...	None

☐ Filter Active
367 of 367 tools

Display mode
○ Tools
○ Assemblies
● Both

• Select the tool in the **Tool Selection** page and then select the **OK** button to exit.

* Make all the necessary changes as shown in Figure: 12.2.1.

Figure: 12.2.1

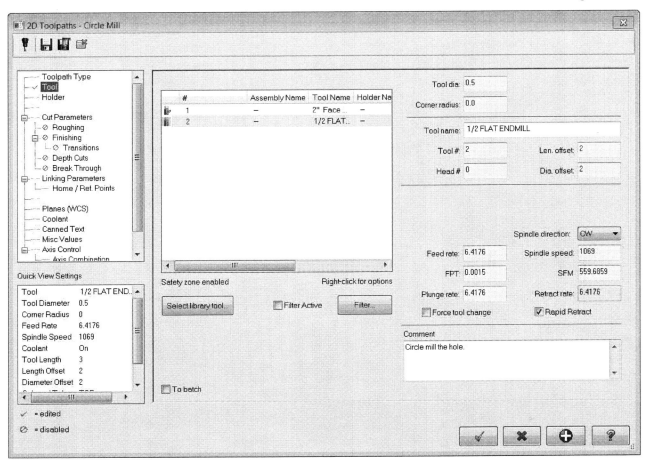

12.3 Cut Parameters

♦ From the **Tree view list**, select **Cut Parameters** and ensure the settings appear as shown in Figure: 12.3.1.

Figure: 12.3.1

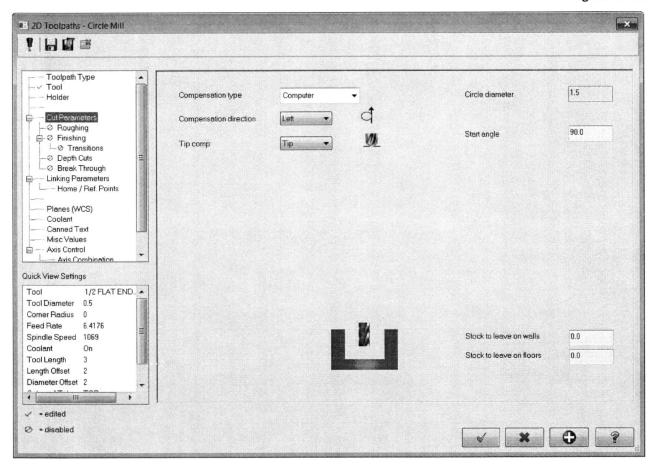

12.4 Roughing

• From the **Tree view list**, select **Roughing** and enabled. Set the Stepover to 50% and enable Helical Entry and set the parameters as shown in Figure: 12.4.1.

Figure: 12.4.1

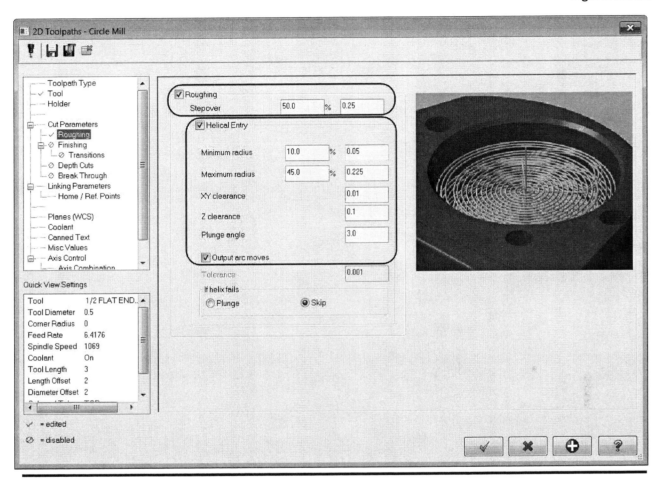

Stepover set the distance between cutting passes in the X and Y axes as a percentage of the tool diameter.

Helical entry creates a helix at the center of the circle to begin the roughing motion.If off, the tool plunges to start the toolpath.

12.5 Depth Cuts

- From the Tree view list, enable Depth Cuts and set the **Max rough step** to **0.5** and enable **Keep tool down**.
- Make any necessary changes as shown in Figure: 12.5.1.

Figure: 12.5.1

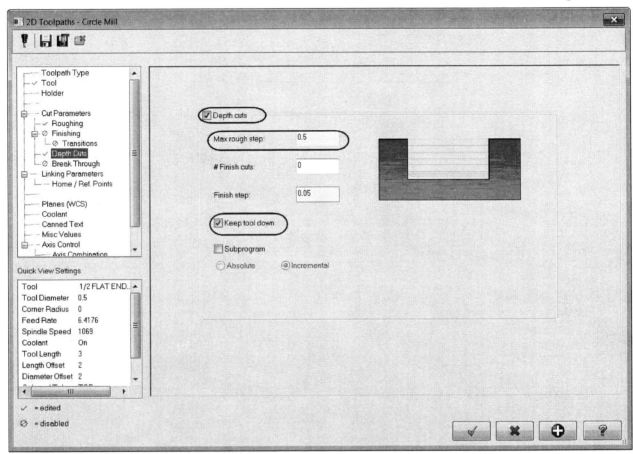

Depth Cuts, Mastercam will take the total depth and divide it into separate depth cuts. Mastercam never performs unequal depth cuts.

Max rough step sets the maximum amount of material removed in the Z axis with each rough cut. Mastercam will calculate equal rough cuts no larger than the maximum rough step until it reaches the final Z depth.

Keep tool down determines whether or not to retract the tool between depth cuts.

12.6 Set the Break Through

◆ From the **Tree view list**, select **Break Through** and set the parameters to completely cut through the material by an amount that you specify as shown in Figure: 12.6.1.

Figure: 12.6.1

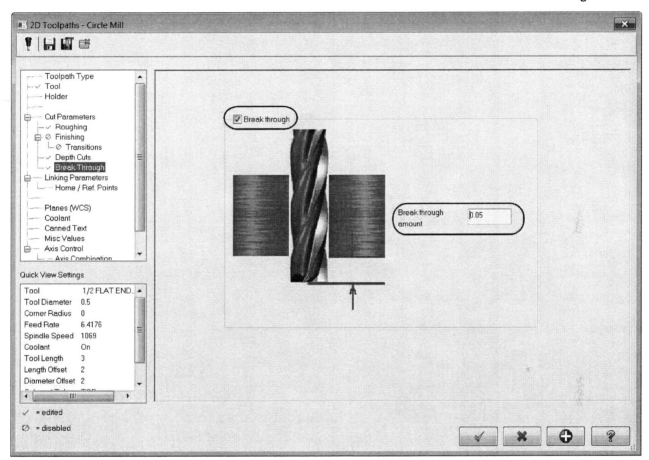

12.7 Linking Parameters

- Select **Linking Parameters** from the **Tree view list.**
- Change the top of stock to **0.0** and set the depth to **-0.75.** Ensure all the values are set to **Absolute** as shown in <u>Figure: 12.7.1</u>.

Figure: 12.7.1

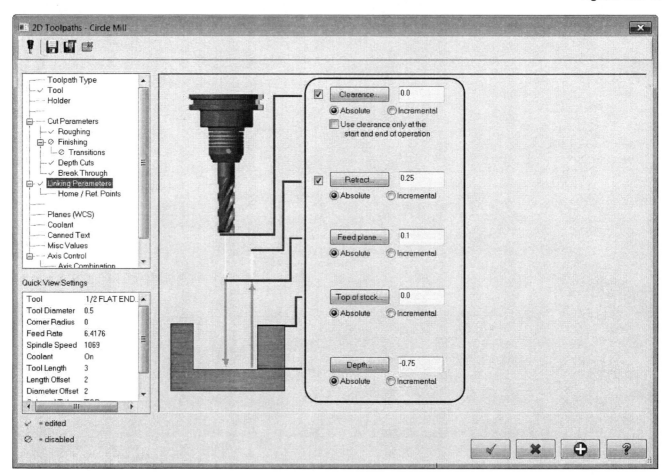

Absolute values are always measured from the origin 0,0,0.

Incremental values are relative to other parameters or chained geometry.

STEP 13: BACKPLOT THE TOOLPATHS

Backplotting shows the path the tools take to cut the part. This display lets you spot errors in the program before you machine the part. As you backplot toolpaths, Mastercam displays additional information such as the X, Y, and Z coordinates, the path length , the minimum and maximum coordinates and the cycle time. It also shows any collisions between the workpiece and the tool.

- Make sure that the toolpaths are selected (signified by the green check mark on the folder icon). If both

  operations are not selected choose the select all operations icon.
- Select the **Backplot** selected operations button.

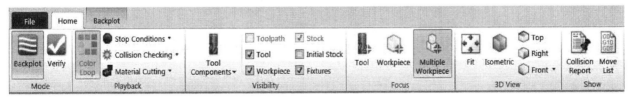

> **NOTE:** Mastercam launches a new window that allows you to check the part using **Backplot** or **Verify**. Note that an error might appear that operation #1 has undercuts. Select the OK button to continue

- To remove the error, select **File** tab.
- Select **Options** and change the **Simulation engine** to **5-axis**.
- Select the Yes button to continue.
- Select the **OK** button to exit **Options**.
- Select the **Backplot** tab and have the following settings enabled as shown.

- Select the **Home** tab and make sure that you have the following settings on as shown.

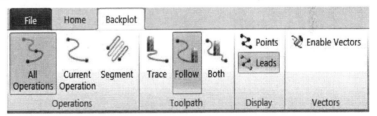

- To see the part from an **Isometric** view select the **Isometric** icon.

- To fit the workpiece to the screen, select the **Fit** icon.

- You can step through the **Backplot** by using the **Step forward**  or **Step back** buttons.

- You can adjust the speed of the backplot. Speed:
- Select the **Play Simulation** button in the **VCR** bar to run **Backplot**.

- The toolpath should look as shown Figure: 13.0.1.

Figure: 13.0.1.

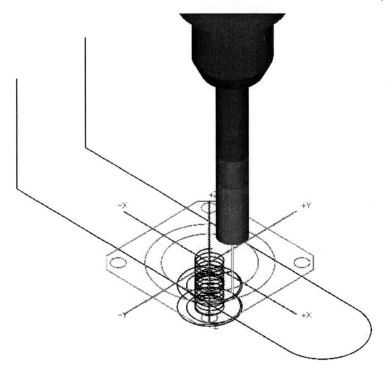

STEP 14: SIMULATE THE TOOLPATH IN VERIFY

Verify Mode shows the path the tools take to cut the part with material removal. This display lets you spot errors in the program before you machine the part. As you verify toolpaths, Mastercam displays additional information such as the X, Y, and Z coordinates, the path length , the minimum and maximum coordinates and the cycle time. It also shows any collisions between the workpiece and the tool.

◆ From **Mastercam Backplot Home** tab, switch to **Verify** and leave the settings for the **Visibility** and **Focus** as shown in Figure: 14.0.1.

Figure: 14.0.1

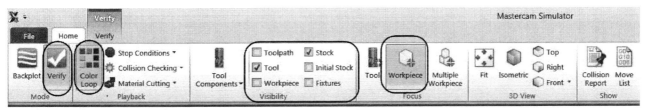

◆ Select the **Play Simulation** button in the **VCR** bar to run **Verify**.

◆ The part should appear as shown in Figure: 14.0.2.

Figure: 14.0.2

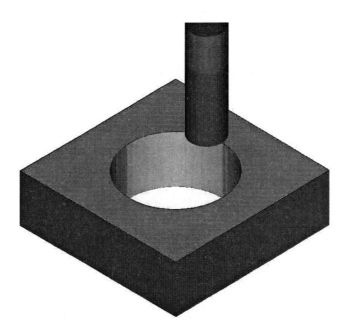

NOTE: To rotate the part, move the cursor to the center of the part and click and hold the mouse wheel and slowly move it in one direction.
To **Zoom In** or **Out** hold down the mouse wheel and scroll up or down as needed.

- Click on the **Isometric** icon and then the **Fit** icon to see the part in the original position if needed.
- To check the part step by step, click first on the **Reset simulation** icon.
- Click on the **Step Forward** to see the tool moving one step at a time.
- The part should look as shown after several steps.

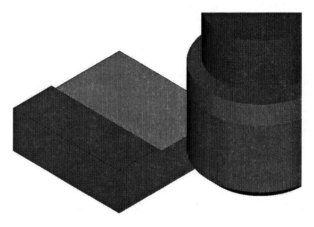

- Click on the **Step Forward** until the toolpath is completed.
- To go back to Mastercam window, minimize **Verify** window as shown.

STEP 15: CONTOUR TOOLPATH

A **Contour** toolpath removes material along a path defined by a chain of curves. A Contour toolpath only follows a chain, it does not clean out an enclosed area.

Toolpath Preview:

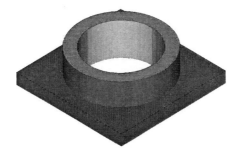

15.1 Chain selection

A chain of entities consists of one or more entities linked together in order and direction. The distance between the endpoints of two consecutive entities of the chain has to be equal or less than the chaining tolerance (0.0001"). In an open chain, the start point is placed at the end of the chain closest to the selection point and the chain direction points to the opposite end of the chain. See the **User Notes** chapter for more information on chaining.

Toolpaths

-  **Contour.**
- Leave the default settings in the **chaining dialog** box.

- Change the **Graphic view** to **Top.**

• Select the chain and ensure the chaining direction is the same as shown in Figure: 15.1.1.

Figure: 15.1.1

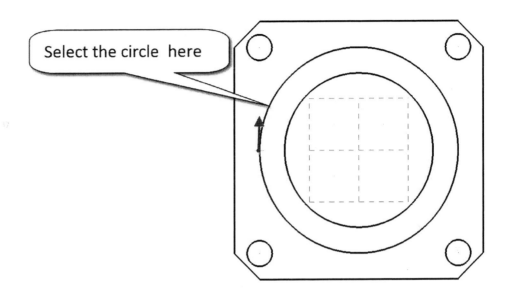

Select the circle here

• Select the **OK** button to exit the **Chaining** dialog box.
• In the **Toolpath Type** page, the **Contour** toolpath will be selected.

Contour   Pocket   Facing   Slot Mill

15.2 Select the 1/2" Flat endmill from the list and set the Tool Parameters

- Select **Tool** from the **Tree view list**.
- Make all the necessary changes as shown in Figure: 15.2.1.

Figure: 15.2.1

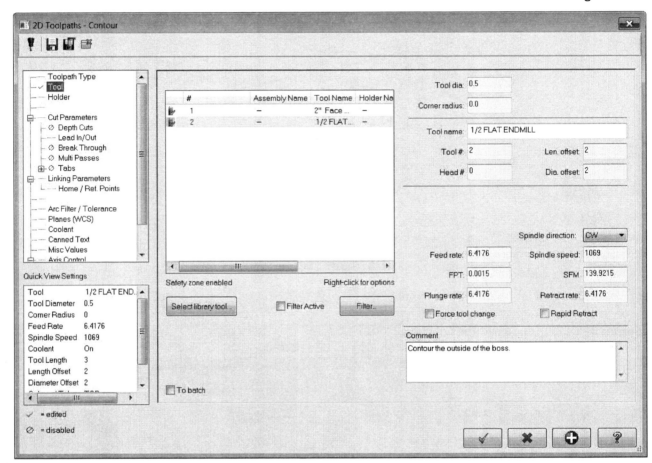

15.3 Cut Parameters

◆ Select the **Cut Parameters** and make the necessary changes as shown in Figure: 15.3.1.

Figure: 15.3.1

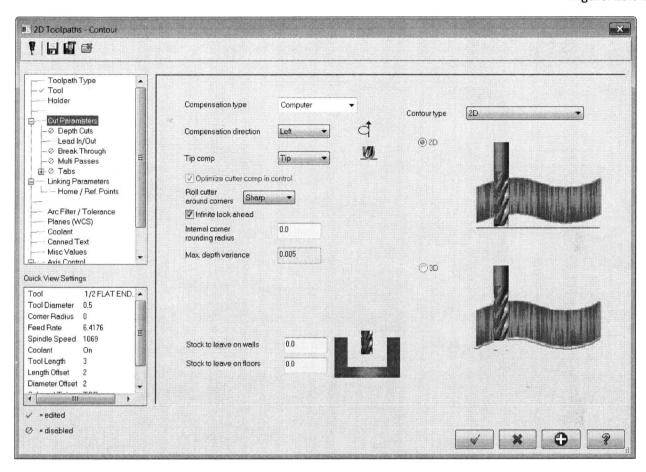

Roll cutter around corners inserts arc moves around corners in the toolpath.

None guarantees all sharp corners.

Sharp rolls the tool around sharp corners (135 degrees or less).

All rolls the tool around all corners and creates smooth tool movement.

15.4 Depth Cuts

♦ Select **Depth cuts** and enable it. Input a **Max rough step** of **0.250** and enable **Keep tool down** as shown in <u>Figure: 15.4.1</u>.

Figure: 15.4.1

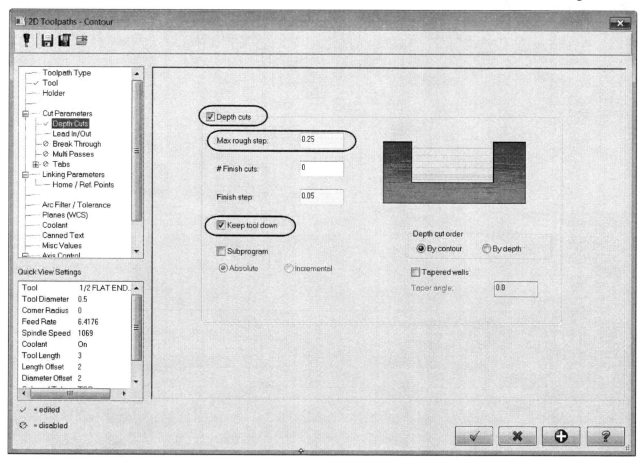

15.5 Lead In/Out

◆ Choose the option **Lead In/Out** and input an **Overlap** value. Make any other necessary changes as shown in Figure: 15.5.1.

Figure: 15.5.1

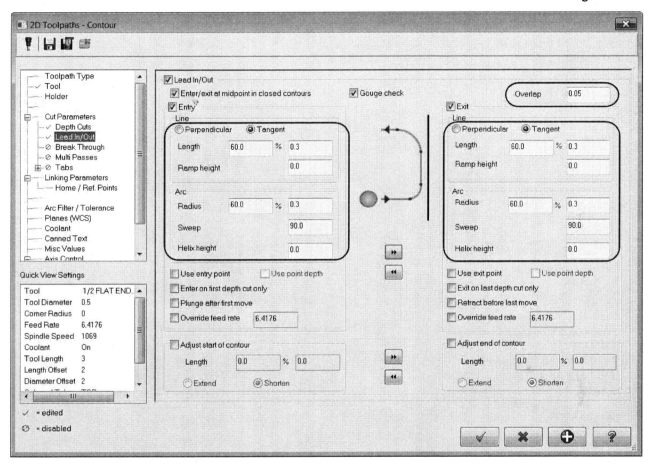

15.6 Multi Passes

◆ Select **Multi Passes** from the **Tree view list** and enable the option.
◆ Set the Number of **Rough** passes to **2** with **spacing** of **0.25** and number of **Finish** passes to **1** with **spacing** of **0.02**. This will have the system make two rough passes and then proceed with a **0.02** finish pass.
◆ Enable the option to **Machine finish passes** at the **Final depth** as shown in Figure: 15.6.1.

Figure: 15.6.1

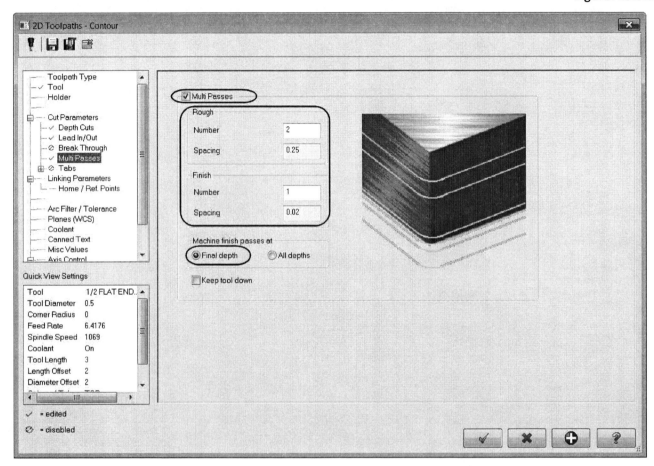

15.7 Linking Parameters

- Select **Linking Parameters** from the **Tree view list**. Set the **Top of stock** to **zero** and the **Depth** to **-0.5** as shown in Figure: 15.7.1.

Figure: 15.7.1

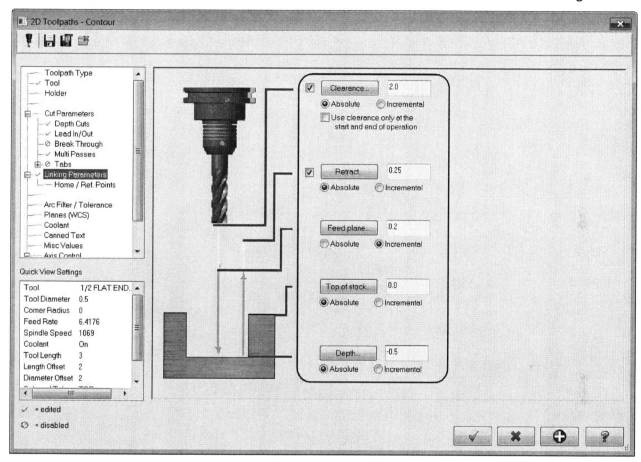

15.8 Verify the toolpaths

♦ Click on the **Verify selected operation** icon.

♦ For information on how to set the verify parameters and to simulate the toolpath, please check page 105.
♦ The part will appear as shown in Figure: 15.8.1.

Figure: 15.8.1

♦ To go back to Mastercam window, minimize **Verify** window as shown..

STEP 16: SPOT DRILL THE HOLES

Spot Drilling the holes allows you to start the hole. In this operation we will use the spot drill to chamfer the hole before drilling it.

Toolpath Preview:

◆ Select all toolpaths and press **Alt +T** to remove the toolpath display if needed.

Toolpaths

◆ 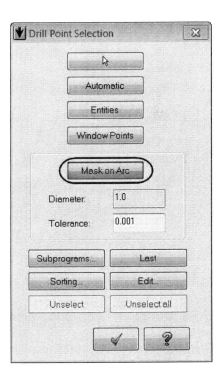 **Drill.**

◆ In the **Drill Point Selection** dialog box choose the option **Mask on Arc**.

* Select one of the four arcs.
* Left click in the upper left corner of the graphics window, holding the left button down drag a rectangle to the lower right corner of the part as shown in <u>Figure: 16.0.1</u>.

Figure: 16.0.1

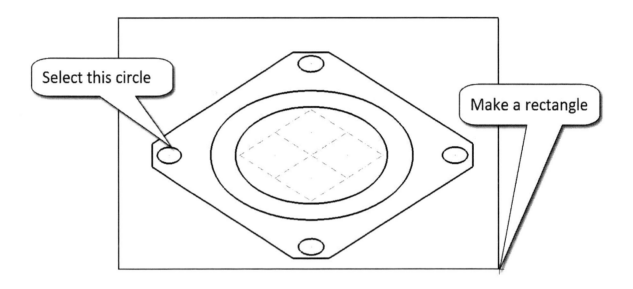

NOTE: **Mask on Arc** is a tool for selecting arcs whose diameters match the one that you select within the specified tolerance.

* Release the left mouse button and click it again once you have created a window encompassing the entire part.
* Hit **Enter** once complete.

* Select the **OK** button in the **Drill Point Selection** dialog box to accept the 4 drill points.
* In the **Toolpath Type** page, the **Drill** toolpath will be selected.

Drill   Circle Mill   Point   Helix Bore   Thread Mill

16.1 Select a 3/4" Spot Drill from the library and set the Tool Parameters

* Select **Tool** from the **Tree view list**.

* Click on the **Select library tool** button. `Select library tool...`

◆ To be able to see just the spot drill, select the filter button.

◆ Under **Tool Types** select the **None** button and then choose the **Spot drill** icon as shown in Figure: 16.1.1.

Figure: 16.1.1

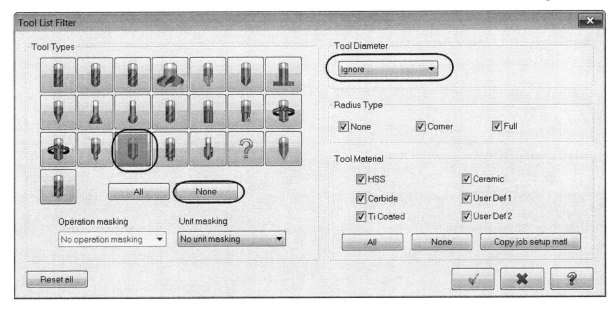

◆ Select the **OK** button to exit the **Tool List Filter** dialog box.
◆ At this point you should only see **Spot Drills**.
◆ From that list select the **3/4" Spot Drill** as shown.

#	Assembly Name	Tool Name	Holder Name	Dia.	Cor. rad.	Length	# Flutes	Type	Rad. Type
4	–	1/8 SPO...	–	0....	0.0	2.0	2	Sp...	None
5	–	1/4 SPO...	–	0.25	0.0	2.0	2	Sp...	None
6	–	1/2 SPO...	–	0.5	0.0	2.0	2	Sp...	None
198	–	3/4 SPO...	–	0.75	0.0	2.0	4	Sp...	None
312	–	1. SPOT...	–	1.0	0.0	2.0	4	Sp...	None
314	–	3/8 SPO...	–	0....	0.0	2.0	4	Sp...	None

◆ Select the tool in the **Tool Selection** page and then select the **OK** button to exit.

♦ Make the necessary changes to the **Tool** page as shown in Figure: 16.1.2.

Figure: 16.1.2

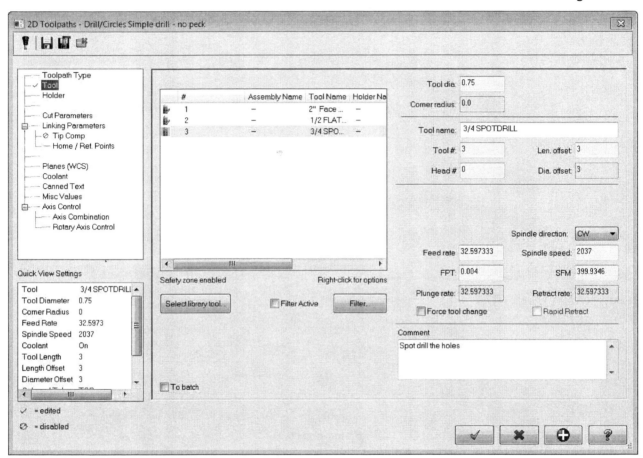

16.2 Set the Cut Parameters

◆ Select **Cut Parameters** and make the necessary changes as shown in Figure: 16.2.1.

Figure: 16.2.1

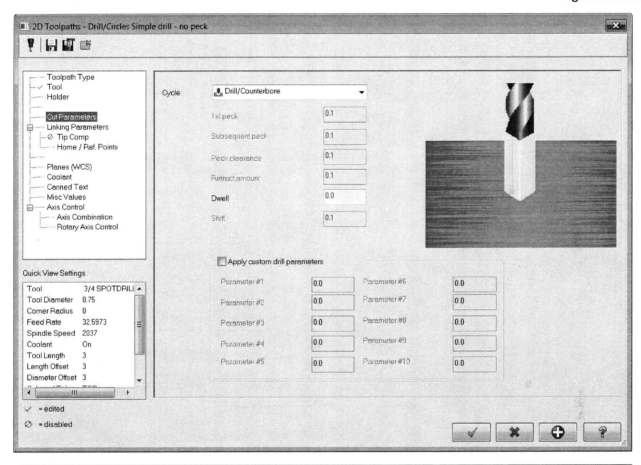

Drill/Counterbore recommended for drilling holes with depths of less than three times the tools diameter.

Dwell sets the amount of time in seconds that the tool remains at the bottom of a drilled hole.

16.3 Linking Parameters

* Choose **Linking Parameters**, ensure clearance is enabled and set the **Top of stock** and the **Depth** to **Absolute** and **-0.5** as shown.
* To input the depth select the **Calculator** icon as shown.

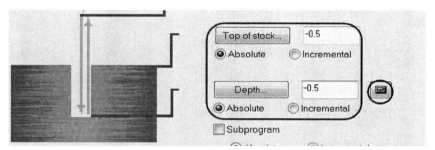

* Input the following equation in the **Finish diameter** area: **0.25+0.05** and hit **Enter** to calculate the **Depth** as shown in Figure: 16.3.1.

Figure: 16.3.1

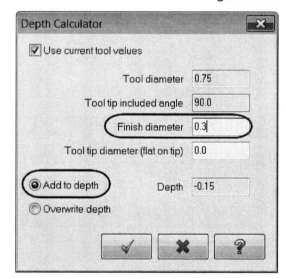

* Select the **OK** button to exit the **Depth Calculator**.

◆ You will now see the depth we calculated for the spot drilling operation set in the **Depth** field. Change the rest of the parameters as shown in <u>Figure: 16.3.2</u>.

Figure: 16.3.2

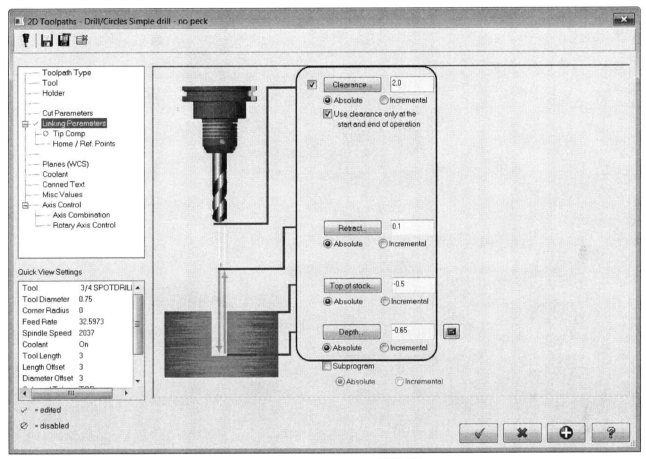

◆ Select the **OK** button to exit the **Drill/Counterbore** parameters.

16.4 Verify the toolpaths

◆ See page 105 to review the procedure.

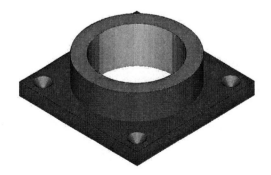

STEP 17: DRILL THE HOLES

In this step we will drill the holes to a specified depth.

Toolpath Preview:

Toolpaths

* **Drill.**
* In the **Drill Point Selection** dialog box choose the option **Last**.

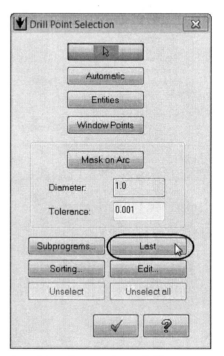

* This option will automatically select the 4 holes for you based off the selection from the previous drill operation.

* Select the **OK** button in the **Drill Point Selection** dialog box to accept the 4 drill points.

◆ In the **Toolpath Type** page, the **Drill** toolpath will be selected as shown in Figure: 17.0.1.

Figure: 17.0.1

Drill   Circle Mill   Point   Helix Bore   Thread Mill

17.1 Select a 1/4" Drill from the library and set the Tool Parameters

◆ Select **Tool** from the **Tree view list**.

◆ Click on the **Select library tool** button.

◆ To be able to see just the spot drill select the **Filter** button.

◆ Under **Tool Types** select the **None** button and then choose the drill Icon. Under **Tool Diameter** select **Equal** and input a value of **0.25**.

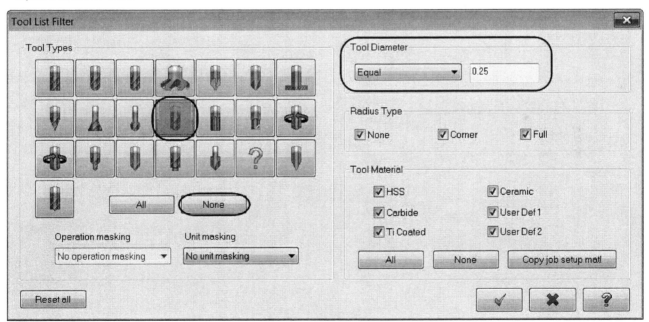

◆ Select **OK** button to exit the **Tool List Filter** dialog box.
◆ At this point you should only see a **1/4" Drill**. Select the drill as shown.

#	Assembly Name	Tool Name	Holder Name	Dia.	Cor. rad.	Length	# Flutes	Type	Rad. Type
104	–	1/4 DRILL	–	0.25	0.0	2.0	2	Drill	None

◆ Select the tool in the **Tool Selection** page and then choose the **OK** button to exit.

• Make the necessary changes to the **Tool** page as shown in Figure: 17.1.1.

Figure: 17.1.1

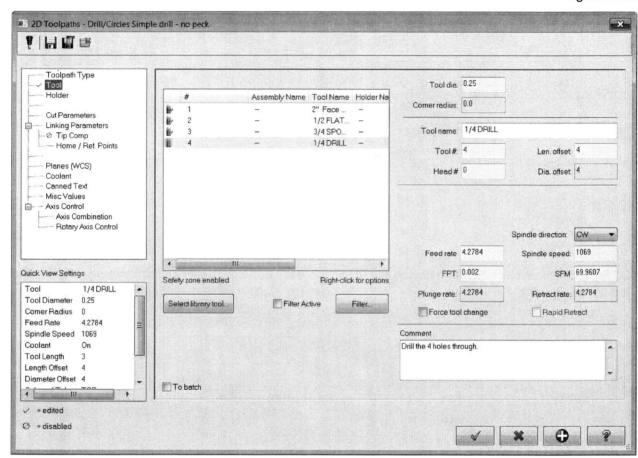

17.2 Cut Parameters

♦ Select **Cut Parameters**, change the drill **Cycle** to **Drill/Counterbore** as shown in Figure: 17.2.1.

Figure: 17.2.1

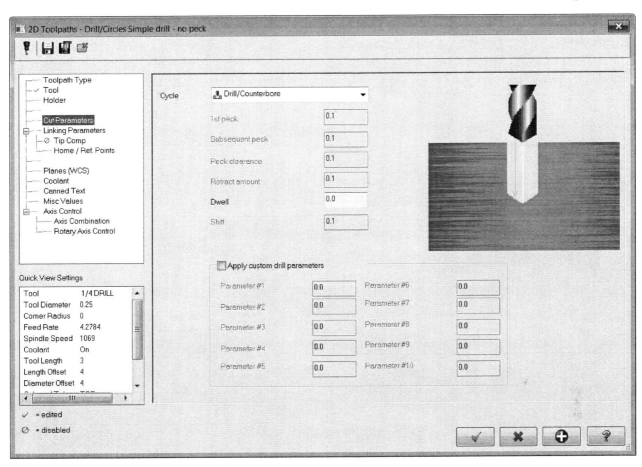

17.3 Linking Parameters

• Choose **Linking Parameters**, and set the **Top of stock** to **-0.5**. Input a depth value of **-0.75**as shown in Figure: 17.3.1.

Figure: 17.3.1

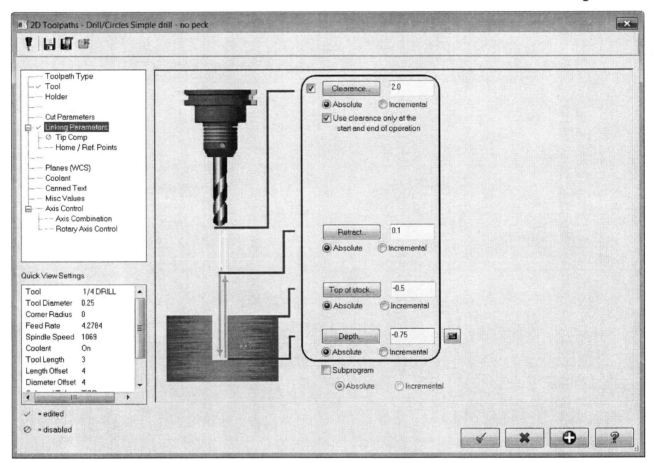

17.4 Set the Tip Compensation

• Select **Tip Comp** and enable it.
• Set the **Breakthrough amount** to **0.01** as shown in Figure: 17.4.1.

Figure: 17.4.1

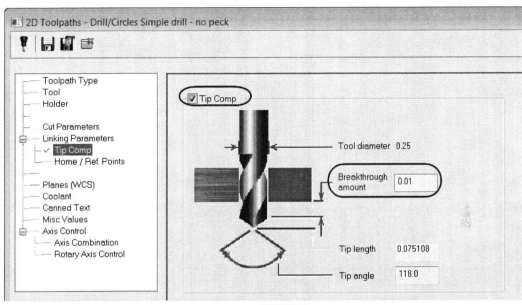

• Select the **OK** button to exit the **Drill/Counterbore** parameters.

17.5 Verify the toolpaths

• To **Verify** the toolpaths see page 105 to review the procedure.

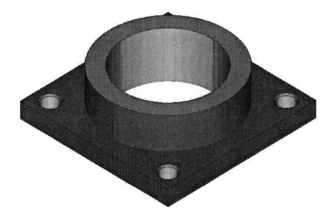

♦ To rotate the part, click in the center of the part with the mouse wheel. Hold down the mouse wheel and slightly drag the cursor to rotate.

STEP 18: CHAMFER THE TOP OF THE PART

Chamfer Toolpath automatically cuts a chamfer around a contour using a chamfer mill.

Toolpath Preview:

Toolpaths

♦  **Contour.**

• Leave the default settings in the **Chaining** dialog box as shown.

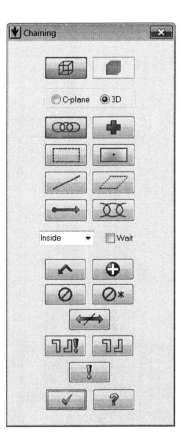

◆ Select the chains and ensure the chaining direction is the same as shown in Figure: 18.0.1.

Figure: 18.0.1

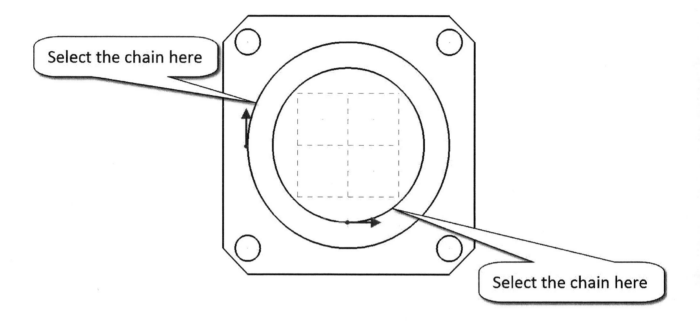

Select the chain here

Select the chain here

> **NOTE:** It does not matter which contour you select first. However the first contour you select will be the first contour cut. Select the contours as shown in Figure: 18.0.1 to ensure that the chaining directions for both chains are correct. Use Reverse button to reverse the chains if needed.

◆ Select the **OK** button to exit the **Chaining** dialog box.
◆ In the **Toolpath Type** page, the **Contour** toolpath will be selected.

Contour   Pocket   Facing   Slot Mill

18.1 Select a 1/2" Chamfer Mill from the library and set the Tool parameters

◆ Select **Tool** from the **Tree view list**.

◆ Click on the **Select library tool** button. `Select library tool...`

◆ To be able to see just the spot drill select the **Filter** button.

◆ Under **Tool Types** select the **None** button and then choose the **Chamfer Mill** Icon.

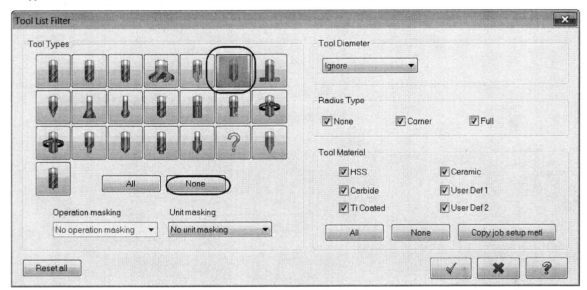

◆ Select the **OK** button to exit the **Tool List Filter** dialog box. ✓

◆ At this point you should only see a list of chamfer mills.

◆ From the **Tool Selection** list select the **1/2" Chamfer Mill**.

#	Assembly Name	Tool Name	Holder Name	Dia.	Cor. rad.	Length	# Flutes	Type	Rad. Type
304	–	1/4 CHA...	–	0....	0.0	0.5	4	Ch...	None
305	–	1/2 CHA...	–	0....	0.0	0.75	4	Ch...	None
306	–	3/4 CHA...	–	0....	0.0	1.0	4	Ch...	None
307	–	1 INCH C...	–	1....	0.0	1.0	4	Ch...	None

◆ In the **Tool Selection** page choose the **OK** button to exit. ✓

◆ A warning message that the tool selected is not defined as being capable of both roughing and finish will appear on the screen.

NOTE: The chamfer mill is defined for finish operation only. For chamfer toolpath we only need a finish operation.

◆ Select the OK button to continue.

♦ Make all the necessary changes as shown in Figure: 18.1.1.

Figure: 18.1.1

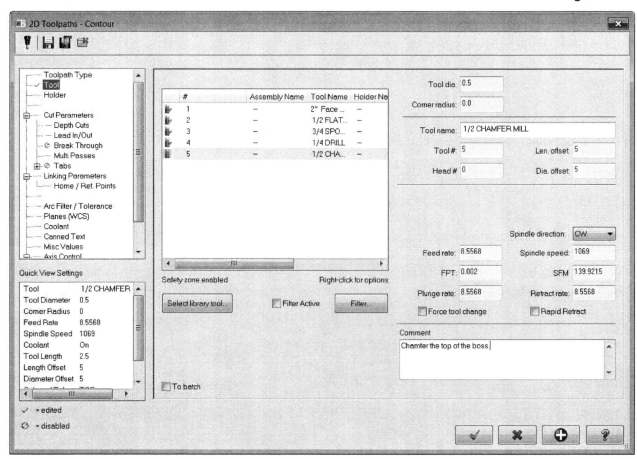

18.2 Cut Parameters

♦ Select the **Cut Parameters** page and change the **Contour type** to **2D chamfer**.
♦ Input a **Width** of **0.025** and a **Tip offset** of **0.05** as shown in Figure: 18.2.1.

Figure: 18.2.1

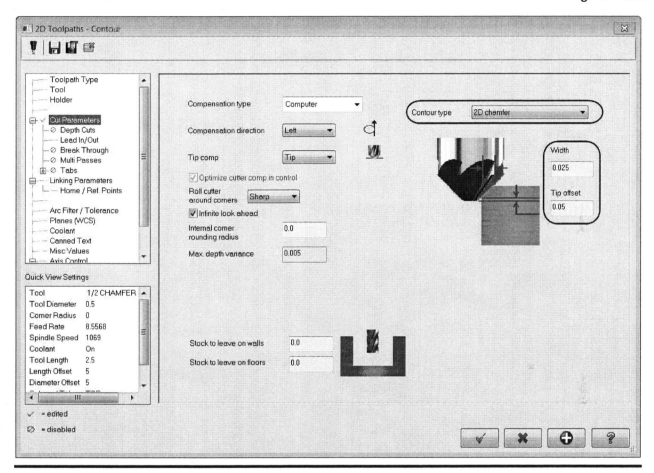

2D chamfer cuts chamfers around a contour.

Width sets the chamfer width. Mastercam measures the width from the chained geometry adjusted by the cut depths defined on the linking parameters page.

Tip offset is an amount to ensure that the tip of the tool clears the bottom of the chamfer.

18.3 Depth Cuts

◆ Select **Depth Cuts** and **disable** it as shown in <u>Figure: 18.3.1</u>.

Figure: 18.3.1

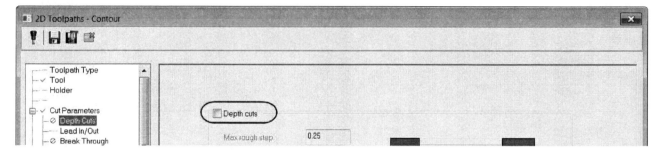

18.4 Lead In/Out

◆ Choose the option **Lead In/Out** and input an **Overlap value** of **0.02**.
◆ Make any other necessary changes as shown in <u>Figure: 18.4.1</u>.

Figure: 18.4.1

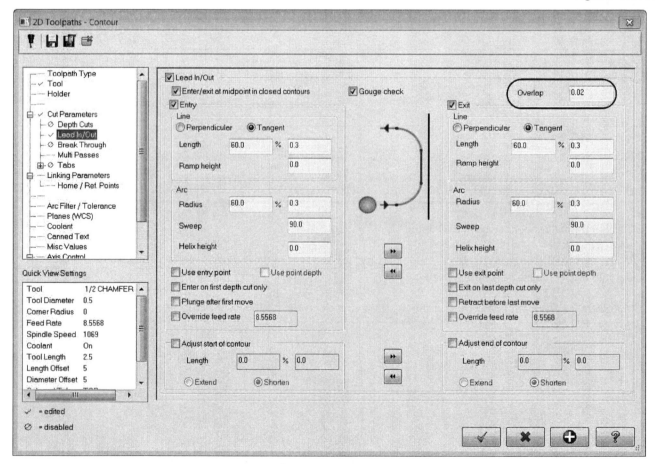

18.5 Multi Passes

◆ Select **Multi Passes**, disable this option as shown in Figure: 18.5.1.

Figure: 18.5.1

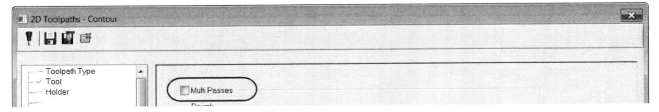

18.6 Linking Parameters

◆ Select the **Linking Parameters** from the **Tree view list**. Set the **Top of stock** to **zero** and the **Depth** to **zero** as shown in Figure: 18.6.1.

Figure: 18.6.1

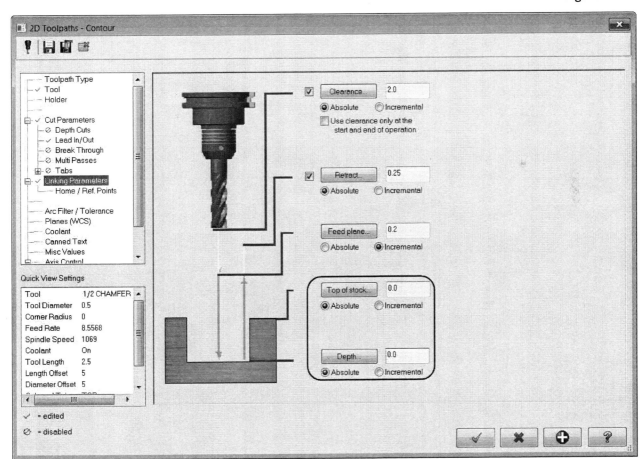

NOTE: The depth of the chamfer is based on the width and tip offset set in the Cut Parameters page. This is why we set the depth here to zero.

18.7 Verify the toolpaths

◆ To **Verify** the toolpaths see page 105 to review the procedure.
◆ Ensure all operations are selected, if they are not use the button **Select all operations** in the **Operations**

 Manager.
◆ Your part will appear as shown.

◆ To exit **Verify** click on the **Close** icon.

STEP 19: MACHINE THE CHAMFERS AT THE CORNERS USING CONTOUR TOOLPATH

In this step you will machine the corners of the part using **ContourToolpath**.

Toolpath Preview:

Toolpaths
◆ 🔲 **Contour.**

• Leave the default settings in the **Chaining** dialog box as shown.

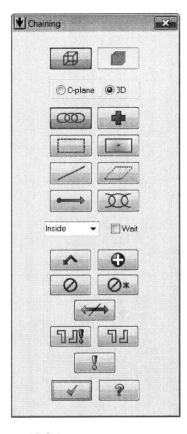

• Select the chain and ensure the chaining direction is the same as shown in Figure: 19.0.1.

Figure: 19.0.1

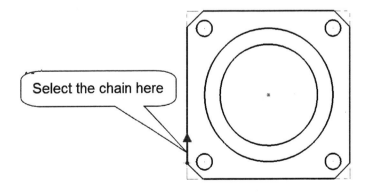

Select the chain here

NOTE: Select the contour as shown in Figure: 19.0.1 to ensure that the chaining directions for both chains are correct. Use Reverse button to reverse the chains if needed.

- Select the **OK** button to exit the **Chaining** dialog box.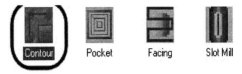
- In the **Toolpath Type** page, the **Contour** toolpath will be selected.

19.1 Select a 1/2" Flat Endmill and set the Tool parameters

- IMake all the necessary changes as shown in <u>Figure: 19.1.1</u>.

Figure: 19.1.1

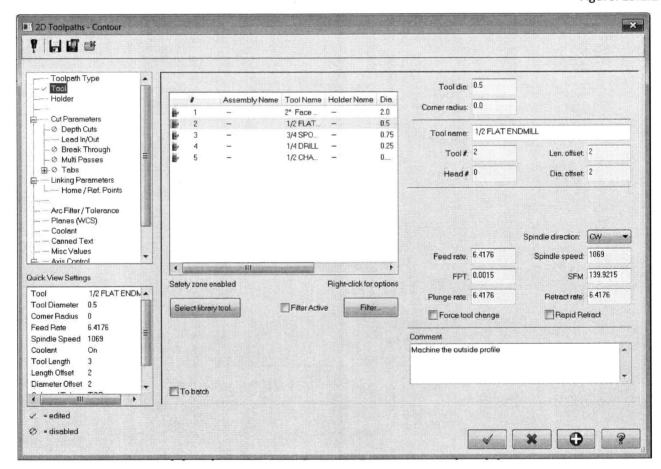

19.2 Cut Parameters

♦ Select the **Cut Parameters** page and change the **Contour type** to **2D** as shown in <u>Figure: 19.2.1</u>.

Figure: 19.2.1

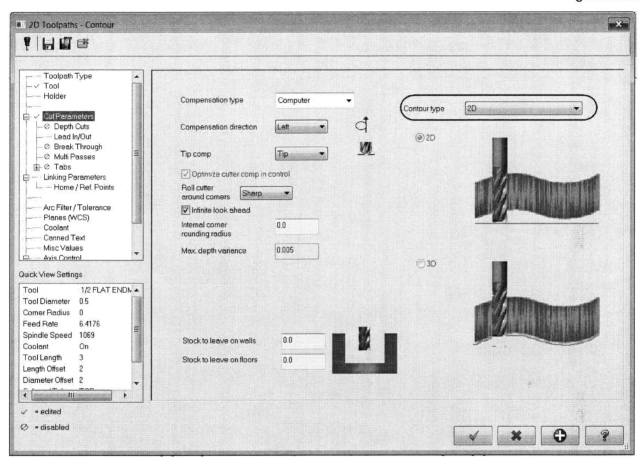

19.3 Depth Cuts

◆ Select **Depth Cuts** and enable it as shown in Figure: 19.3.1.
◆ Make sure that the parameters are set as shown in Figure: 19.3.1.

Figure: 19.3.1

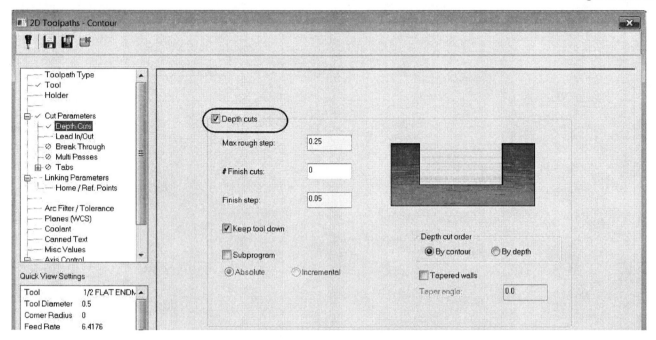

19.4 Lead In/Out

♦ Choose the option **Lead In/Out** and make sure the parameters are set as shown in Figure: 19.4.1.

Figure: 19.4.1

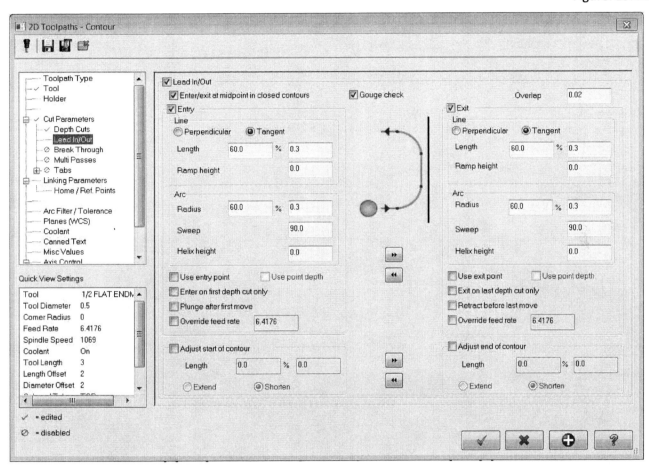

19.5 Linking Parameters

 • Select the **Linking Parameters** from the **Tree view list**. Set the **Top of stock** and the **Depth** as shown in Figure: 19.5.1.

Figure: 19.5.1

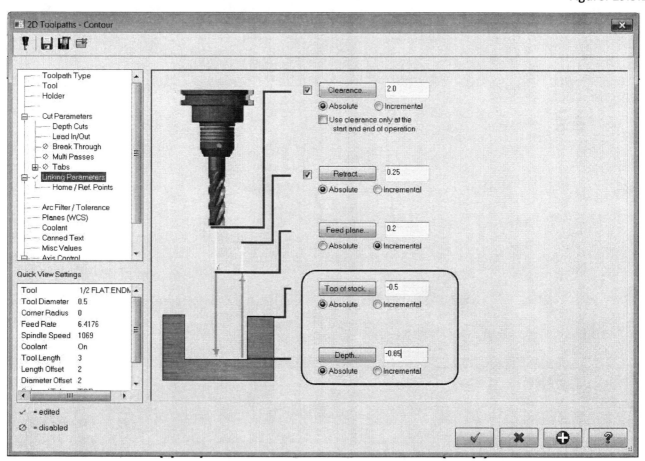

NOTE: The Top of stock is set to -0.5 as the previous contour machine the part up to this depth.

19.6 Verify the toolpaths

• To **Verify** the toolpaths see page 105 to review the procedure.
• Ensure all operations are selected, if they are not use the button **Select all operations** in the **Operations**

Manager.
• Your part will appear as shown.

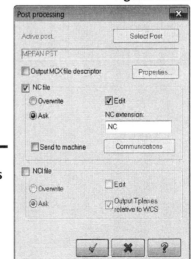

• To exit **Verify** click on the **Close** icon.

STEP 20: POST THE FILE

• Ensure all operations are selected, if they are not use the button **Select all operations** in the **Operations**

Manager.

• Select the **Post selected operations** button from the **Operations Manager.**
• In the **Post processing** window make the necessary changes as shown in Figure: 20.0.1.

Figure: 20.0.1

NC File enabled allows you to keep the NC file and to assign the same name as the MCX file.

Edit enabled allows you to automatically launch the default editor.

• Select the **OK** button to continue.

- Save the NC file.
- A window with Mastercam Code Expert will be lunched and the NC program will appear as shown in Figure: 20.0.2.

Figure: 20.0.2

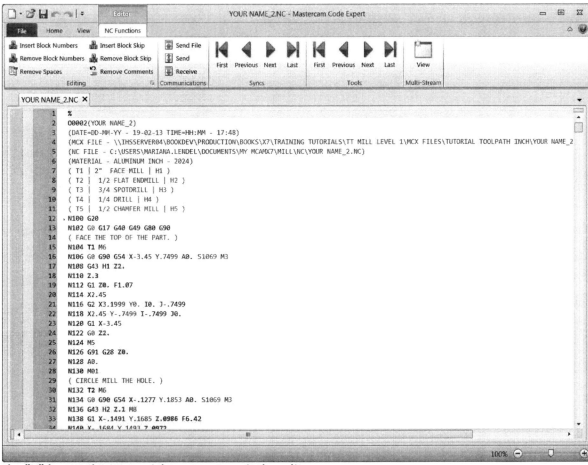

- Select the "X" box at the upper right corner to exit the editor.

STEP 21: SAVE THE UPDATED MCX FILE

REVIEW EXERCISE -STUDENT PRACTICE

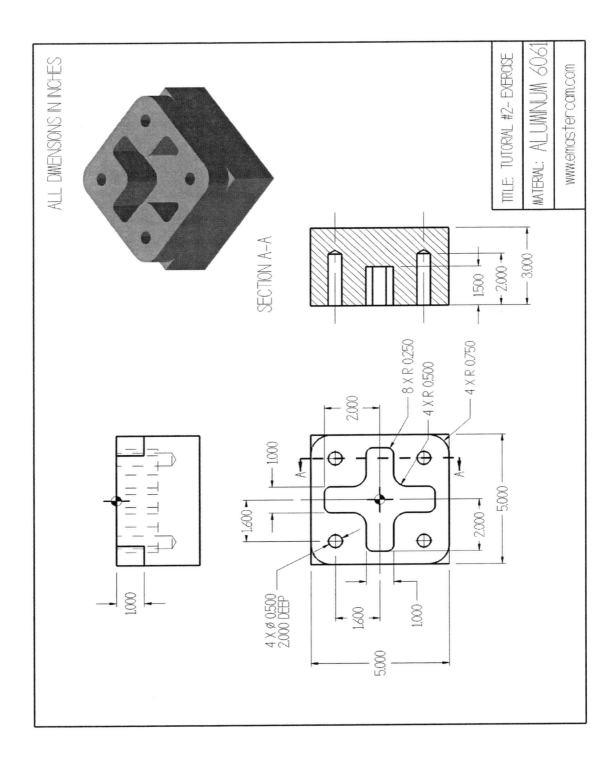

CREATE THE GEOMETRY FOR TUTORIAL #2 EXERCISE

Use these commands to create the geometry.
- Create Rectangle.
- Create Fillets.
- Create Lines.
- Create Line Parallel.
- Create Circle Center Points.
- Fast Point to position the Circles.
- Trim.

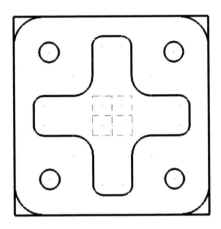

CREATE THE TOOLPATHS FOR TUTORIAL #2 EXERCISE

Create the Toolpaths for Tutorial #2 Exercise as per the instructions below.

Set the machine properties including the stock.
Remove the material on the outside of the part Contour (2D).
- Use a **1/2" Flat Endmill**.
- Based on your chaining direction ensure the **Compensation direction** is set correctly.
- Enable **Depth Cuts** and set the **Max rough step** to **0.25"**.
- **Lead In/Out** set **Length** and **Radius** to **60%** with a **90** degree sweep.
- No **Break Through**, **Multi Passes**.
- Set the depth according to the drawing.

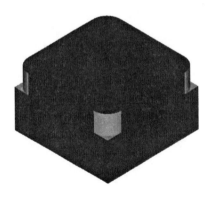

Spot drill the holes.
- Use a **3/4" Spot Drill**.
- Set the **Cycle** to **Drill/Counterbore** and set a **Dwell** to **1.0** second.
- Use the depth calculator to set a **0.05"** chamfer on the hole.

Drill the holes.
- Use a **1/2" Drill**.
- Set the Cycle to Peck Drill and set your peck values.
- Set the depth according to the drawing.

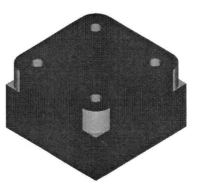

Remove the Material in the center of the part (Pocket Standard).
- Use a **1/2" Flat Endmill**.
- Choose to leave no stock on the walls.
- Set the **Cutting method** to **Constant Overlap Spiral.**
- The **Entry Motion** will be **Helix**.
- Enable **Finish** and set the parameters.
- **Lead In/Out** set **Length** and **Radius** to **60%** with a **90** degree sweep.
- Enable **Depth Cuts** and set the **Max rough step** to **0.25"**.
- Disable **Break Through**.
- Set the depth according to the drawing.

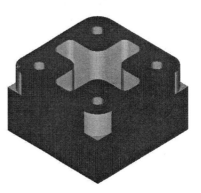

NOTES:

TUTORIAL #2 QUIZ

◆ What is a Facing Toolpath used for?

◆ What does a Pocket Toolpath allow you to do?

◆ What is the difference between Climb and Conventional cutting?

◆ What does verify allow you to do?

Mill Level 1 Training Tutorial

TUTORIAL #3

OVERVIEW OF STEPS TAKEN TO CREATE THE FINAL PART:

From Drawing to CAD Model:
- The student should examine the drawing on the following page to understand what part is being created in the tutorial.
- From the drawing we can decide how to go about creating the geometry in Mastercam.

Create the 2D CAD Model used to generate Toolpaths from:
- The student will create the Top 2D geometry needed to create the toolpaths.
- Geometry creation commands such as rectangle, polygon, fillet entities, fillet chain, arc circle center point, line endpoints, rectangular shapes and trim will be used.

Create the necessary Toolpaths to machine the part:
- The student will set up the stock size to be used and the clamping method used.

Setup 1
- A Slot Mill toolpath will be created to machine the slot.
- 2D High Speed Dynamic Core mill toolpath will be created to rough out the outside profile.
- A Contour toolpath will be created to finish the outside profile.
- 2D High Speed Dynamic Contour mill toolpath will be created to machine the small radii.

Setup 2
- A Facing toolpath will be used to face the bottom of the part.

Backplot and Verify the file:
- The Backplot will be used to simulate a step by step process of the tool's movements.
- The Verify will be used to watch a tool machine the part out of a solid model.

Post Process the file to generate the G-code:
- The Student will then post process the file to obtain an NC file containing the necessary code for the machine.

 This tutorial takes approximately two hours to complete.

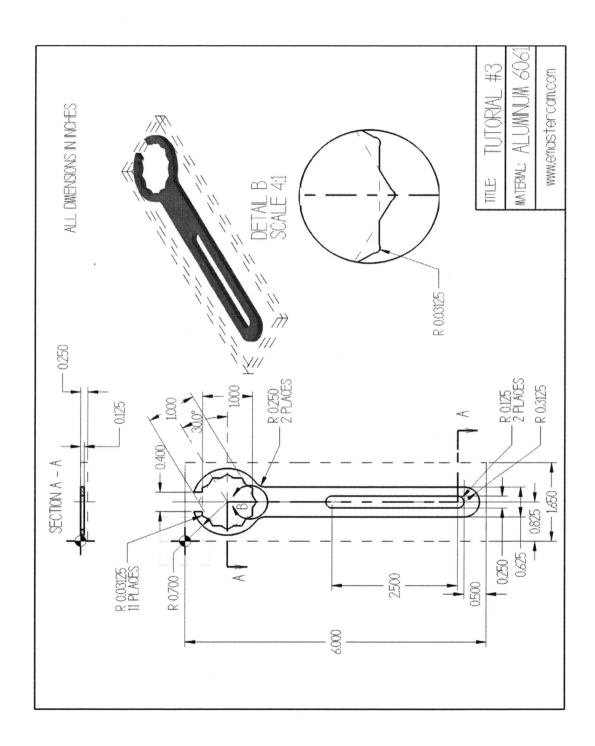

ALL DIMENSIONS IN INCHES

DETAIL B
SCALE 4:1

R 0.03125

SECTION A - A

0.250

0.125

1.000

1.000

30.0°

R 0.250
2 PLACES

R 0.03125
11 PLACES

R 0.700

0.400

R 0.125
2 PLACES

R 0.3125

1.650

0.825

0.250

0.625

0.500

2.500

6.000

A

A

B

TITLE: TUTORIAL #3

MATERIAL: ALUMINUM 6061

www.emastercam.com

GEOMETRY CREATION

STEP 1: SETTING UP THE GRAPHIC USER INTERFACE

Please refer to the **Getting Started** section to set up the graphics user interface.

STEP 2: CREATE A RECTANGLE

In this step you will learn how to create a rectangle knowing the width, the height and the anchor position.

Step Preview:

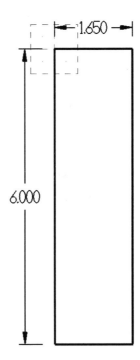

Create

+ 🔲 ▼ **Rectangle.**

+ Enter the **Width** 📐 **1.65** and **Height** 📐 **-6.0** as shown.   `1.65 ▼` `-6.0 ▼`   🔲 🔲
+ Press **Enter** after typing the values to see a preview of the rectangle.

♦ [Select position of first corner]: Select the **Origin** as shown in <u>Figure: 2.0.1</u>.

Figure: 2.0.1

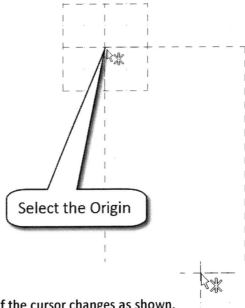

Select the Origin

♦ Make sure that when selecting the origin, the visual cue of the cursor changes as shown.

♦ Select the **OK** button to exit the **Rectangle** command.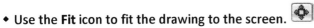

♦ Use the **Fit** icon to fit the drawing to the screen.

NOTE: During the geometry creation of this tutorial, if you make a mistake you can undo the last step using the **Undo** icon. You can undo as many steps as needed. If you delete or undo a step by mistake, just use the **Redo** icon. To delete unwanted geometry, select it first and then press **Delete** from the keyboard.

STEP 3: CREATE TWO POLYGONS

In this step you will learn how to create two six side polygons. To Create A Polygon you need to define the number of sides, the radius of the arc based on which the polygon is created and how it is measured (Corner or Flat) and the center point.

Step Preview:

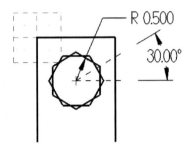

3.1 Create the straight polygon

Create

* ⬠ **Polygon.**
* Change the settings in the dialog box to create a six side polygon with the arc radius **0.5"** measured to the flats as shown in Figure: 3.1.1.

Figure: 3.1.1

* [Select position of base point]: Select the **Fast point** icon 🔧 and enter the coordinates as shown.

> 0.825, -0.875

◆ Press **Enter** to see the polygon created in the windows graphics as shown.

◆ Select the **Apply** button to continue in the same command.

3.2 Create the 30 degrees rotated polygon

◆ Expand the dialog box by selecting the upper left arrow as shown.

◆ Re-enter the arc radius **0.5** (although the value is still showing in the dialog box) and enter the rotation angle **30** degrees as shown in Figure: 3.2.1.

Figure: 3.2.1

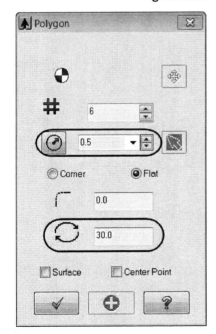

- [Select position of base point]: Select the **Fast point** icon 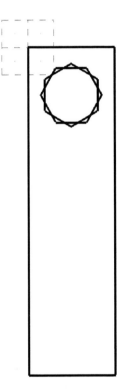 and enter the coordinates as shown.

0.825, -0.875

- Press **Enter** to see the polygon created in the windows graphics as shown.

- Select the **OK** button to exit the command.

STEP 4: USE TRIM DIVIDE TO CLEAN THE POLYGONS

In this step you will learn how to trim the geometry using **Divide** option. **Divide** allows you to trim an entity into two disjointed segments by removing the segment that lies between two dividing intersections. It can also allow you to delete entities based on the nearest intersection. Pick always the segment in the area that has to be removed.

Step Preview:

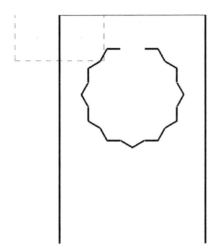

* To better see the area that we are working on, **Zoom in** by moving the cursor as shown and then scroll up the mouse wheel.
* The geometry should look as shown.

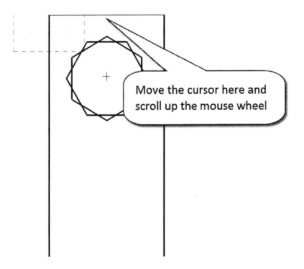

Move the cursor here and scroll up the mouse wheel

Edit
* **Trim/Break.**

*  **Trim/Break/Extend.**
* Select the **Divide** command and ensure the option to **Trim** is enabled as shown.

◆ Select the lines as shown in Figure: 4.0.1.

Figure: 4.0.1

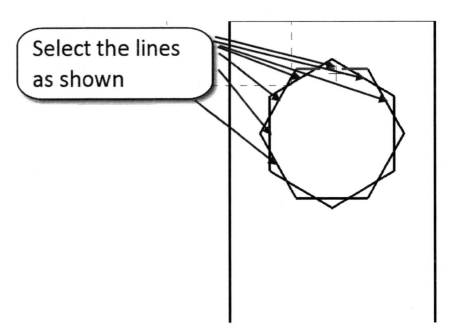

Select the lines as shown

NOTE: When selecting the line you will notice the line change to a hidden line style. This is a preview of what is going to be deleted and lets you select another segment of the line if necessary.

◆ Repeat the step selecting the lines as shown in Figure: 4.0.2.

Figure: 4.0.2

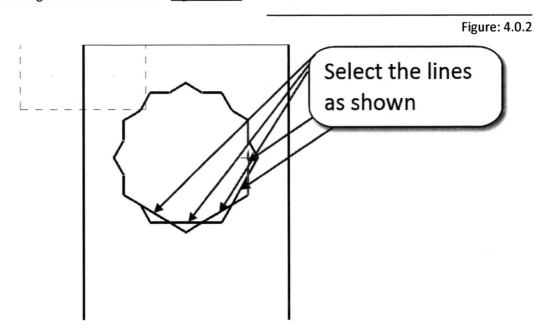

Select the lines as shown

◆ Your drawing will appear as shown.

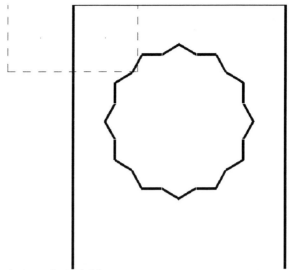

◆ Select the lines shown in <u>Figure: 4.0.3</u> to delete them using **Divide**.

Figure: 4.0.3

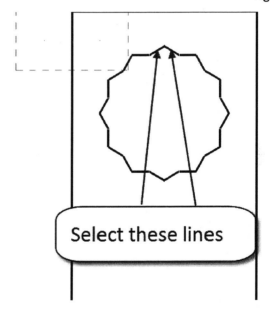

Select these lines

♦ The geometry should look as shown.

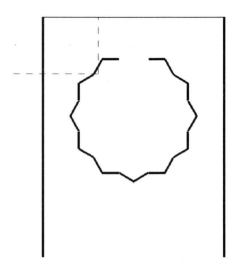

♦ Select the **OK** icon to exit the command.

STEP 5: CREATE THE CLEARANCE STYLE ARCS

In this step you will learn how to use **Fillet chains** command to create the clearance style arcs with the 0.035 radius.

Step Preview:

R 0.035
TYP.

Mastercam. X⁷

Create

♦ **Fillet.**

♦  **Chains.**

♦ The Chaining dialog box appears on the screen as shown.

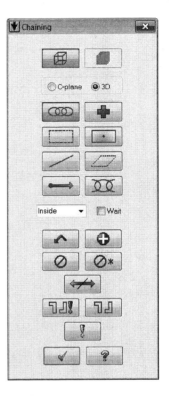

♦ [Select chain1]: Select the chain as shown in Figure: 5.0.1.

Figure: 5.0.1

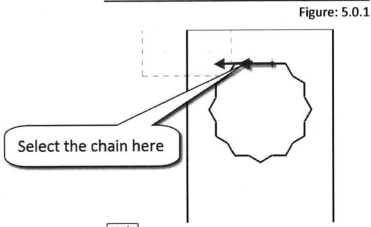

Select the chain here

♦ From the **Chaining** dialog box, select the **OK** button to continue.

♦ In the **Ribbon bar**, enter the **Radius 0.035** and click on the down arrow to change the fillet **Style** to **Clearance** as shown. Make the **Trim** icon is selected too as shown.

• Select the **OK** icon to exit the command.
• The drawing will appear as shown.

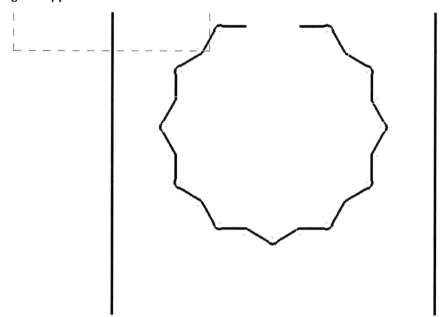

• Select the **Fit** icon to fit the geometry to the screen.

STEP 6: CREATE CIRCLES

In this step you will create two circles knowing the radii and the center locations.

Step Preview:

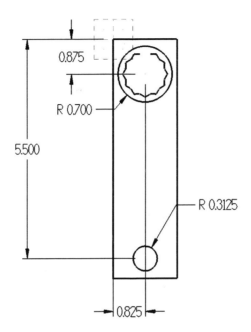

Create
♦ **Arc.**

♦  **Circle Center Point.**

♦ Input the **0.7 Radius** in the **Ribbon bar** as shown.

♦ Select the **Fast Point** icon from the **AutoCursor Ribbon Bar.**

0.825, -0.875

♦ Enter the dimensions as shown, then hit **Enter** on your keyboard to place the circle.

♦ From the **Ribbon bar**, select the **Apply** icon to finish the circle and to continue in the same command.

♦ Input the **0.3125 Radius** in the **Ribbon bar** as shown.

♦ Select the **Fast Point** again.

♦ Enter the dimensions **0.825, -5.5** and hit **Enter** on the keyboard once again.

♦ Once complete choose the **OK** button to exit the command.

♦ The geometry should look as shown.

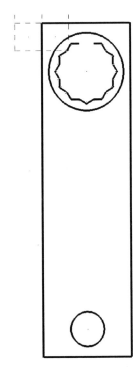

STEP 7: CREATE THE VERTICAL LINES

In this step you will learn how to create vertical lines.

Step Preview:

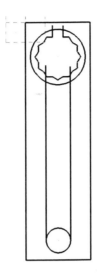

Create

♦ **Line.**

♦  **Endpoint.**

♦ Select the **Vertical** icon as shown.

> **NOTE:** Once this icon has been selected you will only be able to create vertical lines.

♦ [Specify the first endpoint]: Select the **Endpoint** as shown in <u>Figure: 7.0.1</u>.

Figure: 7.0.1

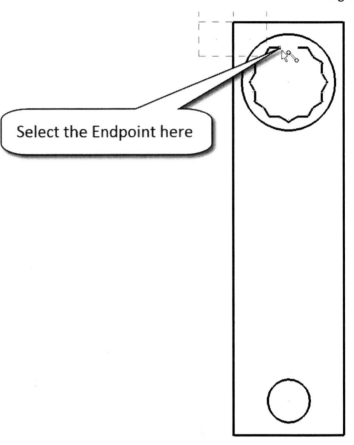

Select the Endpoint here

• [Specify the second endpoint]: Pick a point above the circle to create a vertical line as shown in <u>Figure: 7.0.2</u>.

Figure: 7.0.2

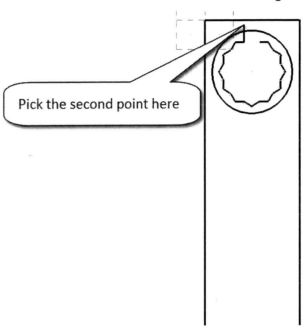

Pick the second point here

• Choose the **Apply** button to continue. ⊕
• Repeat this same step creating the second line as shown in <u>Figure: 7.0.3</u>.

Figure: 7.0.3

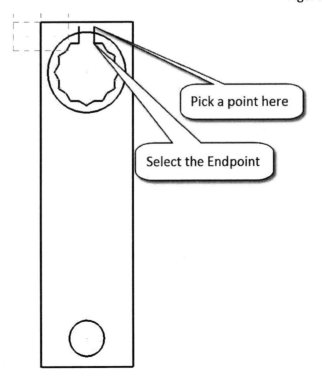

Pick a point here

Select the Endpoint

• Choose the **Apply** button to continue.
• [Specify the first endpoint]: Select the **Midpoint** as shown in Figure: 7.0.4.

Figure: 7.0.4

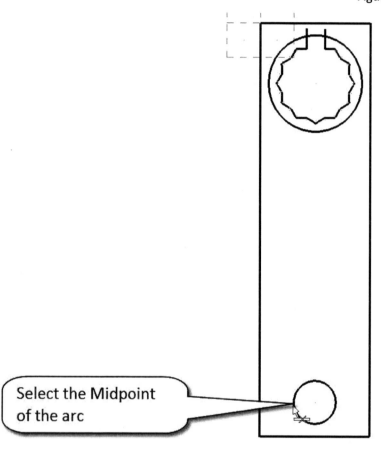

Select the Midpoint
of the arc

• [Specify the second endpoint]: Pick a point inside the polygon shape to create a vertical line as shown in
  Figure: 7.0.5.

Figure: 7.0.5

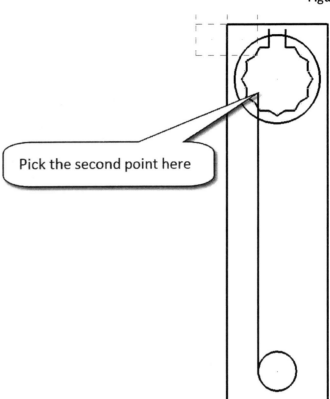

Pick the second point here

• Repeat this same step creating the second line as shown in Figure: 7.0.6.

Figure: 7.0.6

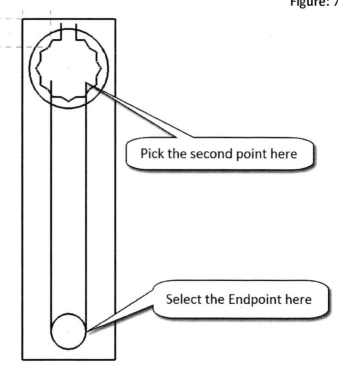

Pick the second point here

Select the Endpoint here

• Select the **OK** button once complete.

STEP 8: USE TRIM DIVIDE TO CLEAN THE GEOMETRY

Step Preview:

- To better see the area that we are working on, **Zoom in** by placing the cursor as shown and then scroll up the mouse wheel.

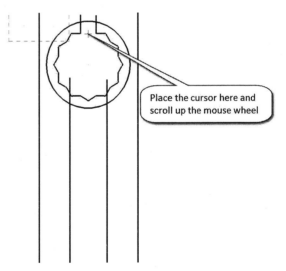

Place the cursor here and scroll up the mouse wheel

Edit
- **Trim/Break.**
- **Trim/Break/Extend.**
- Select the **Divide** command and ensure the option to **Trim** is enabled as shown.

◆ Select the lines and the arcs as shown in <u>Figure: 8.0.1</u>.

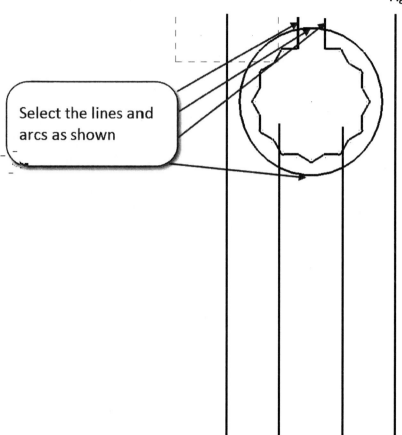

Figure: 8.0.1

Select the lines and arcs as shown

◆ Select the **Fit** icon.

◆ Repeat the step selecting the lines as shown in <u>Figure: 8.0.2</u>.

Figure: 8.0.2

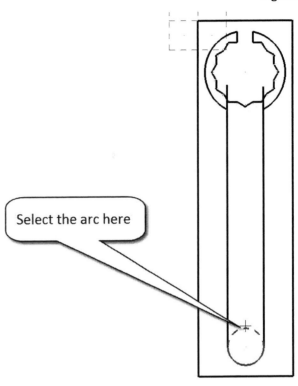

Select the arc here

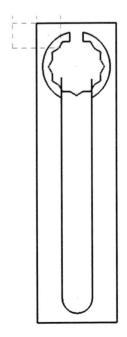

◆ Select the **OK** icon to exit the command.
◆ The geometry should look as shown.

STEP 9: CREATE FILLETS

Fillets are used to round sharp corners.

Step Preview:

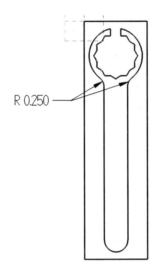

R 0.250

Create
- ◆ **Fillet.**
- ◆  **Entities.**
- ◆ Enter a fillet radius of **0.25**. Ensure the fillet style is set to **Normal** and **Trim** is enabled as shown.

- [Select an entity]: Select Entity A as shown in Figure: 9.0.1.
- [Select another entity]: Select Entity B as shown.

Figure: 9.0.1

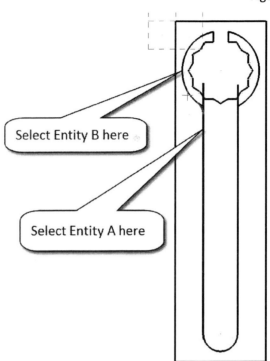

- ◆ [Select an entity]: Select Entity C as shown in <u>Figure: 9.0.2</u>.
- ◆ [Select another entity]: Select Entity D as shown.

Figure: 9.0.2

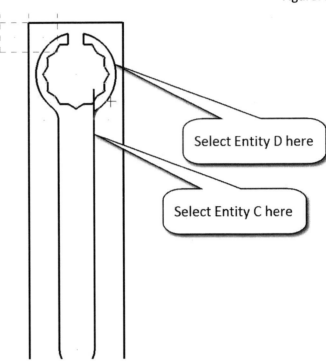

Select Entity D here

Select Entity C here

- ◆ Select the **OK** button to exit the command. ✅
- ◆ The geometry should look as shown.

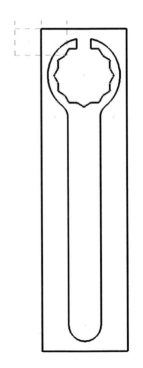

STEP 10: CREATE THE RECTANGULAR SHAPE

Create the **Obround Shape** which consists of 2 straight lines and two 180 degrees arcs at the ends using **Rectangular shapes** command.

Step Preview:

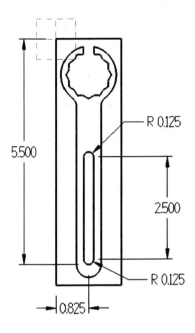

Create

* **Rectangular Shapes.**
* Enter the **Width** and the **Height** in the **Rectangular Shapes Options** dialog box as shown in <u>Figure: 10.0.1</u>.

> **NOTE:** Mastercam can perform basic math functions as shown in <u>Figure: 10.0.1</u>.

Figure: 10.0.1

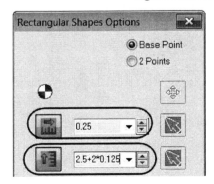

• Set the rest of the parameters as shown in Figure: 10.0.2.

Figure: 10.0.2

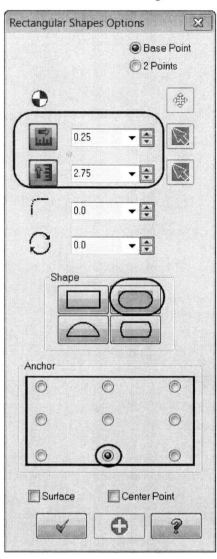

• [Select position of base point]: Select the **Fast point** icon  and enter the values as shown.

```
0.825, -5.5
```

• Press **Enter** to place the obround shape.

◆ The geometry should look as shown.

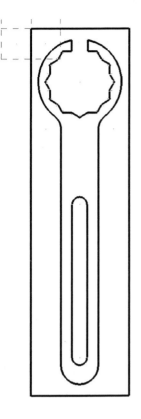

◆ Select the **OK** button to exit the **Rectangular Shape Options**. ✓

STEP 11: SAVE THE FILE

File

◆ 💾 **Save As.**

◆ File name: "Your Name_3".

TOOLPATH CREATION - SETUP 1

SUGGESTED FIXTURE:

> **NOTE:** In order to machine this part we will have 2 setups and output 2 NC files. To view the second setup, see page 233.

SETUP SHEET:

__TOOL LIST__

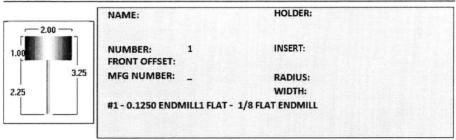

NAME:	HOLDER:
NUMBER: 1	INSERT:
FRONT OFFSET:	
MFG NUMBER: _	RADIUS:
	WIDTH:

#1 - 0.1250 ENDMILL1 FLAT - 1/8 FLAT ENDMILL

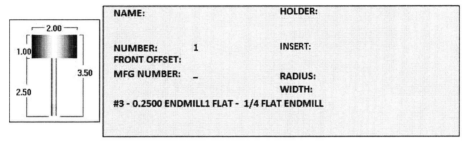

NAME:	HOLDER:
NUMBER: 1	INSERT:
FRONT OFFSET:	
MFG NUMBER: _	RADIUS:
	WIDTH:

#3 - 0.2500 ENDMILL1 FLAT - 1/4 FLAT ENDMILL

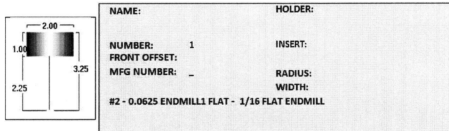

NAME:	HOLDER:
NUMBER: 1	INSERT:
FRONT OFFSET:	
MFG NUMBER: _	RADIUS:
	WIDTH:

#2 - 0.0625 ENDMILL1 FLAT - 1/16 FLAT ENDMILL

STEP 12: SELECT THE MACHINE AND SET UP THE STOCK

In Mastercam, you select a **Machine Definition** before creating any toolpaths. The **Machine Definition** is a model of your machines capabilities and features. It acts like a template for setting up your machine. The machine definition ties together three main components. The schematic model of your machines components. The control definition that models your control capabilities and the post processor that will generate the required machine code (G-code). For a Mill Level 1 exercise (2D toolpaths) we need just a basic machine definition.

> **NOTE:** For the purpose of this tutorial, we will be using the Default milling machine.

- ✦ To display the **Operations Manager** press **Alt + O**.

- ✦ Use the **Fit** icon to fit the drawing to the screen. ⊕
Machine type
- ✦ **Mill.**
- ✦ **Default.**

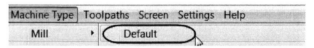

- ✦ Select the plus sign in front of **Properties** in the **Toolpaths Manager** to expand the **Toolpaths Group Properties.**

Select the Plus sign

- ✦ Select **Tool Settings** to set the tool parameters.

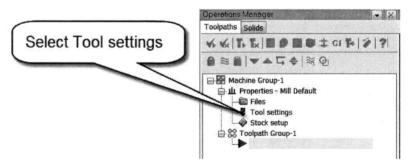

Select Tool settings

◆ Change the parameters to match the screen shot as shown in Figure: 12.0.1.

Figure: 12.0.1

Program # is used to enter a number if your machine tool requires a number for a program name.

Assign tool numbers sequentially allows you to overwrite the tool number from the library with the next available tool number. (First operation tool number 1; Second operation tool number 2, etc.)

Warn of duplicate tool numbers allows you to get a warning if you enter two tools with the same number.

Override defaults with modal values enables the system to keep the values that you enter.

Feed Calculation set From tool uses feed rate, plunge rate, retract rate and spindle speed from the tool definition.

◆ Select the Stock setup tab to define the stock.
◆ Select the All Entities button near the bottom of the Stock Setup page as shown.

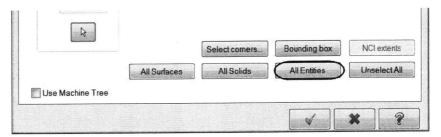

◆ If the Bounding box message "Override 2D construction mode?" appears select the Yes button to continue.

- In the **Stock thickness** enter **0.25** as shown in Figure: 12.0.2. This will add **0.125"** of stock on the bottom of the model.
- Click in the graphics area at the upper left corner to move the arrow where the origin is set and then change the **Stock origin** values to zero as shown in Figure: 12.0.2.

Figure: 12.0.2

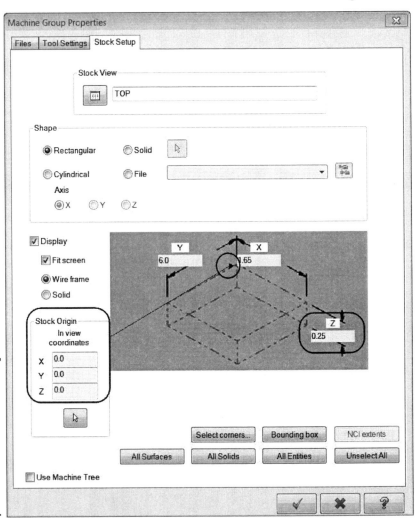

The **Stock Origin** values adjust the positioning of the stock, ensuring that you have equal amount of extra stock around the finished part.

Display options allow you to set the stock as **Wireframe** and to fit the stock to the screen. (Fit Screen)

- Select the **OK** button to exit **Machine Group Properties**.

- Select the **Isometric** view from the graphics view toolbar to see the stock.

- Use the **Fit** icon to fit the drawing to the screen.

◆ The stock model will appear as shown.

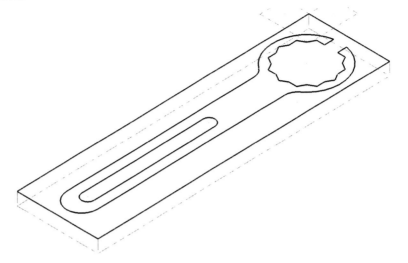

> **NOTE:** The stock is not geometry and can not be selected.

◆ Select the **Top** view from the view toolbar to see the part from the top.

> **NOTE:** There will not be facing toolpath because the stock is already to size.

STEP 13: SLOT MILLING

Slot Mill toolpath allows Mastercam to efficiently machine obround slots. These are slots that consist of 2 straight lines and two 180-degree arcs at the ends.

Toolpath Preview:

Toolpaths
- **Circle Paths.**

- 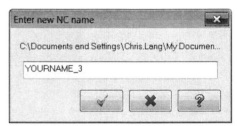 **Slot Mill.**

- If a prompt appears, **Enter new NC name**, select the **OK** button to accept the default.

- When the chaining dialog box appears, choose **Chain** as the chaining method as shown.

◆ Select the chain as shown in <u>Figure: 13.0.1</u>.

Figure: 13.0.1

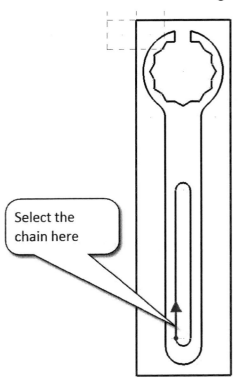

Select the
chain here

◆ Choose the **OK** button to exit the **Chaining** dialog box.
◆ In the **Toolpath Type** page, the **Slot Mill** icon will be selected.

Contour   Pocket   Facing   Slot Mill

NOTE: Mastercam updates the pages as you modify them and then marks them, in the **Tree view list,** with a green check mark. Pages that are not changed are marked with a red circle and slash.

13.1 Select a 1/8" Flat Endmill and set the Tool Parameters

◆ Select **Tool** from the **Tree view list.**

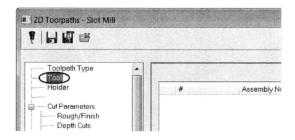

◆ Click on **Select library tool** button.
◆ Select the **Filter** button.

◆ Select the **None** button and then under **Tool Types** choose the **Flat Endmill** icon.
◆ Under tool diameter pick **Equal** and input a value **0.125** as shown in Figure: 13.1.1.

Figure: 13.1.1

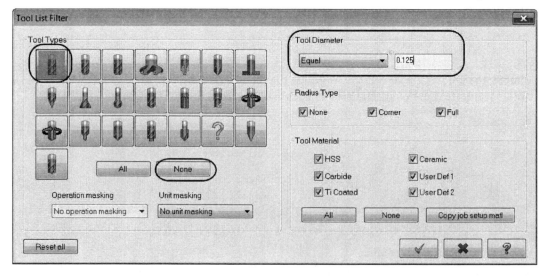

◆ Select the **OK** button to exit the **Tool List Filter.**
◆ In the **Tool Selection** dialog box you should only see a **1/8" Flat Endmill.**

◆ Select the **1/8" Flat Endmill** in the **Tool Selection** page and then select the **OK** button to exit.

◆ Make all the necessary changes as shown in Figure: 13.1.2.

Figure: 13.1.2

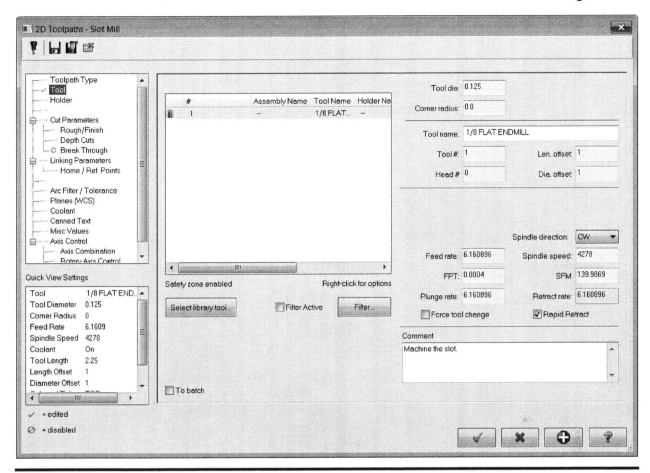

The **Feed rate**, **Plunge rate**, **Retract rate** and **Spindle speed** are based on the tool definition as set in the **Tool Settings**. You may change these values as per your part material and tools.

In the **Comment** field enter a comment to help identify the toolpath in the **Toolpaths/Operations Manager** such as the one shown above.

13.2 Cut Parameters

◆ Select **Cut Parameters** and make the necessary changes as shown in <u>Figure: 13.2.1</u>.

Figure: 13.2.1

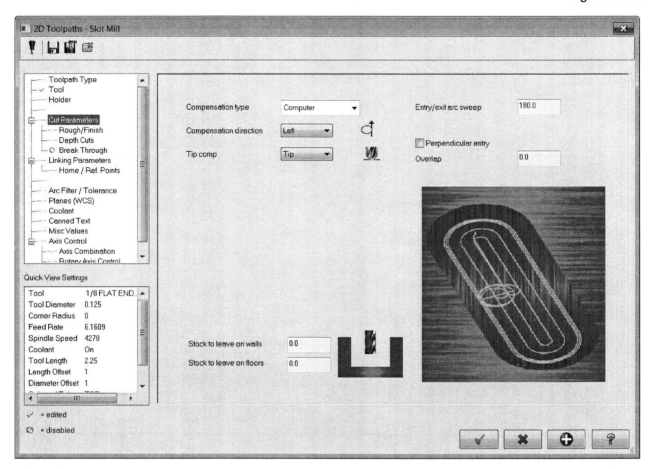

Compensation type allows you to choose how you want to handle cutter compensation. Computer sets Mastercam to compute the compensated toolpath and does not output control codes for compensation.

Entry/exit arc sweep sets the included angle of each entry and exit arc. If the entry/exit arc sweep is less than 180 degrees, the system applies an entry/exit line.

Perpendicular entry enters the toolpath perpendicular to the first tool move.

13.3 Rough/Finish

♦ Select **Rough/Finish** and make the necessary changes as shown in Figure: 13.3.1.

Figure: 13.3.1

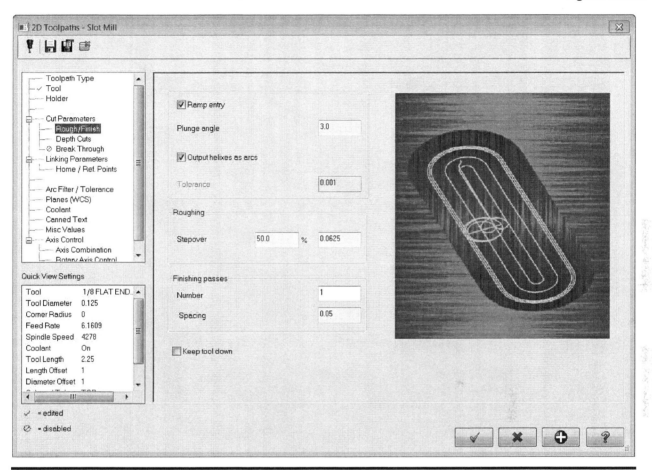

Ramp entry creates a smoother entry motion rather than plunging directly.

Plunge angle sets the angle of descent for the entry move, and determines the pitch. A smaller plunge angle means that the entry move takes longer to descend in the Z axis. A recommended angle is 3 to 5 degrees.

Output arc moves writes the entry helix to the NCI file as arcs. Using this option can create shorter NC files. If you turn off this option, the helix breaks into linear segments in the NCI file.

Roughing Stepover sets the distance between cutting passes in the X and Y Axes. Enter a percentage of the tool diameter or a distance.

Finish passes allows you to set the finish cuts for the toolpath. This **Number** multiplied by the finish **Spacing** value equals the total amount of stock cut by the finish passes. Setting the number of finish cuts to 0 creates no finish cuts.

Keep tool down enabled does not allow the tool to retract between multipasses.

13.4 Depth Cuts

◆ Choose **Depth Cuts** and enable this option. Input a **Max rough step** of **0.1**.

◆ Enable the option **Keep tool down** as shown in <u>Figure: 13.4.1</u>.

Figure: 13.4.1

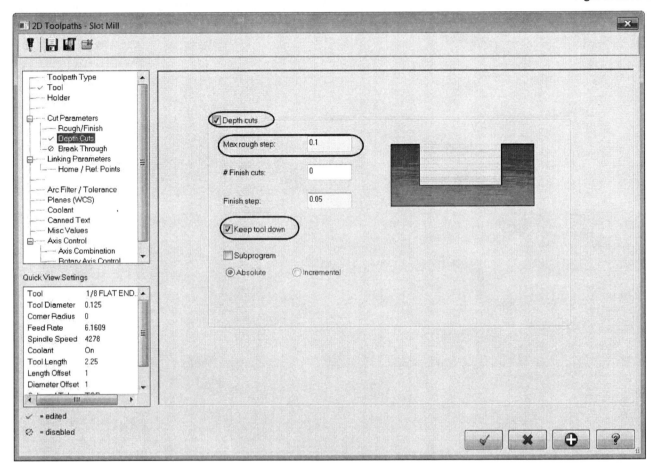

13.5 Break Through

◆ Pick **Break Through** from the **Tree view list**. Enable this option and input a break through amount of **0.1** as shown in Figure: 13.5.1.

Figure: 13.5.1

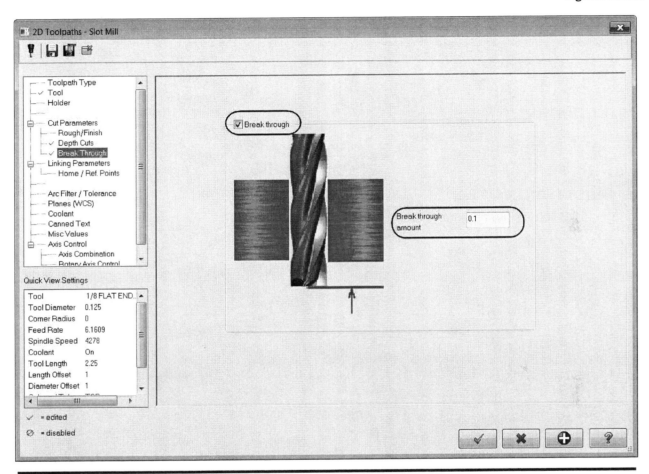

Break Through allows you to specify an amount that the tool will completely cut through the material by. This values is always a positive number.

13.6 Linking Parameters

♦ Pick **Linking Parameters** and make the necessary changes as shown in Figure: 13.6.1.

Figure: 13.6.1

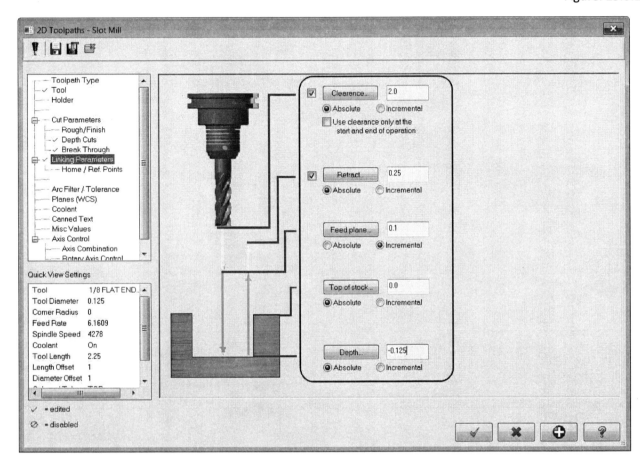

Clearance sets the height at which the tool moves to and from the part.

Retract sets the height that the tool moves up to before the next tool pass.

Feed Plane sets the height that the tool rapids to before changing to the plunge rate to enter the part.

Top of stock sets the height of the material in the Z axis.

Depth determines the final machining depth that the tool descends into the stock.

♦ Select the **OK** button to exit the Slot Mill parameters.

STEP 14: BACKPLOT THE TOOLPATHS

Backplotting shows the path the tools take to cut the part. This display lets you spot errors in the program before you machine the part. As you backplot toolpaths, Mastercam displays additional information such as the X, Y, and Z coordinates, the path length , the minimum and maximum coordinates and the cycle time. It also shows any collisions between the workpiece and the tool.

♦ Make sure that the toolpaths are selected (signified by the green check mark on the folder icon). If the operation is not selected choose the **Select all operations** icon.

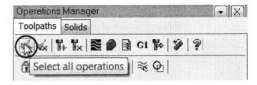

♦ Select the **Backplot selected operations** button.

> **NOTE:** Mastercam launches a new window that allows you to check the part using **Backplot** or **Verify.**

♦ Select the **Backplot** tab and have the following settings enabled as shown.

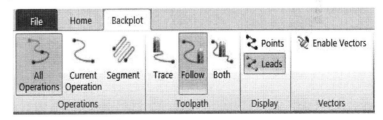

♦ Select the **Home** tab and make sure that you have the following settings on as shown.

♦ To see the part from an **Isometric** view select the **Isometric** icon. Isometric

- To fit the workpiece to the screen, select the **Fit** icon.

- You can step through the **Backplot** by using the **Step forward**  or **Step back** buttons.

- You can adjust the speed of the **Backplot**.
- Select the **Play Simulation** button in the **VCR** bar to run **Backplot**.

- The toolpath should look as shown in Figure: 14.0.1.

Figure: 14.0.1.

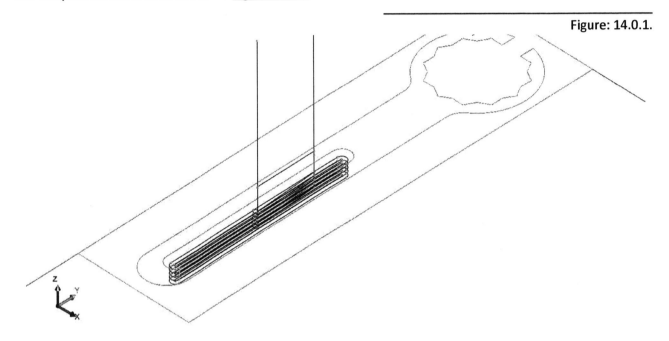

STEP 15: SIMULATE THE TOOLPATH IN VERIFY

Verify Mode shows the path the tools take to cut the part with material removal. This display lets you spot errors in the program before you machine the part. As you verify toolpaths, Mastercam displays additional information such as the X, Y, and Z coordinates, the path length, the minimum and maximum coordinates and the cycle time. It also shows any collisions between the workpiece and the tool.

• From **Mastercam Backplot Home** tab, switch to **Verify** and change the settings for the **Visibility** and **Focus** as shown in Figure: 15.0.1.

Figure: 15.0.1

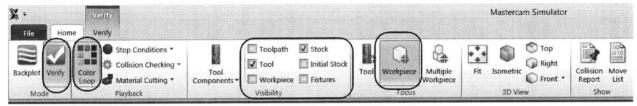

• Select the **Play Simulation** button in the **VCR** bar to run **Verify**.

• The part should appear as shown in Figure: 15.0.2.

Figure: 15.0.2

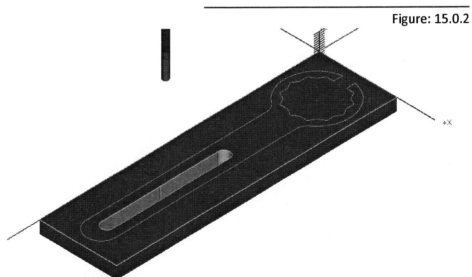

• To go back to Mastercam window, minimize **Verify** window as shown.

STEP 16: ROUGH THE OUTSIDE USING HIGH SPEED DYNAMIC CORE MILL

In this step you will machine the outside profile using **2D HS Dynamic Core Mill** toolpath. **Dynamic Core Mill** machines open pocket shapes or standing core shapes using the outmost chain as the stock boundary. The tool moves freely outside of this area; the inner chain defines the limit of the toolpath. They are designed to utilize the entire flute length of their cutting tools to maximize material removal while minimizing tool wear.

Toolpath Preview:

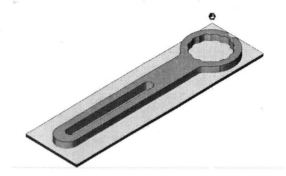

16.1 Chain selection

- Press **Alt** + **T** to remove the toolpath display.

Toolpaths
- **2D High Speed.**

- **Dynamic Core.**

◆ Leave the default setting in the chaining dialog box and pick the chain as shown.

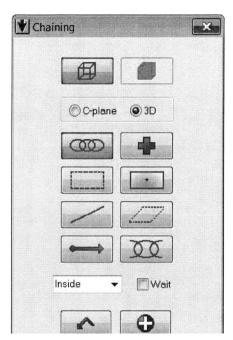

◆ Select the rectangle as shown in <u>Figure: 16.1.1</u>.

Figure: 16.1.1

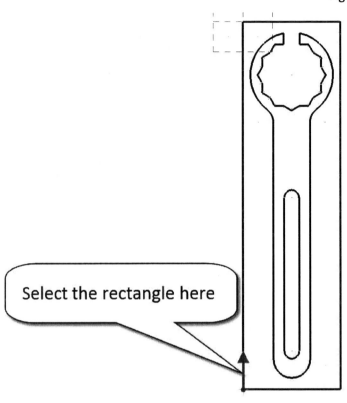

Select the rectangle here

◆ Select the **OK** button to exit the **Chaining** dialog box.
◆ In the **Chain Options** dialog box and enable the **Multiple regions** enabled.

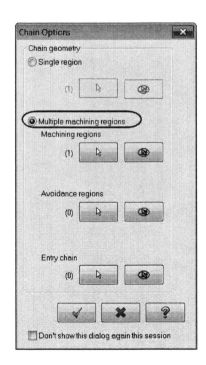

Mastercam. X^7

♦ Click on the select button in the **Avoidance regions** as shown.

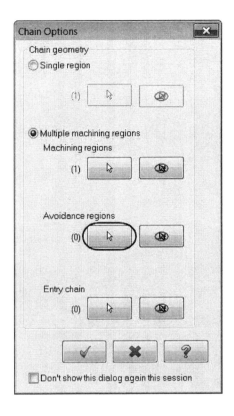

♦ Select the profile as shown in <u>Figure: 16.1.2</u>.

Figure: 16.1.2

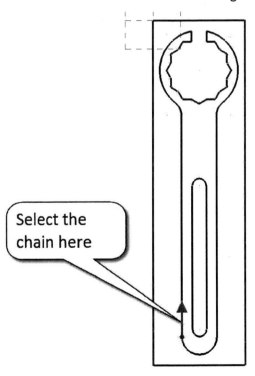

Select the chain here

* Select the **OK** button to exit the **Chaining** dialog box. ✓

* Select the **OK** button to exit the **Chain Options** dialog box. ✓
* In the **Toolpath Type** page, select **Dynamic Core Mill** as shown in Figure: 16.1.3.

Figure: 16.1.3

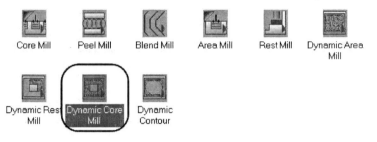

16.2 Select a 1/4" Flat endmill from the library and set the Tool Parameters

* Select **Tool** from the **Tree view list**.

* Click on **Select library tool** button. | Select library tool... |
* Select the **Filter** button.

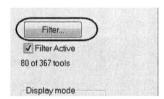

* Select the **None** button and then under **Tool Types** choose the **Flat Endmill** Icon.
* Under tool diameter pick **Equal** and input a value **0.25** as shown in Figure: 16.2.1.

Figure: 16.2.1

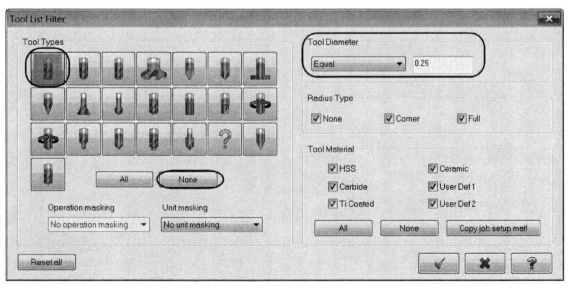

• Select the **OK** button to exit the **Tool List Filter.**
• In the **Tool Selection** dialog box you should only see a **1/4" Flat Endmill.**

#	Assembly Name	Tool Name	Holder Name	Dia.	Cor. rad.	Length	# Flutes	Type	Rad. Type
235	–	1/4 FLAT...	–	0.25	0.0	0.5	4	En...	None

• Select the **1/4" Flat Endmill** in the **Tool Selection** page and then select the **OK** button to exit.
• Make all the necessary changes as shown in Figure: 16.2.2.

Figure: 16.2.2

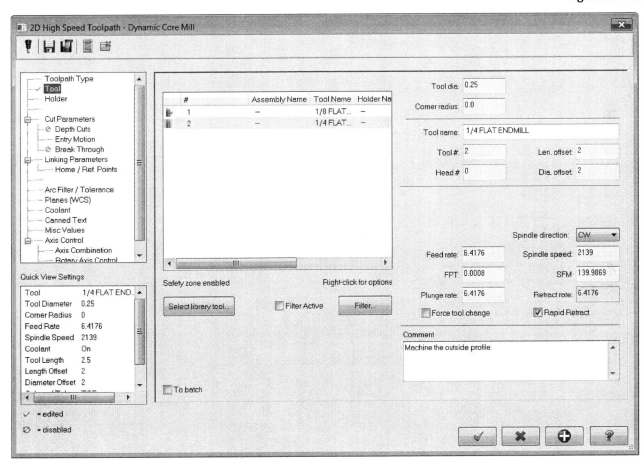

16.3 Set the Cut Parameters

♦ From the **Tree view list**, select **Cut Parameters**. Change the settings as shown in <u>Figure: 16.3.1</u>.

Figure: 16.3.1

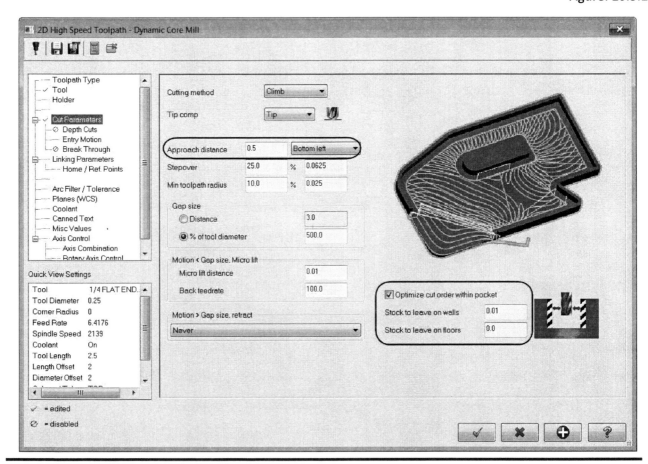

Stepover sets the distance between cutting passes in the X and Y axis.

Toolpath radius reduces sharp corner motion between cut passes.

Micro lift distance enters the distance the tool lifts off the part on the back moves. Microlifts are slight lifts that help clear chips and minimize excessive tool heating.

Back feedrate controls the speed of the backfeed movement of the tool.

Motion > Gap Size, retract controls retracts in the toolpath when making a non-cutting move within an area where the tool can be kept down or microlifted.

Optimize cut order defines the cut order Mastercam applies to different cutting passes in the dynamic mill toolpath.

16.4 Set the Entry Motion

♦ Entry motion configures an entry method for the dynamic mill toolpath which determines not only how and where the tool enters the part, but the cutting method/machining strategy used by the toolpath. Set the Entry method to Helix only as shown in <u>Figure: 16.4.1</u>.

Figure: 16.4.1

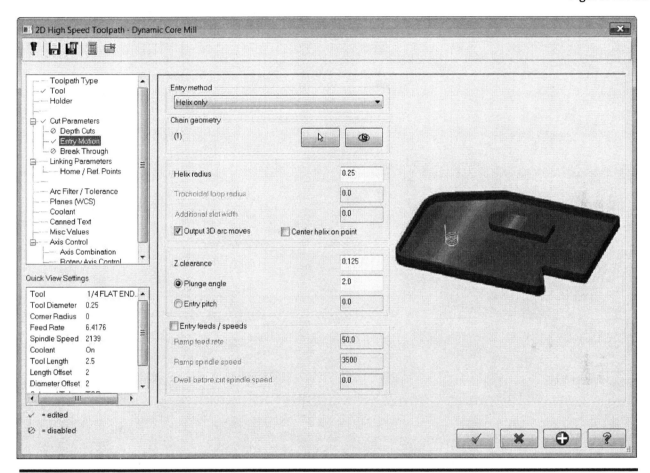

Entry method set to **Helix only** creates a helical entry into the part.

16.5 Set the Break through

• From the Tree view list, select and enable **Break Through** to cut completely through the material by an amount that you specify as shown in Figure: 16.5.1.

Figure: 16.5.1

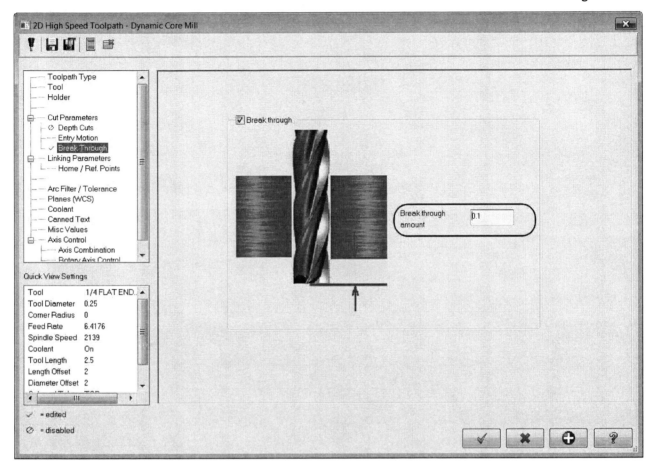

16.6 Set the Linking Parameters

• Select **Linking Parameters** and change the **Depth** to **-0.125** as shown in <u>Figure: 16.6.1</u>.

Figure: 16.6.1

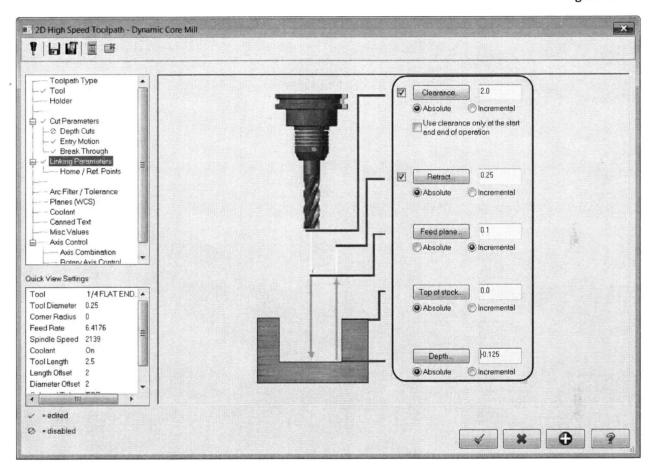

• Select the **OK** button to generate the toolpath.
• To remove the toolpath display, if needed, pres **Alt** + **T**.

16.7 Verify the toolpath

♦ From the **Toolpaths Operations Manager**, click on the **Select all operations** icon.

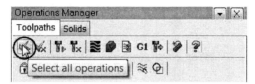

♦ Set the **Machine simulation** parameters as shown on page 201.
♦ The part will appear as shown in <u>Figure: 16.7.1</u>.

Figure: 16.7.1

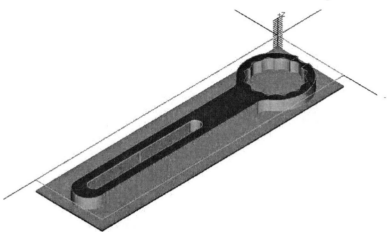

♦ To go back to Mastercam window, minimize **Verify** window as shown.

♦ To remove the toolpath display press **Alt + T** or click on the **Toggle display on selected operations**.

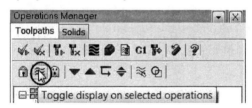

STEP 17: FINISH THE OUTSIDE PROFILE USING CONTOUR TOOLPATH

Contour toolpaths remove material along a path defined by a chain of curves. **Contour** toolpaths only follow a chain; they do not clean out an enclosed area.

Toolpath Preview:

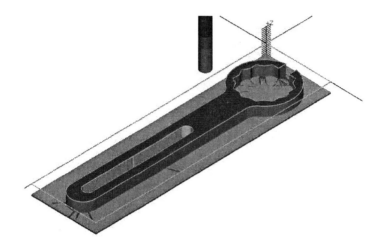

17.1 Chain selection

Toolpaths

◆ Contour.

◆ Leave the **Chain** button enabled in the **Chaining** dialog box as shown.

• Select the profile as shown in Figure: 17.1.1.

Figure: 17.1.1

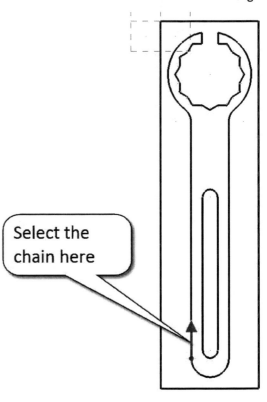

Select the
chain here

• Select the **OK** button to exit **Chaining**.
• In the **Toolpath Type** page, the **Contour** icon will be selected as shown.

 Contour   Pocket   Facing   Slot Mill

17.2 Select a 1/4" Flat endmill from the list and set the Tool page parameters

• From the Tree view list, select Tool and make all the necessary changes as shown in Figure: 17.2.1.

Figure: 17.2.1

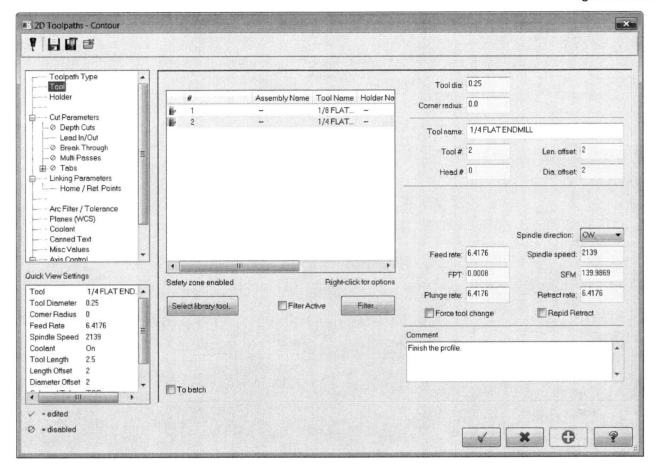

17.3 Cut Parameters

• From the **Tree view list**, select **Cut Parameters** and ensure the settings appear as shown in <u>Figure: 17.3.1</u>.

Figure: 17.3.1

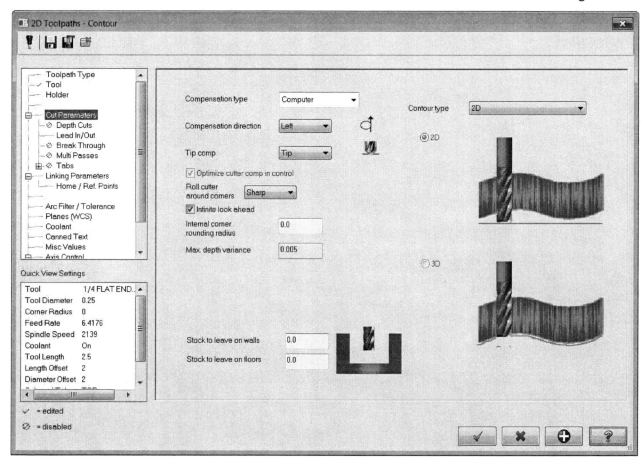

NOTE: For more information regarding these parameters please check Step 8 in Tutorial #1.

17.4 Lead In/Out

* Select **Lead In/Out** from the **Tree view list.**
* Change the parameters as shown in Figure: 17.4.1.

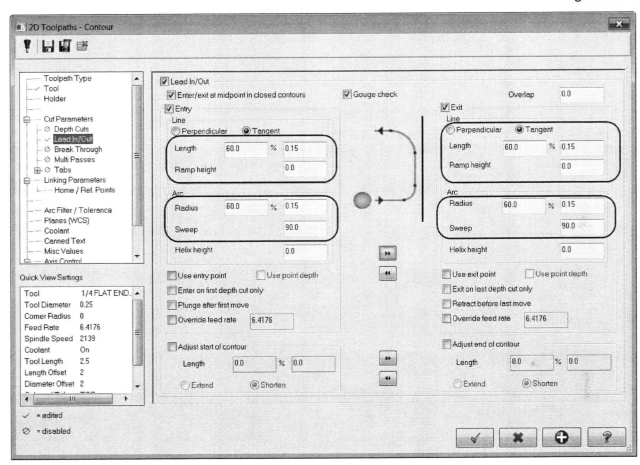

17.5 Break Through

◆ From the **Tree view list**, select **Break Through** and make the necessary changes as shown in Figure: 17.5.1.

Figure: 17.5.1

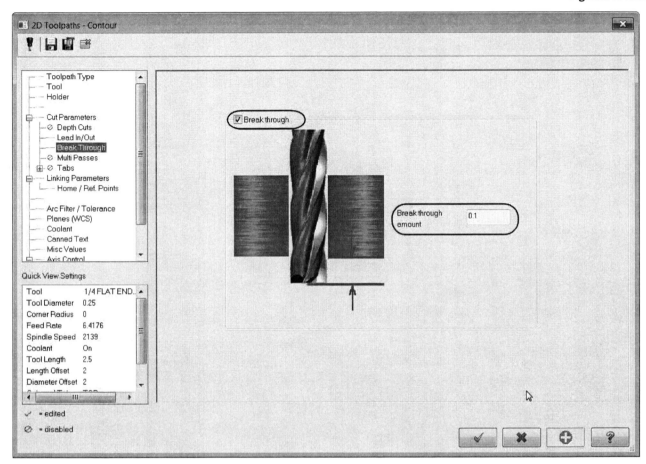

17.6 Linking Parameters

♦ Select **Linking Parameters** and input the **Depth** as shown as shown in Figure: 17.6.1.

Figure: 17.6.1

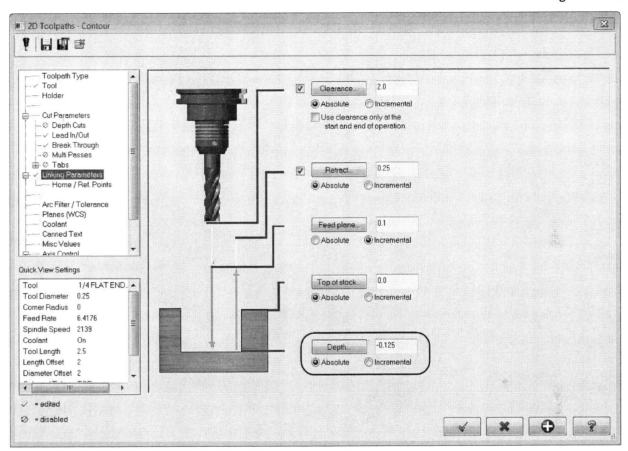

♦ Once complete pick the **OK** button to generate the toolpath.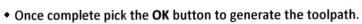
♦ To remove the toolpath display, if needed, pres **Alt** + **T**.

17.7 Backplot and Verify the toolpaths

- To **Backplot** and **Verify** the toolpaths see page 199 to review the procedures.
- To select all the operations, from the **Toolpaths Operations Manager**, click on the **Select all operations** icon.

- The part should look as shown.

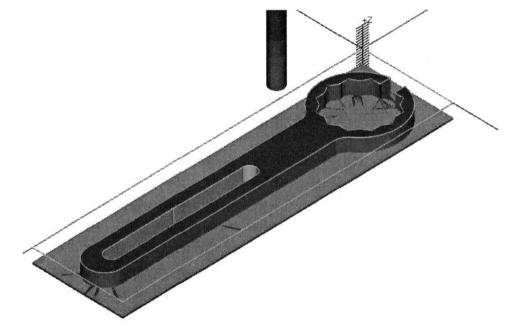

STEP 18: CLEAN THE INSIDE SHAPE USING 2D HS DYNAMIC CONTOUR

2D HS Dynamic Contour toolpath utilizes the entire flute length of the cutting tools and is used to mill material off walls. It does support both closed or open chains.

Toolpath Preview:

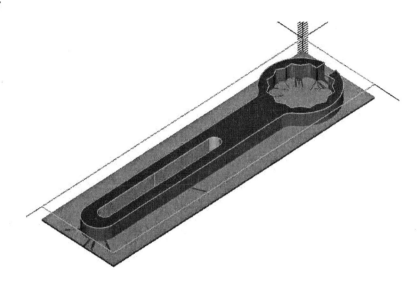

Toolpaths
* **2D High Speed.**

* 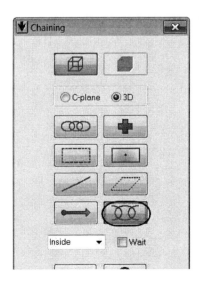 **Dynamic Contour.**

18.1 Select the Geometry

* Enable **Partial** button in the **Chaining** dialog box as shown.

• Select the first entity of the chain as shown in <u>Figure: 18.1.1</u>. Make sure that the arrows are pointing downwards as shown otherwise select the reverse button 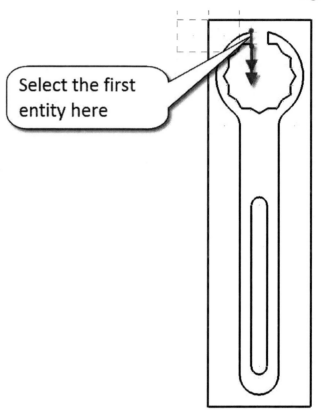 from the **Chaining** dialog box.

Figure: 18.1.1

◆ Select the last entity of the chain as shown in Figure: 18.1.2.

Figure: 18.1.2

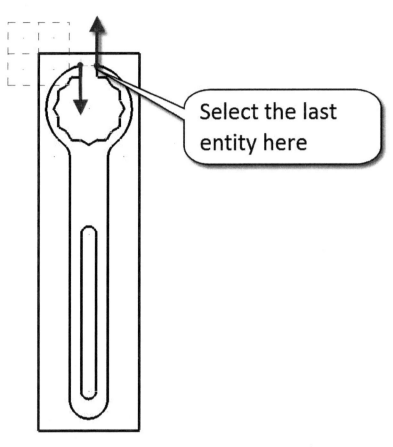

Select the last entity here

◆ Choose the **OK** button to exit **Chaining** dialog box.

♦ Leave the **Chain Options** parameters set to **Single region** as shown.

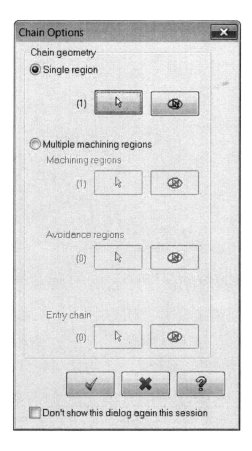

♦ Select the **OK** button to exit **Chain Options** dialog box and to continue.
♦ On the **Toolpath Type** page, **Dynamic Contour** will be picked.

Core Mill   Peel Mill   Blend Mill   Area Mill   Rest Mill   Dynamic A
                                                                  Mill

Dynamic Rest Dynamic Core   Dynamic
    Mill   Mill   Contour

18.2 Select the 1/16" Tool

♦ Select **Tool** from the **Tree view list**.

♦ Click on **Select library tool** button.
♦ Select the **Filter** button.

♦ Select the **None** button and then under **Tool Types** choose the **Flat Endmill** icon.
♦ Under tool diameter pick **Equal** and input a value **0.0625** as shown in Figure: 18.2.1.

Figure: 18.2.1

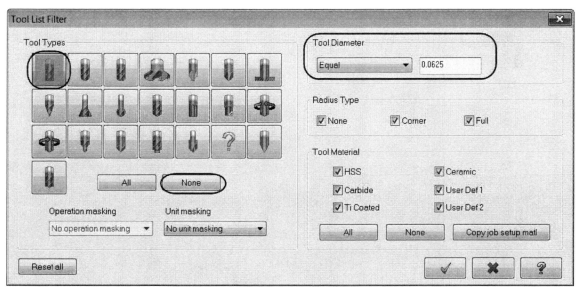

♦ Select the **OK** button to exit the **Tool List Filter**.
♦ In the **Tool Selection** dialog box you should only see a **1/16" Flat Endmill**.

#	Assembly Name	Tool Name	Holder Name	Dia.	Cor. rad.	Length	# Flutes	Type	Rad. Type
230	–	1/16 FLA...	–	0....	0.0	0.375	4	En...	None

♦ Select the **1/16" Flat Endmill** in the **Tool Selection** page and then select the **OK** button to exit.

◆ Make any other changes as shown in <u>Figure: 18.2.2</u>.

Figure: 18.2.2

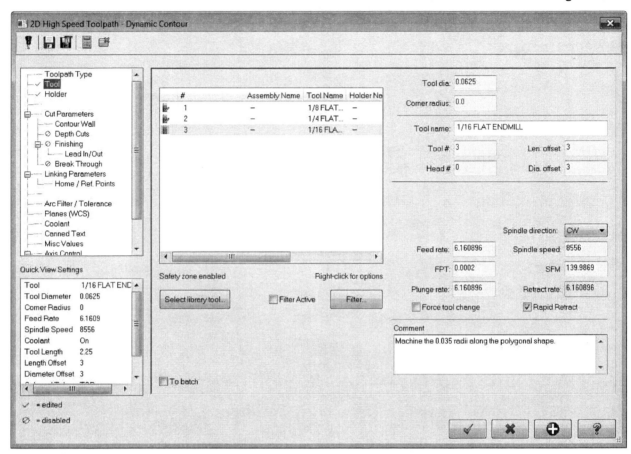

Mastercam. X^7

18.3 Cut Parameters

* From the **Tree view list** select **Cut Parameters** ensure the parameters appear the same.

Figure: 18.3.1

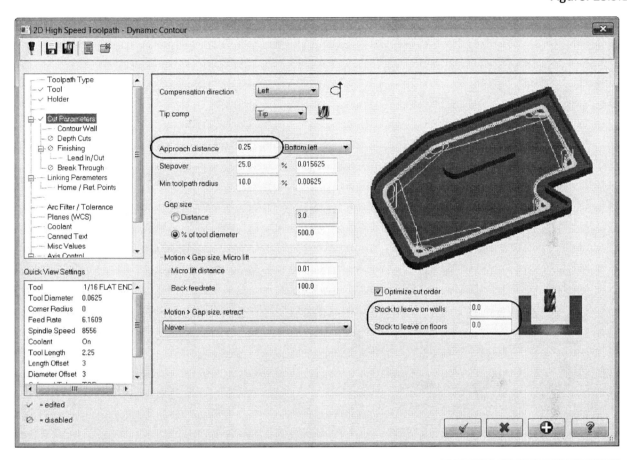

Compensation direction offsets the tool to the **Left** in our case.

Approach distance adds the specified absolute distance to the beginning of the toolpath's first cut.

Stepover sets the distance between cutting passes in the X and Y axes. Enter a percentage of the tool diameter or an absolute distance.

Min toolpath radius sets the minimum toolpath radius used in combination with the **Microlift distance** and **Back feedrate** parameters to calculate 3D arc moves between cut passes.

18.4 Contour Wall

• From the Tree view list, select **Contour Wall** and ensure your parameters appear as shown in <u>Figure: 18.4.1</u>.

Figure: 18.4.1

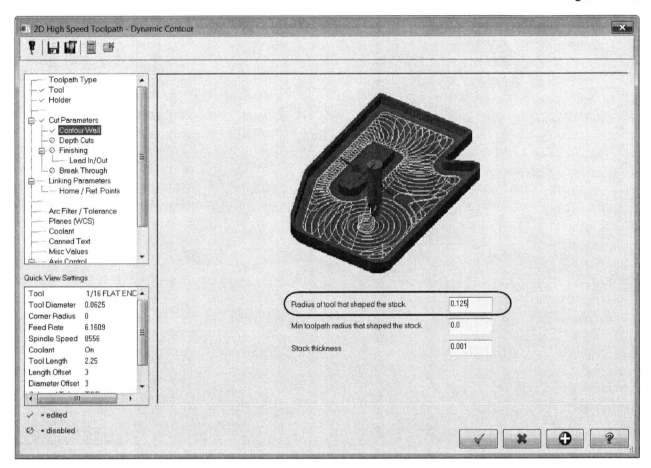

Radius of tool that shaped the stock is the radius of the tool used in a toolpath that already cut this area. Mastercam calculates the stock to remove along the contour wall using the stock thickness (required) and, if provided, the **Radius of the tool that shaped the stock** and the **Toolpath radius that shaped the stock**.

In our case, in the previous contour operation you used a 0.25 " Flat Endmill and no toolpath radius.

18.5 Depth Cuts

♦ From the Tree view list, choose **Depth Cuts** and enable it. Input a **Max rough step** of **0.05** as shown in Figure: 18.5.1.

Figure: 18.5.1

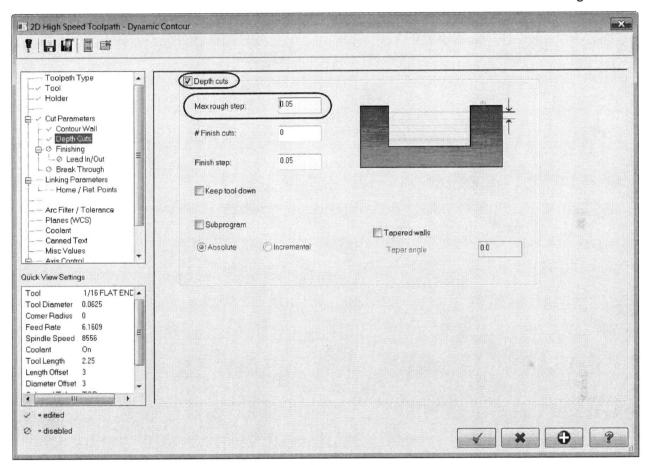

18.6 Break Through

♦ From the **Tree view list**, select **Break Through** and make the necessary changes as shown in <u>Figure: 18.6.1</u>.

Figure: 18.6.1

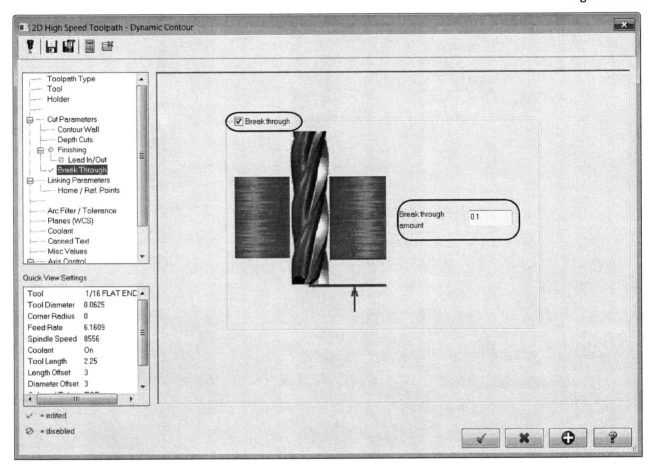

Mill Level 1 Training Tutorial   *Mastercam.* X[7]

18.7 Linking Parameters

◆ Select **Linking Parameters** from the **Tree View** list.
◆ Set the **Depth** to **-0.125** as shown in Figure: 18.7.1.

Figure: 18.7.1

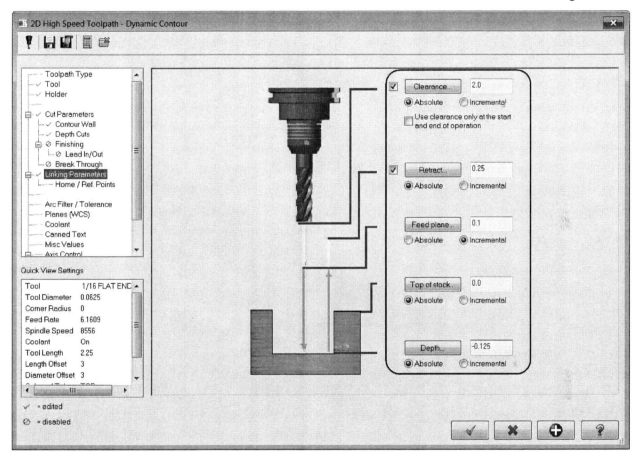

◆ Select the **OK** button to exit the **Dynamic Contour** parameters.

18.8 Backplot and Verify

* To **Backplot** and **Verify** your toolpath page 199 to review these procedures.
* To select all the operations, from the **Toolpaths Operations Manager**, click on the **Select all operations** icon.

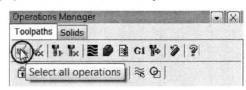

* The part should look as shown.

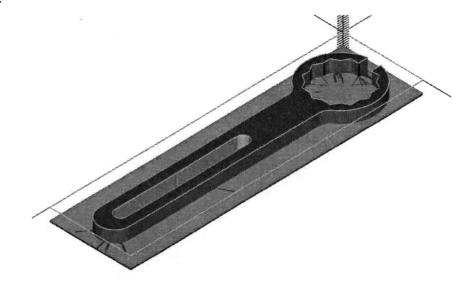

TOOLPATH CREATION - SETUP 2

SUGGESTED FIXTURE:

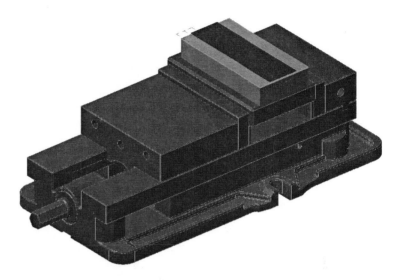

> **NOTE:** In order to machine this part we will have 2 setups and output 2 NC files.

SETUP SHEET:

TOOL LIST

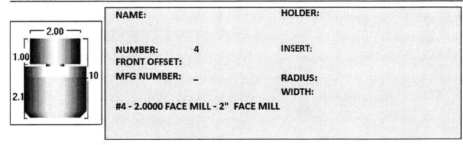

NAME:		HOLDER:
NUMBER:	4	INSERT:
FRONT OFFSET:		
MFG NUMBER:	_	RADIUS:
		WIDTH:

#4 - 2.0000 FACE MILL - 2" FACE MILL

STEP 19: CREATING AND RENAMING TOOLPATH GROUPS

To machine the part in two different setups, we will need to have two separate programs. To be able to post process separately the operations of each setup, we will create them under different toolpath groups with different NC names.

19.1 Rename the current Toolpath Group - 1 and NC file

• Click once on the Toolpath Group - 1 to highlight it and then click again on it to rename it "Setup #1" as shown in Figure: 19.1.1.

Figure: 19.1.1

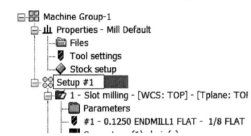

• Right mouse click on the **Setup #1 Toolpath group** and select **Edit selected operations** and then, select **Change NC file name.**

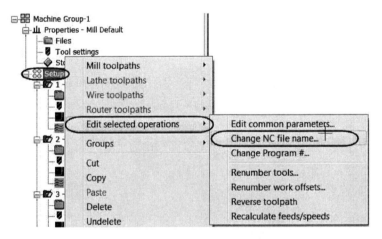

• Enter the new NC name: **Setup #1.**

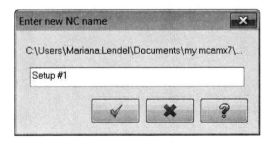

• Select the **OK** button to accept the new **NC name.**

19.2 Create a new Toolpath Group

♦ Right mouse click on the **Machine Group-1** and select **Groups** and then **New Toolpath group** as shown.

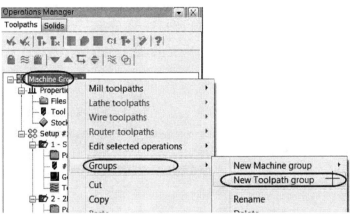

♦ Rename the toolpath group "**Setup #2**" as shown.

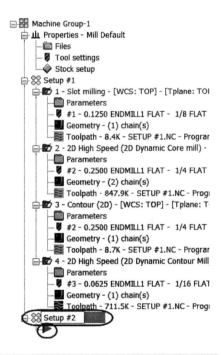

NOTE: The red insert arrow controls where the new operation will be inserted. In our case should be located below the Setup #2 group.

♦ If the insert arrow needs to be moved, from the **Toolpaths Operations Manager**, click on the **Move insert arrow down** icon.

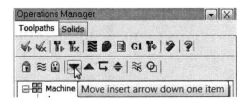

STEP 20: SET WCS TO BOTTOM

Work coordinate system (WCS) is the active coordinate system in use by Mastercam at any given time. The WCS contains the orientation of the X-Y-Z axes plus the location of the zero point (the origin). This tells Mastercam how your part is positioned or orientated in the machine.

◆ Select **WCS** located in the status bar.

◆ When the **WCS** menu appears select **"View Manager"** from it.

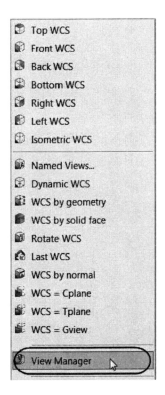

- When the **View Manager** dialog box appears pick **Geometry** to set the new view based on existing geometry as shown.

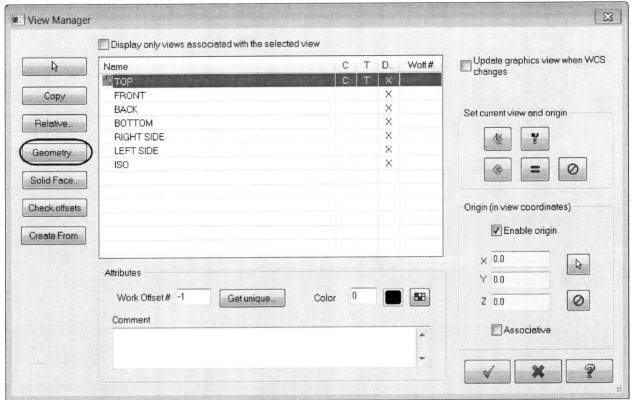

- Change the graphic view to **Isometric**.

♦ Pick first the line along the X-axis of the new view and then the second select the line along the Y-axis of the new view as shown in <u>Figure: 20.0.1</u>.

Figure: 20.0.1

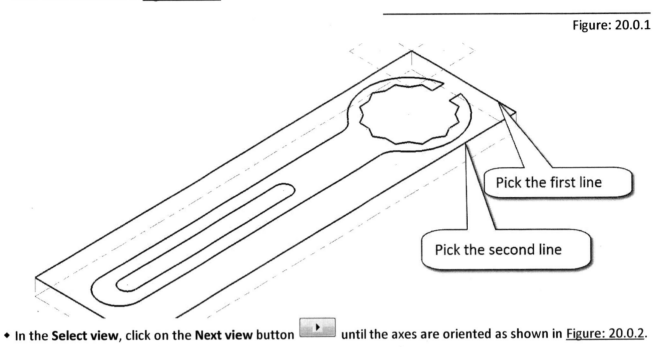

♦ In the **Select view**, click on the **Next view** button 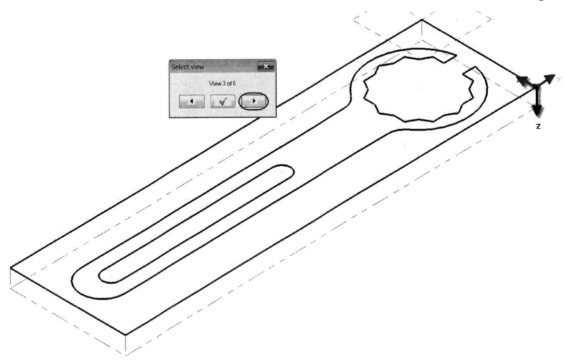 until the axes are oriented as shown in <u>Figure: 20.0.2</u>.

Figure: 20.0.2

♦ From the **Select view** click on the **OK** button to continue.

◆ In the **New View** named the view **Bottom View** as shown.

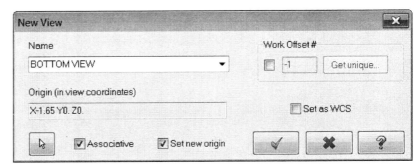

◆ Select the **OK** button to continue.
◆ Set the **Work Coordinate System (WCS)**, **Tool plane**, **Construction plane** to the **Bottom View,** by selecting the equal icon as shown in Figure: 20.0.3.
◆ Enable and set the **Origin** as shown in Figure: 20.0.3.

Figure: 20.0.3

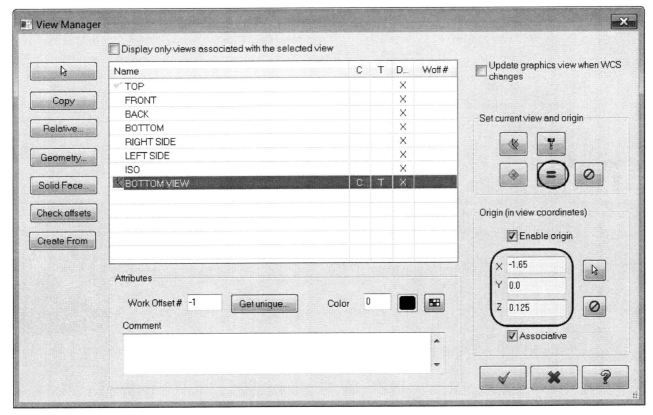

◆ Select the **OK** button to exit the **View Manager**.

◆ Pick the **Isometric graphics view** to see the part in its new orientation.

◆ Select **Fit** screen icon.

• The part should look as shown.

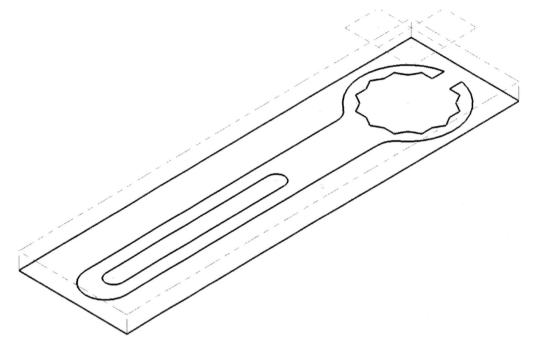

NOTE: **Z zero** is at **0.125** below the stock.

STEP 21: FACE THE PART

A **Facing** toolpath quickly removes material from the top of the part to create an even surface.

Toolpath Preview:

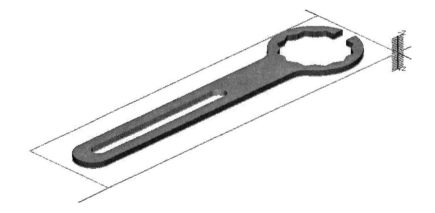

Toolpaths

♦ **Face.**

♦ When the chaining dialog box appears choose the **OK** button to use defined stock and exit the **Chaining** dialog

box.

NOTE: Mastercam will create the Facing toolpath defined from the stock setup.

♦ In the **Toolpath Type** page, the **Facing** icon will be automatically selected.

Contour   Pocket   Facing   Slot Mill

21.1 Select a 2.0" Face Mill from the library and set the Tool parameters

♦ Select **Tool** from the **Tree view list.**

♦ Click on the **Select library tool** button.   Select library tool...

♦ To be able to see all the tools from the library disable **Filter Active.**

♦ Pick the **2" Face Mill (#316)** as shown.

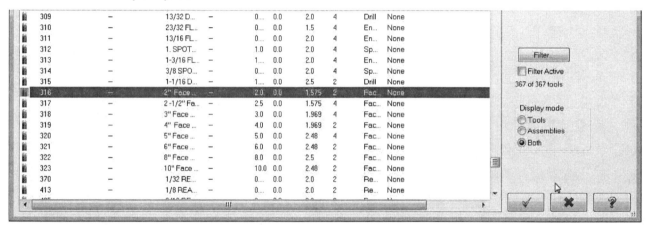

♦ Select the tool in the **Tool Selection** page and then select the **OK** button to exit.

- Make all the necessary changes as shown in Figure: 21.1.1.

Figure: 21.1.1

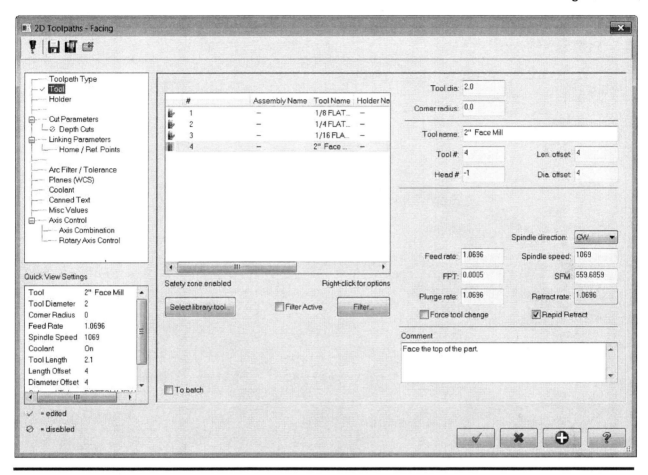

The **Feed rate, Plunge rate, Retract rate** and **Spindle speed** are based on the tool definition as set in the **Tool Settings**. You may change these values as per your part material and tools.

In the **Comment** field enter a comment to help identify the toolpath in the **Toolpaths/Operations Manager** such as the one shown above.

◆ Select **Cut Parameters** and make the necessary changes as shown in Figure: 21.1.2.

Figure: 21.1.2

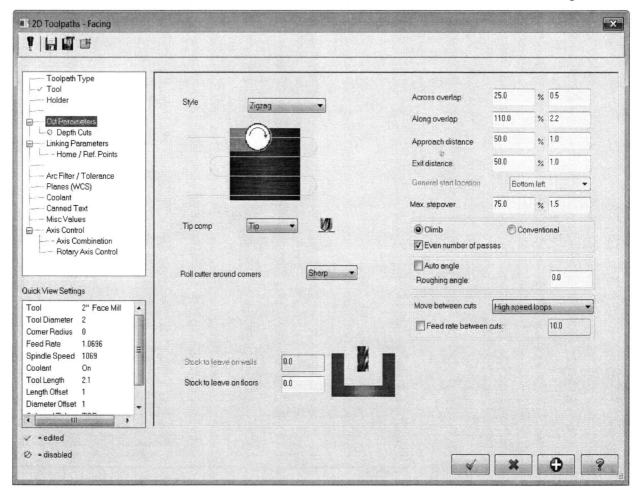

The **Style** (facing cutting method) **Zigzag** creates a back and forth cutting motion.

Move between cuts determines how the tool moves between each cut. This is only available if you select the zigzag cutting method.

High speed loops to create 180 degrees arcs between each cut.

♦ Select the **Linking Parameters** page and make the necessary changes as shown in Figure: 21.1.3.

Figure: 21.1.3

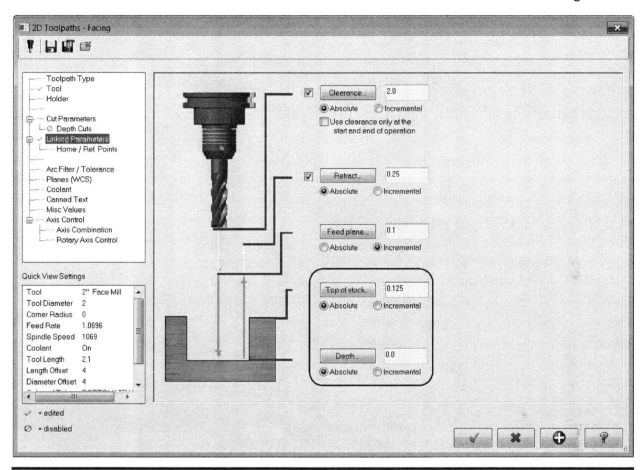

Clearance sets the height at which the tool moves to and from the part.

Retract sets the height that the tool moves up to before the next tool pass.

Feed Plane sets the height that the tool rapids to before changing to the plunge rate to enter the part.

Top of stock sets the height of the material in the Z axis.

Depth determines the final machining depth that the tool descends into the stock.

• Select the **OK** button to exit the **Facing Parameters**.

> **NOTE:** The top of stock is set to **0.125"** because in our **Bottom view** we have **Origin Z** value set to **0.125"** above the first setup origin. The depth is set to **0.0"** because this is the depth of the finish part we want the tool to go to.

• To **Backplot** and **Verify** your toolpath page 199 to review these procedures.
• To select all the operations, from the **Toolpaths Operations Manager**, click on the **Select all operations** icon.

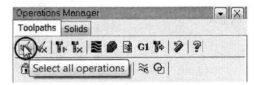

• The toolpaths should look as shown.

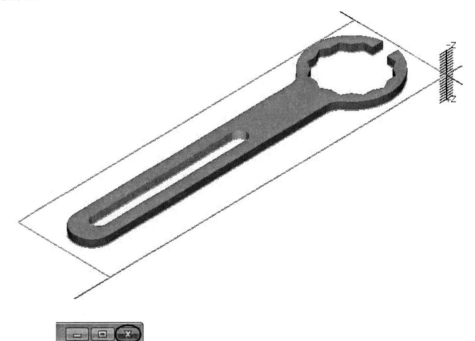

• To exit **Verify** click on the **Close** icon.

STEP 22: RENAME THE NC FILE

The Facing operation in Setup #2 kept the NC name from Setup #1. We need to rename this operation.

- Right click on Setup #2 group, choose the option **Edit selected operations** and then pick **Change NC file name**.

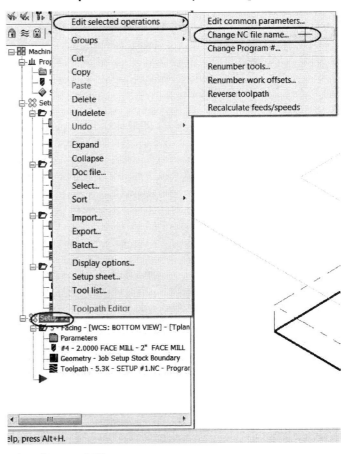

- When the **Enter new NC name** dialog box appears select **"Setup #2"**.

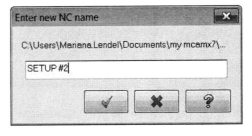

- Select the **OK** button apply the changed **NC name** to **Operation #5**.

* The result you should see **Setup #2.NC** in the last item of text for Operation #5.

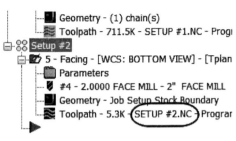

```
        Geometry - (1) chain(s)
        Toolpath - 711.5K - SETUP #1.NC - Progi
 Setup #2
    5 - Facing - [WCS: BOTTOM VIEW] - [Tplan
        Parameters
        #4 - 2.0000 FACE MILL - 2"  FACE MILL
        Geometry - Job Setup Stock Boundary
        Toolpath - 5.3K - SETUP #2.NC - Progran
```

STEP 23: POST THE FILE

* Ensure all operations are selected, if they are not use the button **Select all operations** in the **Operations Manager.**

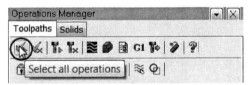

* Select the **Post selected operations** G1 button from the **Operations Manager.**
* In the **Post processing** window make the necessary changes as shown in Figure: 23.0.1.

Figure: 23.0.1

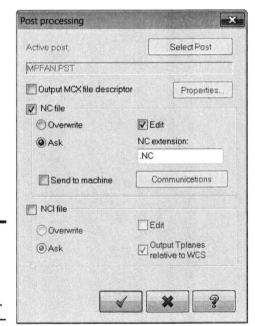

NC File enabled allows you to keep the NC file and to assign the same name as the MCX file.

Edit enabled allows you to automatically launch the default editor.

* Select the **OK** button to continue.
* Save Setup #1 NC file.
* Save Setup #2 NC file.

• A window with Mastercam Code Expert will be lunched and the NC program will appear as shown in
<u>Figure: 23.0.2</u>.

Figure: 23.0.2

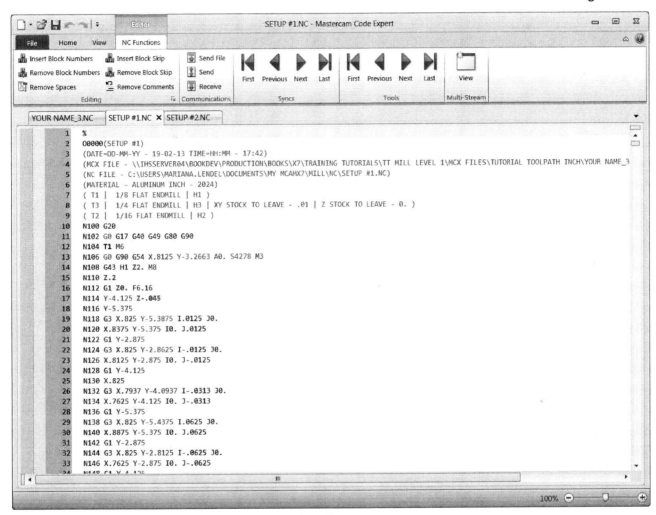

• Select the **"X"** at the upper right corner to exit the editor.

STEP 24: SAVE THE UPDATED MCX FILE

REVIEW EXERCISE -STUDENT PRACTICE

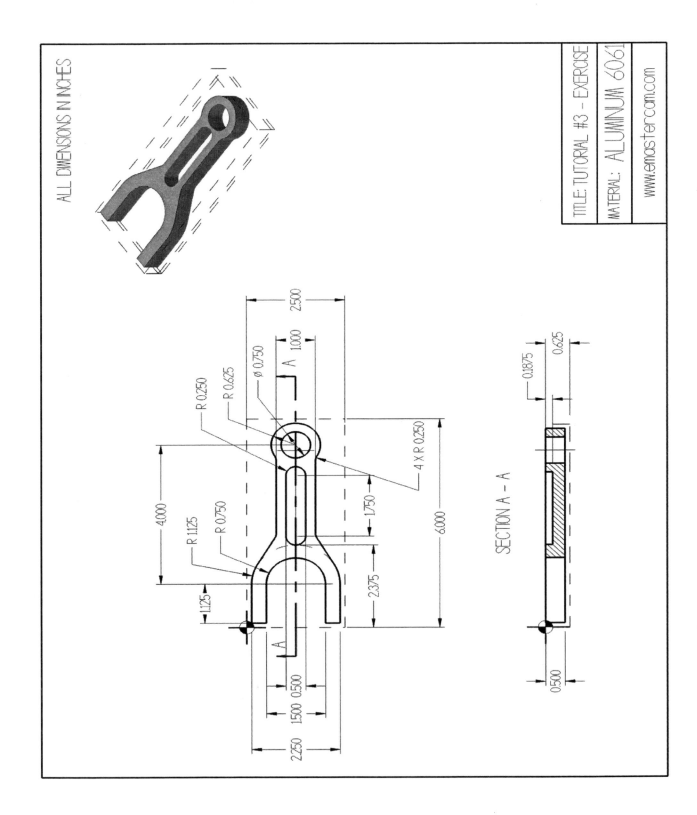

ALL DIMENSIONS IN INCHES

TITLE: TUTORIAL #3 – EXERCISE

MATERIAL: ALUMINUM 6061

www.emastercam.com

SECTION A – A

Mastercam X⁷

CREATE THE GEOMETRY FOR TUTORIAL #3 EXERCISE

Use these commands to create the geometry:

◆ Create 1/2 of the geometry.
◆ Create circle center point.
◆ Fast Point to locate arcs.
◆ Create Vertical and Horizontal lines.
◆ Create Tangent Lines.
◆ Edit Trim/Break Two Pieces.
◆ Create Line Parallel.
◆ Create fillet entities.

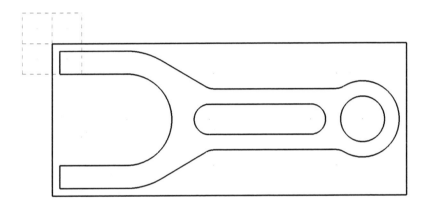

CREATE THE TOOLPATHS FOR TUTORIAL #3 EXERCISE

Create the Toolpaths for Tutorial #3 Exercise as per the instructions below.

Setup #1
Set the machine properties including the stock setup.
• Remove the material in the slot.
• Use a 1/4" Flat Endmill.
• Set the Depth according to the drawing.

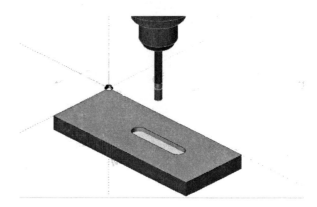

Circle Mill the 1/4" Hole.
• Choose a 1/4" Drill.
• Enable Roughing.
• Set appropriate Depth of cuts and Break through amount.
• Input a Depth according to the drawing.

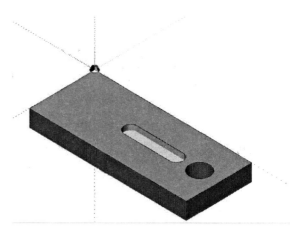

Rough the outside profile using 2D HS Dynamic Core.
• Use a 1/2" Flat Endmill.
• Leave stock on the wall only.
• Enable Break through.
• Set the Depth according to the drawing.

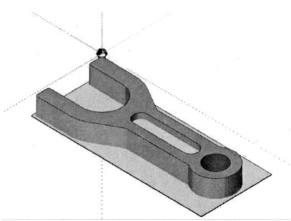

Finish the outside profile using Contour.
* Use a 1/2" Flat Endmill.
* Enable **Break through**.
* Set the final **Depth** according to the drawing.

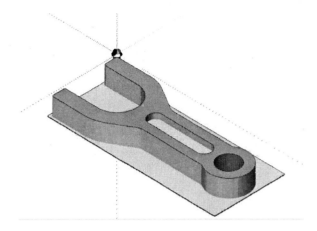

Setup #2.
* Rename the previous Toolpath Group.
* Rename all the existing operation NC file
* Create a new Toolpath Group and rename it.

Use WCS View Manager and set the Bottom plane
* Use Geometry to define the plane.
* Set WCS, Cplane and Tplane to the new view.
* Set the z origin to 0.125

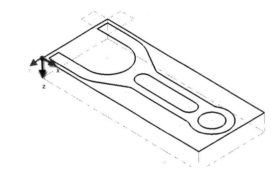

Face the part the part (Contour 2D).
* Select the 2"Face Mill from the Tool page.
* Set the Depth according to the drawing.

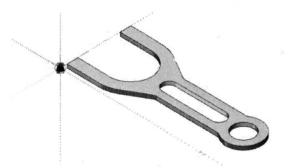

NOTES:

Mastercam. X⁷

TUTORIAL #3 QUIZ

◆ What does Slot mill toolpath do?

◆ What does 2D HS Dynamic Core mill do?

◆ What does the 2D HS Dynamic Contour mill do?

◆ What is the process used to be able to post different operations as different programs?

TUTORIAL #4

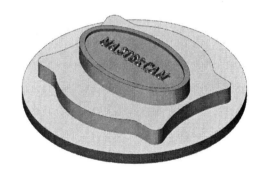

OVERVIEW OF STEPS TAKEN TO CREATE THE FINAL PART:

From Drawing to CAD Model:
- The student should examine the drawing on the following page to understand what part is being created in the tutorial.
- From the drawing we can decide how to go about creating the geometry in Mastercam.

Create the 2D CAD Model used to generate Toolpaths from:
- The student will create the Top 2D geometry needed to create the toolpaths.
- Geometry creation commands such as arc polar, circle center point, line tangent at an angle, mirror, arc tangent, ellipse, letters, bounding box and translate will be used.

Create the necessary Toolpaths to machine the part:
- The student will set up the stock size to be used and the clamping method used.
- A 2D High Speed Core Mill toolpath will be created to remove the material from the outside step.
- A 2D High Speed Dynamic Core Mill toolpath will be created to remove the outside material.
- A Pocket Island Facing toolpath will be created to machine the and face the letters.
- A Pocket Remachining toolpath will be used to machine the remaining material.

Backplot and Verify the file:
- The Backplot will be used to simulate a step by step process of the tool's movements.
- The Verify will be used to watch a tool machine the part out of a solid model.

Post Process the file to generate the G-code:
- The Student will then post process the file to obtain an NC file containing the necessary code for the machine.

 This tutorial takes approximately two hours to complete.

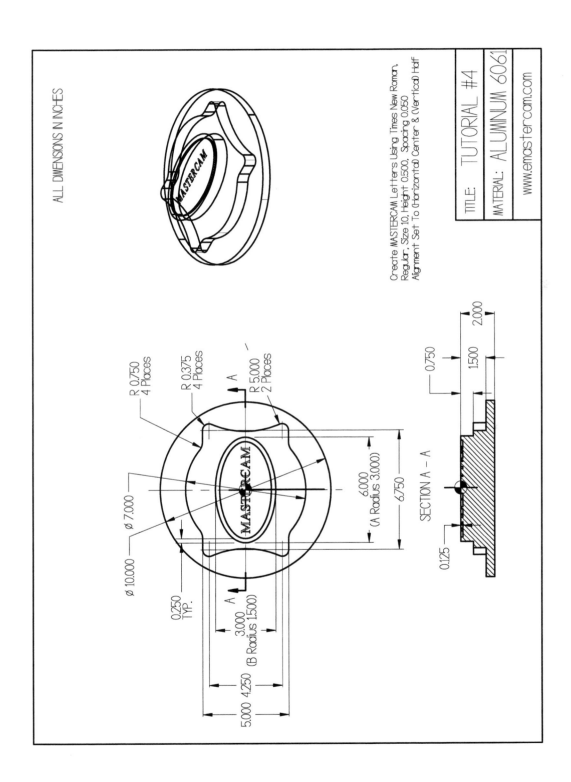

ALL DIMENSIONS IN INCHES

Create MASTERCAM Letters Using Times New Roman,
Regular, Size 10, Height 0.500, Spacing 0.050
Alignment Set To (Horizontal) Center & (Vertical) Half

TITLE:	TUTORIAL #4
MATERIAL:	ALUMINUM 6061
	www.emastercam.com

R 0.750
4 Places

R 0.375
4 Places

R 5.000
2 Places

A

Ø 7.000

6.000
(A Radius 3.000)

6.750

MASTERCAM

0.250
TYP.

Ø 10.000

A

3.000
(B Radius 1.500)

5.000 4.250

SECTION A - A

0.750

1.500

2.000

0.125

GEOMETRY CREATION

STEP 1: SETTING UP THE GRAPHIC USER INTERFACE

Please refer to the **Getting Started** section to set up the graphics user interface.

NOTE: In the next steps you will create a quater of the entire geometry. You will use the Mirror command to generate the rest.

STEP 2: CREATE TWO POLAR ARCS

In this step you will create two arcs using arc polar command. To create an arc polar you need to know the Radius, the Start Angle, the End Angle and the center point of the arc.

Step Preview:

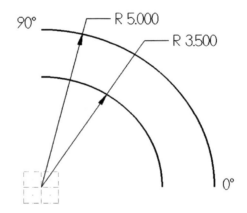

2.1 Create the 10.0" diameter arc

Create

♦ **Arc.**

♦  **Arc Polar.**

♦ Enter the radius in the **Ribbon bar** as shown, and then press the **Tab key** to move through all the fields and enter the rest of the values.

♦ [Enter the center point]: Select the Origin as shown in Figure: 2.1.1.

Figure: 2.1.1

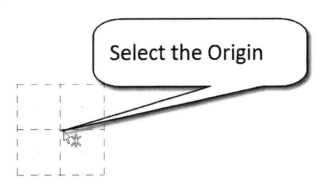

♦ Make sure that when selecting the origin, the visual cue of the cursor changes as shown.

♦ Use the **Fit** icon to fit the drawing to the screen.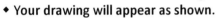

♦ Your drawing will appear as shown.

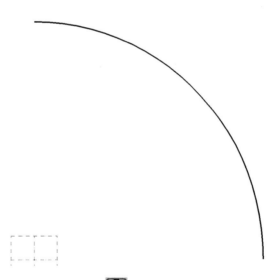

♦ Choose the **Apply** button to continue in the same command.

> **NOTE:** During the geometry creation of this tutorial, if you make a mistake you can undo the last step using the **Undo** icon. You can undo as many steps as needed. If you delete or undo a step by mistake, just use the **Redo** icon. To delete unwanted geometry, select it first and then press **Delete** from the keyboard.

2.2 Create the 7.0" diameter arc

♦ Enter the values in the **Ribbon bar** as shown.

♦ [Enter the center point]: Select the Origin as shown in Figure: 2.1.1.

Figure: 2.2.1

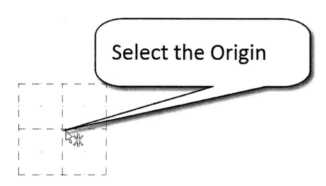

Select the Origin

♦ The drawing will appear as shown.

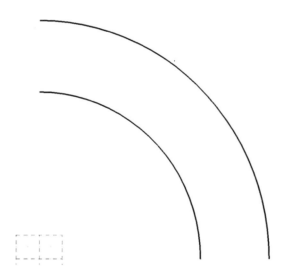

♦ Choose the **OK** button to continue.

STEP 3: CREATE A CIRCLE

In this step you will learn how to create a crcle knowing the radius and the center point.

Step Preview:

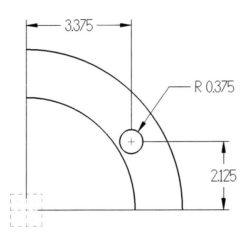

Create
* **Arc.**

*  **Circle Center Point.**

* Enter the **Radius** of **0.375** then pick the **Fast Point** command.
* Enter the coordinates of **3.375, 2.125** as shown and then hit **Enter** on your keyboard.

3.375,2.125

* Select the **OK** button to exit the command.

• The drawing should look as shown.

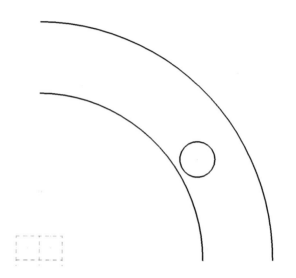

STEP 4: CREATE A LINE TANGENT TO THE CIRCLE

In this step you will use **Create Line Endpoind** command to create a line tangent to the circle at a 180 degree angle. Mastercam angles are measured counter clockwise and will always total 360 degrees.

Step Preview:

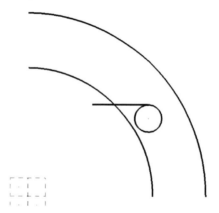

Create
• **Line.**

• **Endpoint.**

• In the **Ribbon bar** make sure that only the tangent icon is enabled and none of the other icons are selected as shown.

• [Specify the first point]: Select the arc approximatelly as shown in Figure: 4.0.1. For this exercise purpose, make

sure that the quadrant point does not appear while selecting the arc.

Figure: 4.0.1

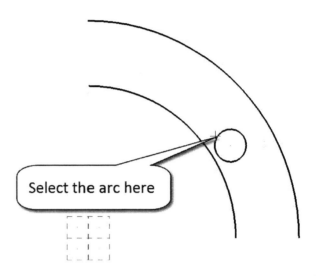

Select the arc here

• Sketch the line by moving the cursor to the left of the arc and click to select the second endpoint as shown
in Figure: 4.0.2.

Figure: 4.0.2

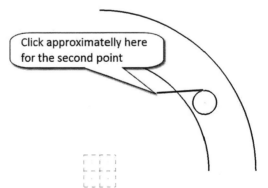

Click approximatelly here
for the second point

• In the **Ribbon bar** type the angle **180** as shown and press **Enter**.

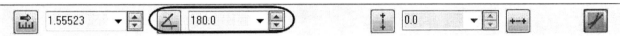

> **NOTE:** Once you enter the angle the line will be updated.

• Select the **OK** button to exit the command.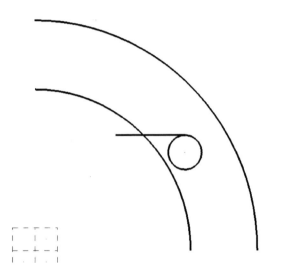
• The geometry should look as shown.

STEP 5: CREATE A FILLET

In this step you will use **Create Fillet Entities** command to create a fillet with the radius 0.75. Fillets are used to round sharp corners.

Step Preview:

R 0.750

Create
* **Fillet.**

*  **Entities.**
* Enter a fillet radius of **0.75**. Ensure the fillet style is set to **Normal** and **Trim** is enabled as shown.

- [Select an entity]: Select Entity A as shown in <u>Figure: 5.0.1</u>.
- [Select another entity]: Select Entity B as shown in <u>Figure: 5.0.1</u>.

Figure: 5.0.1

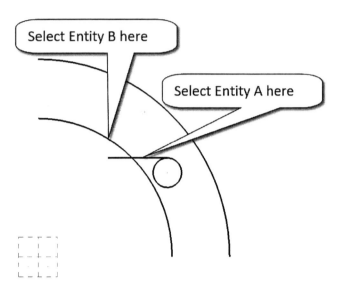

- Select the **OK** button to exit the command.
- The geometry should look as shown.

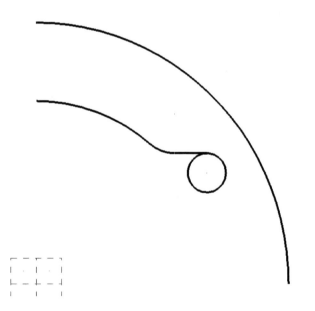

STEP 6: MIRROR THE GEOMETRY

In this step you will Mirror the inside geometry about the X-axis.

Step Preview:

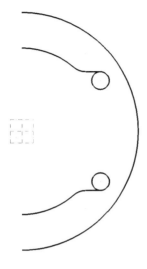

Xform

♦ 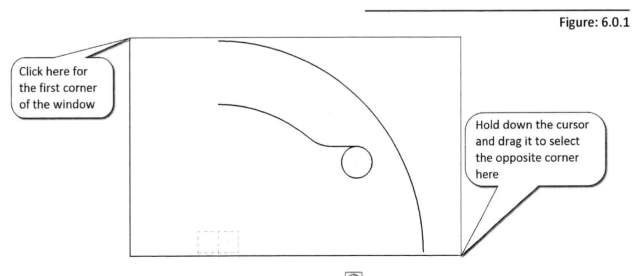 **Mirror.**

♦ [Mirror: select entities to mirror]: Make a Window aroud the entire geometry as shown in Figure: 6.0.1.

Figure: 6.0.1

♦ Press **Enter** or choose the **End Selection** button to continue.

♦ [Select the entity that the arc is to be tangent]: Select Entity A as shown in <u>Figure: 7.0.1</u>.
♦ [Select the entity that the arc is to be tangent]: Select Entity B as shown in <u>Figure: 7.0.1</u>.

Figure: 7.0.1

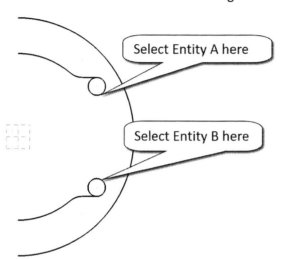

♦ [Select the fillet to use]: Select the hidden line arc as shown in <u>Figure: 7.0.2</u>.

Figure: 7.0.2

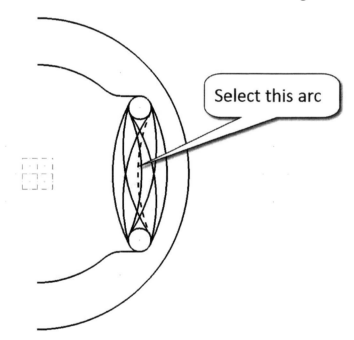

♦ Select the **OK** button to exit the **Create Arc Tangent** function.

◆ The geometry should look as shown.

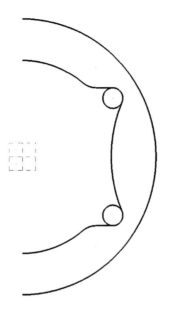

STEP 8: TRIM THE GEOMETRY USING TRIM 3 ENTITIES COMMAND

In this step you will use trim three entities command to clean the geometry. The first two entities that you select are trimmed to the third, which acts as a trimming curve. The third entity is then trimmed to the first two.

This function is useful for trimming two lines to a circle that is tangent to both lines. The arc is selected last, and the results vary depending on whether you select to keep the top or the bottom of the arc.

Step Preview:

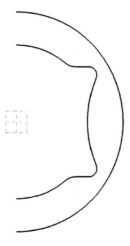

Edit
◆ **Trim/Break.**

◆  **Trim/Break/Extend.**

- Select the option to **Trim 3 Entities**.

- [Select the first entity to trim/extend]: Select Entity A as shown in Figure: 8.0.1.
- [Select the first second to trim/extend]: Select Entity B as shown in Figure: 8.0.1.
- [Select the entity to trim/extend to]: Select Entity C as shown in Figure: 8.0.1.

Figure: 8.0.1

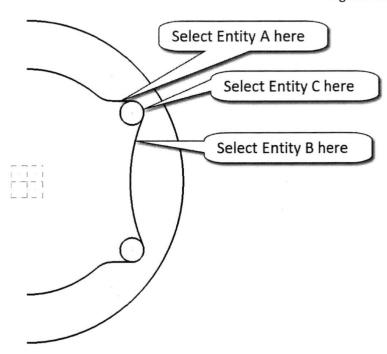

- The geometry should look as shown.

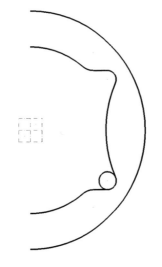

• Repeat the steps to clean the second circle as shown.

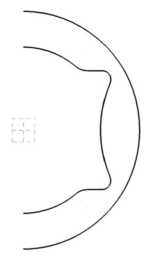

• Select the **OK** button to exit the command.

STEP 9: MIRROR THE GEOMETRY

In this step you will Mirror the inside geometry about the Y-axis.

Step Preview:

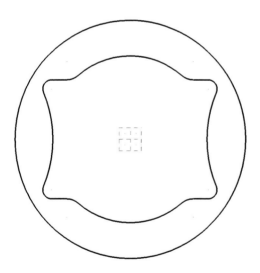

Xform

•  **Mirror.**

- [Mirror: select entities to mirror]: To select the entire geometry, hold down the Shift key and click on both contours as shown in Figure: 9.0.1.

Figure: 9.0.1

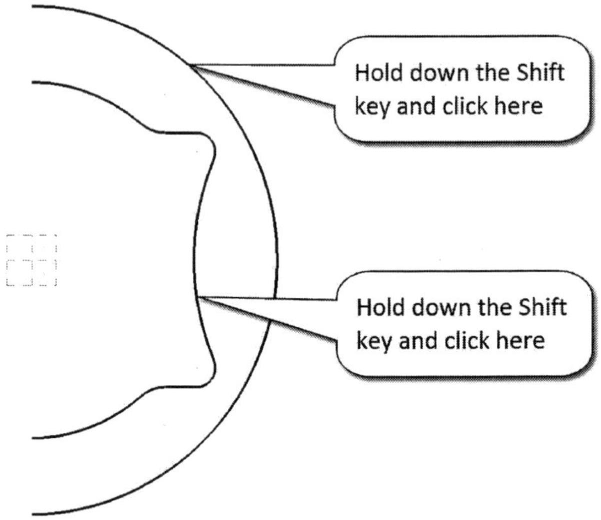

Hold down the Shift key and click here

Hold down the Shift key and click here

NOTE: By holding the **Shift** key and selecting one entity of a chain, Mastercam selects all the other entities that are in the chain.

- Choose the **End Selection** button.

• Pick the option to mirror the entities about the **Y Axis** as shown in <u>Figure: 9.0.2</u>.

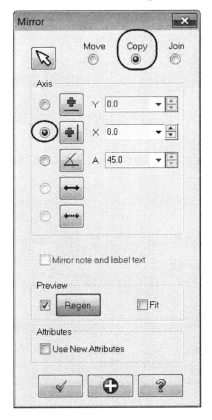

• Pick the **OK** button to exit the **Mirror** dialog box.

• Select the **Fit** icon to fit the drawing to the screen.
• The geometry should look as shown.

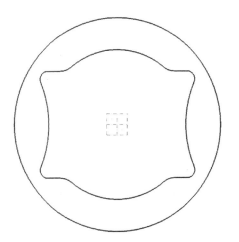

• Select the **Clear Colors** icon from the toolbars to reset the colours back to the original colours.

STEP 10: CREATE THE ELLIPSES

In this step you will learn how to create an ellipse knowing the point of origin, A radius and B radius.

Step Preview:

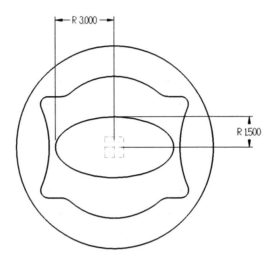

Create

◆ 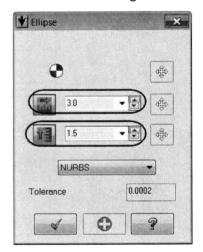 **Ellipse.**

◆ Pick the **Origin** as the position of base point.

◆ Enter a **A radius** of **3.0**, a **B radius** of **1.5** and press **Enter** as shown in <u>Figure: 10.0.1</u>.

Figure: 10.0.1

◆ Pick the **OK** button to exit the **Ellipse** command.

STEP 11: OFFSET THE ELLIPSE

In this step you will offset the ellipse with a given distance.

Step Preview:

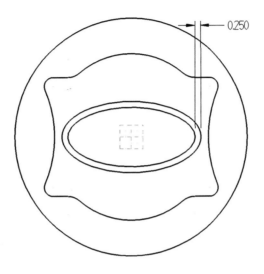

Xform

•  **Offset.**

• [Select the line, arc, spline or curve to offset]: Select the ellipse as shown in <u>Figure: 11.0.1</u>.

Figure: 11.0.1

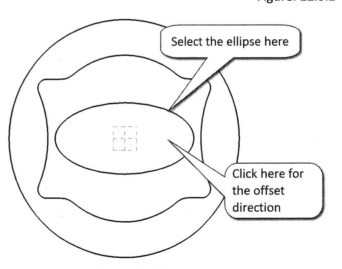

Select the ellipse here

Click here for the offset direction

• [Indicate the offset direction]: Click inside of the ellipse as shown in <u>Figure: 11.0.1</u>.

• Change the distance in the **Offset** dialog box to **0.25** and leave **Copy** enabled as shown in <u>Figure: 11.0.2</u>.

Figure: 11.0.2

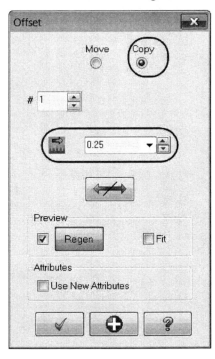

• Select the **OK** button to exit **Offset** dialog box.

• Pick the **Clear Color** icon to return the colours to the original colours.

• The geometry should look as shown.

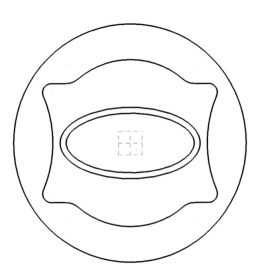

STEP 12: ADD THE TEXT

In this step we will create the **Letters,** then using **Bounding box** you will create a point at their center and then you will use **Translate** command to move them in the center of the part.

Creating letters uses lines, arcs and **NURBS** splines. There are various fonts found in this command as well. When using **TrueType** fonts the height of the letters may not match the value you entered for the letter height because Mastercam scales the letters based on all the information encoded into the **TrueType** font.

Step Preview:

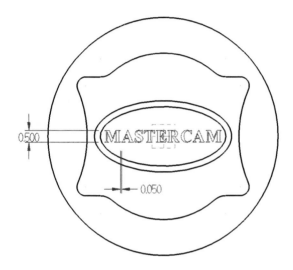

12.1 Change the main color to red

* From the **Ribbon bar**, click on the **System color** as shown.

- Select the **red color no. 12** as shown.

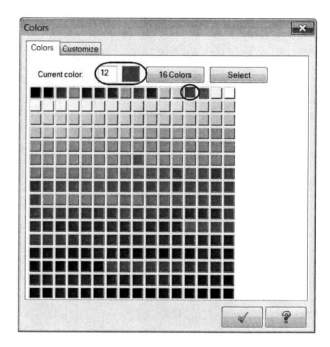

- Select the **OK** button to continue.

12.2 Create the letters

Create

- **L** **Letters.**
- When the **Create Letters** dialog box appears select the **TrueType(R)** button as shown in Figure: 12.2.1.

Figure: 12.2.1

- Scroll down the font list and find the font **Times New Roman**.

◆ Select **Bold** for the **Font style** as shown in <u>Figure: 12.2.2</u>.

Figure: 12.2.2

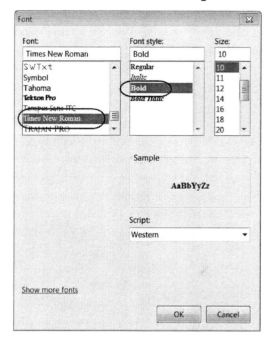

◆ Select the **OK** button.
◆ Input the word **Mastercam** under the area titled **Letters** as shown in <u>Figure: 12.2.3</u>.

Figure: 12.2.3

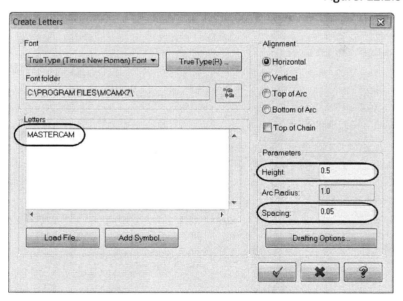

◆ Change the **Height** to **0.50** and the **Spacing** to **0.05**.

◆ Select the **OK** button.

* [Enter the starting location]: Pick a point to the right of the part as the text starting location as shown in
  <u>Figure: 12.2.4</u>.

Figure: 12.2.4

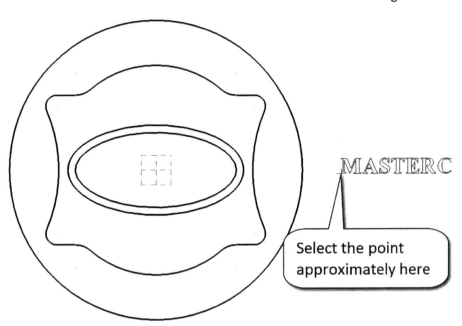

Select the point
approximately here

* Press your Esc key on your keyboard to exit the command.

NOTE: Next we will move the text within the part.

* Select the **Fit** icon.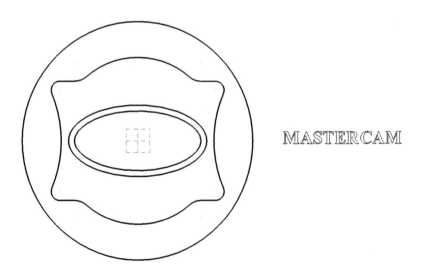

12.3 Create a point at the center of the letters using Bounding Box

Create

• 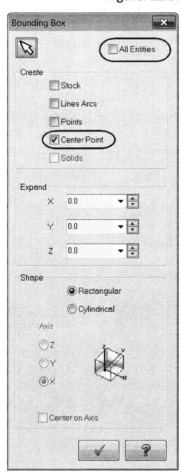 **Bounding Box.**
• When the **Bounding Box dialog** box appears disable the option to create **Lines Arcs** and enable only the **Center Point.**
• Uncheck **All Entities** as shown in Figure: 12.3.1.

Figure: 12.3.1

NOTE: Once you unchecked All Entities, Mastercam brings you to the graphics window where you can select the letters.

• [Select entities]: Click on the **QM Color** icon located to the right of the graphics window as shown.

• From the **Select All** dialog box click on the red color as shown.

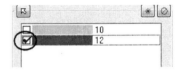

• Select the **OK** button to exit **Select All** dialog box.

• Press **Enter** or pick the **End Selection** button.

• Select the **OK** button to exit **Bounding box** dialog box.

> **NOTE:** A point should appear in the middle of the letters.

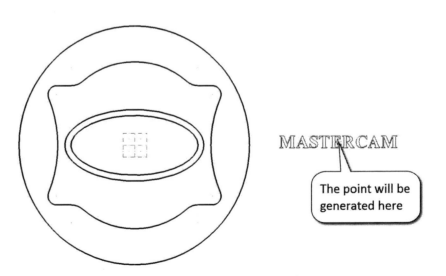

The point will be generated here

12.4 Move the letters using Translate

Xform

+ 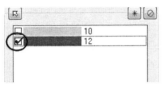 **Translate.**
+ [Translate: select entities to translate]: Click on the **QM Color** icon as shown.

+ Select the red color again as shown.

+ Select the **OK** button to exit **Select All** dialog box.
+ Choose the **End Selection** button to finish the selection.

• When the **Translate dialog** box appears, select the **Move** button and then choose the **From Point** icon 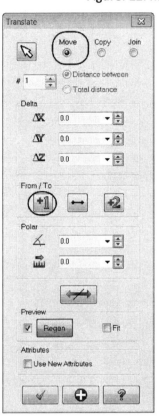 as shown in Figure: 12.4.1.

Figure: 12.4.1

• Choose the **Zoom Window** icon and create a window around the letters as shown in Figure: 12.4.2.

Figure: 12.4.2

- Select the point inside the "**E**" as shown in <u>Figure: 12.4.3</u>.

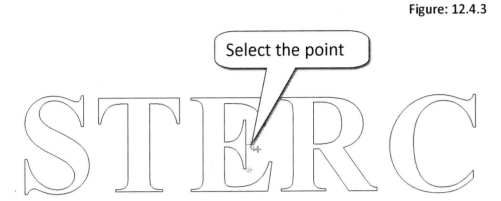

Select the point

- Pick the **Fit** icon.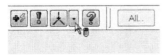
- Choose the drop down arrow in the **AutoCursor** ribbon bar.

- From the list select the option **Origin**.

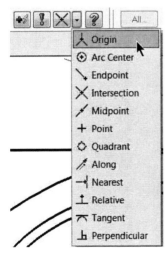

- Select the **OK** button in the **Translate** dialog box.

- Select **Fit** screen to see the geometry.

- Pick the **Clear Color** icon to return the colours to the original colours.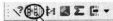

• Once complete the geometry should look as shown.

STEP 13: DELETE THE POINT

In this step you will use QM Point selection to select the center point and then you will delete it.

• From the **Quick Mask** toolbar select **QM Point** as shown to select all the existing point.

• Select the **Delete** key from your keyboard or select the **Delete entities** icon.

STEP 14: SAVE THE FILE

File

• 💾 Save As.
• File name: "Your Name_4".

TOOLPATH CREATION

SUGGESTED FIXTURE:

SETUP SHEET:

TOOL LIST

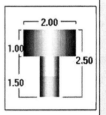

NAME:		HOLDER:
NUMBER:	2	INSERT:
FRONT OFFSET:		
MFG NUMBER:	_	RADIUS:
		WIDTH:
#2 - 0.7500 ENDMILL1 FLAT - 3/4 FLAT ENDMILL		

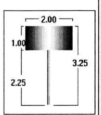

NAME:		HOLDER:
NUMBER:	2	INSERT:
FRONT OFFSET:		
MFG NUMBER:	_	RADIUS:
		WIDTH:
#3 - 0.1250 ENDMILL1 FLAT - 1/8 FLAT ENDMILL		

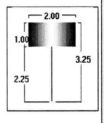

NAME:		HOLDER:
NUMBER:	2	INSERT:
FRONT OFFSET:		
MFG NUMBER:	_	RADIUS:
		WIDTH:
#4 - 0.0313 ENDMILL1 FLAT - 1/32 FLAT ENDMILL		

STEP 15: SELECT THE MACHINE AND SET UP THE STOCK

In Mastercam, you select a **Machine Definition** before creating any toolpaths. The **Machine Definition** is a model of your machines capabilities and features. It acts like a template for setting up your machine. The machine definition ties together three main components. The schematic model of your machines components. The control definition that models your control capabilities and the post processor that will generate the required machine code (G-code). For a Mill Level 1 exercise (2D toolpaths) we need just a basic machine definition.

> **NOTE:** For the purpose of this tutorial, we will be using the Default milling machine.

• To display the **Operations Manager** press **Alt + O**.

• Use the **Fit** icon to fit the drawing to the screen.

Machine type
• **Mill.**
• **Default.**

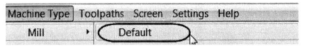

• Select the plus sign in front of **Properties** in the **Toolpaths Manager** to expand the **Toolpaths Group Properties.**

• Select **Tool settings** to set the tool parameters.

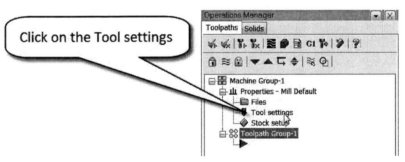

◆ Change the parameters to match the screenshot as shown in <u>Figure: 15.0.1</u>.

Figure: 15.0.1

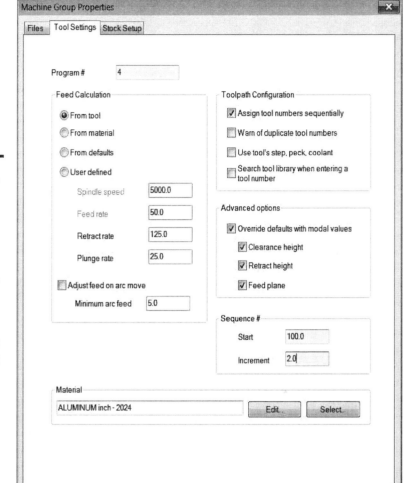

Program # is used to enter a number if your machine tool requires a number for a program name.

Assign tool numbers sequentially allows you to overwrite the tool number from the library with the next available tool number. (First operation tool number 1; Second operation tool number 2, etc.)

Warn of duplicate tool numbers allows you to get a warning if you enter two tools with the same number.

Override defaults with modal values enables the system to keep the values that you enter.

Feed Calculation set From tool uses feed rate, plunge rate, retract rate and spindle speed from the tool definition.

- Select the **Stock Setup** tab to define the stock.
- Select the **Cylindrical Shape** and enter the values as shown in Figure: 15.0.2.

Figure: 15.0.2

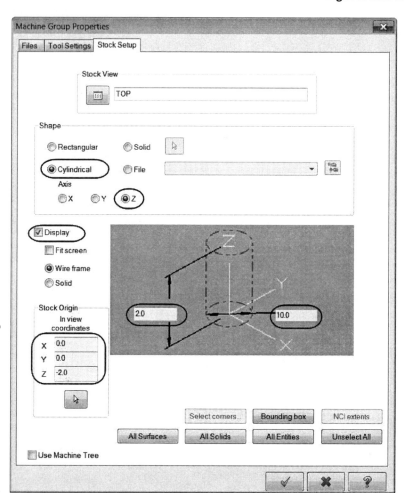

The **Stock Origin** values adjust the positioning of the stock, ensuring that you have equal amount of extra stock around the finished part.

Display options allow you to set the stock as Wireframe and to fit the stock to the screen. (Fit Screen)

- Select the **OK** button to exit the **Machine Group Properties**.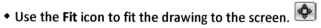

- Select the **Isometric** view from the graphics view toolbar to see the stock.

- Use the **Fit** icon to fit the drawing to the screen.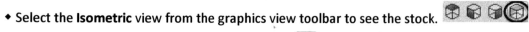

Mill Level 1 Training Tutorial
Mastercam. X ⁷

◆ The stock model will appear as shown.

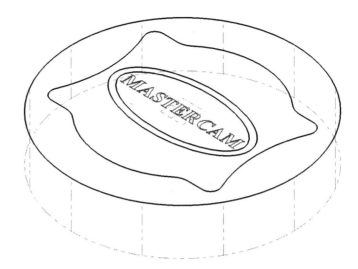

| **NOTE:** The stock is not geometry and can not be selected.

◆ Select the **Top** view from the view toolbar to see the part from the top.

| **NOTE:** There will not be facing toolpath because the stock is already to size.

STEP 16: 2D HIGH SPEED CORE MILL

2D High Speed Core Mill generates the free-flowing motion needed to machine features, such as standing bosses and cores in a single operation. Core Mill requires two chains. An outside chain defining the stock boundary, allowing the toolpath to move freely outside this area. An inner chain defines the limit of the toolpath.

Toolpath Preview:

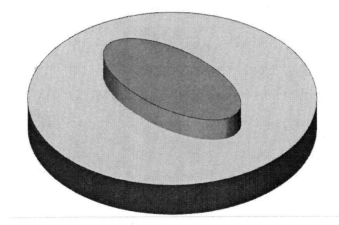

Toolpaths
* **2D High Speed.**

* 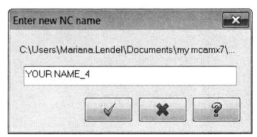 **Core.**

* If a prompt appears, enter new **NC name**, select the **OK** button to accept the default.

* Leave the default settings in the chaining dialog box.

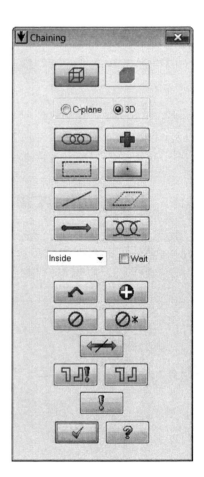

◆ [2D HST: define chain 1]: Select the first chain as shown in Figure: 16.0.1.

Figure: 16.0.1

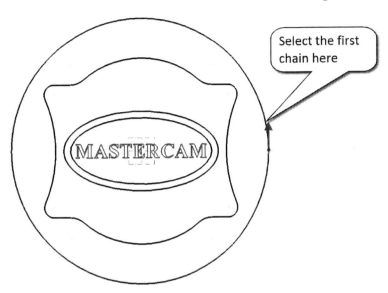

Select the first
chain here

◆ [2D HST: define chain 2]: Select the second chain as shown in Figure: 16.0.2.

Figure: 16.0.2

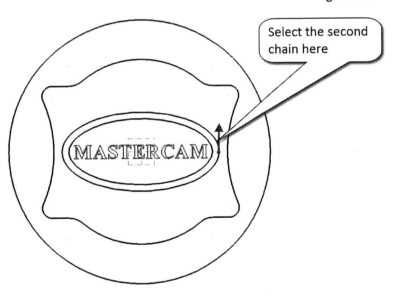

Select the second
chain here

• Choose the **OK** button to continue.

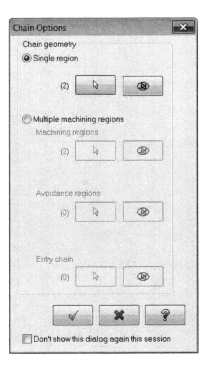

• Select the **OK** button to exit the **Chain Options** dialog box.
• In the **Toolpath Type** page select the toolpath **Core Mill**.

Core Mill   Peel Mill   Blend Mill   Area Mill   Rest Mill   Dynamic Area Mill

Dynamic Rest Mill   Dynamic Core Mill   Dynamic Contour

NOTE: Mastercam updates the pages as you modify them and then marks them, in the **Tree view** list, with a green check mark. Pages that are not changed are marked with a red circle and slash.

16.1 Select a 3/4" Flat Endmill from the Tool Library and set the Tool Parameters

• From the **Tree view list**, select **Tool.**

• Click on **Select library tool** button. `Select library tool...`
• Select the **Filter** button.

- Select the **None** button and then under **Tool Types** choose the **Flat Endmill** Icon.
- Under tool diameter pick **Equal** and input a value of **0.75** as shown in Figure: 16.1.1.

Figure: 16.1.1

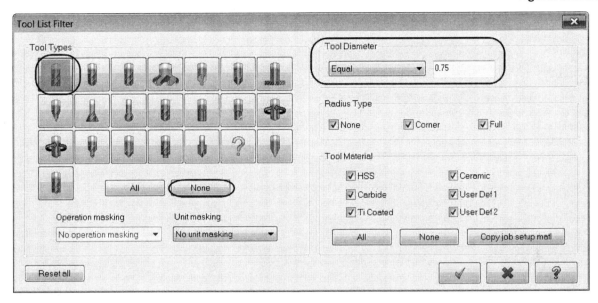

- Select the **OK** button to exit the **Tool List Filter**.
- In the **Tool Selection** dialog box you should only see a **3/4" Flat Endmill**.

#	Assembly Name	Tool Name	Holder Name	Dia.	Cor. rad.	Length	# Flutes	Type	Rad. Type
241	–	3/4 FLAT...	–	0.75	0.0	2.0	4	En...	None

- Select the **3/4" Flat Endmill** in the **Tool Selection** page and then select the **OK** button to exit.

♦ Make all the necessary changes as shown in <u>Figure: 16.1.2</u>.

Figure: 16.1.2

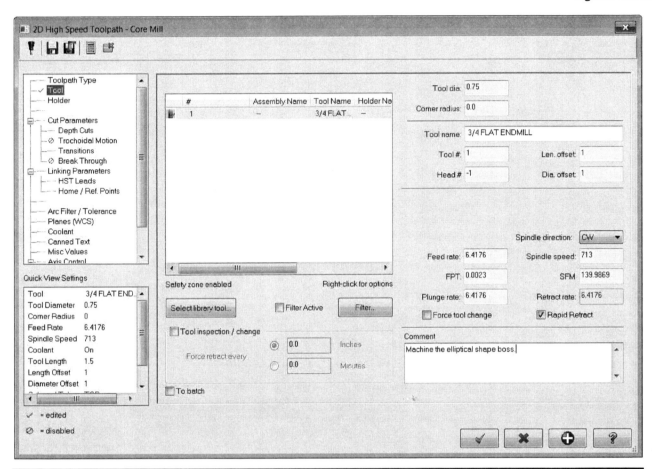

Tool Inspection/change forces a retract move at set intervals so that your machine operator can inspect the tool. When the tool reaches an inspection point, it retracts and rapid off the part to the clearance plane.

16.2 Set the Cut Parameters

♦ Select **Cut Parameters** and enable **Corner rounding** as shown in <u>Figure: 16.2.1</u>.

Figure: 16.2.1

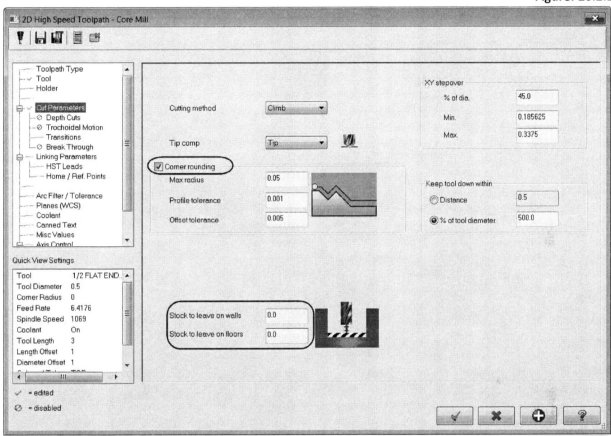

Corner Rounding replaces sharp corners with arcs for faster and smoother transitions in tool direction.

Max Radius is the largest arc that you allow Mastercam to insert to replace a corner. Larger arcs will create a smoother toolpath but with greater deviation from the originally programmed toolpath.

Profile Tolerance represents the maximum distance that the outermost profile of a toolpath created a corner with a corner rounding can deviate from the original toolpath.

Offset Tolerance represents the maximum distance that a profile of a toolpath created with corner rounding can deviate from the original toolpath. This is the same measurement as the profile tolerance but is applied to all the profiles except the outermost one.

XY Stepover expresses the maximum XY stepover as a percentage of the tool diameter. Mastercam will use the largest value possible that does not leave unwanted upstands of material between the passes.

Keep Tool Down Within keeps the tool down if the distance from the end pass to the start of the next pass is less than the value here. Mastercam will not create a retract move as defined on the linking parameters page. Instead the tool will stay down and move directly between the passes at the feed rate.

16.3 Set the Depth Cuts Parameters

• Select **Depth cuts** and make the necessary changes as shown in Figure: 16.3.1.

Figure: 16.3.1

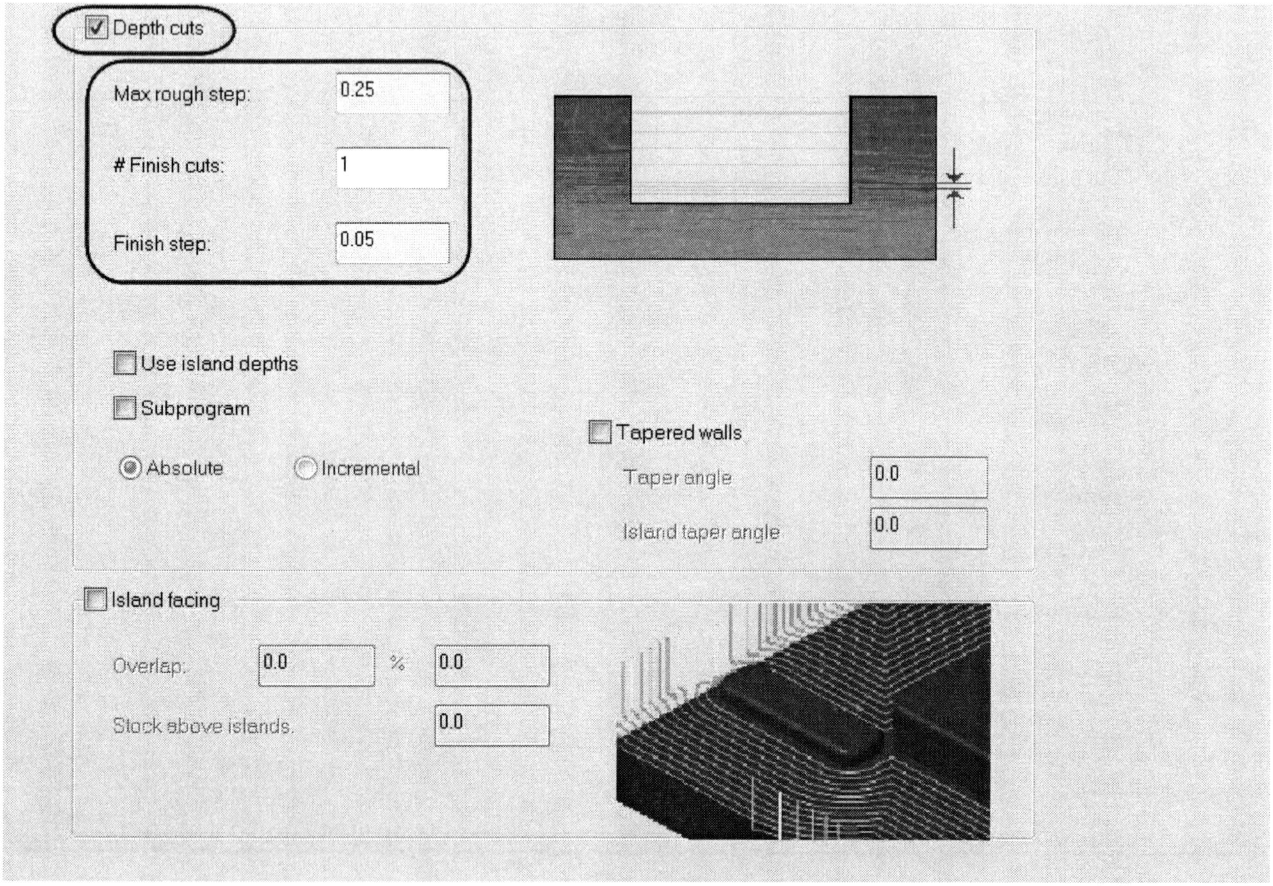

☑ Depth cuts

Max rough step: 0.25

Finish cuts: 1

Finish step: 0.05

☐ Use island depths

☐ Subprogram

◉ Absolute   ○ Incremental

☐ Tapered walls

Taper angle   0.0

Island taper angle   0.0

☐ Island facing

Overlap: 0.0   %   0.0

Stock above islands.   0.0

16.4 Set the Transitions Parameters

- ◆ Select **Transitions**, choose the **Entry method Entry helix** and enter a **Radius** of **0.25**.
- ◆ Enable **Output 3D arc moves** and ensure the value set in **Skip pockets smaller than** is **0.55** as shown in <u>Figure: 16.4.1</u>.

Figure: 16.4.1

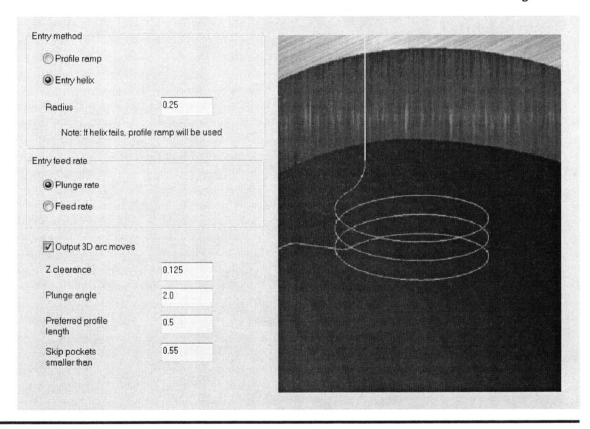

Entry method sets the entry move that the tool makes as it transitions to new Z depths. If you choose to create a helical entry and there is not enough room, Mastercam creates a ramp entry instead.

Entry feed rate sets the rate that the tool feeds into the material.

Output 3d arc moves using this option Mastercam creates the helix with arc (G2/G3) moves. If this option is disabled the helix will be created with many small linear moves.

Z clearance is extra height used in the ramping motion down from a top profile. It ensures the tool has fully slowed down from the rapid speeds before touching the material.

16.5 Set the Linking Parameters

• Select **Linking Parameters** and make the necessary changes as shown in Figure: 16.5.1.

Figure: 16.5.1

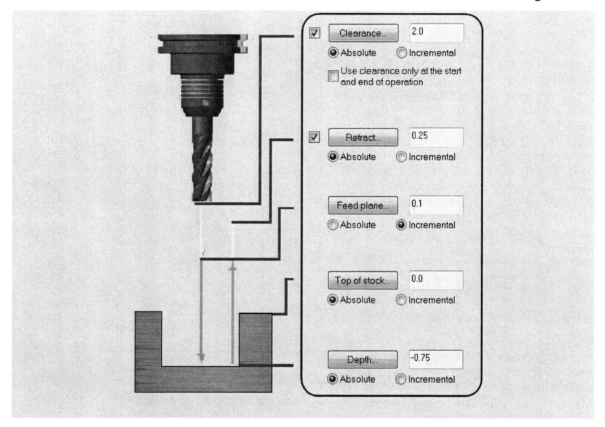

16.6 Set the HST Leads

♦ From the Tree view list, select HST Leads and make any necessary changes as shown in Figure: 16.6.1.

Figure: 16.6.1

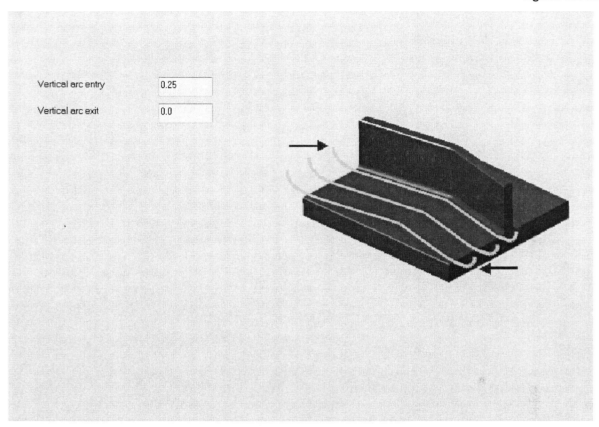

HST Leads page allows you to specify an entry and exit arc radius value for the **2D High Speed Toolpaths**. The arc is created vertically to lead on and off the material.

16.7 Set the Arc Filter / Tolerance

♦ Choose **Arc Filter / Tolerance** from the **Tree view list** and make the necessary changes as shown in <u>Figure: 16.7.1</u>.

Figure: 16.7.1

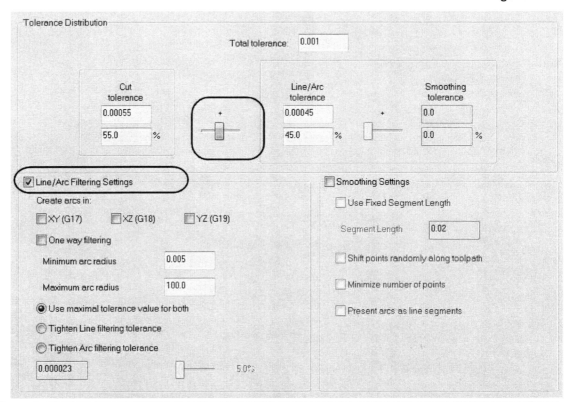

Tolerance Distribution allows you to dynamically adjust the toolpath's total tolerance. Total tolerance is the sum of the cut tolerance and the line/arc and smoothing tolerances. Move the sliders between the **Cut tolerance**, **Line/Arc tolerance** and/or **Smoothing tolerance** fields, the ratios update in 5% increments and the toolpath's total tolerance remains at its current value.

Line/Arc Filtering Settings allows you to activate Line/Arc filtering for the toolpath and apply the settings you define in this section to the toolpath refinement. Toolpath filtering lets you replace multiple very small linear moves — within the filter tolerance — with single arc moves to simplify the toolpath. Smoothing distributes a toolpath's node points, avoiding the clustering and grouping of points that can cause marks and other imperfections.

Create arcs in creates arcs in the selected plane. Your post processor must be able to handle arcs and output the code G17, G18, G19 to select this option.

♦ Select the **OK** button once the parameters have been set.

STEP 17: BACKPLOT THE TOOLPATHS

Backplotting shows the path the tools take to cut the part. This display lets you spot errors in the program before you machine the part. As you backplot toolpaths, Mastercam displays additional information such as the X, Y, and Z coordinates, the path length , the minimum and maximum coordinates and the cycle time. It also shows any collisions between the workpiece and the tool.

◆ Make sure that the toolpaths are selected (signified by the green check mark on the folder icon). If the operation is not selected choose the **Select all operations** icon.

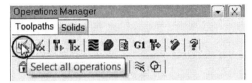

◆ Select the **Backplot selected operations** button.

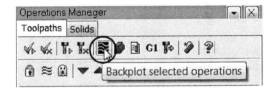

> **NOTE:** Mastercam launches a new window that allows you to check the part using **Backplot** or **Verify**.

◆ Select the **Backplot** tab and have the following settings enabled as shown.

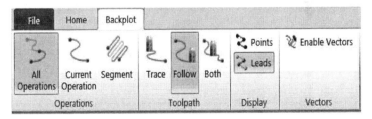

◆ Select the **Home** tab and make sure that you have the following settings on as shown.

◆ To see the part from an **Isometric** view select the **Isometric** icon.

* To fit the workpiece to the screen, select the **Fit** icon.

* You can step through the **Backplot** by using the **Step forward** or **Step back** buttons.

* You can adjust the speed of the backplot.
* Select the **Play Simulation** button in the **VCR** bar to run **Backplot**.

* The toolpath should look as shown.

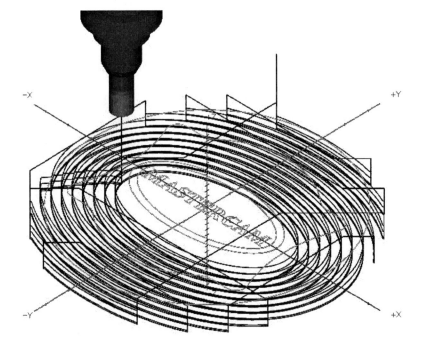

STEP 18: SIMULATE THE TOOLPATH IN VERIFY

Verify Mode shows the path the tools take to cut the part with material removal. This display lets you spot errors in the program before you machine the part. As you verify toolpaths, Mastercam displays additional information such as the X, Y, and Z coordinates, the path length , the minimum and maximum coordinates and the cycle time. It also shows any collisions between the workpiece and the tool.

◆ From **Mastercam Backplot Home** tab, switch to **Verify** and change the settings for the **Visibility** and **Focus** as shown in Figure: 18.0.1.

Figure: 18.0.1

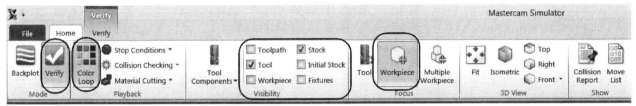

◆ Select the **Play Simulation** button in the **VCR** bar to run **Verify**.

◆ The part should appear as shown in <u>Figure: 18.0.2</u>.

Figure: 18.0.2

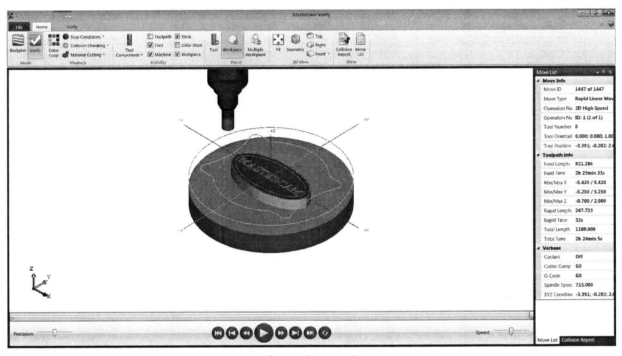

◆ To go back to Mastercam window, minimize **Verify** window as shown.

STEP 19: 2D HIGH SPEED DYNAMIC CORE MILL

In this step you will machine the outside profile using **2D HS Dynamic Core Mill** toolpath. **Dynamic Core Mill** machines open pocket shapes or standing core shapes using the outmost chain as the stock boundary. The tool moves freely outside of this area; the inner chain defines the limit of the toolpath. They are designed to utilize the entire flute length of their cutting tools to maximize material removal while minimizing tool wear.

Toolpath Preview:

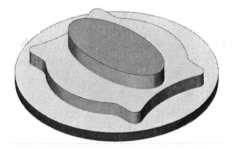

19.1 Chain Selection

- To remove the toolpath display press **Alt + T** or click on the **Toggle display on selected operations** in the **Toolpaths Operations Manager**.

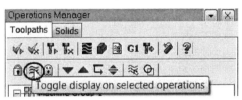

Toolpaths
- **2D High speed.**
- **Dynamic Core.**
- Leave the default setting in the chaining dialog box.

- [2D HST: define chain 1]: Pick the first chain as shown in Figure: 19.1.1.

Figure: 19.1.1

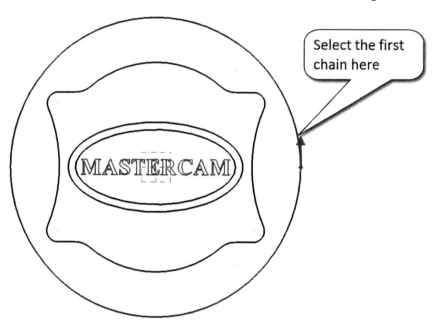

Select the first chain here

- Then pick the second chain as shown in Figure: 19.1.2.

Figure: 19.1.2

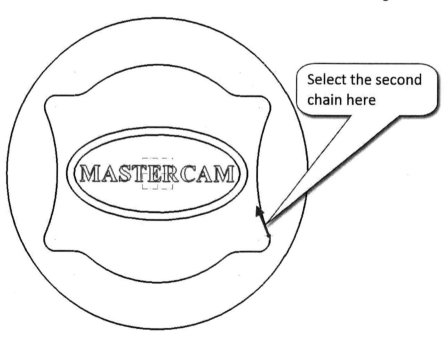

Select the second chain here

- Select the **OK** button to exit the **Chaining** dialog box.

• Select the **OK** button exit the **Chain Options** dialog box.
• In the **Toolpath Type** page, the **Dynamic Core Mill** should already be selected.

19.2 Select the existing 3/4" Flat endmill from the list and set the Tool Parameters

• Make all the necessary changes as shown in Figure: 19.2.1.

Figure: 19.2.1

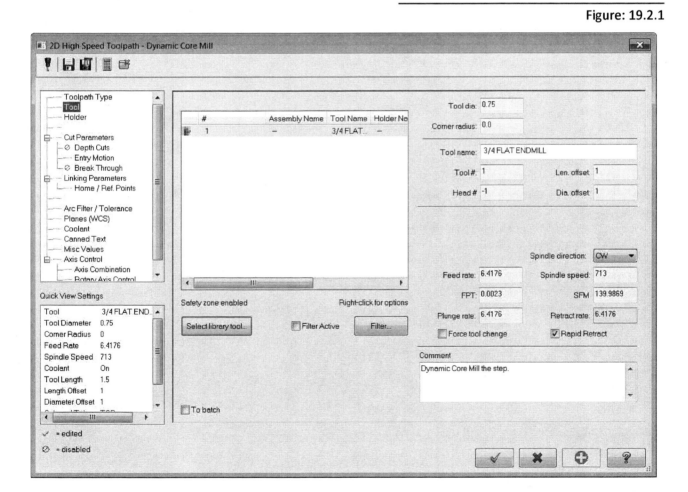

19.3 Set the Cut Parameters

♦ From the **Tree view list**, select **Cut Parameters**. Input a **Stepover** value of **25%** as shown in Figure: 19.3.1.

Figure: 19.3.1

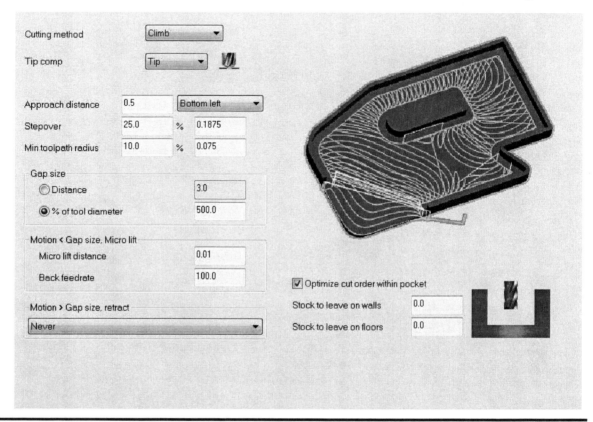

Approach Distance available only when open pocket machining is selected. Adds the specified absolute distance to the beginning of the toolpaths first cut.

Stepover sets the distance between cutting passes in the X and Y axis.

Toolpath Radius reduces sharp corner motion between cut passes.

Micro Lift Distance enter the distance the tool lifts off the part on the back moves. Microlifts are slight lifts that help clear chips and minimize excessive tool heating.

Back Feedrate controls the speed of the backfeed movement of the tool.

Retract controls retracts in the toolpath when making a non-cutting move within an area where the tool can be kept down or microlifted.

Optimize Cut Order defines the cut order Mastercam applies to different cutting passes in the dynamic mill toolpath.

19.4 Disable the Depth cuts parameters

♦ From the **Tree view list**, select the **Depth Cuts** and make sure is disabled as shown.

19.5 Set the Entry Motion

♦ From the **Tree view** list, select **Entry Motion**.
♦ Input a **Z clearance** of **0.05**and a **Plunge angle** of **2.0** degrees.
♦ Enable **Entry feeds / speeds** and set a **Ramp feed rate** of **10.0** Inches per minute, a **Ramp spindle speed** of **4000** RPM and **Dwell before cut spindle speed** of **3.0** seconds as shown in Figure: 19.5.1.

Figure: 19.5.1

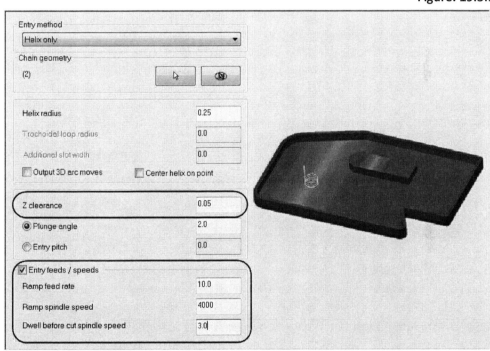

Entry method defines the entry point and cutting strategy used to create the toolpath.

Z clearance adds an extra height used in the ramping motion down from a top profile. It ensures that the tool has fully slowed down from rapid speeds before touching the material.

Plunge angle sets the angle of descent for the entry move, and determines the pitch.

Rapid feed rate overrides the feed rate set on the tools page and uses the specified feed rate for entry ramps into the material.

Ramp spindle speed overrides the spindle speed set in the tools page and uses the specified spindle speed for entry ramps into the material.

19.6 Set the Linking Parameters

• Select **Linking Parameters** and input the **Depth** as shown in <u>Figure: 19.6.1</u>.

Figure: 19.6.1

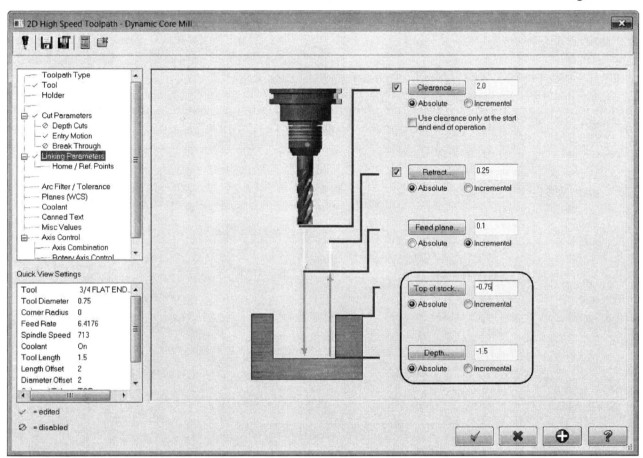

• Once complete pick the **OK** button to generate the toolpath.

19.7 Backplot the toolpath

• To **Backplot** the toolpath page 307 to review this procedure.

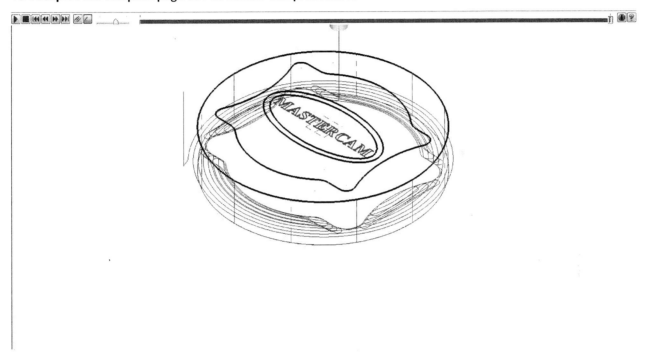

• To go back to Mastercam window, minimize **Backplot** window as shown.

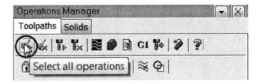

19.8 Simulate the toolpaths using Verify

• To select all operations, in the **Toolpaths Operations Manager**, click on the **Select all operation** icon.

• To **Verify** the toolpath see page 309.

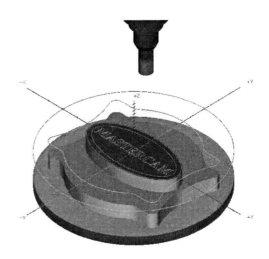

• To go back to Mastercam window, minimize **Verify** window as shown.

STEP 20: POCKET

Toolpath Preview:

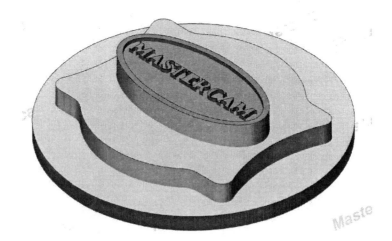

• Press **Alt** + **T** to remove the toolpath display.

Toolpaths

• **Pocket.**

20.1 Select the Geometry

• Choose the **Top** graphics view from the toolbars.

Mastercam X[7]

◆ When the chaining dialog box appears select the **Window** chaining option.

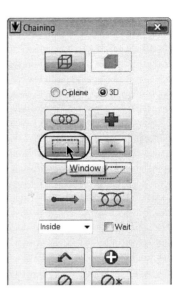

• Create a window around the letters and the inner ellipse as shown in <u>Figure: 20.1.1</u>.

> **NOTE:** Make sure that the window is big enough to include the inside ellipse completed but avoid the outside ellipse.

Figure: 20.1.1

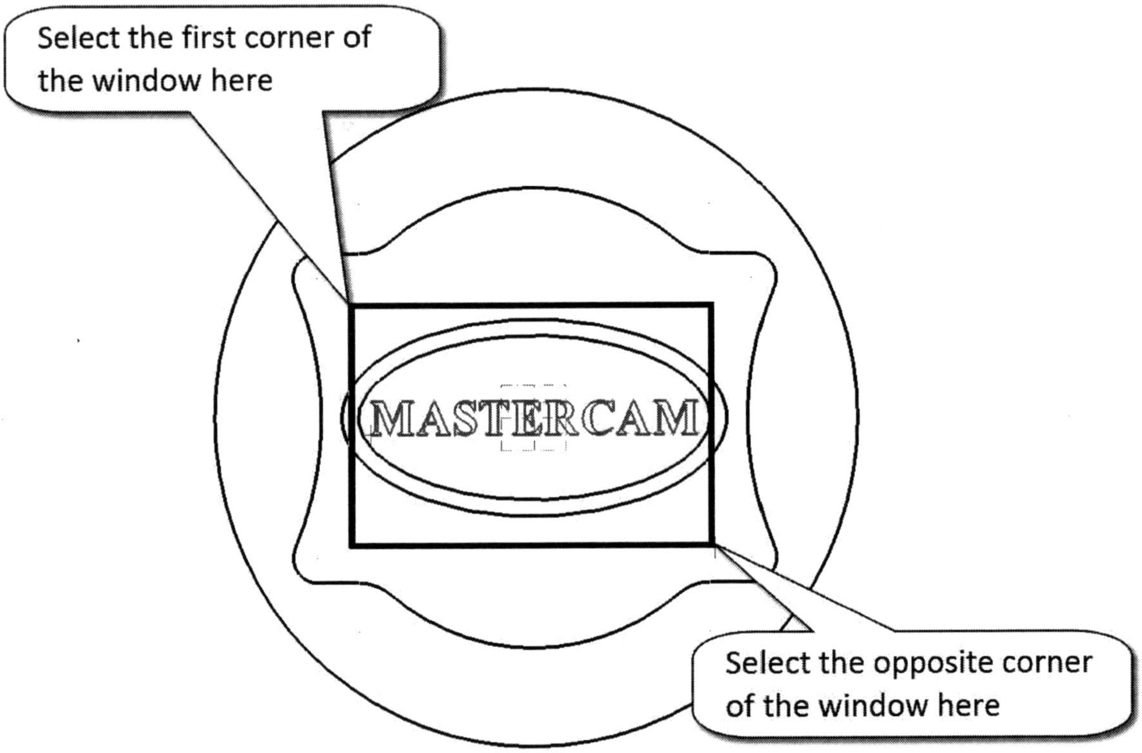

Select the first corner of the window here

MASTERCAM

Select the opposite corner of the window here

• [Sketch approximate start point]: Pick an approximate starting point near the bottom of the letter "M" as shown in Figure: 20.1.2.

Figure: 20.1.2

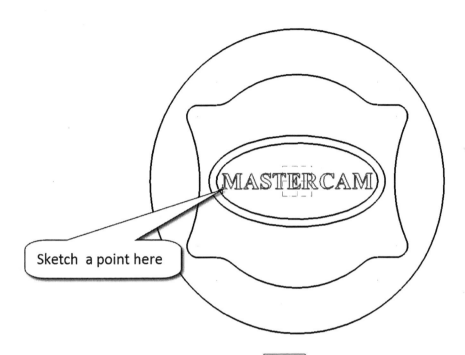

Sketch a point here

• Choose the **OK** button to exit the **Chaining** dialog box.
• On the **Toolpath Type** page **Pocket** will be picked.

Contour   Pocket   Facing   Slot Mill

20.2 Select a 1/8" Flat endmill from the library and set the Tool Parameters

• Select **Tool** from the **Tree view** list.

• Click on **Select library tool** button.
• Select the **Filter** button.

• Select the **None** button and then under **Tool Types** choose the **Flat Endmill** icon.

• Under tool diameter pick **Equal** and input a value **0.125** as shown in Figure: 20.2.1.

Figure: 20.2.1

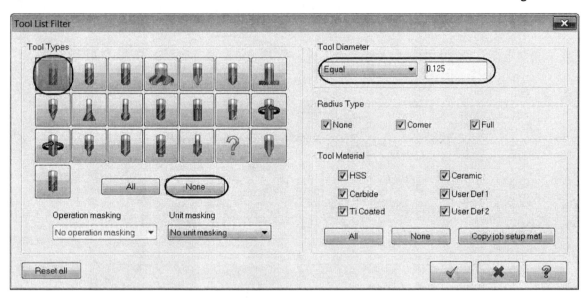

• Select the **OK** button to exit the **Tool List Filter**.
• In the **Tool Selection** dialog box you should only see a **1/8" Flat Endmill**.

#	Assembly Name	Tool Name	Holder Name	Dia.	Cor. rad.	Length	# Flutes	Type	Rad. Type
232	–	1/8 FLAT...	–	0...	0.0	0.375	4	En...	None

• Select the **1/8" Flat Endmill** in the **Tool Selection** page and then select the **OK** button to exit.

♦ Make all the necessary changes as shown in <u>Figure: 20.2.2</u>.

Figure: 20.2.2

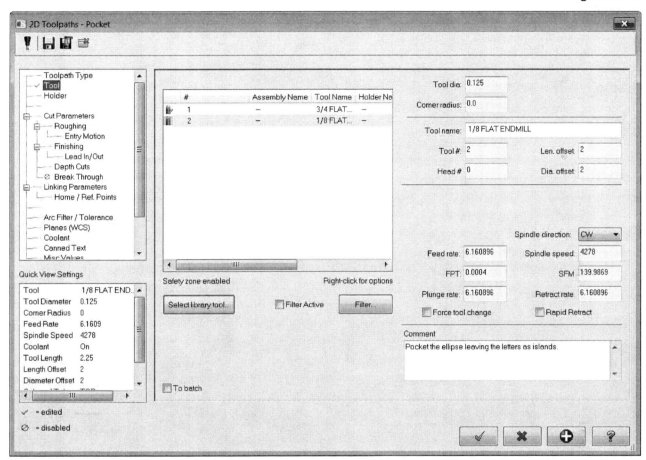

20.3 Set the Cut Parameters

♦ From the **Tree view** list select **Cut Parameters,** and ensure **Pocket type** is set to **Standard** as shown in
<u>Figure: 20.3.1</u>.

Figure: 20.3.1

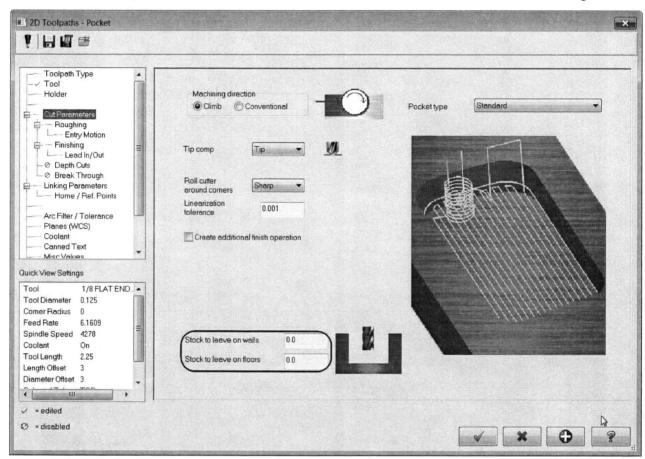

20.4 Set the Roughing Parameters

◆ Enable **Roughing** and ensure your parameters appear as shown in Figure: 20.4.1.

Figure: 20.4.1

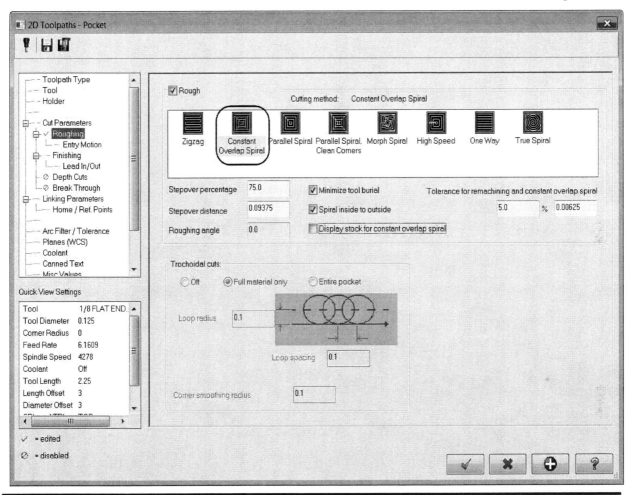

Constant Overlap Spiral creates one roughing pass, determines the remaining stock and recalculates based on the new stock amount. This process repeats until the pocket is cleared.

20.5 Set the Entry Motion

♦ Choose **Entry Motion** from the **tree view list.** Ensure your settings appear as shown in <u>Figure: 20.5.1</u>.

Figure: 20.5.1

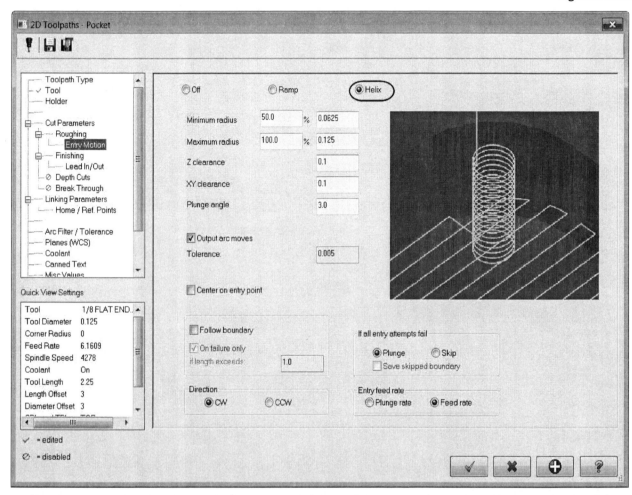

Minimum Radius sets the smallest possible radius for the entry helix.

Maximum Radius sets the largest possible radius for the entry helix.

20.6 Set the Finishing Parameters

♦ Select **Finishing** and ensure you options appear as shown in Figure: 20.6.1.

Figure: 20.6.1

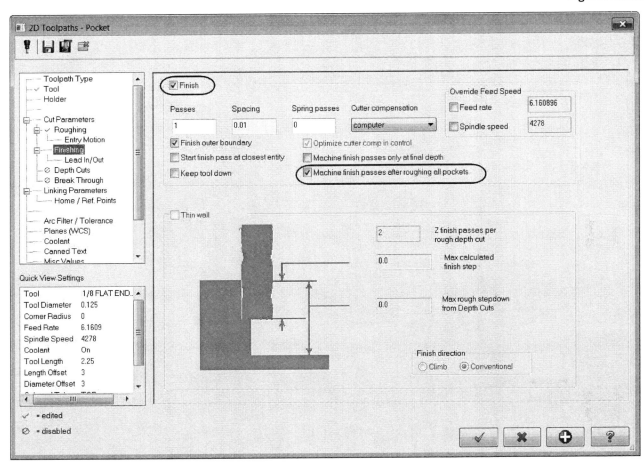

20.7 Set the Lead In/Out Parameters

◆ Select **Lead In/Out** from the **Tree view list.** Set the length and arc percentage to **60%** and input an **Arc Sweep** of **90** degrees as shown in Figure: 20.7.1.

Figure: 20.7.1

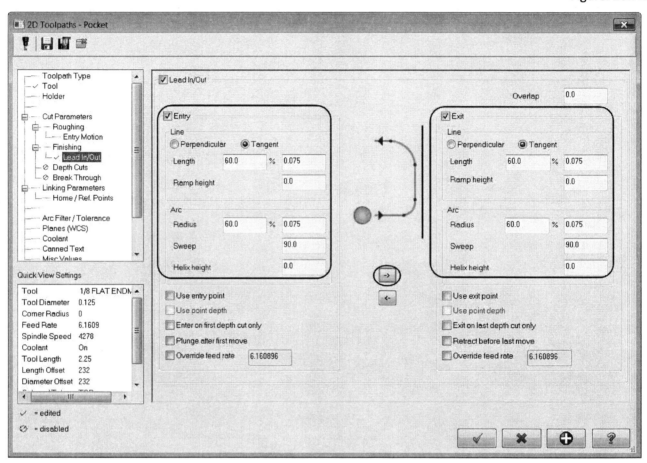

POCKET   **TUTORIAL #4**

20.8 Setup Depth Cuts Parameters

• Pick **Depth Cuts** and enable this option. Set the **Max rough step** to **0.05** as shown in <u>Figure: 20.8.1</u>.

Figure: 20.8.1

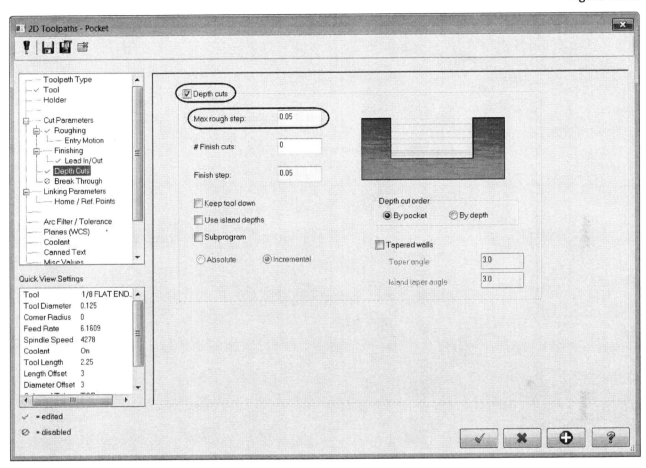

20.9 Set the Linking Parameters

* Choose **Linking Parameters** and input a final **Depth** of **-0.125** as shown in Figure: 20.9.1.

Figure: 20.9.1

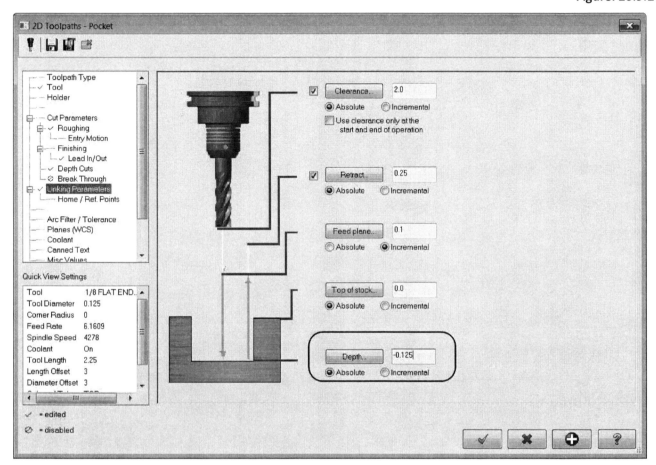

* Select the **OK** button to exit the **Pocket** parameters.

20.10 Backplot and Verify the toolpath

◆ To **Backplot** and **Verify** your toolpath see page 307 to review these procedures.

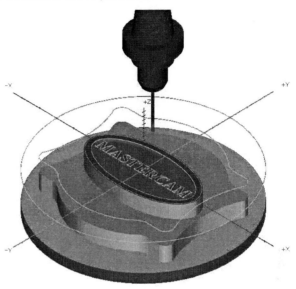

STEP 21: POCKET REMACHINING

Pocket Remachining is only used with closed chains. It calculates areas where the pocket roughing tool could not machine the stock and creates a remachining pocket toolpath to clear the remaining material.

Toolpath Preview:

21.1 Select the Geometry

Toolpaths

- **Pocket.**
- When the **Chaining** dialog box appears choose the **Last** button to reselect the chains used in the previous toolpath.

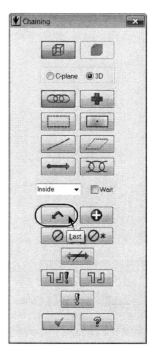

- Select the **OK** button to exit the chaining dialog box.
- On the **Toolpath Type** page **Pocket** will be picked.

| Contour | Pocket | Facing | Slot Mill |

21.2 Select a 1/32" Flat endmill from the library and set the Tool Parameters

- Select **Tool** from the **Tree view list**.

- Click on **Select library tool** button.
- Select the **Filter** button.

• Select the **None** button and then under **Tool Types** choose the **Flat Endmill** Icon.
• Under tool diameter pick **Equal** and input a value **0.03125** as shown in Figure: 21.2.1.

Figure: 21.2.1

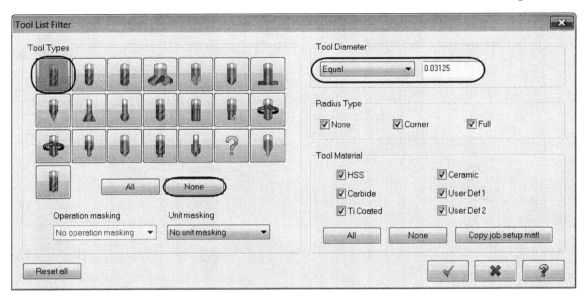

• Select the **OK** button to exit the **Tool List Filter.**
• In the **Tool Selection** dialog box you should only see a **1/32" Flat Endmill**.

#	Assembly Name	Tool Name	Holder Name	Dia.	Cor. rad.	Length	# Flutes	Type	Rad. Type
229	–	1/32 FLA...	–	0....	0.0	0.375	4	En...	None

• Select the **1/32" Flat Endmill** in the **Tool Selection** page and then select the **OK** button to exit.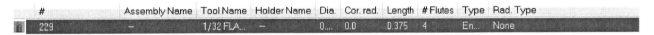

• Make all the necessary changes as shown in Figure: 21.2.2.

Figure: 21.2.2

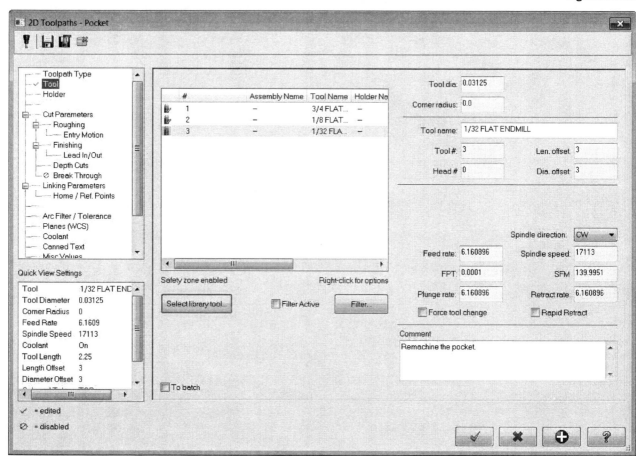

21.3 Set the Cut Parameters

◆ Select **Cut Parameters** and change the **Pocket Type** to **Remachining.**
◆ Ensure your settings appear as shown in Figure: 21.3.1.

Figure: 21.3.1

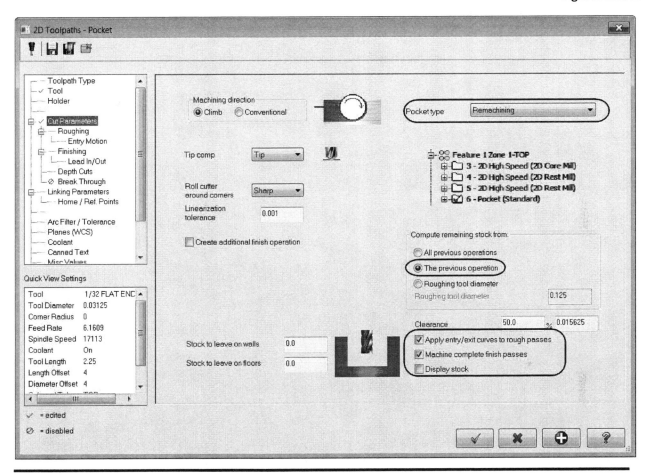

Compute remaining stock from The previous operation determines remaining stock for remachining by calculating stock removed during the previous toolpath.

Clearance extends the remachining toolpath at the beginning and end to prevent cusps of material from being left behind.

21.4 Set the Roughing Parameters

◆ Choose **Roughing** and change the stepover percentage to **55** as shown in Figure: 21.4.1.

Figure: 21.4.1

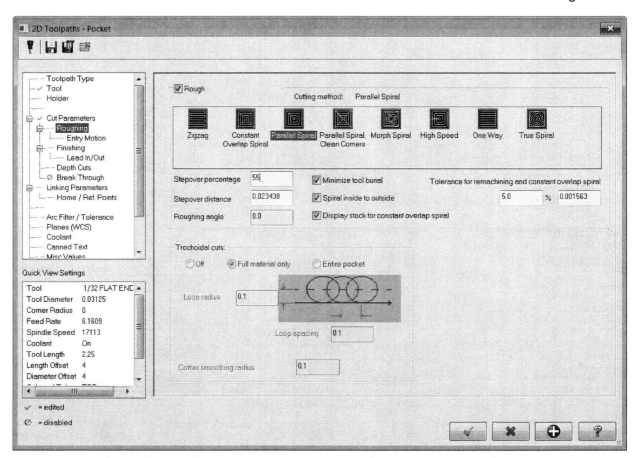

> **NOTE:** The **Cutting method** is defined by the **Pocket type** and can not be modified for **Remachining**. The **Finishing, Lead In/Out** and **Depth Cuts** parameters are the same as the previous toolpath therefore we do not need to view them.

21.5 Set the Linking Parameters

• Choose **Linking Parameters**, and set the **Depth** to **-0.125** as shown in <u>Figure: 21.5.1</u>.

Figure: 21.5.1

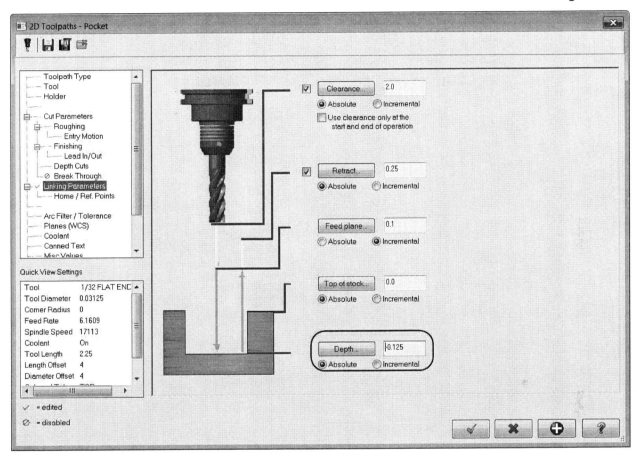

• Select the **OK** button to exit the pocket parameters.
• A warning that the remachining complete finish passes option requires the machining finish passes after roughing all pockets will appear and will automatically be enabled.
• Select the **OK** button to continue.

21.6 Backplot and Verify the toolpaths

◆ To **Backplot** and **Verify** your toolpath page 307 to review these procedures.

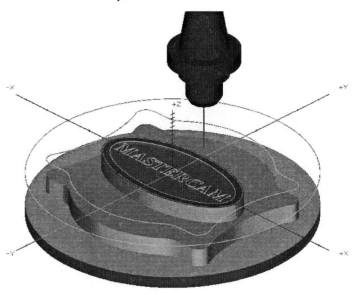

◆ To exit exit Verify select the close button as shown.

STEP 22: POST THE FILE

- Ensure all operations are selected, if they are not use the button **Select all operations** in the **Operations Manager.**

- Select the **Post selected operations** button from the **Operations Manager.** G1

- In the **Post processing** window make the necessary changes as shown in Figure: 22.0.1.

Figure: 22.0.1

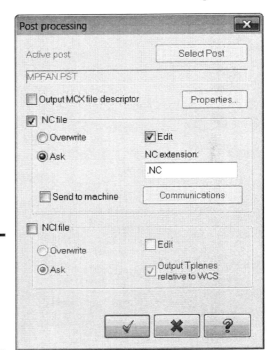

NC File enabled allows you to keep the NC file and to assign the same name as the MCX file.

Edit enabled allows you to automatically launch the default editor.

- Select the **OK** button to continue.

- Save the NC file.

+ A window with Mastercam Code Expert will be lunched and the NC program will appear as shown in
  Figure: 22.0.2

Figure: 22.0.2

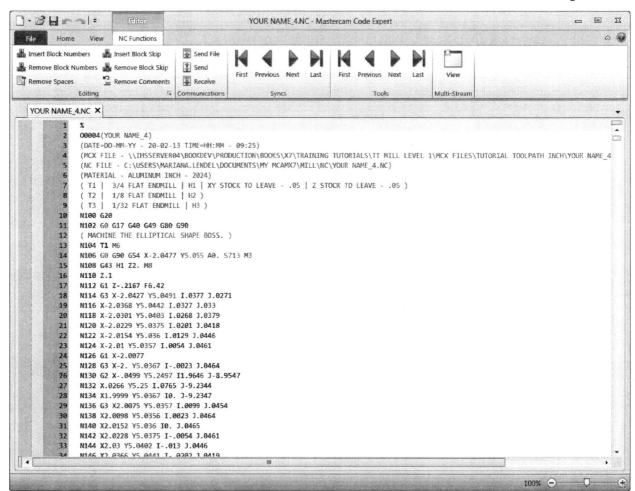

+ Select the red "**X**" box at the upper right corner to exit the editor.

STEP 23: SAVE THE UPDATED MCX FILE

REVIEW EXERCISE - STUDENT PRACTICE

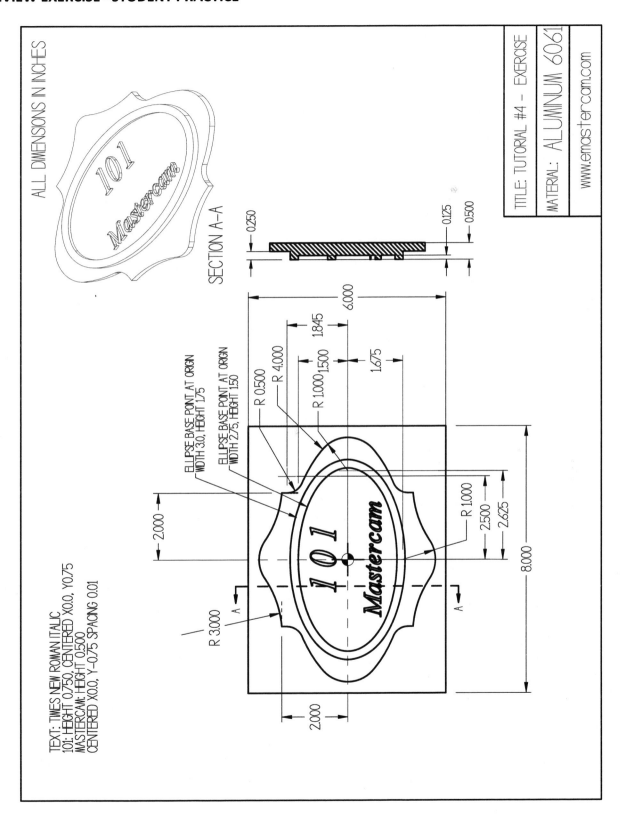

ALL DIMENSIONS IN INCHES

SECTION A-A

0.250
0.125
0.500

TITLE: TUTORIAL #4 - EXERCISE

MATERIAL: ALUMINUM 6061

www.emastercam.com

6.000
1.845
1.500
1.675
R 0.500
R 4.000
R 1.000
2.000
R 1.000
2.500
2.625
8.000
R 3.000
2.000

ELLIPSE BASE POINT AT ORIGIN
WIDTH 3.0, HEIGHT 1.75

ELLIPSE BASE POINT AT ORIGIN
WIDTH 2.75, HEIGHT 1.50

TEXT: TIMES NEW ROMAN ITALIC
101: HEIGHT 0.750, CENTERED X0.0, Y0.75
MASTERCAM: HEIGHT 0.500
CENTERED X0.0, Y-0.75 SPACING 0.01

CREATE THE GEOMETRY FOR TUTORIAL #4 EXERCISE

Use these commands to create the geometry:
- Create Arc Circle Center Point.
- Create Horizontal line.
- Create Arc Tangent 2 Entities.
- Trim/Break/Extend.
- Xform Mirror.
- Create Ellipse.

CREATE THE TOOLPATHS FOR TUTORIAL #4 EXERCISE

Create the Toolpaths for Tutorial #4 Exercise as per the instructions below.

Set the machine properties including the stock setup.
- Remove the material around the part using Core Mill.
- Use a 1" Flat Endmill.
- Enable Corner Rounding.
- Set the Entry method.
- Use Depth Cuts.
- Enable Break through.
- Set the Depth according to the drawing.

Remove the material at the step using Dynamic Core Mill.
- Use the 1" Flat Endmill.
- Enable smoothing.
- Disable Depth cuts.
- Set your entry method.
- Disable Break through.
- Set the Depth according to the drawing.

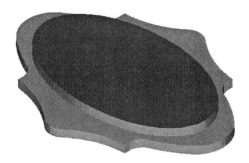

Pocket out the Center.
- Use a 1/4" Flat Endmill.
- Choose a cutting method.
- Set the Entry Motion.
- Disable Finishing.
- Enable Depth cuts and set a cut depth of 0.125".
- Set the Depth according to the drawing.

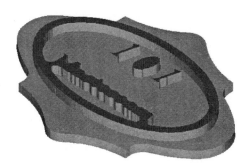

Remachine the Pocket

- Use a 1/16" Flat Endmill.
- Change the Pocket Type to Remachining.
- Disable Display stock.
- Change the Stepover Percentage to 55%.
- Set the Entry Motion.
- Enable Depth cuts and set a cut depth of 0.0625".
- Set the Depth according to the drawing.

Mastercam. X⁷

NOTES:

TUTORIAL #4 QUIZ

◆ What does Core Mill require and what do those requirements do?

◆ What does smoothing do?

◆ What does pocket remachining do?

TUTORIAL #5

OVERVIEW OF STEPS TAKEN TO CREATE THE FINAL PART:

From Drawing to CAD Model:
+ The student should examine the drawing on the following page to understand what part is being created in the tutorial.
+ From the drawing we can decide how to go about creating the geometry in Mastercam.

Create the 2D CAD Model used to generate Toolpaths from:
+ The student will create the Top 2D geometry needed to create the toolpaths.
+ Geometry creation commands such as circle center point, line tangent, mirror, arc tangent, arc polar, trim, fillet, rotate and translate will be used.

Create the necessary Toolpaths to machine the part:
+ The student will set up the stock size and the clamping method used. Two setups will be used to machine the part from the top and then from the bottom.
+ A 2D High Speed Area Mill toolpath will be created to remove the material inside of the step.
+ A 2D High Speed Dynamic Area Mill toolpath will be created to remove the material inside of the deeper pockets.
+ A 2D High Speed Area Mill toolpath will be created to remove the material inside of the smaller pocket.
+ Transform-Rotate toolpath is used to machine the rest of the smaller pocket.
+ Two Drill toolpath will be created to machine the holes.
+ A Circle Mill toolpath will be created to remove the material inside of the center hole.
+ A Contour-Chamfer toolpath will be created to chamfer all edges.
+ A 2D High Speed Dynamic Area Mill toolpath will be created to remove the material inside of the part from the bottom.

Backplot and Verify the file:
+ The Backplot will be used to simulate a step by step process of the tool's movements.
+ The Verify will be used to watch a tool machine the part out of a solid model.

Post Process the file to generate the G-code:
+ The Student will then post process the file to obtain an NC file containing the necessary code for the machine.

 This tutorial takes approximately two hours to complete.

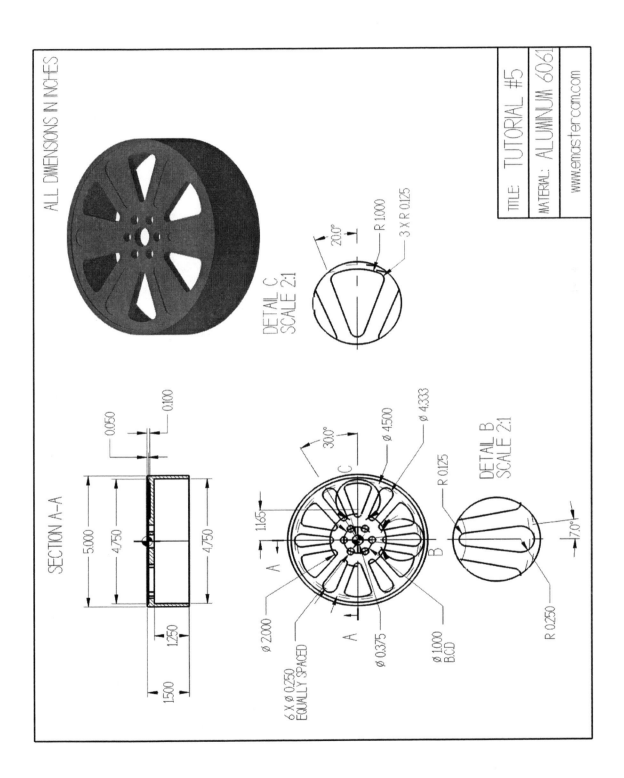

ALL DIMENSIONS IN INCHES

TITLE: TUTORIAL #5

MATERIAL: ALUMINUM 6061

www.emastercam.com

DETAIL C
SCALE 2:1

20.0°

R 1.000

3 X R 0.125

SECTION A-A

0.050

0.100

5.000

4.750

4.750

1.250

1.500

30.0°

Ø 4.500

Ø 4.333

C

1.165

A

R 0.125

B

A

DETAIL B
SCALE 2:1

7.0°

Ø 2.000

6 X Ø 0.250
EQUALLY SPACED

Ø 0.375

Ø 1.000
B.C.D

R 0.250

GEOMETRY CREATION

STEP 1: SETTING UP THE GRAPHIC USER INTERFACE

Please refer to the Getting Started section to set up the graphics user interface.

STEP 2: CREATE ARCS

In this step you will create the arcs used for the main body of the part.

Step Preview:

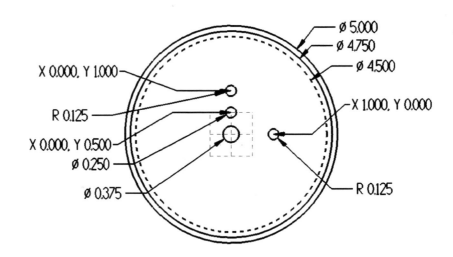

2.1 Create Circles

Create
- **Arc.**
- **Circle Center Point.**
- Enter the **Diameter** of **5.0**.

* [Enter the center point]: Select the **Origin** as shown in <u>Figure: 2.1.1</u>.

Figure: 2.1.1

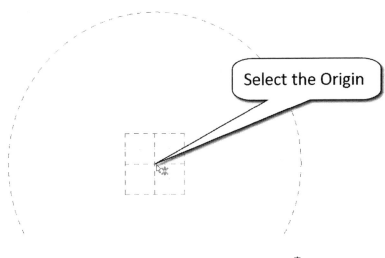

Select the Origin

* Make sure that when selecting the origin, the visual cue of the cursor changes as shown.
* Choose the **Apply** button to continue.

NOTE: During the geometry creation of this tutorial, if you make a mistake you can undo the last step using the **Undo** icon. You can undo as many steps as needed. If you delete or undo a step by mistake, just use the **Redo** icon. To delete unwanted geometry, select it first and then press **Delete** from the keyboard.

* Use the **Fit** icon to fit the drawing to the screen.

* Enter a **Diameter** value of **4.75.**
* [Enter the center point]: Select the **Origin**.

* Choose the **Apply** button to continue.

* Enter a **Diameter** value of **0.375.**
* [Enter the center point]: Select the **Origin**.

* Choose the **Apply** button to continue.

* Enter a **Diameter** value of **0.25** and lock the value by selecting the diameter icon as shown.

• [Enter the center point]: Select the **Fast Point** icon.
• Enter the coordinates as shown and hit **Enter** on your keyboard.

0.0, 0.5

• Choose the **Apply** button to continue.

• [Enter the center point]: Select the **Fast Point** icon.
• Enter the coordinate value of **1.0, 0.0** and hit **Enter** on your keyboard.

• Choose the **Apply** button to continue.

• [Enter the center point]: Select the **Fast Point** icon.
• Enter the coordinate value of **0.0, 1.0**and hit **Enter** on your keyboard.

• Choose the **OK** button to continue.
• The geometry should look as shown.

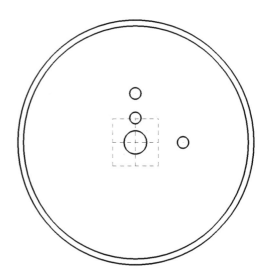

2.2 Change the Line Style and create the 4.5"diameter circle

• Left click on the **Line Style** options in the **Status Bar** as shown in Figure: 2.2.1.

Figure: 2.2.1

• Select from the list the **hidden line style** (2nd style in the list) as shown in Figure: 2.2.2.

Figure: 2.2.2

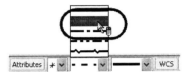

Create

♦ **Arc.**

♦ 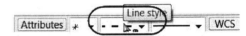 **Circle Center Point.**

♦ Click on the **Diameter** icon to unlock the value.

♦ Enter the **Diameter** of **4.5**.

♦ [Select position for the center of the arc]: Select the **Origin**.

♦ Choose the **OK** button to continue.

2.3 Change the Line Style back to Solid

♦ Left click on the **Line Style** options in the **Status Bar** as shown in Figure: 2.3.1.

Figure: 2.3.1

♦ Select from the list the **solid line style** (1st style in the list) as shown in Figure: 2.3.2.

Figure: 2.3.2

◆ The geometry should look as shown.

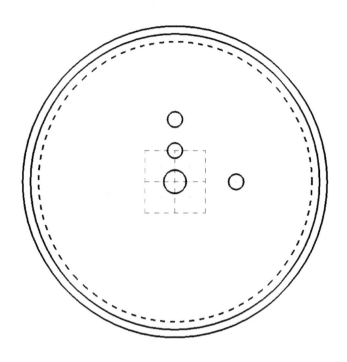

STEP 3: CREATE TANGENT LINES

In this step you will learn how to create tangent lines knowing the angle of the lines.

Step Preview:

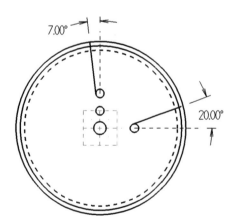

Mill Level 1 Training Tutorial

Mastercam. X^7

Create
- **Line.**

-  **Endpoint.**

- In the **Ribbon Bar** ensure the **Tangent** option is on and **Vertical** or **Horizontal** are not enabled as shown.

- Select the **Zoom Window** button and zoom in on the area as shown in Figure: 3.0.1.

Figure: 3.0.1

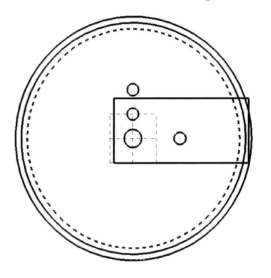

- Select the arc as shown in Figure: 3.0.2.

NOTE: Make sure that you are not selecting any endpoints, midpoints or quadrants from the arc. If you select one of these points Mastercam snaps to the points and disregards the tangent option.

Figure: 3.0.2

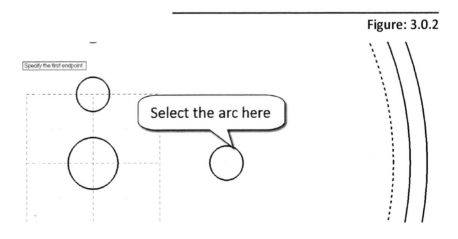

• Sketch a line at any angle to the point as shown in <u>Figure: 3.0.3</u>.

Figure: 3.0.3

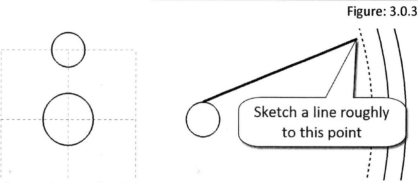

Sketch a line roughly to this point

• In the **Ribbon bar** enter a line **Length** of **1.5** and an **Angle** of **20**.

• Hit **Enter** on your keyboard to preview this line.

• Choose the **Apply** button to continue making lines.

• Pick the **Fit** button.

• Select the **Zoom Window** button and zoom in on the area as shown in <u>Figure: 3.0.4</u>.

Figure: 3.0.4

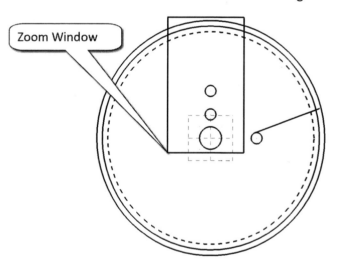

Zoom Window

• Select the arc as shown in Figure: 3.0.5.

> **NOTE:** Make sure that you are not selecting any endpoints, midpoints or quadrants from the arc. If you select one of these points Mastercam snaps to the points and disregards the tangent option.

Figure: 3.0.5

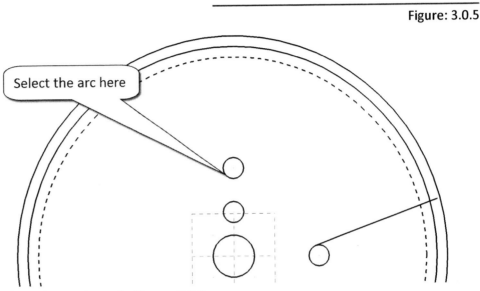

Select the arc here

• Sketch a line at any angle to the point as shown in Figure: 3.0.6.

Figure: 3.0.6

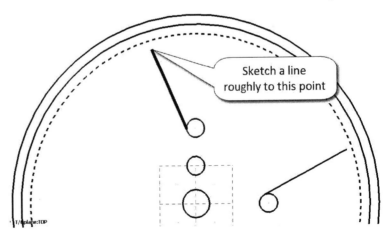

Sketch a line roughly to this point

• In the Ribbon bar enter a line **Length** of **1.5** and an **Angle** of **7+90**.

• Hit **Enter** to preview this line.

• Choose the **OK** button exit the command.

• Pick the **Fit** button.

* The drawing should appear as shown.

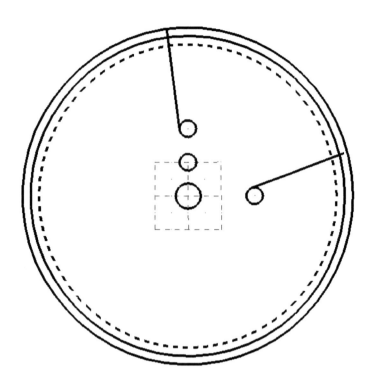

STEP 4: MIRROR THE TANGENT LINES

In this step you will learn how to Mirror the lines we created in the previous step.

Step Preview:

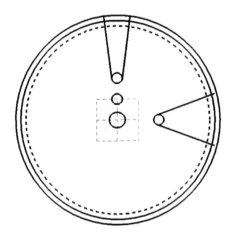

Mastercam. X⁷

Xform

◆ **Mirror.**

◆ Select the line to mirror it as shown in <u>Figure: 4.0.1</u>.

Figure: 4.0.1

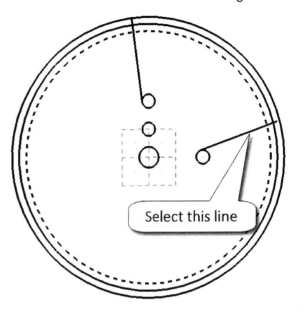

Select this line

◆ Press Enter or select the **End Selection** button.

- In the **Mirror** dialog box ensure **Copy** is enabled and pick the option to **Mirror about X axis** as shown in <u>Figure: 4.0.2</u>.

Figure: 4.0.2

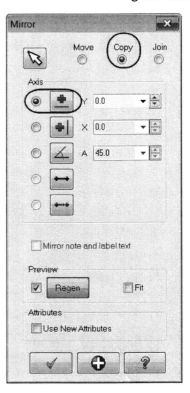

- Pick the **Apply** button to select the next line to mirror.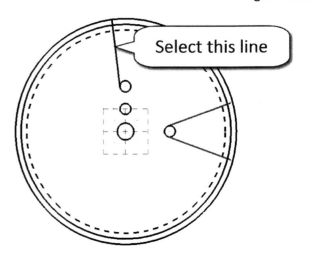
- Select the line to mirror as shown in <u>Figure: 4.0.3</u>.

Figure: 4.0.3

Select this line

- Choose the **End Selection** button.

• In the **Mirror** dialog box ensure **Copy** is enabled and pick the option to **Mirror about Y axis** as shown in
  Figure: 4.0.4.

Figure: 4.0.4

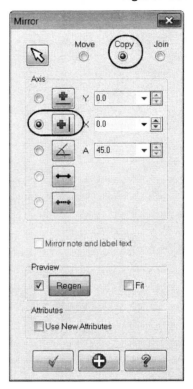

• Choose the **OK** button to exit the command.

• Pick the **Clear Colors** icon to return the colors to the original system colors.

STEP 5: CREATE ARC TANGENT

In this step you will learn how to create an arc tangent to 3 entities.

Step Preview:

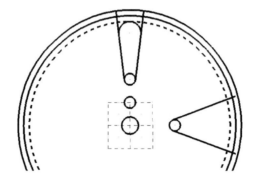

Create

◆ **Arc.**

◆  **Arc Tangent.**

◆ Choose the **Arc Tangent 3 Entities** button in the **Ribbon bar**.

◆ Pick the entities in the order as shown in <u>Figure: 5.0.1</u>.

Figure: 5.0.1

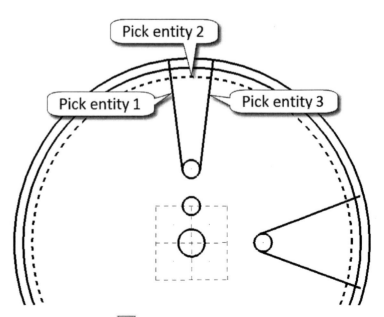

◆ Select the **OK** button to exit the **Create Arc Tangent** command.

STEP 6: CREATE ARC POLAR

In this step you will learn how to create an arc polar, knowing the center point, radius, start angle and end angle.

Step Preview:

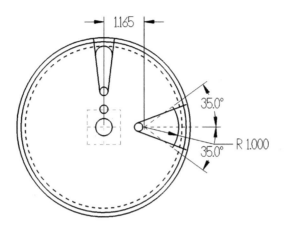

Create

◆ **Arc.**

◆  **Arc Polar.**

◆ Choose the **Fast Point** 🖉 icon to enter the center point.

◆ Input the coordinates **1.165, 0.0** as shown.

◆ Press **Enter**.

◆ Enter the arc **Radius** ⊙ of **1.0**, a **Start Angle** 🔺 of **-35.0** degrees and a **End Angle** 🔺 of **35.0**.

| ⊙ | 1.0 | | ⊙ | 2.0 | | 🔺 | -35.0 | | 🔺 | 35.0 | | ✎ |

◆ Select the **OK** button to exit the command. ✅

◆ Select **Fit** screen. ✣

STEP 7: TRIM THE LINES

In this step you will learn how to Trim 3 entities and use the Divide function.

Step Preview:

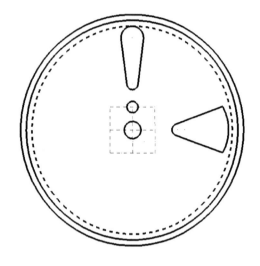

Edit
- **Trim / Break.**
- **Trim / Break/ Extend.**
- From the Ribbon bar select the **Trim 3 Entities** button.
- Choose the entities in the order shown in <u>Figure: 7.0.1</u>.

Figure: 7.0.1

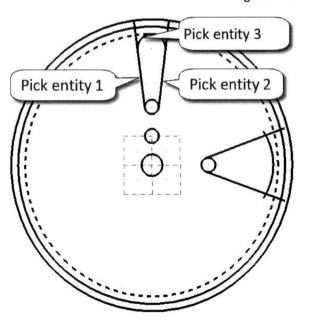

• Repeat the step selecting the entities as shown in <u>Figure: 7.0.2</u>.

Figure: 7.0.2

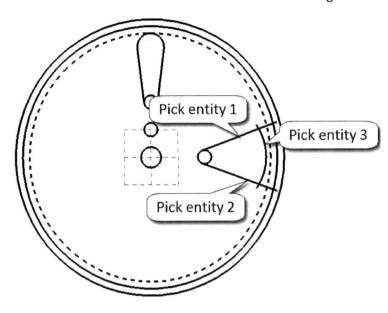

• Repeat the step selecting the entities as shown in <u>Figure: 7.0.3</u>.

Figure: 7.0.3

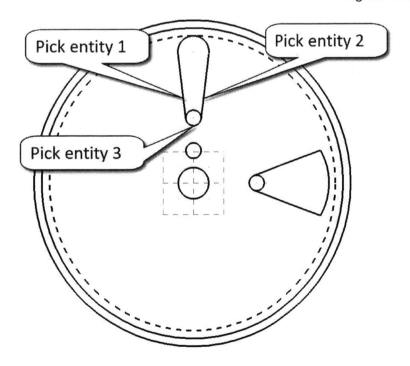

• Once the entities have been picked choose the **Divide** icon.

• Pick the arcs as shown in <u>Figure: 7.0.4</u>.

Figure: 7.0.4

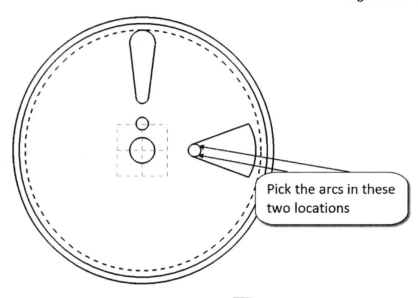

Pick the arcs in these two locations

• Once the arcs have been selected choose the **OK** button to exit the command. ☑
• Your part will appear as shown up to this point.

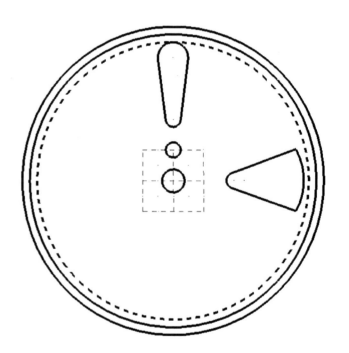

STEP 8: CREATE FILLETS

In this step you will learn how to create filleted corners. Filleted corners apply round corners to sharp corners.

Step Preview:

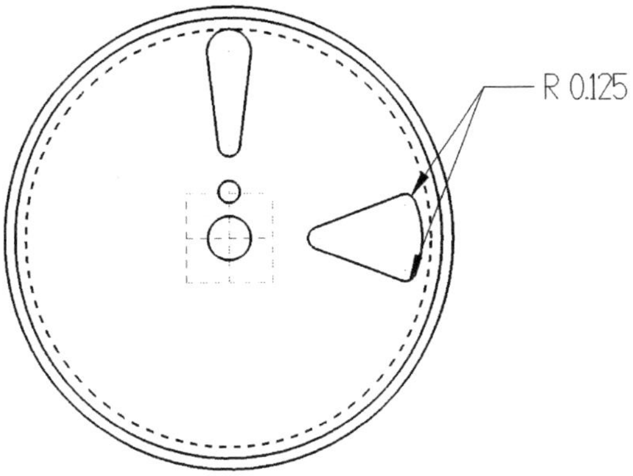

Create

- **Fillet.**
- 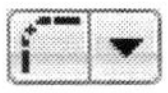 **Entities.**
- Input a **Radius**  value of **0.125.**
- Select the entities as shown in Figure: 8.0.1.

Figure: 8.0.1

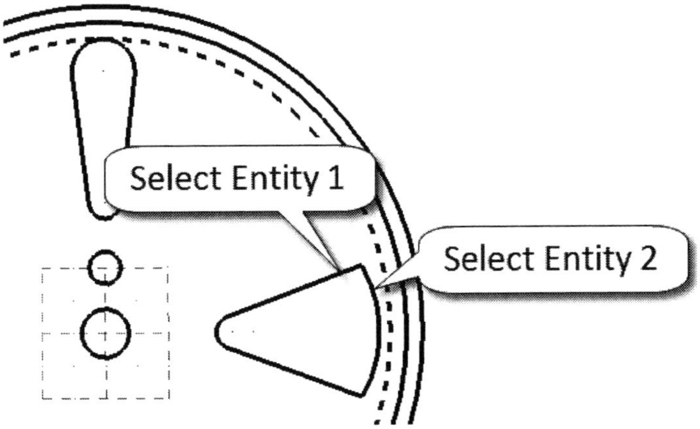

- Pick the entities as shown in <u>Figure: 8.0.2</u>.

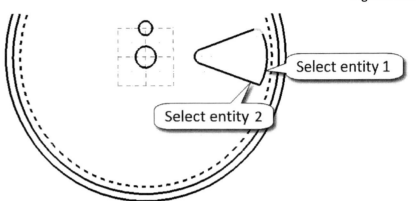

Select entity 1

Select entity 2

- Select the **OK** button to exit the command.

STEP 9: DELETE THE CONSTRUCTION ARC

In this step we will delete the arc.

Step Preview:

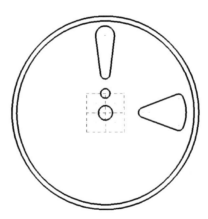

- Choose the **Delete** icon.

• Select the arc as shown in <u>Figure: 9.0.1</u>.

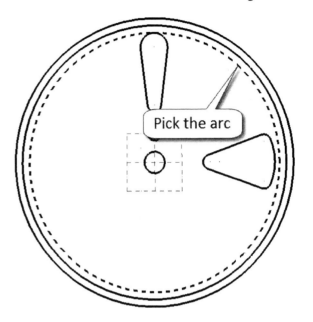

Pick the arc

• Choose the **End Selection** button.

STEP 10: XFORM ROTATE

In this step you will learn how to rotate entities around a center point by a specified angle.

Step Preview:

Xform

- 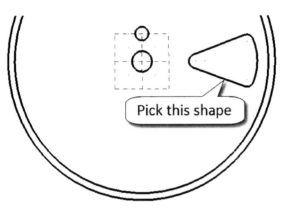 **Rotate.**
- Hold the shift key and pick the shape as shown in <u>Figure: 10.0.1</u>.

> **NOTE:** By holding down the Shift key and selecting one entity of a chain, Mastercam selects the whole chain.

Figure: 10.0.1

Pick this shape

- Choose the **End Selection** button.

♦ When the **Rotate** dialog box appears ensure **Move** is enabled and input a number of copies **#** to **6** as shown in Figure: 10.0.2.
♦ Press **Enter**.
♦ Choose the option **Total sweep** and input a value of **360.0** degrees.

Figure: 10.0.2

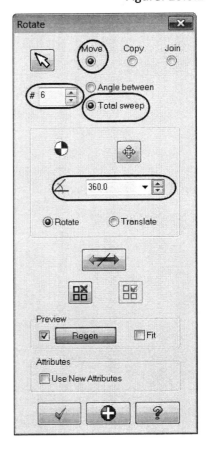

♦ Select the **Apply** button to accept these parameters.
♦ Select the **Repaint** icon as shown.

♦ The geometry should look as shown.

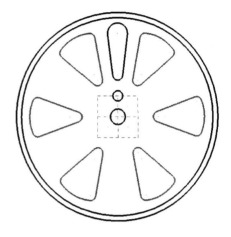

♦ Hold the **Shift** key again and pick the shape as shown in <u>Figure: 10.0.3</u>.

Figure: 10.0.3

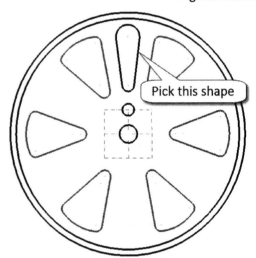

Pick this shape

♦ Choose the **End Selection** button.

• When the **Rotate** dialog box appears ensure that **Copy** is enabled and the number of copies **#** is set to **5** as shown in <u>Figure: 10.0.4</u>.

• Choose the option **Angle between** and input **360.0/6** and hit **Enter**.

Figure: 10.0.4

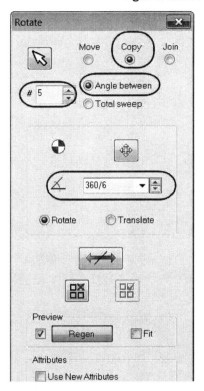

• Select the **Apply** button to accept these parameters.

● Pick the arc as shown in <u>Figure: 10.0.5</u>.

Pick this arc

● Choose the **End Selection** button.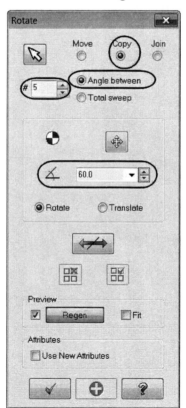
● When the **Rotate** dialog box appears ensure that **Copy** is enabled, the number of copies # is set to **5** and **Angle between** is set to **60** and hit **Enter**. <u>Figure: 10.0.6</u>.

• Select the **OK** button to accept these parameters.

• Pick the **Clear Colors** icon to set the colors back to the system colors.
• The geometry will appear as shown.

STEP 11: XFORM TRANSLATE

In this step you will learn how to translate entities to a different Z depth. This geometry will be used when creating a toolpath from the bottom of the part.

Step Preview:

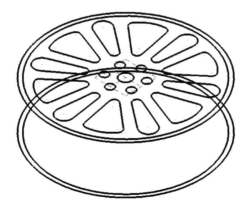

Xform

- 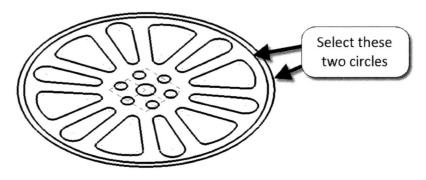 **Translate.**

- Select the graphic view **Isometric** from the toolbars.
- [Translate: select entities to translate]: Select the two outer circles as shown in Figure: 11.0.1.

Figure: 11.0.1

Select these two circles

- Choose the **End Selection** button from the ribbon bar.
- When the **Translate** dialog box appears ensure **Copy** is enabled and input a depth of **-1.5** as shown in Figure: 11.0.2.

Figure: 11.0.2

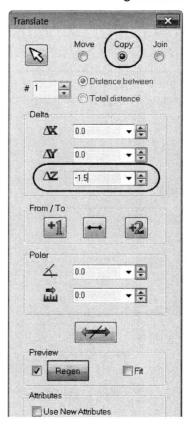

- ◆ Choose the **Apply** button to accept these parameters.
- ◆ Hold down the **Shift** key and select all the entities within those two circles as shown in <u>Figure: 11.0.3</u>.

Figure: 11.0.3

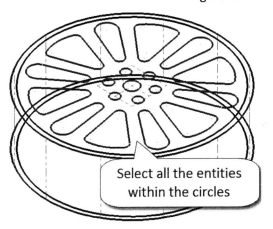

Select all the entities within the circles

- ◆ Choose the **End Selection** button from the ribbon bar.
- ◆ When the **Translate** dialog box appears ensure **Move** is enabled and input a depth of **-0.05** as shown in <u>Figure: 11.0.4</u>.

Figure: 11.0.4

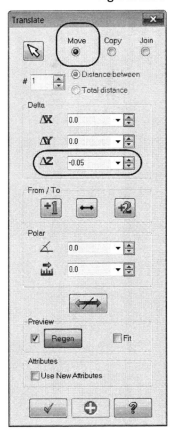

♦ Choose the **OK** button to accept these parameters.

♦ Pick the **Clear Colors** icon to set the colors back to the system colors.
♦ The geometry should look as shown.

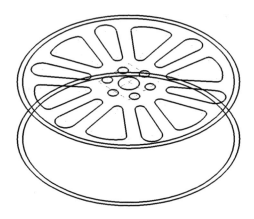

STEP 12: SAVE THE FILE

File

♦ 💾 **Save As.**
♦ File name: "Your Name_5".

TOOLPATH CREATION - SETUP 1

SUGGESTED FIXTURE 1:

> **NOTE:** In order to machine this part we will have 2 setups and output 2 NC files. To view the second setup see page 441.

SETUP SHEET 1:

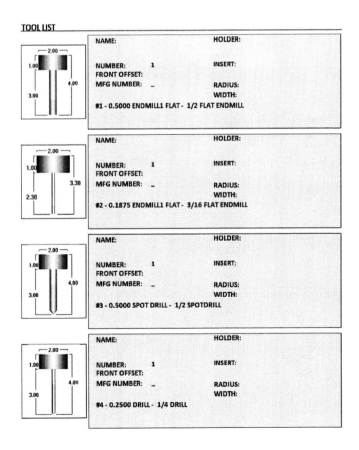

TOOL LIST

NAME:		HOLDER:
NUMBER:	1	INSERT:
FRONT OFFSET:		
MFG NUMBER:	_	RADIUS:
		WIDTH:

#1 - 0.5000 ENDMILL1 FLAT - 1/2 FLAT ENDMILL

NAME:		HOLDER:
NUMBER:	1	INSERT:
FRONT OFFSET:		
MFG NUMBER:	_	RADIUS:
		WIDTH:

#2 - 0.1875 ENDMILL1 FLAT - 3/16 FLAT ENDMILL

NAME:		HOLDER:
NUMBER:	1	INSERT:
FRONT OFFSET:		
MFG NUMBER:	_	RADIUS:
		WIDTH:

#3 - 0.5000 SPOT DRILL - 1/2 SPOTDRILL

NAME:		HOLDER:
NUMBER:	1	INSERT:
FRONT OFFSET:		
MFG NUMBER:	_	RADIUS:
		WIDTH:

#4 - 0.2500 DRILL - 1/4 DRILL

STEP 13: SELECT THE MACHINE AND SET UP THE STOCK

In Mastercam, you select a **Machine Definition** before creating any toolpaths. The **Machine Definition** is a model of your machines capabilities and features. It acts like a template for setting up your machine. The machine definition ties together three main components. The schematic model of your machines components. The control definition that models your control capabilities and the post processor that will generate the required machine code (G-code). For a Mill Level 1 exercise (2D toolpaths) we need just a basic machine definition.

NOTE: For the purpose of this tutorial, we will be using the Default milling machine.

• To display the **Operations Manager** press **Alt + O**.

• Use the **Fit** icon to fit the drawing to the screen.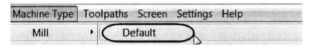
Machine type
• **Mill.**
• **Default.**

• Select the plus sign in front of **Properties** in the **Toolpaths** Manager to expand the **Toolpaths Group Properties.**

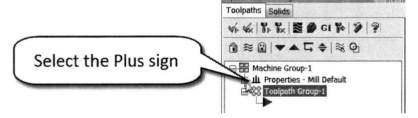

• Select **Tool Settings** to set the tool parameters.

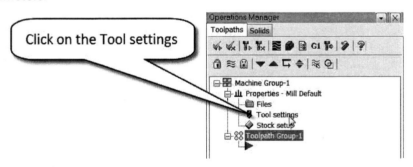

Mill Level 1 Training Tutorial   *Mastercam.* X^7

• Change the parameters to match the screen shot as shown in Figure: 13.0.1.

Figure: 13.0.1

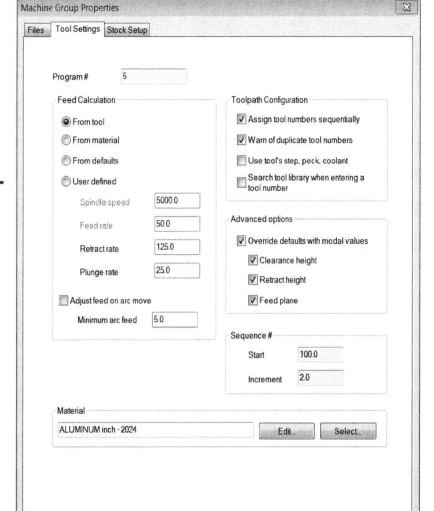

Program # is used to enter a number if your machine tool requires a number for a program name.

Assign tool numbers sequentially allows you to overwrite the tool number from the library with the next available tool number. (First operation tool number 1; Second operation tool number 2, etc.)

Warn of duplicate tool numbers allows you to get a warning if you enter two tools with the same number.

Override defaults with modal values enables the system to keep the values that you enter.

Feed Calculation set From tool uses feed rate, plunge rate, retract rate and spindle speed from the tool definition.

* Select the **Stock setup** tab to define the stock.
* Pick the **Cylindrical** shape option and the axis which the stock will be set to select **"Z."**
* Pick the **All Entities** button to define the stock size as shown in <u>Figure: 13.0.2</u>.

Figure: 13.0.2

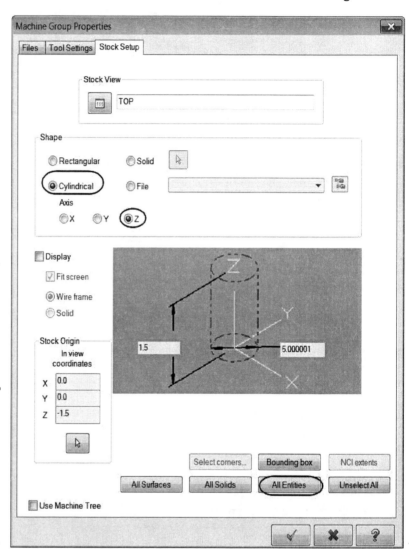

The **Stock Origin** values adjust the positioning of the stock, ensuring that you have equal amount of extra stock around the finished part.

Display options allow you to set the stock as Wireframe and to fit the stock to the screen. (Fit Screen)

NOTE: The **stock** model that you create can be displayed with the part geometry when viewing the file or the toolpaths, during backplot, or while verifying toolpaths.

* Select the **OK** button to exit **Machine Group Properties**.

* Select the **Isometric** view from the graphics view toolbar to see the stock.

* Use the **Fit** icon to fit the drawing to the screen.

◆ The stock model will appear as shown in Figure: 13.0.3.

Figure: 13.0.3

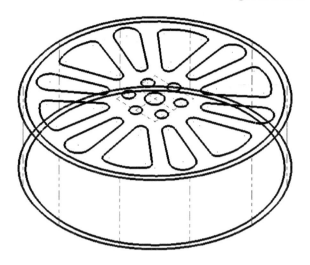

NOTE: The stock is not geometry and can not be selected.
There will not be a facing toolpath because the stock is already to size.

STEP 14: 2D HIGH SPEED AREA MILL

2D High Speed Area Mill machines pockets using a smooth clean motion. Helical entries and tangent stepovers create efficient motion for your machine tools. Cut parameters let you control corner rounding to create the best toolpath, avoiding sharp corners or direction changes.

Toolpath Preview:

14.1 Chain Selection

Toolpaths
* **2D High speed.**

* **Area.**

* When the new NC name dialog box appears select the **OK** button to accept the name. ✓

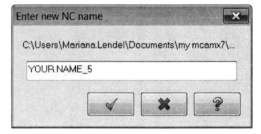

• Leave the default setting in the chaining dialog box and chain the inner circle as shown in
Figure: 14.1.1.

Figure: 14.1.1

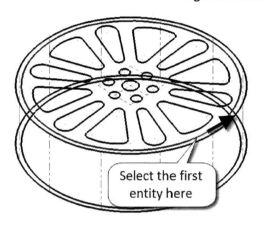

Select the first entity here

• Select the **OK** button to exit the **Chaining** dialog box.

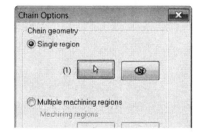

• Select the **OK** button to exit the **Chain Options** dialog box.
• In the **Toolpath Type** page, select **Area Mill.**

Core Mill   Peel Mill   Blend Mill   Area Mill   Rest Mill   Dynamic Area Mill

Dynamic Rest   Dynamic Core   Dynamic
Mill   Mill   Contour

14.2 Select a 1/2" Flat Endmill from the Library and set the Tool Parameters

• Select **Tool** from the **Tree view** list.

• Click on **Select library tool** button.

• Select the **Filter** button.

• Select the **None** button and then under **Tool Types** choose the **Flat Endmill** icon.

• Under tool diameter pick **Equal** and input a value of **0.5** as shown in Figure: 14.2.1.

Figure: 14.2.1

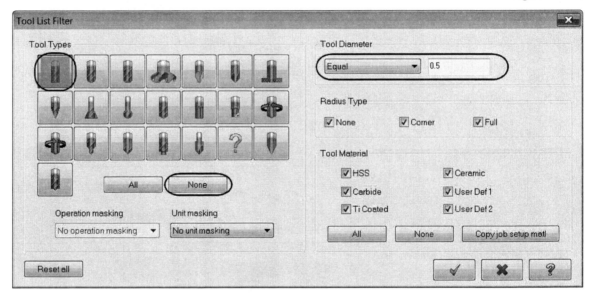

• Select the **OK** button to exit the **Tool List Filter.**

• In the **Tool Selection** dialog box you should only see a **1/2" Flat Endmill**.

#	Assembly Name	Tool Name	Holder Name	Dia.	Cor. rad.	Length	# Flutes	Type	Rad. Type
239	–	1/2 FLAT...	–	0.5	0.0	1.0	4	En...	None

• Select the **1/2" Flat Endmill** in the **Tool Selection** page and then select the **OK** button to exit.

Page |386   **Mill Level 1 Training Tutorial**   *Mastercam. X*⁷

♦ Make all the necessary changes as shown in <u>Figure: 14.2.2</u>.

Figure: 14.2.2

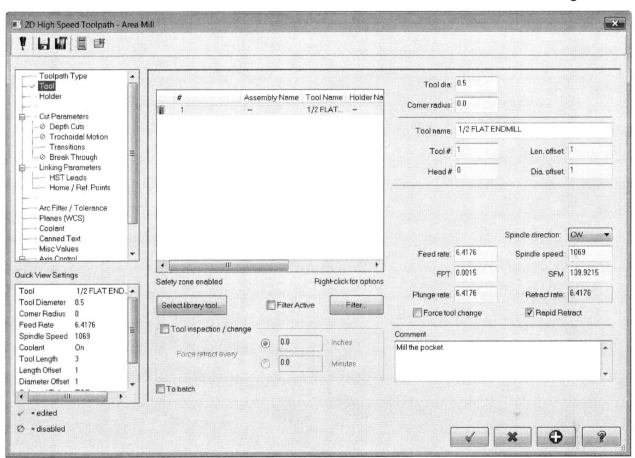

14.3 Set the Cut Parameters

♦ From the **Tree view list**, select **Cut Parameters**.
♦ Set the parameters as shown in Figure: 14.3.1.

Figure: 14.3.1

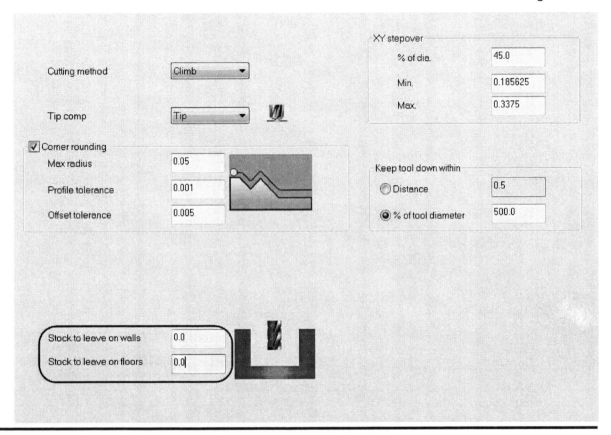

Cutting method set to **Climb** cuts in one direction with the tool rotating in the opposite direction of the tool motion.

XY stepover sets the distance between cutting passes in the X and Y axis.
% of dia expresses the maximum XY stepover as a percentage of the tool diameter. The Max. XY stepover field will update automatically when you enter a value in this field. The actual stepover is calculated by Mastercam between the Min. and Max. values.

Corner rounding activates toolpath corner rounding, which replaces sharp corners with arcs for faster and smoother transitions in tool direction.

Profile tolerance represents the maximum distance that the outermost profile of a toolpath created with corner rounding can deviate from the original toolpath.

Offset tolerance represents the maximum distance that a profile of a toolpath created with corner rounding can deviate from the original toolpath. This is the same measurement as the profile tolerance but is applied to all the profiles except the outermost one.

14.4 Set the Depth Cuts Parameters

◆ From the **Tree view list**, select the **Depth Cuts** and disable it as shown.

☐ Depth cuts

14.5 Set the Transitions

◆ From the Tree view list, select Transitions and make sure the parameters are set as shown in Figure: 14.5.1.

Figure: 14.5.1

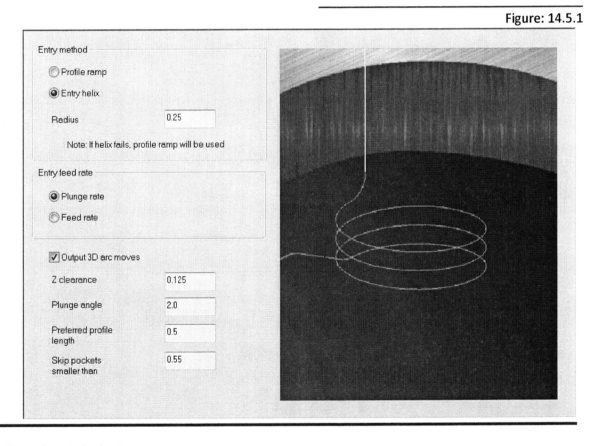

Entry helix creates a helical entry move.

Output 3D arc moves generates the g-code of the helix with arc (G2/G3) moves. Otherwise, the helix will be rendered with many small linear moves. This can be useful for some types of machines:Many machines have built-in "look ahead" capabilities. Using small linear moves with these capabilities can be more efficient than arc moves.

Z clearance adds an extra height used in the ramping motion down from a top profile. It ensures that the tool has fully slowed down from rapid speeds before touching the material.

Plunge angle sets the angle of descent for the entry move, and determines the pitch.

Skip pockets smaller than allows you to specify a minimum pocket size that Mastercam will consider creating a cutting pass for.

14.6 Set the Linking Parameters

♦ Select **Linking Parameters** and input a **Depth** of **-0.05** as shown in <u>Figure: 14.6.1</u>.

Figure: 14.6.1

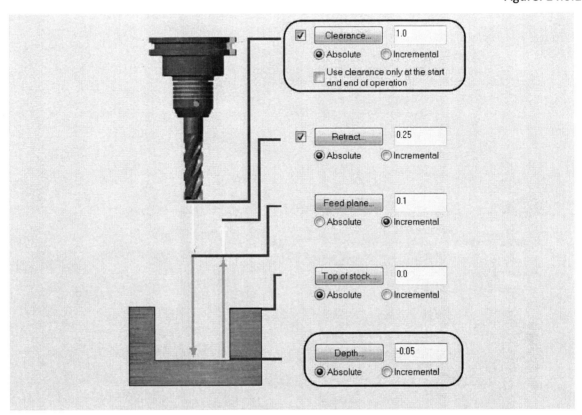

♦ Once complete pick the **OK** button to generate the toolpath.

STEP 15: BACKPLOT THE TOOLPATHS

Backplotting shows the path the tools take to cut the part. This display lets you spot errors in the program before you machine the part. As you backplot toolpaths, Mastercam displays additional information such as the X, Y, and Z coordinates, the path length , the minimum and maximum coordinates and the cycle time. It also shows any collisions between the workpiece and the tool.

♦ Make sure that the toolpaths are selected (signified by the green check mark on the folder icon). If the operation is not selected choose the **Select all operations** icon.

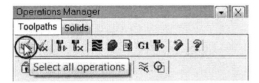

♦ Select the **Backplot selected operations** button.

♦ Select the **Backplot** tab and have the following settings enabled as shown.

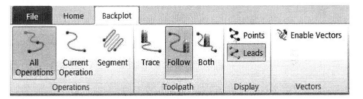

♦ Select the **Home** tab and make sure that you have the following settings on as shown.

♦ To see the part from an **Isometric** view select the **Isometric** icon.

♦ To fit the workpiece to the screen, select the **Fit** icon.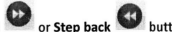

♦ You can step through the **Backplot** by using the **Step forward** or **Step back** buttons.

+ You can adjust the speed of the backplot.
+ Select the **Play Simulation** button in the **VCR** bar to run **Backplot**.

+ The toolpath should look as shown.

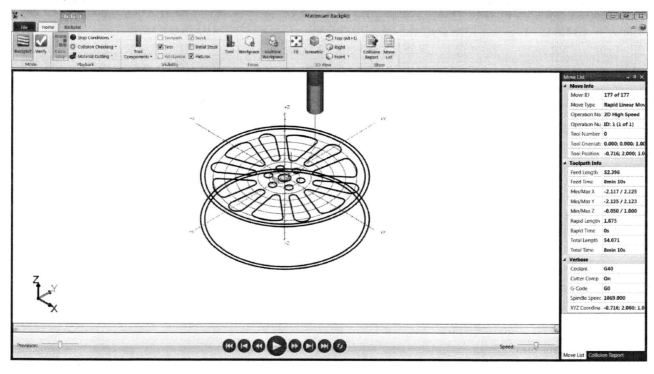

STEP 16: SIMULATE THE TOOLPATH IN VERIFY

Verify Mode shows the path the tools take to cut the part with material removal. This display lets you spot errors in the program before you machine the part. As you verify toolpaths, Mastercam displays additional information such as the X, Y, and Z coordinates, the path length , the minimum and maximum coordinates and the cycle time. It also shows any collisions between the workpiece and the tool.

♦ From **Mastercam Backplot Home** tab, switch to **Verify** and change the settings for the **Visibility** and **Focus** as shown in <u>Figure: 16.0.1</u>.

Figure: 16.0.1

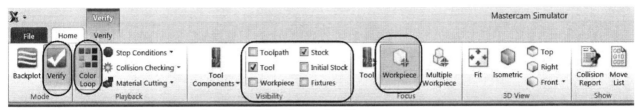

♦ Select the **Play Simulation** button in the **VCR** bar to run **Verify**.

♦ The part will appear as shown.

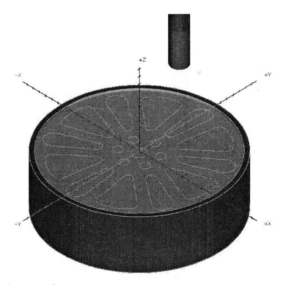

♦ To go back to Mastercam window, minimize **Verify** window as shown.

STEP 17: 2D HIGH SPEED DYNAMIC AREA MILL

2D High Speed Dynamic Area Mill utilizes the entire flute length of their cutting tools to produce the smoothest, most efficient tool motion for high speed pocketing. The toolpath supports a custom entry method and many others. Micro lifts further refine the dynamic milling motion and avoid excessive heat build up. Custom feeds and speeds optimize and generate safe tool motion. Dynamic Area Mill machines pockets using one or more chains to drive the toolpath. The outside chain contains the toolpah; all inside chains are considered islands.

In this step you will machine the six bigger pockets using 2D HS Dynamic Area Mill toolpath. To select all chains, you will use the **Chain Feature** option.

Toolpath Preview:

17.1 Chain selection using Chain Feature Option

◆ Press **Alt** + **T** to remove the toolpath display.

Toolpaths
◆ **2D High speed.**

◆ 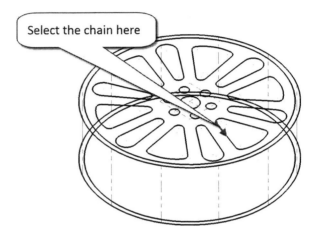 **Dynamic Area.**
◆ Leave the default setting in the chaining dialog box and pick the chain as shown in <u>Figure: 17.1.1</u>.

Figure: 17.1.1

Select the chain here

• From the **Chaining** dialog box select the **Chain Feature** button.

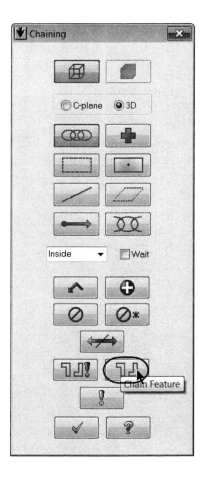

NOTE: Chain Feature allows you to automatically select chains based on the initial chain. Chain Feature is most useful when you have a large number of chains in a part with groups of similar shapes and window chaining is not an option.

• Select the **OK** button to exit the **Chaining** dialog box.

♦ In the **Chain Options** dialog box enable **Multiple machining regions** to instruct Mastercam to machine all the chains.

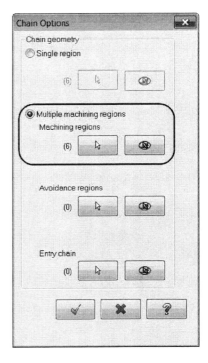

♦ Select the **OK** button to exit the **Chain Options** dialog box.
♦ In the **Toolpath Type** page, select **Dynamic Area Mill** as shown in Figure: 17.1.2.

Figure: 17.1.2

| Core Mill | Peel Mill | Blend Mill | Area Mill | Rest Mill | Dynamic Area Mill |

| Dynamic Rest Mill | Dynamic Core Mill | Dynamic Contour |

17.2 Select a 3/16" Flat endmill from the library and set the Tool Parameters

* Select **Tool** from the Tree view list.

* Click on **Select library tool** button. Select library tool...
* Select the **Filter** button.

* Select the **None** button and then under **Tool Types** choose the **Flat Endmill** icon.
* Under tool diameter pick **Equal** and input a value **0.1875** as shown in Figure: 17.2.1.

Figure: 17.2.1

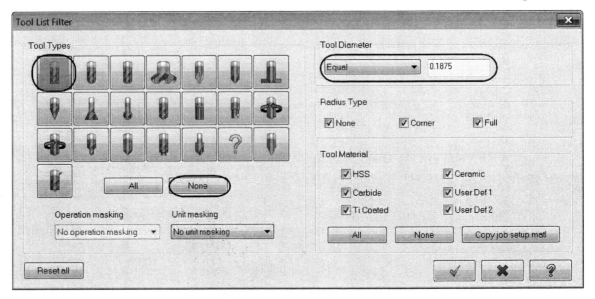

* Select the **OK** button to exit the **Tool List Filter.**
* In the **Tool Selection** dialog box you should only see a **3/16" Flat Endmill**.

#	Assembly Name	Tool Name	Holder Name	Dia.	Cor. rad.	Length	# Flutes	Type	Rad. Type
234	–	3/16 FLA...	–	0....	0.0	0.4375	4	En...	None

* Select the **3/16" Flat Endmill** in the **Tool Selection** page and then select the **OK** button to exit.

- Make all the necessary changes as shown in <u>Figure: 17.2.2</u>.

Figure: 17.2.2

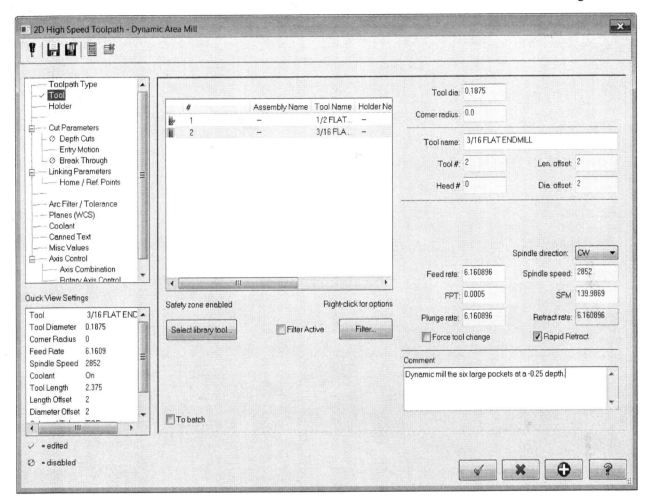

17.3 Set the Cut Parameters

- From the **Tree view list**, select **Cut Parameters**. The previously used settings will still be there.
- Change the settings for this second toolpath as shown in Figure: 17.3.1.

Figure: 17.3.1

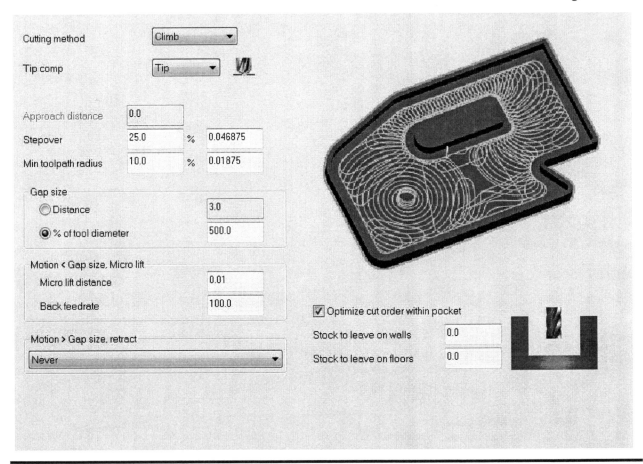

Stepover sets the distance between cutting passes in the X and Y axis.

Toolpath radius reduces sharp corner motion between cut passes.

Micro lift distance enters the distance the tool lifts off the part on the back moves. Microlifts are slight lifts that help clear chips and minimize excessive tool heating.

Back feedrate controls the speed of the backfeed movement of the tool.

Motion > Gap Size, retract controls retracts in the toolpath when making a non-cutting move within an area where the tool can be kept down or microlifted.

Optimize cut order defines the cut order Mastercam applies to different cutting passes in the dynamic mill toolpath.

17.4 Set the Entry Motion

* Entry motion configures an entry method for the dynamic mill toolpath which determines not only how and where the tool enters the part, but the cutting method/machining strategy used by the toolpath.The previous settings will be saved.
* All we want to do is change the **Entry method** to **Profile** as shown in <u>Figure: 17.4.1</u>.

Figure: 17.4.1

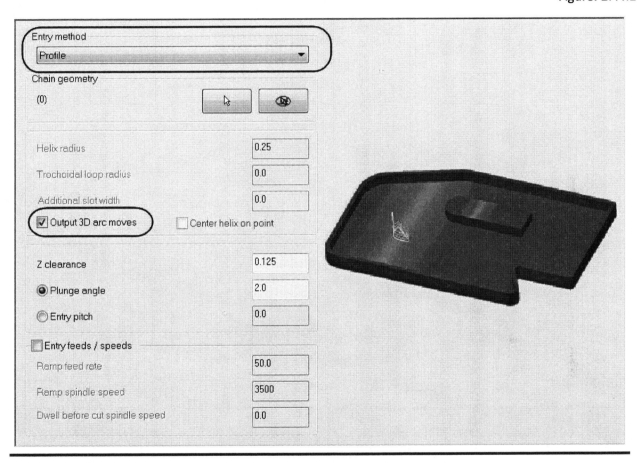

Entry method set to **Profile** creates a boundary based on the shape of the selected chain and uses the tool to ramp into the part. The slot is cleared by taking lighter cuts in the Z axis until the tool reaches the full depth.

Z clearance adds an extra height used in the ramping motion down from a top profile. It ensures that the tool has fully slowed down from rapid speeds before touching the material.

Plunge angle sets the angle of descent for the entry move, and determines the pitch.

17.5 Set the Linking Parameters

• Select **Linking Parameters** and change the **Top of Stock** value to **Incremental 0.0** and the **Depth** to **-0.25 Incremental** as shown in <u>Figure: 17.5.1</u>.

Figure: 17.5.1

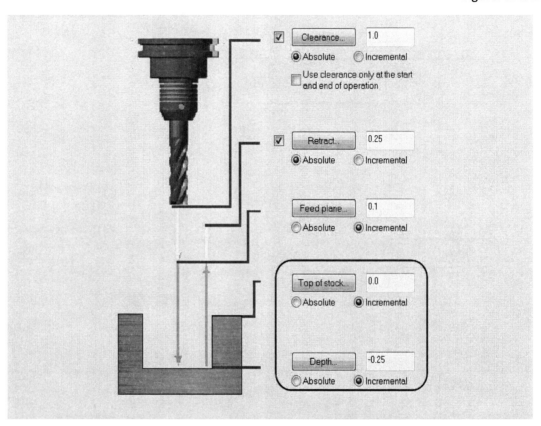

Incremental values are relative to other parameters or chained geometry. In this tutorial the pocket chains were moved **0.05** along Zaxis, below zero. The **Top of stock** and the the **Depth** set to **Incremental** is measure from the z depth of the chains. If you want to set the **Top of stock** and the **Depth** to **Absolute**, the values should be **- 0.05** and **-0.3** respectively .

• Select the **OK** button to generate the toolpath.

• To **Backplot** the toolpath see page 391 to review this procedure.

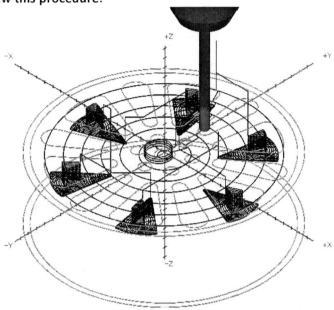

• To go back to Mastercam window, minimize **Backplot** window as shown.

• To **Verify** the toolpaths see page 393.
• To select both toolpaths click on the **Select all operations** icon.

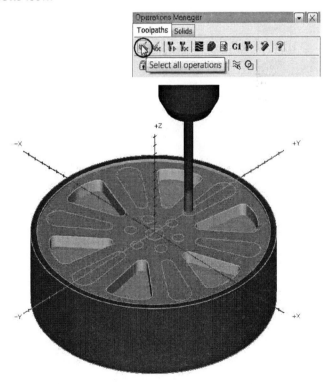

• To go back to Mastercam window, minimize **Verify** window as shown.

STEP 18: MACHINE ONE SMALLER POCKET USING 2D HIGH SPEED AREA MILL

In this step you will machine one smaller pocket using 2D HS Area Mill.

Toolpath Preview:

18.1 Chain Selection

♦ Press **Alt** + **T** to remove the toolpath display.

Toolpaths
♦ **2D High speed.**

♦ 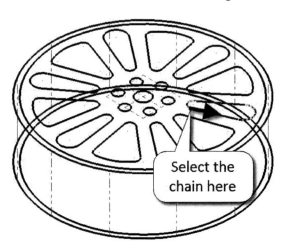 **Area.**

♦ Leave the default setting in the chaining dialog box and pick the chain as shown in <u>Figure: 18.1.1</u>.

Figure: 18.1.1

- Select the **OK** button to exit the **Chaining** dialog box.

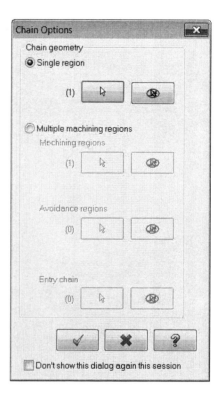

- Select the **OK** button to exit the **Chain Options** dialog box.
- In the **Toolpath Type**, **Area Mill** should be already selected as shown.

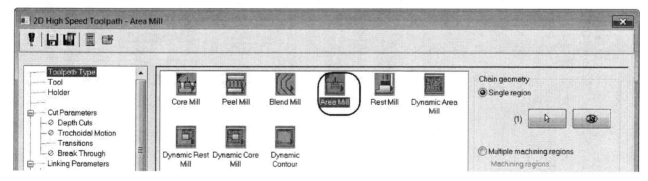

- Fom the **Tree view list** select **Tool**.
- Select the **3/16" Flat Endmill** and make all the necessary changes as shown in <u>Figure: 18.1.2</u>.

Figure: 18.1.2

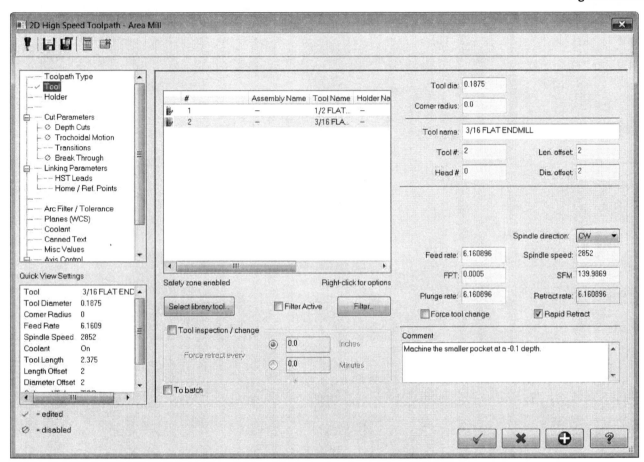

18.2 Set the Cut Parameters

◆ From the **Tree view list**, select **Cut Parameters**. The previously used settings will still be there. Use these
settings for this third toolpath as shown in <u>Figure: 18.2.1</u>.

Figure: 18.2.1

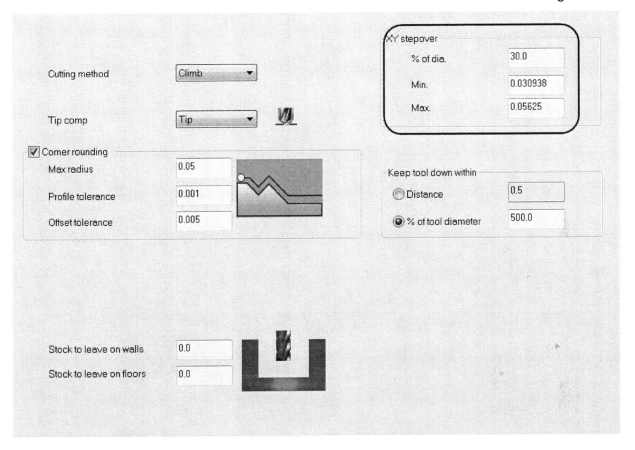

18.3 Set the Depth Cuts parameters

- From the **Tree view list**, select **Depth Cuts** and set the parameters as shown in <u>Figure: 18.3.1</u>.

Figure: 18.3.1

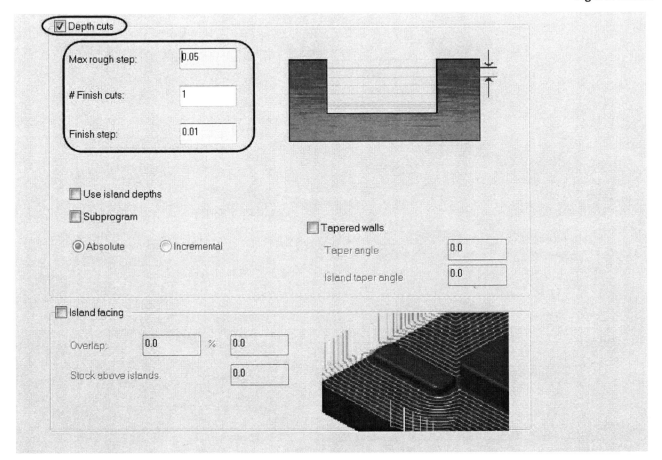

Mill Level 1 Training Tutorial *Mastercam.* X[7]

18.4 Set the Transitions

• From the **Tree view list**, select **Transitions** and leave the **Entry method** set to **Entry helix** as shown in <u>Figure: 18.4.1</u>.

Figure: 18.4.1

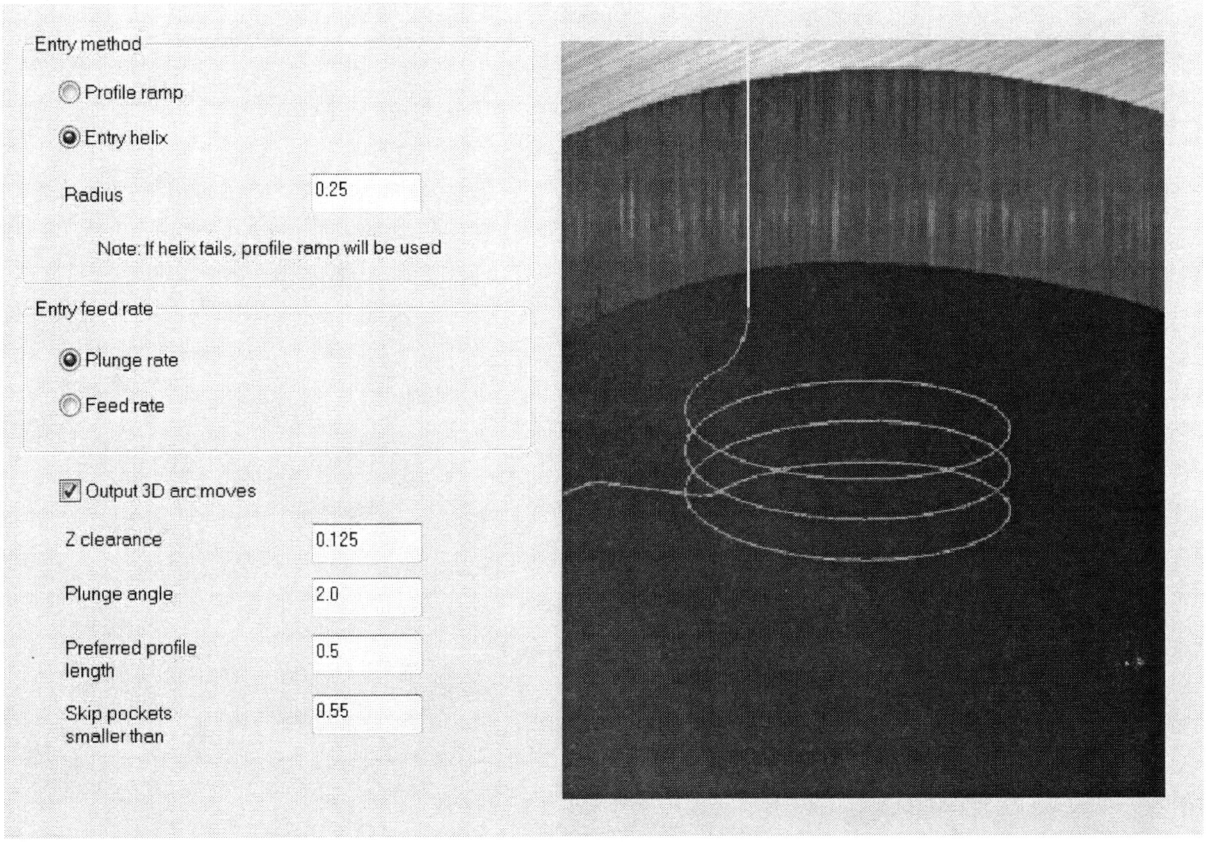

18.5 Set the Linking Parameters

♦ Select **Linking Parameters** and input the **Depth** as shown in <u>Figure: 18.5.1</u>.

Figure: 18.5.1

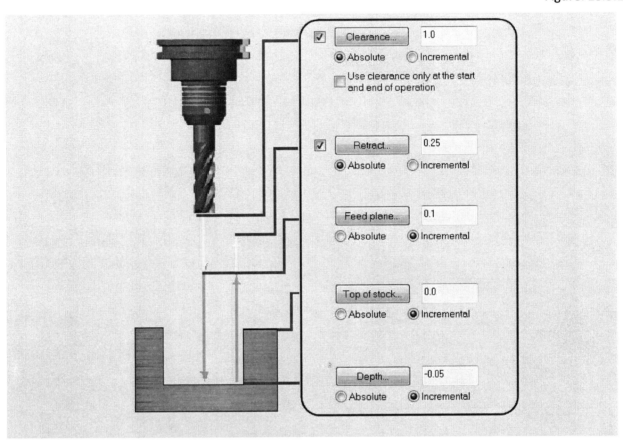

♦ Once complete pick the **OK** button to generate the toolpath.
♦ **Backplot** the toolpath as shown at page 391.

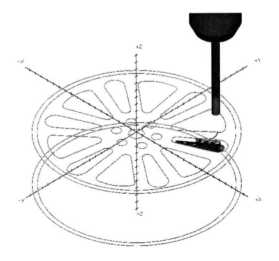

◆ Minimize **Backplot** window, select all toolpaths and then **Verify** them as shown at page 393.

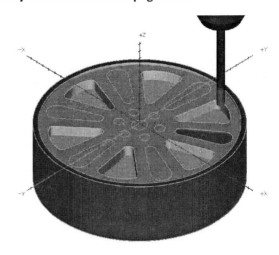

STEP 19: TRANSFORM TOOLPATHS

Transform toolpaths are used when you want to run the same toolpath in different locations. You can transform a single toolpath or several at a time.

Toolpath Preview:

Toolpaths

◆  **Transform.**
◆ For the **Type** select **Rotate**, **Coordinate** for **Method.**
◆ Select **Operation 3.**

• Pick **Group NCI output by** the **Operation order** as shown in Figure: 19.0.1.

Figure: 19.0.1

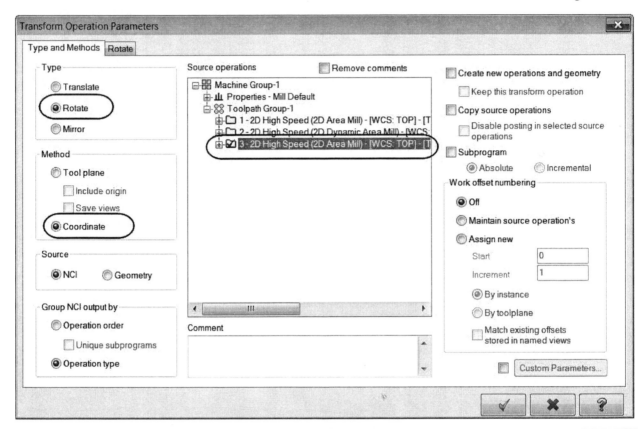

Rotate revolves the toolpath about the construction origin or a specified point. Activate the Rotate tab and you can set the rotation point and number of copies.

Coordinate creates new coordinate positions for the new toolpaths in the original tool plane.

Operation order sorts the transformed operations by the order they were selected. In our example we choose the large pocket then small pocket. It will execute them in that order (large pocket, small pocket, large pocket, small pocket, etc.).

- Choose the **Rotate** tab.
- Input the **Number of steps 6,** a **Start angle** of **0.0, and a Rotation angle** of **60.0** degrees as shown in
  Figure: 19.0.2.

Figure: 19.0.2

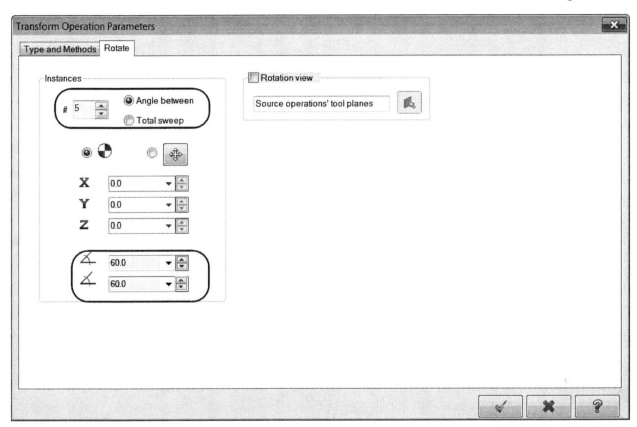

Number of steps is the number of times to rotate the toolpath.

Start angle sets the beginning angle for the rotate toolpath.

Rotation angle sets the angle of rotation for the transformed toolpath.

- Once complete pick the **OK** button to generate the toolpath.

◆ **Backplot** the toolpath as shown at page 391.

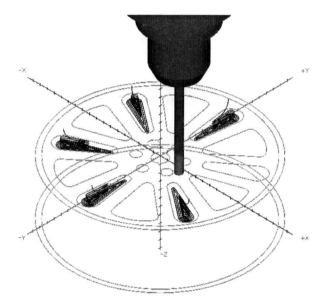

◆ Minimize **Backplot** and select all toolpaths to **Verify** them as shown at page 393.

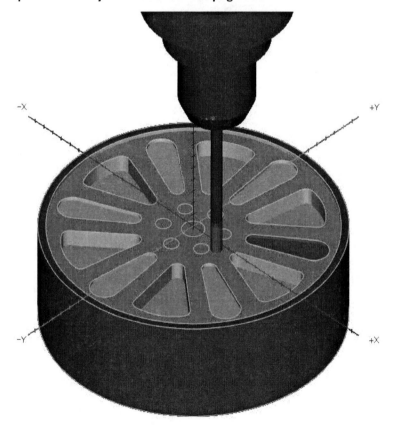

STEP 20: SPOT DRILL THE HOLES

Spot Drilling the holes allows you to start the hole. In this operation we will use the spot drill to chamfer the hole before drilling it.

Toolpath Preview:

Toolpaths

* 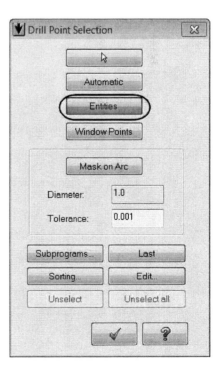 **Drill.**
* In the **Drill Point Selection** dialog box choose the option **Entities.**

• Select the arcs as shown in <u>Figure: 20.0.1</u>.

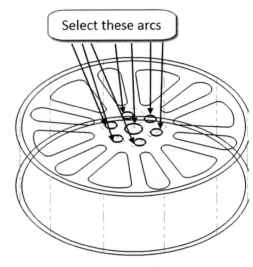

Select these arcs

• Select the **OK** button in the **Drill Point Selection** dialog box once you have picked the arc.
• In the **Toolpath Type** page, the **Drill** toolpath will be selected.

Drill   Circle Mill   Point   Helix Bore   Thread Mill

20.1 Select a 1/2" Spot Drill from the Library and set the Tool Parameters

♦ Select **Tool** from the Tree view list.

♦ Click on **Select library tool** button.

♦ To be able to see just the spot drill select the **Filter** button.

♦ Under **Tool Types** select the **None** button and then choose the **Spot drill** icon as shown in Figure: 20.1.1.

Figure: 20.1.1

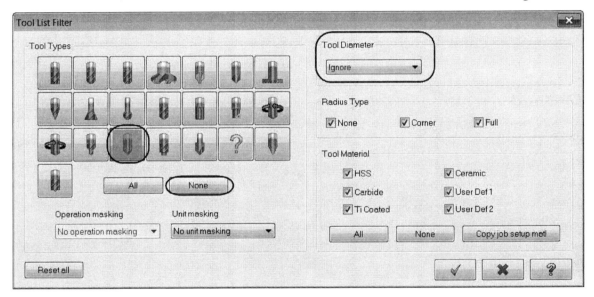

♦ Select **OK** button to exit the **Tool List Filter** dialog box.
♦ At this point you should only see **Spot Drills**.
♦ From that list select the **1/2" Spot Drill**.

#	Assembly Name	Tool Name	Holder Name	Dia.	Cor. rad.	Length	# Flutes	Type	Rad. Type
4	–	1/8 SPO...	–	0....	0.0	2.0	2	Sp...	None
5	–	1/4 SPO...	–	0.25	0.0	2.0	2	Sp...	None
6	–	1/2 SPO...	–	0.5	0.0	2.0	2	Sp...	None
198	–	3/4 SPO...	–	0.75	0.0	2.0	4	Sp...	None
312	–	1. SPOT...	–	1.0	0.0	2.0	4	Sp...	None
314	–	3/8 SPO...	–	0....	0.0	2.0	4	Sp...	None

♦ Select the tool in the **Tool Selection** page and then select the **OK** button to exit.

• Make the necessary changes to the **Tool** page as shown in Figure: 20.1.2.

Figure: 20.1.2

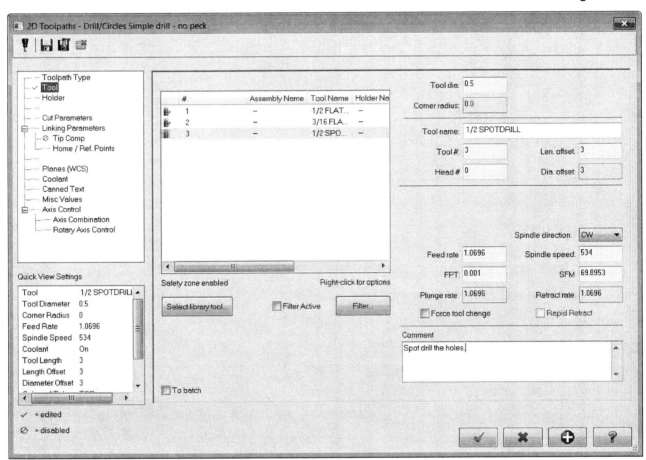

20.2 Set the Cut Parameters

◆ Select **Cut Parameters** and make the necessary changes as shown in <u>Figure: 20.2.1</u>.

Figure: 20.2.1

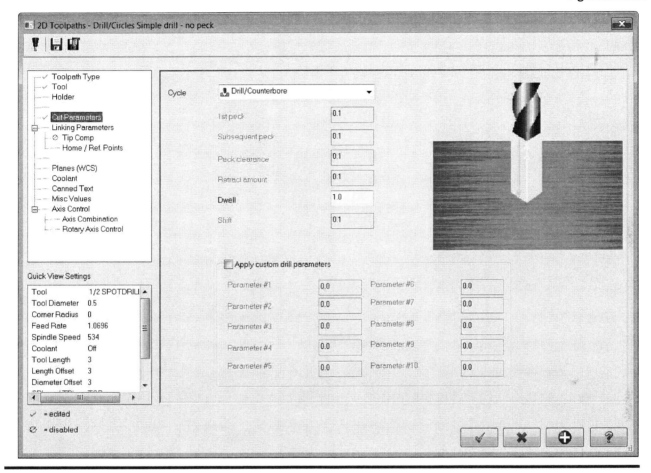

Drill/Counterbore is recommended for drilling holes with depths of less than three times the tools diameter.

Dwell sets the amount of time in seconds that the tool remains at the bottom of a drilled hole.

20.3 Set the Linking Parameters

♦ Choose **Linking Parameters**, ensure **Clearance** is enabled and set to **1.0**, the **Top of stock** is set to **Incremental** and **zero**.

♦ Set the **Depth** to **Incremental** and select the **Calculator** icon.
♦ Input the following equation in the **Finish diameter** area. **0.25+0.05** and hit **Enter** to calculate the **Depth** as shown in <u>Figure: 20.3.1</u>.

Figure: 20.3.1

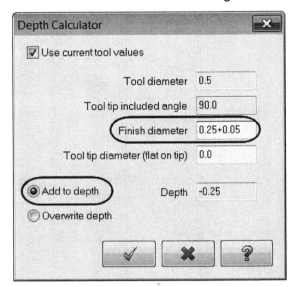

♦ Select the **OK** button to exit the **Depth Calculator**.

♦ You will now see the depth we calculated for the spot drilling operation set in the **Depth** field as shown in Figure: 20.3.2.

Figure: 20.3.2

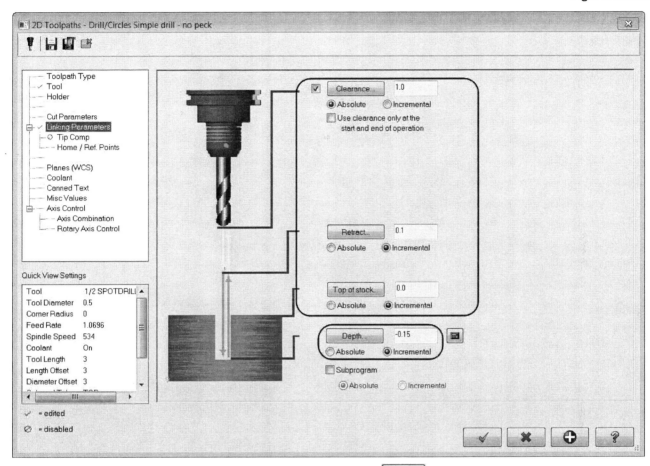

♦ Select the **OK** button to exit the **Drill/Counterbore** parameters.
♦ To **Backplot** and **Verify** the toolpaths see page 391 and page 393 to review these procedures.

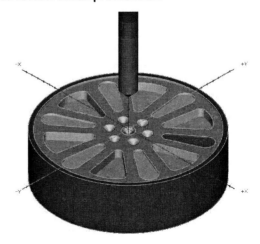

STEP 21: DRILL ALL HOLES

In this example we will drill the 1/4" holes to a specified depth.

Toolpath Preview:

Toolpaths

+ **Drill.**
+ In the **Drill Point Selection** dialog box choose the option **Last**.

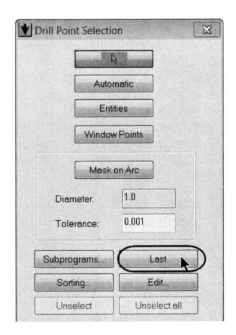

NOTE: This option will automatically select the hole for you based off the selection from the previous drill operation.

- Select the **OK** button in the **Drill Point Selection** dialog box to accept the 7 drill points.
- In the **Toolpath Type** page, the **Drill** toolpath will be selected.

Drill   Circle Mill   Point   Helix Bore   Thread Mill

21.1 Select a 1/4" Drill from the Library and set the Tool Parameters

- Select **Tool** from the **Tree view** list.

- Click on **Select library tool** button.
- To be able to see just the spot drill select the **Filter** button.

- Under **Tool Types** select the **None** button and then choose the drill icon.
- Under **Tool Diameter** select **Equal** and enter **0.25** as shown in Figure: 21.1.1.

Figure: 21.1.1

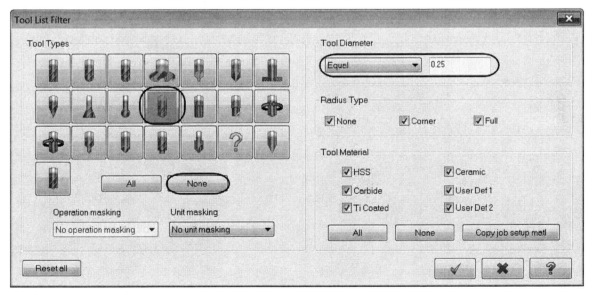

- Select **OK** button to exit the **Tool List Filter** dialog box.
- From that list select a **1/4" Drill**.

#	Assembly Name	Tool Name	Holder Name	Dia.	Cor. rad.	Length	# Flutes	Type	Rad. Type
104	–	1/4 DRILL	–	0.25	0.0	2.0	2	Drill	None

• Select the tool in the **Tool Selection** page and then choose the **OK** button to exit.
• Make the necessary changes to the **Tool** page as shown in <u>Figure: 21.1.2</u>.

Figure: 21.1.2

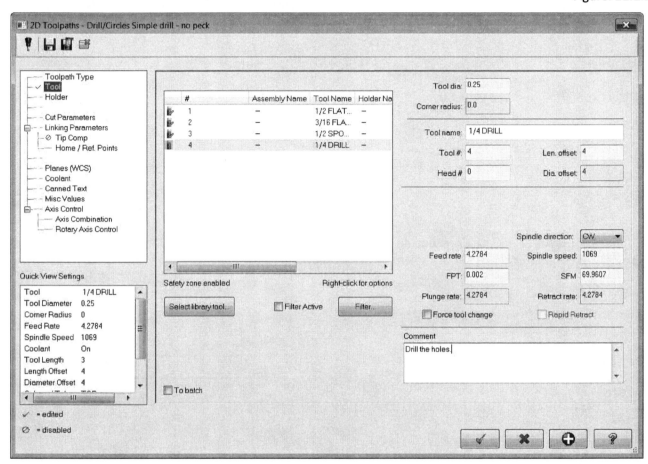

Mastercam. X⁷

21.2 Set the Cut Parameters

- Select **Cut Parameters**, change the drill **Cycle** to **Chip Break** and input a **1st peck** value of **0.1** as shown in <u>Figure: 21.2.1</u>.

Figure: 21.2.1

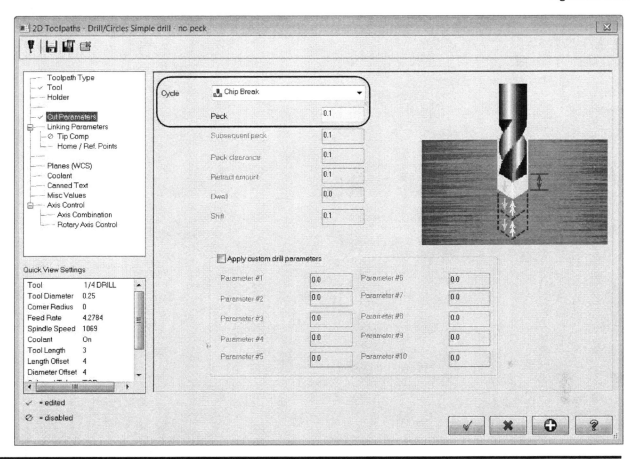

Chip Break drills holes with depths of more than three times the tool diameter. The tool retracts partially out of the drilled hole to break material chips.

1st peck sets the depth for the first peck move which plunges in and out of the material to clear and break chips.

21.3 Set the Linking Parameters

♦ Choose **Linking Parameters** and input a **Top of Stock** value of **0.0 Incremental** and **depth** value of **-0.5 Incremental** as shown in <u>Figure: 21.3.1</u>.

Figure: 21.3.1

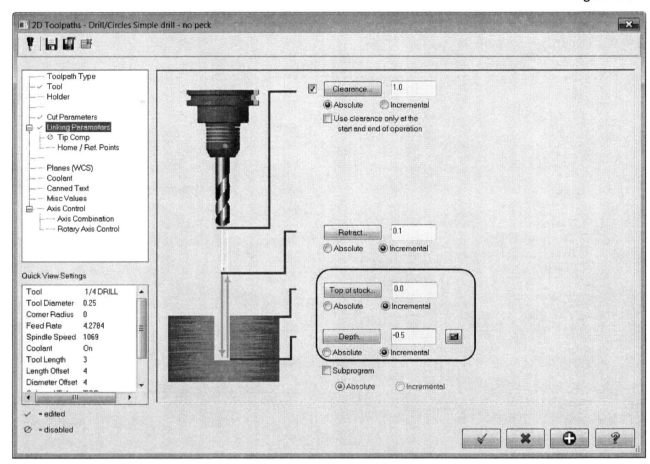

♦ Select the **OK** button to exit the **Drill/Counterbore** parameters.

• To **Backplot** and **Verify** your toolpath see page 391 and page 393 to review these procedures.

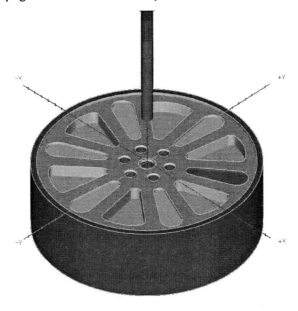

STEP 22: CIRCLE MILL THE CENTER HOLE

Circle mill toolpath is used to mill circular pockets based on a single point. Mastercam will pocket out a circular area of the diameter and to the depth that you specify. After milling the center of the circle, Mastercam calculates an entry arc before approaching the perimeter and then a similar exit arc. You can add enhancements such as multiple passes, multiple depth cuts and helical plunge moves as well fine tuning the entry and exit arcs.

Toolpath Preview:

Toolpaths
* **Circle Path.**

* 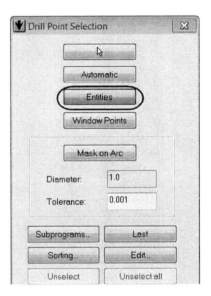**Circle Mill.**

22.1 Select the Geometry

* When the **Drill Point Selection** dialog box appears choose entities.

* Select the arc as shown in <u>Figure: 22.1.1</u>.

Figure: 22.1.1

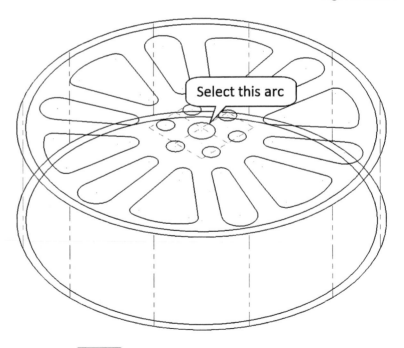

Select this arc

* Choose the **OK** button once the arc has been selected.

• On the **Toolpath Type** page **Circle Mill** will be picked.

Drill Circle Mill Point Helix Bore Thread Mill

22.2 Select the 3/16" Tool

• From the **Tree view list**, select **Tool**.
• Select the existing tool and change the parameters as shown in <u>Figure: 22.2.1</u>.

Figure: 22.2.1

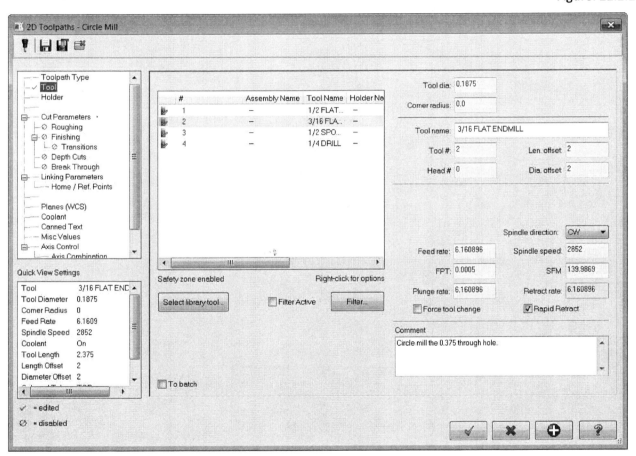

NOTE: Picking the 3/16" Flat Endmill will allow us to use the tool for this toolpath.

22.3 Set the Cut Parameters

- From the **Tree view list** select **Cut Parameters** and ensure the parameters appear the same as shown in Figure: 22.3.1.

Figure: 22.3.1

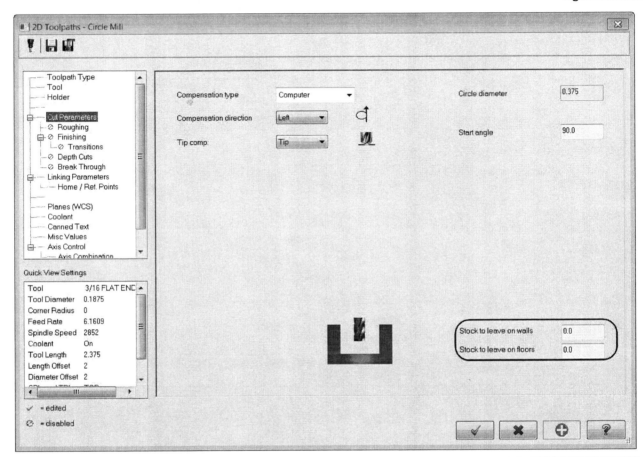

Start Angle sets the angle where the helix bore toolpath begins.

Entry/exit arc sweep sets the included angle of each entry and exit arc.

Start at center begins the toolpath at the center of the arc.

Perpendicular entry enters the thread toolpath perpendicular to the first tool move.

Overlap sets how far the tool goes past the end of the toolpath.

22.4 Set the Roughing Parameters

♦ Make sure the **Roughing** is disabled as shown.

22.5 Set the Finishing parameters

♦ From the **Tree view list**, select Finishing and enable it. Change the parameters as shown in <u>Figure: 22.5.1</u>.

Figure: 22.5.1

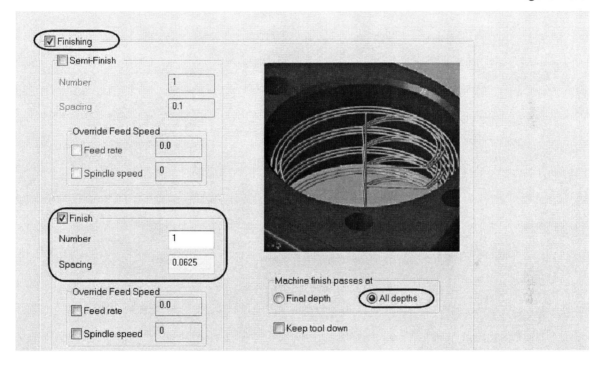

22.6 Set the Linking Parameters

• Select **Linking Parameters** from the **Tree view list**. Set the **Top of stock** and set the **Depth** as shown in <u>Figure: 22.6.1</u>.

Figure: 22.6.1

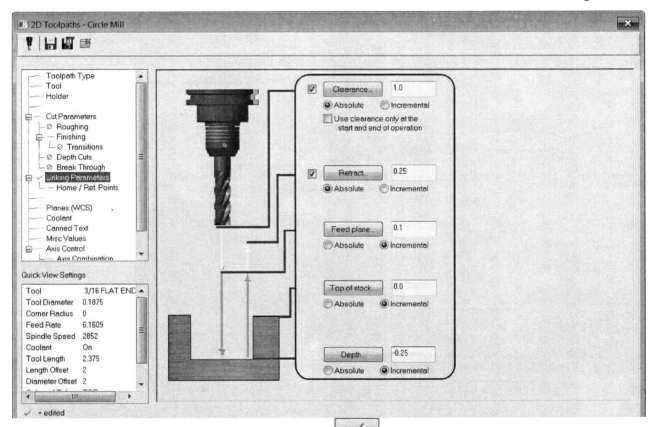

• Select the **OK** button to exit the **Circle Mill** parameters.
• To **Backplot** and **Verify** the toolpaths see page 391 and page 393 to review these procedures.

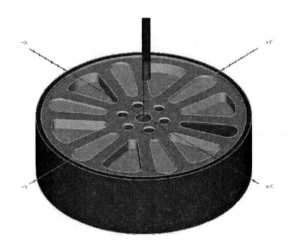

STEP 23: CHAMFER THE PART

Contour - Chamfer toolpath automatically cuts a chamfer around a contour using a chamfer mill.

Toolpath Preview:

Toolpaths

◆  **Contour.**

◆ Leave the default settings in the **Chaining** dialog box as shown in <u>Figure: 23.0.1</u>.

Figure: 23.0.1

• Select the chains and ensure the chaining direction is the same as shown in <u>Figure: 23.0.2</u>.

Figure: 23.0.2

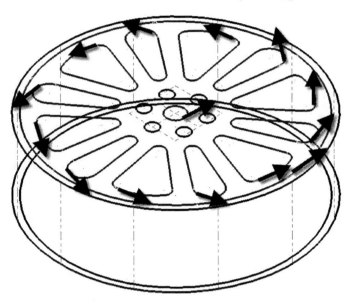

> **NOTE:** It does not matter which contour you select first. However the first contour you select, will be the first
>
> contour cut. Make sure that all chains are selected in the same direction. Use **Reverse** button to change the
>
> direction of chain if needed. [⟷]

• Select the **OK** button to exit the **Chaining** dialog box. [✓]

> **NOTE:** The depth of the chamfer is based on the width and tip offset set in the Cut Parameters page. This is
> why we set the depth here to zero.

• In the **Toolpath Type** page, the **Contour** toolpath will be selected.

Contour   Pocket   Facing   Slot Mill

23.1 Select a 1/4" Chamfer Mill from the Library and set the Tool Parameters

◆ Select **Tool** from the **Tree view list**.

◆ Click on **Select library tool** button.

◆ To be able to see just the spot drill select the **Filter** button.

◆ Under **Tool Types** select the **None** button and then choose the **Chamfer Mill** icon as shown in Figure: 23.1.1.

Figure: 23.1.1

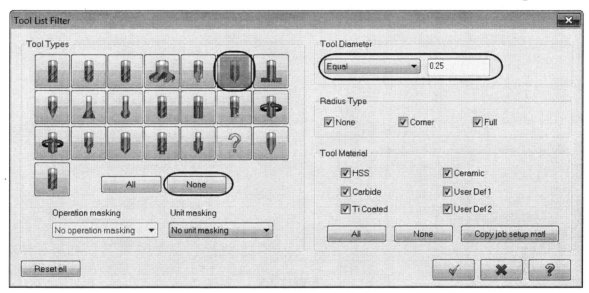

◆ Select the **OK** button to exit the **Tool List Filter** dialog box.

NOTE: You will only see a list of chamfer mills.

◆ From that list select the **1/4" Chamfer Mill**.

#	Assembly Name	Tool Name	Holder Name	Dia.	Cor. rad.	Length	# Flutes	Type	Rad. Type
304	—	1/4 CHA..	—	0...	0.0	0.5	4	Ch..	None

◆ Select the tool in the **Tool Selection** page and then choose the **OK** button to exit. A warning might appear stating that the **Tool Settings** were modified to conform with your current **Machine Definition/ Control Definition**.

◆ Select the **OK** buttong to continue.

• Make all the necessary changes as shown in <u>Figure: 23.1.2</u>.

Figure: 23.1.2

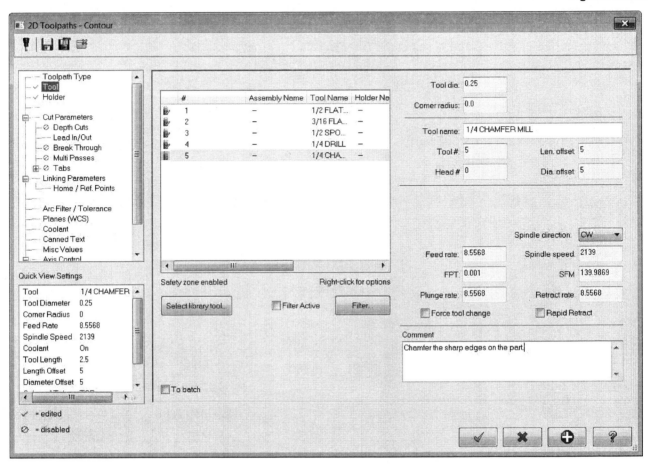

23.2 Set the Cut Parameters

- Select the **Cut Parameters** page and change the **Contour type** to **2D chamfer**.
- Input a **Width** of **0.025** and a **Tip offset** of **0.02** as shown in Figure: 23.2.1.

Figure: 23.2.1

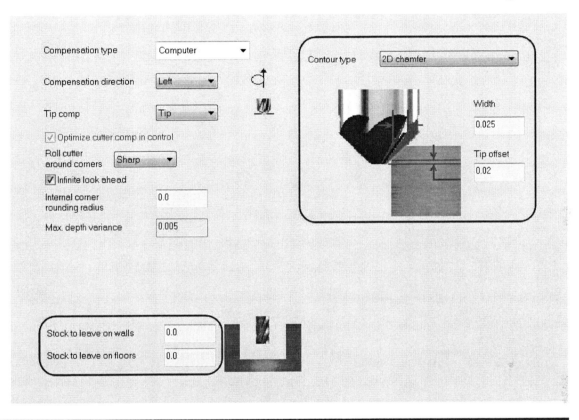

2D chamfer cuts chamfers around a contour.

Width sets the chamfer width. Mastercam measures the width from the chained geometry adjusted by the cut depths defined on the linking parameters page.

Tip offset is an amount to ensure that the tip of the tool clears the bottom of the chamfer.

23.3 Set the Lead In/Out Parameters

- Choose the option **Lead In/Out** and input an **Overlap** value.
- Make any other necessary changes as shown in Figure: 23.3.1.

Figure: 23.3.1

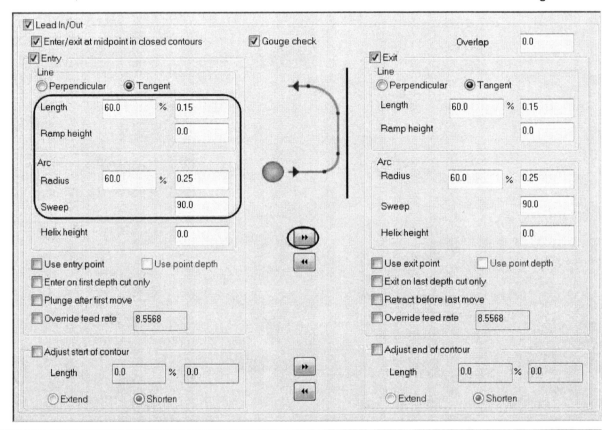

Lead In/Out allows you to can create either entry moves, exit moves, or both. **Lead in/out** move can include both lines and arcs.

Enter/Exit at midpoint in closed contours starts and ends a toolpath with closed chains at the midpoint of the first chained entity.

Gouge check entry/exit motion ensures that the entry/exit moves do not gouge the part. If the entry/exit moves cause a gouge, they are removed from the toolpath.

23.4 Set the Linking Parameters

♦ Select the **Linking Parameters** from the **Tree view list**. Set the **Top of stock** to **zero** and the **Depth** to **0.0 Incremental** as shown in Figure: 23.4.1.

Figure: 23.4.1

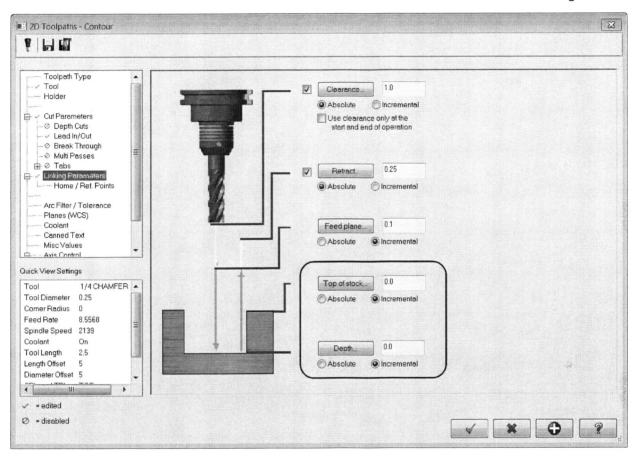

♦ Select the **OK** button to exit the toolpath parameters.

NOTE: The depth of the chamfer is based on the width and tip offset set in the Cut Parameters page. This is why we set the depth here to zero.

23.5 Backplot and Verify

♦ To **Backplot** and **Verify** the toolpath see page 391 and page 393 to review the procedures.
♦ Your part will appear as shown.

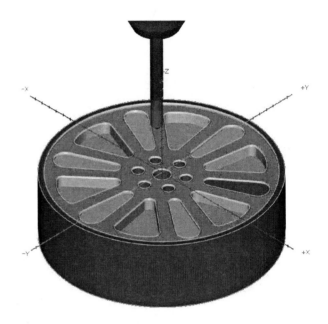

TOOLPATH CREATION - SETUP 2

SUGGESTED FIXTURE 2:

> **NOTE:** The part is now flipped over and we will machine the part from the bottom.

SETUP SHEET 2:

TOOL LIST

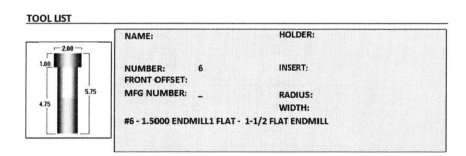

NAME:		HOLDER:
NUMBER:	6	INSERT:
FRONT OFFSET:		
MFG NUMBER:	_	RADIUS:
		WIDTH:

#6 - 1.5000 ENDMILL1 FLAT - 1-1/2 FLAT ENDMILL

STEP 24: CREATING AND RENAMING TOOLPATH GROUPS

To machine the part in two different setups, we will need to have two separate programs. To be able to post process separately the operations of each setup, we will create them under different toolpath groups with different NC names.

24.1 Rename the current Toolpath Group - 1 and the NC file

♦ Click on the **Toolpath Group - 1** to highlight and then click again on it and rename it "**Setup #1.**"

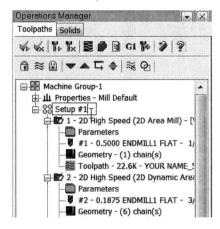

♦ Right mouse click on the toolpath group and select **Edit selected operations** and then, select **Change NC file name** as shown in <u>Figure: 24.1.1</u>.

Figure: 24.1.1

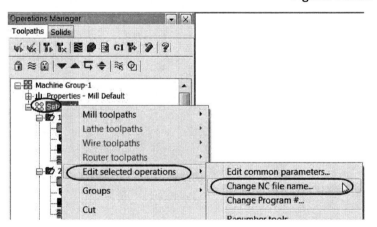

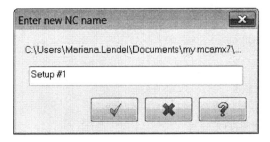

• Enter the new NC name: **Setup #1.**

• Select the **OK** button to accept the new NC name.

24.2 Create a New Toolpath Group

• Right mouse click on the **Machine Group-1** and select **Groups** and then the **New Toolpath group.**

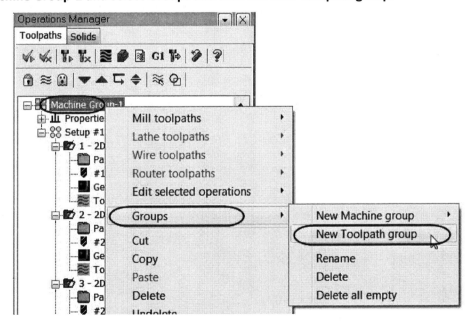

• Rename the toolpath group "**Setup #2**" as shown.

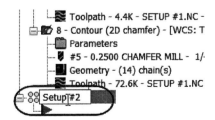

* Make sure that the **Insert arrow** is below the **Setup #2**, otherwise click on the **Move the insert arrow down an item** icon until the arrow is below the **Setup #2** group.

NOTE: The next operation is going to be generated at the insert arrow location.

STEP 25: SET THE WCS TO BOTTOM

Work coordinate system (WCS) is the active coordinate system in use by Mastercam at any given time. The WCS contains the orientation of the X, Y, Z axes plus the location of the zero point (the origin). This tells Mastercam how your part is position or orientated in the machine.

---

* Select **WCS** located in the **Status bar.** ▼ WCS Groups ! ?
* When the **WCS** menu appears select **"View Manager"** from it.

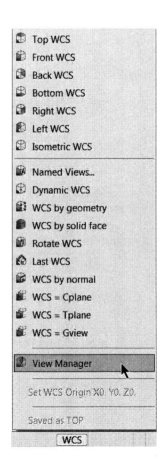

◆ When the **View Manager** dialog box appears pick bottom and then choose to set the **Work Coordinate System** (WCS), tool plane, construction plane, and their origins, to the selected view as shown in <u>Figure: 25.0.1</u>.

Figure: 25.0.1

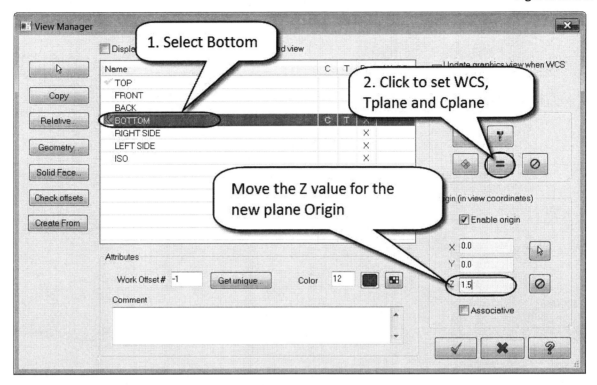

◆ Input a Z value of **1.5** to tell Mastercam where the new origin is located on the part.

◆ Select the **OK** button to exit the **View Manager**.

◆ Pick the **Isometric** graphics view to see the part in its new orientation.

◆ Press **F9** on your keyboard to display the coordinate axes.

NOTE: The brown axes are the original axes and the blue axes are the current axes.

♦ Your part will appear as shown up to this point.

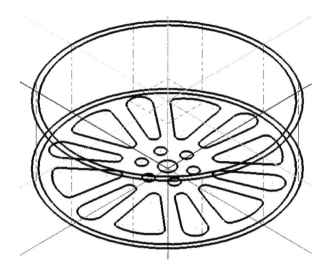

♦ Press **F9** to remove the axes display.

STEP 26: 2D HS DYNAMIC AREA MILL

In this step we will utilize the 2D High Speed Dynamic Area Mill toolpath to remove the material in the middle of the part with the part now flipped over.

Toolpath Preview:

26.1 Chain Selection

Toolpaths
♦ **2D High speed.**

♦ **Dynamic Area.**

- Leave the default settings in the **Chaining** dialog box and pick the first chain on the inner circle as shown in <u>Figure: 26.1.1</u>.

Figure: 26.1.1

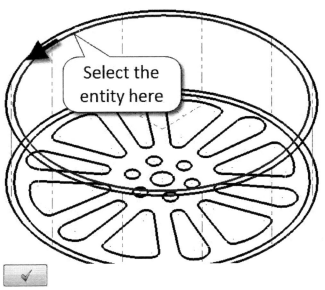

- Select the **OK** button to exit the **Chaining** dialog box.
- In the **Chain Options** select **Single region**.

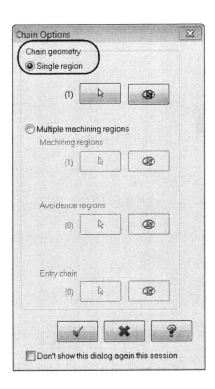

- Select the **OK** button to exit the **Chain Options** dialog box.

* In the **Toolpath Type** page, select **Dynamic Area Mill.**

Core Mill   Peel Mill   Blend Mill   Area Mill   Rest Mill   Dynamic Area Mill

Dynamic Rest Mill   Dynamic Core Mill   Dynamic Contour

26.2 Select a 1 - 1/2" Flat Endmill from the Library and set the Tool parameters

* Select **Tool** from the **Tree view list.**

* Click on **Select library tool** button.
* Select the **Filter** button as shown.

* Select the **None** button and then under **Tool Types** choose the **Flat Endmill** icon.

- Under tool diameter pick **Greater Than** and input a value **1.0** as shown in <u>Figure: 26.2.1</u>.

Figure: 26.2.1

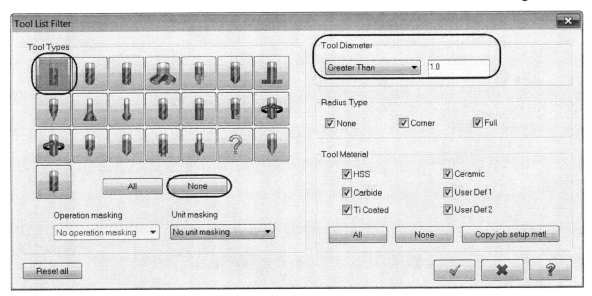

- Select the **OK** button to exit the **Tool List Filter**.
- In the **Tool Selection** dialog box you should only see **Flat Endmill's** larger than **1.0"**.

#	Assembly Name	Tool Name	Holder Name	Dia.	Cor. rad.	Length	# Flutes	Type	Rad. Type
244	–	1-1/2 FL...	–	1.5	0.0	2.5	4	En...	None
245	–	2 INCH F...	–	2.0	0.0	2.75	4	En...	None
313	–	1-3/16 FL...	–	1....	0.0	2.0	4	En...	None

- Select the **1 - 1/2" Flat Endmill** in the **Tool Selection** page.

- Select the **OK** button to exit.

◆ Make all the necessary changes as shown in <u>Figure: 26.2.2</u>.

Figure: 26.2.2

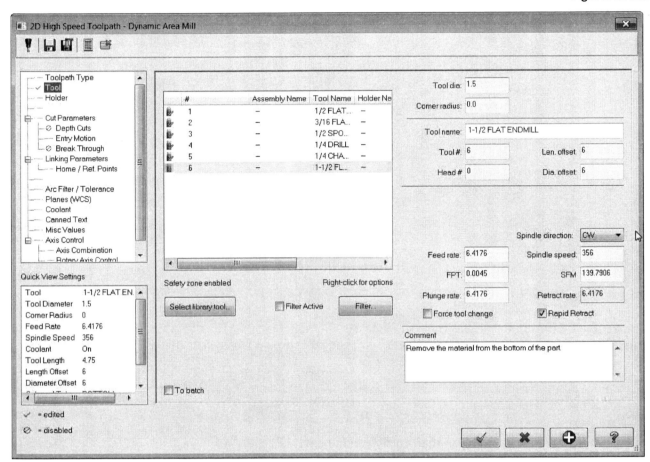

26.3 Set the Cut Parameters

◆ From the **Tree view list**, select **Cut Parameters** and make sure that the parameters are set as shown
<u>Figure: 26.3.1</u>.

Figure: 26.3.1

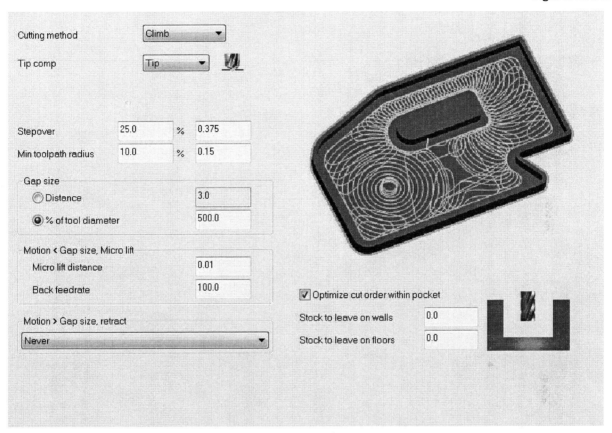

| NOTE: For more information on these settings see page 400.

26.4 Set the Depth Cuts Parameters

* From the **Tree view list**, disable the **Depth Cuts** if needed as shown.

26.5 Set the Entry Motion

* Set the **Entry method** to **Helix only**.
* Set the **Helix radius** to **1.0** and the rest of the parameters as shown in Figure: 26.5.1.
* Enable **Entry feeds / speeds** and set a **Ramp feed rate** of **10.0** Inches per minute, a **Ramp spindle speed** of **800** RPM and **Dwell before cut spindle speed** of **3.0** seconds as shown in Figure: 26.5.1.

Figure: 26.5.1

Entry method
Helix only

Chain geometry
(1)

Helix radius	1.0
Trochoidal loop radius	0.0
Additional slot width	0.0

☑ Output 3D arc moves   ☐ Center helix on point

Z clearance	0.125
⦿ Plunge angle	2.0
◯ Entry pitch	0.0

☑ Entry feeds / speeds
Ramp feed rate	10.0
Ramp spindle speed	800
Dwell before cut spindle speed	3.0

NOTE: For more information on these settings see page 401.

26.6 Set the Linking Parameters

♦ Select **Linking Parameters** and input the **Depth** of **-1.25** as shown in <u>Figure: 26.6.1</u>.

Figure: 26.6.1

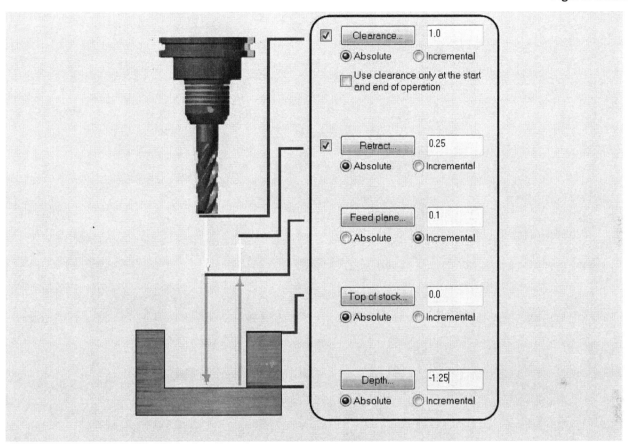

♦ Once complete pick the **OK** button to generate the toolpath.

♦ To **Backplot** and **Verify** your toolpath see page 391 and page 393 to review these procedures.

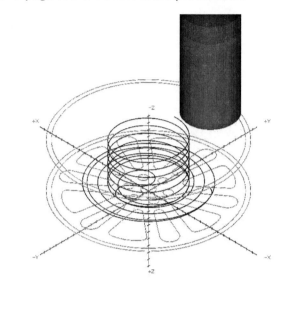

♦ Once complete the part will appear as shown.

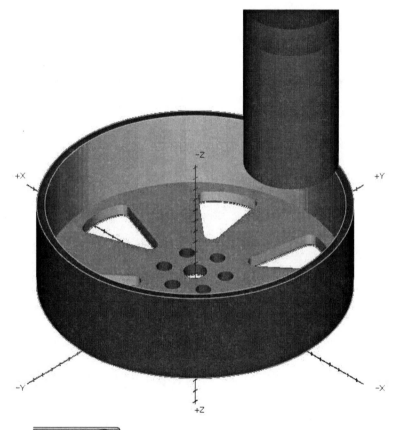

♦ To exit **Verify** click on the **Close** icon.

Mastercam. X⁷

STEP 27: RENAME THE NC FILE

The **2D High Speed dynamic mill** operation in Setup #2 kept the NC name from Setup #1. We need to rename this operation so it will create 2 separate programs.

• Select only operation #8.
• Right click on Operation #8, choose the option **Edit selected operations** and then pick **Change NC file name**.

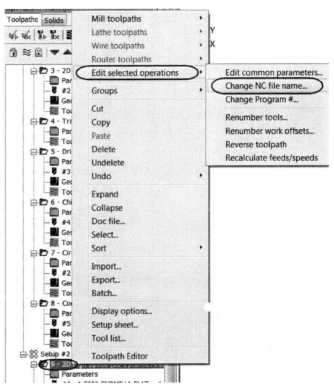

• When the **Enter new NC name** dialog box appears select **"Setup #2"**.

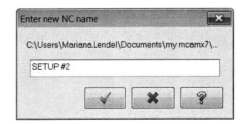

• Select the **OK** button to apply the changed **NC name** to operation #9.

• The result you should see **Setup #2.NC** in the last item of text for operation **#8**.

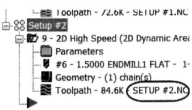

STEP 28: POST THE FILE

• Ensure all operations are selected, if they are not use the button **Select all operations** in the **Operations**

Manager.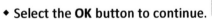

• Select the **Post selected operations** button from the **Operations Manager.** `G1`
• In the **Post processing** window make the necessary changes as shown in Figure: 28.0.1.

Figure: 28.0.1

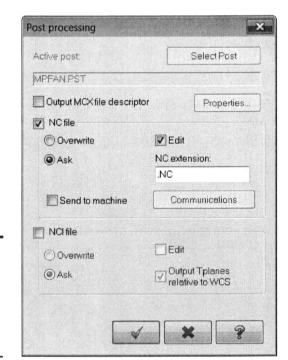

NC File enabled allows you to keep the NC file and to assign the same name as the MCX file.

Edit enabled allows you to automatically launch the default editor.

• Select the **OK** button to continue.
• Save Setup #1 NC file.

- Save Setup #2 NC file.
- A window with Mastercam Code Expert will be lunched and the NC program will appear as shown in <u>Figure: 28.0.2</u>.

Figure: 28.0.2

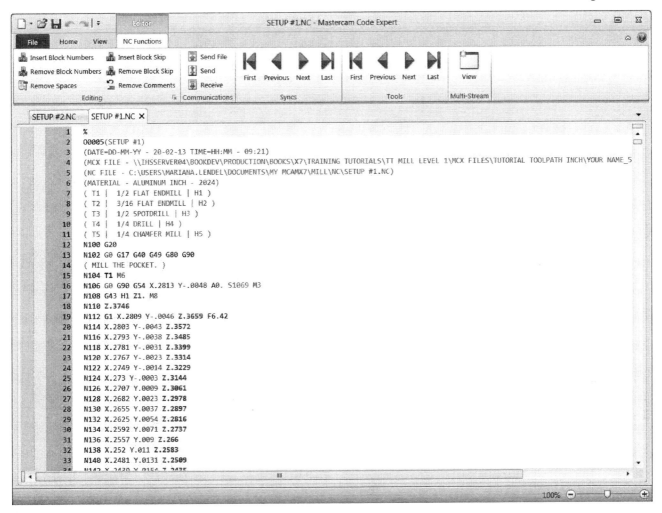

- Select the **"X"** box at the upper right corner to exit the editor.

STEP 29: SAVE THE UPDATED MCX FILE

REVIEW EXERCISE -STUDENT PRACTICE

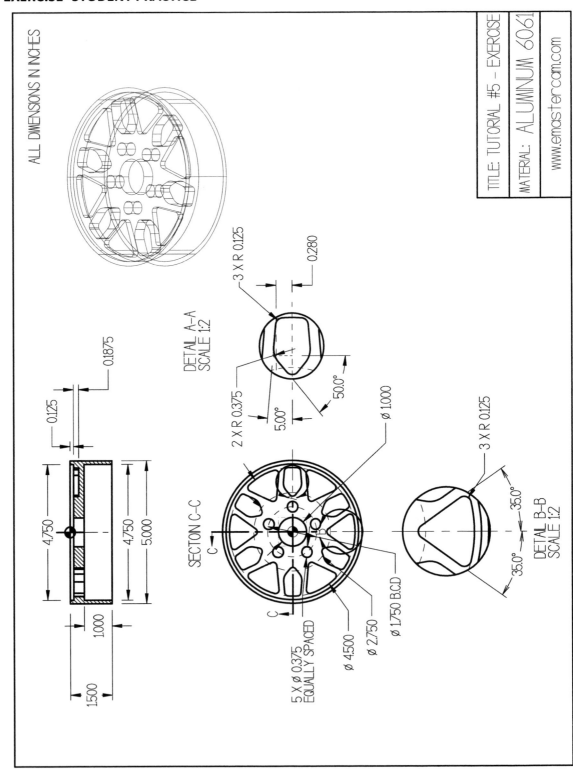

ALL DIMENSIONS IN INCHES

TITLE: TUTORIAL #5 – EXERCISE

MATERIAL: ALUMINUM 6061

www.emastercam.com

DETAIL A-A
SCALE 1:2

3 X R 0.125

0.280

2 X R 0.375

5.00°

50.0°

Ø 1.000

3 X R 0.125

35.0°

DETAIL B-B
SCALE 1:2

35.0°

0.1875

0.125

4.750

4.750

5.000

1.000

1.500

SECTION C-C

C

C

5 X Ø 0.375
EQUALLY SPACED

Ø 4.500

Ø 2.750

Ø 1.750 B.C.D

CREATE THE GEOMETRY FOR TUTORIAL #5 EXERCISE

Use these commands to create the geometry:
- Create Circle Center Point.
- Create Tangent Lines.
- Xform Mirror.
- Create Arc Tangent.
- Create Arc Polar.
- Trim/Break/Extend.
- Create Fillets.
- Delete Entities.
- Xform Rotate.
- Xform Translate.

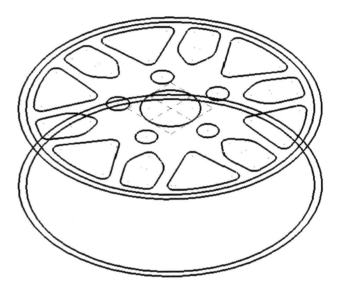

CREATE THE TOOLPATHS FOR TUTORIAL #5 EXERCISE

Create the Toolpaths for Tutorial #5 Exercise as per the instructions below.

Set the machine properties including the stock setup.
Remove the material in the center of the part.
- Use a **1" Flat Endmill**.
- Disable **Depth Cuts**.
- Set the **Entry Motion**.
- Set the **Depth** according to the drawing.

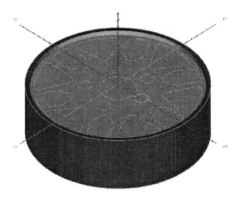

Area Mill one of the large pockets.
- Select Pocket and take note of the angle which the pocket is set at.
- Use a **1/4" Flat Endmill**.
- Disable **Depth Cuts**.
- Set the **Entry Motion**.
- Set the **Top of Stock** and **Depth** according to the drawing.

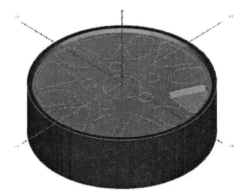

Dynamic Mill one of the small pockets.
- Select Pocket and take note of the angle which the pocket is set at.
- Use a **1/4" Flat Endmill**.
- Enable and set **Depth Cuts**.
- Set the **Entry Motion**.
- Set the **Top of Stock** and **Depth** according to the drawing.

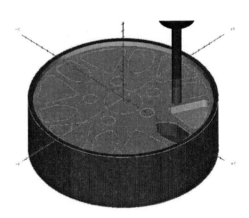

Mastercam. X[7]

Transform Toolpaths.
* Choose **Rotate** and select **Operation #2** and **#3**.
* Select **Coordinate** and **Operation order**.
* Enable **Copy** source operations.
* Ensure disable posting in selected source operations is enabled.
* Select the **Rotate** tab.
* Input the number of steps # = **5**.
* **Start angle = 60.0**.
* **Rotation angle = 60.0**.

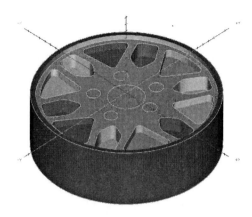

Spot Drill the holes.
* Use a **1/2" Spot Drill**.
* Set the **Cycle** and **Dwell**.
* Set the **Top of Stock** and **Depth** using the depth calculator.

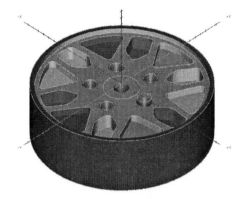

Drill the holes.
* Use a **3/8"Drill**.
* Set the **Cycle** to **Peck** and input your increments.
* Set the **Top of Stock** and **Depth** using the depth calculator.

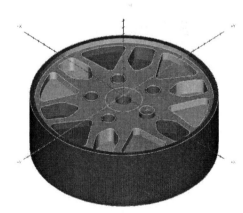

Circle Mill the Center Hole.
* Use the **1/4" Flat Endmill.**
* Enable **Roughing**.
* Enable **Depth Cuts** and set **Max rough step** to **0.25"**.
* Enable **Multi Passes** and set **1 Finish** at a **Spacing** of **0.02"**.
* Set the depth to the appropriate depth.

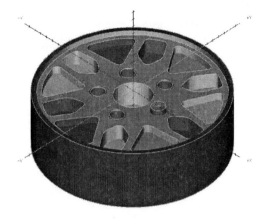

Flip the part over Setup #2.
Set WCS to Bottom and input correct depth.
* Use **Dynamic Area Mill** to remove the material starting from the center.
* Use the **1" Flat Endmill**.
* Disable **Depth cuts**.
* Set the **Entry Motion**.
* Set the **Depth** according to the drawing.

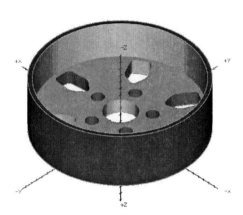

* Your part should appear as shown once complete.

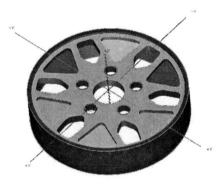

NOTES:

TUTORIAL #5 QUIZ

◆ Define a dynamic toolpath?

◆ What does a "Dwell before cut spindle speed" do?

◆ What does a transform toolpath operation do?

TUTORIAL #6

OVERVIEW OF STEPS TAKEN TO CREATE THE FINAL PART:

From Drawing to CAD Model:
- The student should examine the drawing on the following page to understand what part is being created in the tutorial.
- From the drawing we can decide how to go about creating the geometry in Mastercam.

Create the 2D CAD Model used to generate Toolpaths from:
- The student will create the 3D geometry needed to create the toolpaths.
- You will learn how to set the Construction planes, the Tool planes and the WCS.
- Geometry creation commands such as rectangle, rectangular shapes, circle center point, line parallel, arc tangent, arc endpoints and translate will be used.
- The student will also learn how to clean up the geometry using the trimming functions.

Create the necessary Toolpaths to machine the part:
- The student will set up the stock size to be used and the clamping method used. Three setups will be used to machine the part from the top and then from the bottom.
- A 2D High Speed Area Mill toolpath will be created to remove the material inside of the step.
- Two 2D High Speed Rest Mill toolpaths will be created to remove the material inside the pockets.
- Drill toolpaths will be created to machine the three holes in the front view.
- A Slot Mill toolpath will be created to remove the material inside of the slot from the left side view.

Backplot and Verify the file:
- The Backplot will be used to simulate a step by step process of the tool's movements.
- The Verify will be used to watch a tool machine the part out of a solid model.

Post Process the file to generate the G-code:
- The Student will then post process the file to obtain an NC file containing the necessary code for the machine.

 This tutorial takes approximately two hours to complete.

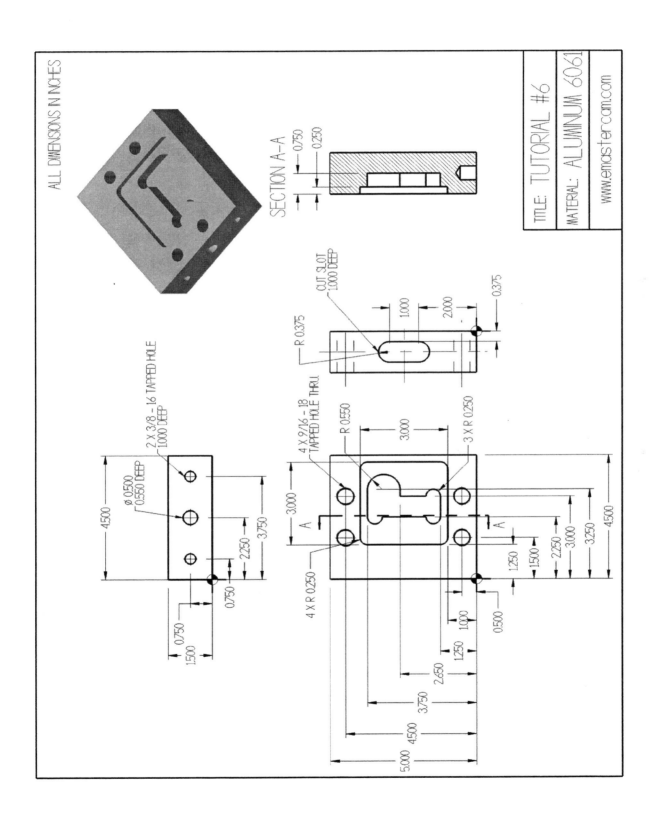

ALL DIMENSIONS IN INCHES

SECTION A-A

0.750
0.250

TITLE: TUTORIAL #6

MATERIAL: ALUMINUM 6061

www.emastercam.com

CUT SLOT 1.000 DEEP

R 0.375

1.000

2.000

0.375

2 X 3/8 - 16 TAPPED HOLE 1.000 DEEP

Ø 0.500 0.550 DEEP

4 X 9/16 - 18 TAPPED HOLE THRU

R 0.550

3.000

3 X R 0.250

4 X R 0.250

4.500

3.750

2.250

0.750

0.750

1.500

3.000

3.000

3.250

4.500

2.250

1.500

1.250

1.000

0.500

2.650

1.250

3.750

4.500

5.000

GEOMETRY CREATION

STEP 1: SETTING UP THE GRAPHIC USER INTERFACE

Please refer to the **Getting Started** section to set up the graphics user interface.

STEP 2: CREATE RECTANGLES

In this step you will create rectangles using the rectangular shapes option command. In this command you can create a rectangle using a base point or 2-point method. You can set a corner fillet radius, rotation angle and general shape.

Step Preview:

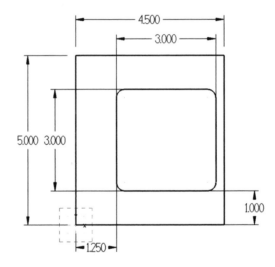

2.1 Create Rectangles

Create

♦ 　Rectangular Shapes.

♦ When the dialog box appears input a **Width** 　of **4.5** and a **Height** 　of **5.0**. Ensure the **Anchor position** is set to the **bottom left corner** as shown in Figure: 2.1.1.

Figure: 2.1.1

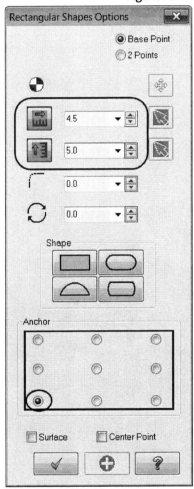

◆ [Select position of the base point]: Select the **Origin** as shown in <u>Figure: 2.1.2</u>.

Figure: 2.1.2

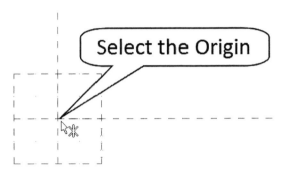

◆ Make sure that when selecting the origin, the visual cue of the cursor changes as shown.

◆ Use the **Fit** icon to fit the drawing to the screen.

◆ Choose the **Apply** button to continue.

NOTE: During the geometry creation of this tutorial, if you make a mistake you can undo the last step using the **Undo** icon. You can undo as many steps as needed. If you delete or undo a step by mistake, just use the **Redo** icon. To delete unwanted geometry, select it first and then press **Delete** from the keyboard.

- Enter a **Width** of **3.0** and a **Height** of **3.0**.
- Enter a **Corner Fillet Radius** of **0.25**.
- Ensure the **Anchor position** is set to the bottom left corner as shown in <u>Figure: 2.1.3</u>.

Figure: 2.1.3

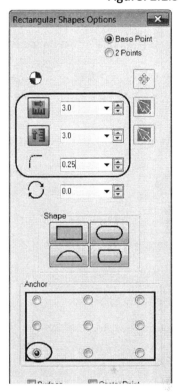

- Pick the **Fast Point** icon.
- Enter the coordinate values of **1.25, 1.0**.
- Hit **Enter** on your keyboard to place the rectangle.

- Choose the **OK** button to exit the command.
- The geometry should look as shown.

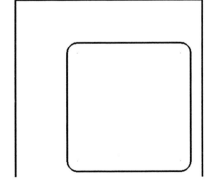

STEP 3: SET CONSTRUCTION DEPTH AND MODE

In this step you will learn how to set your construction depth or Z depth. This is where your geometry will be created. As well we will set our construction mode to 2D. This will allow us to only create geometry parallel to the current construction plane at the current construction depth.

3.1 Set Construction Mode to 2D

◆ Make sure that the construction mode is **2D**. From the **Status bar,** click on **3D** as shown in Figure: 3.1.1. This will toggle the construction mode to **2D**.

Figure: 3.1.1

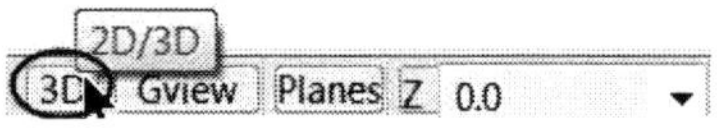

3.2 Set Construction Depth to -0.25"

◆ In the status bar click next to the "Z".

Figure: 3.2.1

◆ Input a value of **-0.25** and hit **Enter** to apply this change.

Figure: 3.2.2

NOTE: When we create our geometry we will be creating it at a depth of **-0.25"** and in the Top construction plane.

STEP 4: CREATE PARALLEL LINES

In this step you will learn how to create parallel lines knowing the side which the lines will fall on and the distance from the original line selected.

Step Preview:

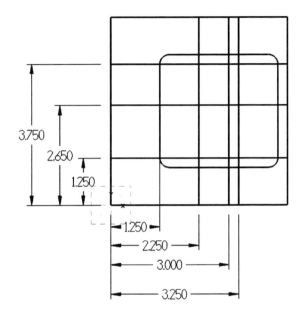

Create
* **Line.**
* 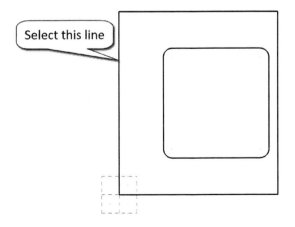 **Parallel.**
* [Select a line]: Select the left vertical line as shown in <u>Figure: 4.0.1</u>.

Figure: 4.0.1

* [Select the point to place a parallel line through]: Pick a point to the right of it.

• Input a **Distance** 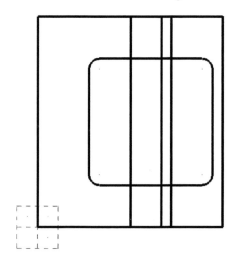 in the **Ribbon bar** of **2.25.**

• Select the **Apply** button.
• [Select a line]: Select the same vertical line.
• [Select the point to place a parallel line through]: Pick a point to the right of it.

• Input a **Distance** in the **Ribbon bar** of **3.0.**

• Select the **Apply** button.
• [Select a line]: Select the same vertical line.
• [Select the point to place a parallel line through]: Pick a point to the right of it.

• Input a **Distance** in the **Ribbon bar** of **3.25.**

• Select the **Apply** button.
• The geometry should look as shown in Figure: 4.0.2.

Figure: 4.0.2

◆ [Select a line]: Select the bottom horizontal line as shown in <u>Figure: 4.0.3</u>.

Figure: 4.0.3

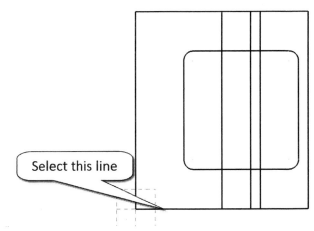

Select this line

◆ [Select the point to place a parallel line through]: Pick a point above it.

◆ Input a **Distance**  in the **Ribbon bar** of **1.25**.

◆ Select the **Apply** button. ⊕

◆ [Select a line]: Select the bottom horizontal line.

◆ [Select the point to place a parallel line through]: Pick a point above it.

◆ Input a **Distance** in the **Ribbon bar** of **2.65**.

◆ Select the **Apply** button. ⊕

◆ [Select a line]: Select the bottom horizontal line.

◆ [Select the point to place a parallel line through]: Pick a point above it.

◆ Input a **Distance** in the **Ribbon bar** of **3.75**.

◆ Select the **OK** button. ✓

◆ The geometry should look as shown in <u>Figure: 4.0.4</u>.

Figure: 4.0.4

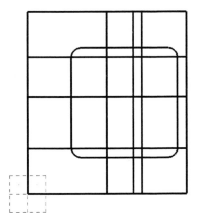

STEP 5: CREATE ARC TANGENT

Tangent 1 Entity allows you to create an arc tangent to a single existing entity. You will be prompted to select an entity to which the arc will be tangent. When Mastercam detects more than one solution, multiple arcs are created and you will be prompted to select the one you want to keep.

Step Preview:

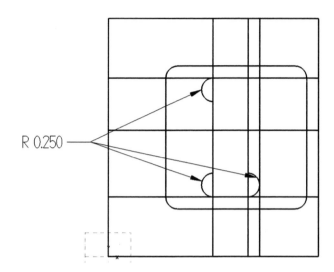

R 0.250

Create

* **Arc.**

*  **Arc Tangent.**

* From the **Ribbon bar** ensure you have **Tangent 1 Entity** selected.

* Enter a **Radius** of **0.25** as shown.

* [Select the entity that the arc is to be tangent to]: Select the horizontal line as shown in <u>Figure: 5.0.1</u>.
* [Specify the tangent point]: Select the intersection as shown in <u>Figure: 5.0.1</u>.

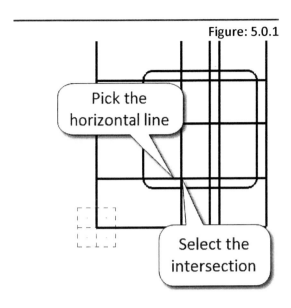

Figure: 5.0.1

• [Select an arc]: Pick the arc to keep as shown in Figure: 5.0.2.

Figure: 5.0.2

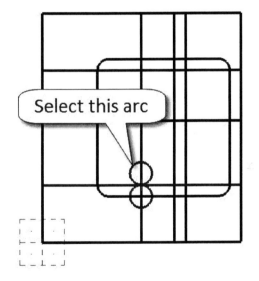

• Choose the **Apply** button to continue.

• [Select the entity that the arc is to be tangent to]: Select the horizontal line as shown in <u>Figure: 5.0.3</u>.
• [Specify the tangent point]: Select the intersection as shown in <u>Figure: 5.0.3</u>.

Figure: 5.0.3

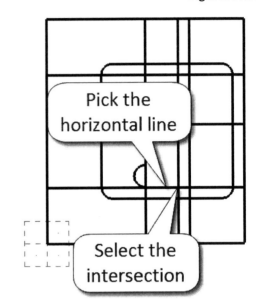

• [Select an arc]: Pick the arc to keep as shown in <u>Figure: 5.0.4</u>.

Figure: 5.0.4

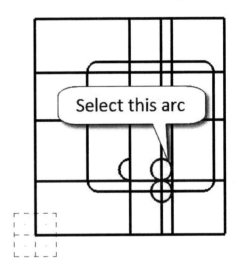

• Choose the **Apply** button to continue.

◆ [Select the entity that the arc is to be tangent to]: Select the horizontal line as shown in Figure: 5.0.5.
◆ [Specify the tangent point]: Select the intersection as shown in Figure: 5.0.5.

Figure: 5.0.5

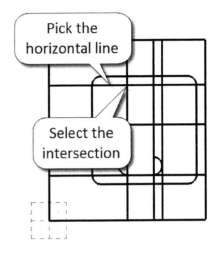

◆ [Select an arc]: Pick the arc to keep as shown in Figure: 5.0.6.

Figure: 5.0.6

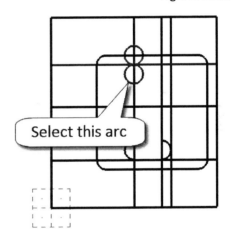

◆ Choose the **OK** button to exit the command.

STEP 6: CREATE ARC ENDPOINTS

In this step you will learn how to create arcs defined by endpoints and a radius or diameter.

Step Preview:

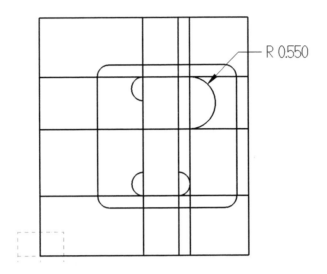

R 0.550

Create
* ◆ **Arc.**
* ◆ 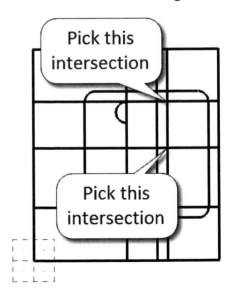 **Arc Endpoints.**
* ◆ Enter the **Radius** ⊚ value of **0.55**.
* ◆ Select the two intersections as shown in Figure: 6.0.1.

Figure: 6.0.1

Pick this intersection

Pick this intersection

◆ Pick the arc to keep as shown in <u>Figure: 6.0.2</u>.

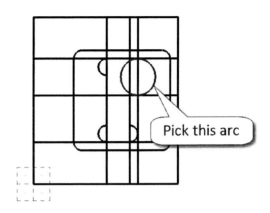

◆ Select the **OK** button to exit the command.

STEP 7: TRIM THE ENTITIES

In this step you will learn how to trim entities to clean up the geometry.

Step Preview:

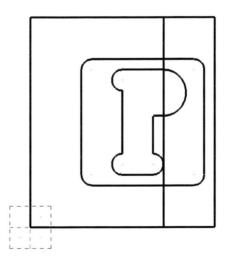

Edit

◆ **Trim/Break.**

◆ **Trim/Break/Extend.**

◆ From the **Ribbon bar** select the option to **Trim 3 Entities**.

- [Select the first entity to trim/extend]: Select **Entity A** as shown in <u>Figure: 7.0.1</u>.
- [Select the second entity to trim/extend]: Select **Entity C** in <u>Figure: 7.0.1</u>.
- [Select the third entity to trim/extend]: Select **Entity B** in <u>Figure: 7.0.1</u>.

Figure: 7.0.1

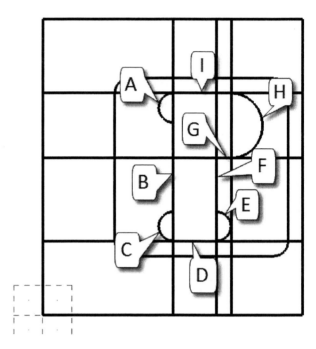

- [Select the first entity to trim/extend]: Select **Entity C** in <u>Figure: 7.0.1</u>.
- [Select the second entity to trim/extend]: Select **Entity E** in <u>Figure: 7.0.1</u>.
- [Select the third entity to trim/extend]: Select **Entity D** in <u>Figure: 7.0.1</u>.

- [Select the first entity to trim/extend]: Select **Entity E** in <u>Figure: 7.0.1</u>.
- [Select the second entity to trim/extend]: Select **Entity G** in <u>Figure: 7.0.1</u>.
- [Select the third entity to trim/extend]: Select **Entity F** in <u>Figure: 7.0.1</u>.

- [Select the first entity to trim/extend]: Select **Entity G** in <u>Figure: 7.0.1</u>.
- [Select the second entity to trim/extend]: Select **Entity I** in <u>Figure: 7.0.1</u>.
- [Select the third entity to trim/extend]: Select **Entity H** in <u>Figure: 7.0.1</u>.

- [Select the first entity to trim/extend]: Select **Entity H** in <u>Figure: 7.0.1</u>.
- [Select the second entity to trim/extend]: Select **Entity A** in <u>Figure: 7.0.1</u>.
- [Select the third entity to trim/extend]: Select **Entity I** in <u>Figure: 7.0.1</u>.

- Select the **OK** button to exit the command.

STEP 8: DELETE AN ENTITY

In this step you will learn how to delete an entity from the graphic user interface.

Step Preview:

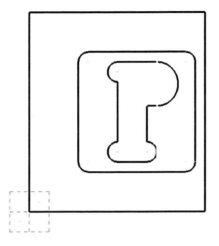

Edit
* **Delete.**
* **Delete Entities.**
* Select the line as shown in <u>Figure: 8.0.1</u>.

Figure: 8.0.1

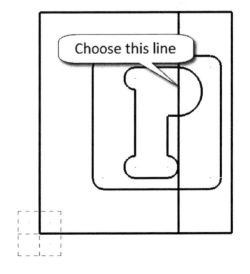

* Pick the **End Selection** button.

STEP 9: CREATE CIRCLES

Create circle center point lets you create circles from the center point.

Step Preview:

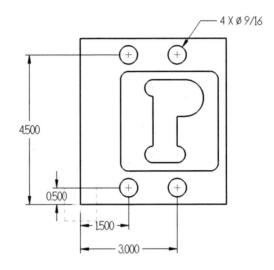

Create
* **Arc.**

*  **Circle Center Point.**

* Set the **Construction depth** to **zero**.
* To see more information regarding this step see page 472.

* Input a **Diameter** value of **9/16** and select the **Diameter** icon to lock this value.

> **NOTE:** When you lock a value the area behind the value turns red.

* Select the **Fast Point** command and input the following coordinates: **1.5, 0.5** and press **Enter**.

* Select the **Apply** button to continue.

* Choose the **Fast Point** command.
* Input the following coordinates: **3.0, 0.5** and press **Enter**.

* Select the **Apply** button to continue.

* Choose the **Fast Point** command.
* Input the following coordinates: **1.5, 4.5** and press **Enter**.

* Select the **Apply** button to continue.

*Mastercam. X*⁷

◆ Choose the **Fast Point** command.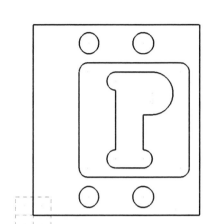
◆ Input the following coordinates: **3.0, 4.5.**

◆ Select the **OK** button to exit the command.
◆ The geometry should look as shown.

STEP 10: TRANSLATE THE ENTITIES

Translate Join transforms a copy of the selected entities to a new position in the graphics window and maintains the position of the original entities. Mastercam creates lines or arcs to connect the endpoints of the original entities to the endpoints of the transformed entities.

Step Preview:

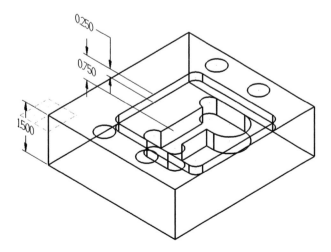

Xform

- 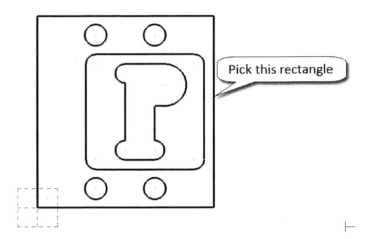 **Translate.**
- [Select entities to translate]: Hold the **Shift** key and select the rectangle as shown in <u>Figure: 10.0.1</u>.

Figure: 10.0.1

Pick this rectangle

- Pick the **End Selection** button.

◆ In the **Translate** dialog box enable **Join** and enter a **Delta Z** value of **-1.5** as shown in <u>Figure: 10.0.2</u>.

Figure: 10.0.2

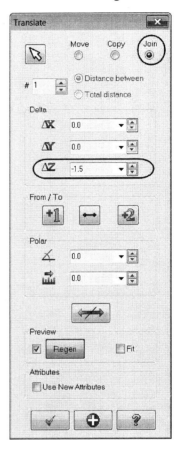

◆ Pick the **Apply** button to continue using the **Translate** command.

◆ Choose the **Isometric Graphics view.**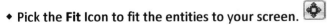

◆ Pick the **Fit** Icon to fit the entities to your screen.

◆ Your part will appear as shown up to this point.

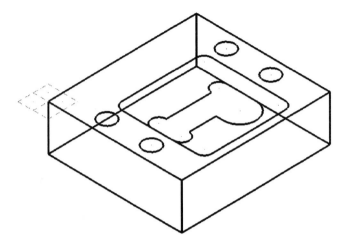

◆ [Select entities to translate]: Hold the **Shift** key and select the rectangle as shown in <u>Figure: 10.0.3</u>.

Figure: 10.0.3

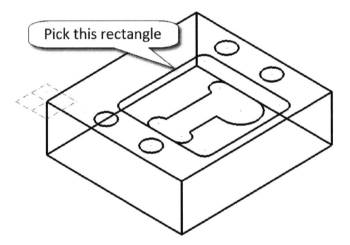

Pick this rectangle

◆ Pick the **End Selection** button.

• In the **Translate** dialog box enter a **Delta Z** value of **-0.25**as shown in <u>Figure: 10.0.4</u>.

Figure: 10.0.4

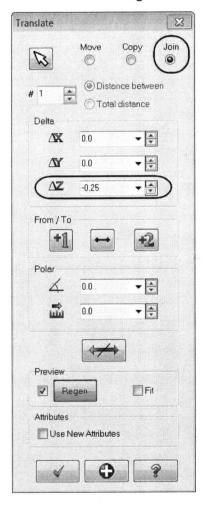

• Pick the **Apply** button to continue to use the translate command.

- [Select entities to translate]: Hold the **Shift** key and select the shape as shown in <u>Figure: 10.0.5</u>.

Figure: 10.0.5

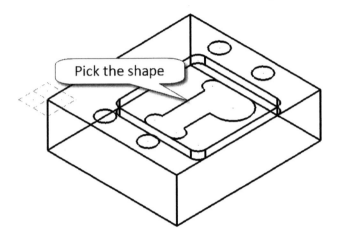

Pick the shape

- Choose the **End Selection** button.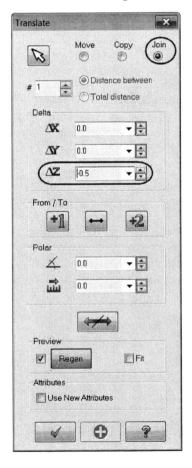
- In the **Translate** dialog box enter a **Delta Z** value of **-0.5** as shown in <u>Figure: 10.0.6</u>.

Figure: 10.0.6

• Pick the **OK** button to exit the translate command.

> **NOTE:** We only enter a value of -0.5" because it is based off where the geometry is created or selected. This will give us the desired depth of -0.75".

• The part will appear as shown up to this point.

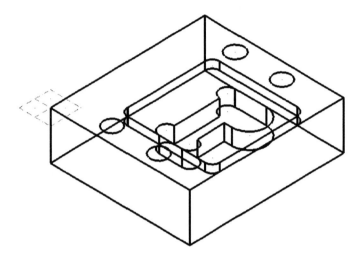

• Select the **Clear color** icon to remove the group and result colors.

> **NOTE:** When performing a transform function (Xform), Mastercam creates a temporary group from the originals (red) and a result (purple) from the transformed entities. These system groups appear in the Groups dialog box. However, they stay in effect only until you use the **Screen, Clear Colors** function or perform another transform function.

STEP 11: CREATE CIRCLES ON THE FRONT PLANE

In this step you will change the construction plane to the front and create circles.

11.1 Change the Construction Plane

• Select the drop down arrow next to the construction plane.

● From the list select **Front**.

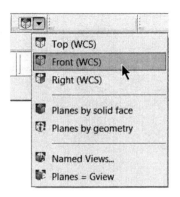

NOTE: This will allow you to create geometry on the front of the part.

● Choose the **Front** graphics view.

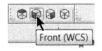

NOTE: This will allow you to view the part from the front.

11.2 Create the Circles

Step Preview:

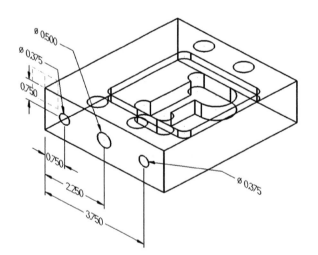

Create
● **Arc.**

● Circle Center Point.

• Enter a **Diameter**  of **0.375** and pick the icon to lock the value if needed as shown.

• [Enter the center point]: Select the **Fast Point** icon.
• Enter the coordinates **0.75, -0.75** and press **Enter**.

• Select the **Apply** button to continue.

• [Enter the center point]: Choose **Fast Point**.
• Enter the coordinates **3.75, -0.75** and press **Enter**.

• Select the **Apply** button to continue.

• Change the **Diameter** value to **0.5**.

• [Enter the center point]: Select the **Fast Point** icon.
• Enter the coordinates **2.25, -0.75** and press **Enter**.

• Select the **OK** button to exit the command.

• Select the **Isometric Gview**.
• Your part will appear as shown.

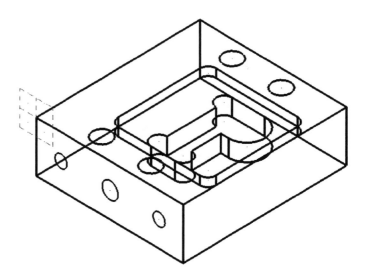

STEP 12: CREATE THE SLOT ON THE LEFT PLANE

In this step you will change the construction plane to the right and create a slot using the construction depth to determine the location of the slot.

12.1 Change the Construction Plane and Graphics View

• Select the drop down arrow next to the construction plane.

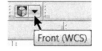

• From the list select **Right**.

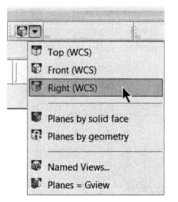

NOTE: This will allow you to create geometry on the right or left side of the part depending upon the construction depth.

• Make sure the construction depth is set to **0.0**.

Mastercam. X⁷

♦ In the status bar select **Gview** and choose the **Right** view.

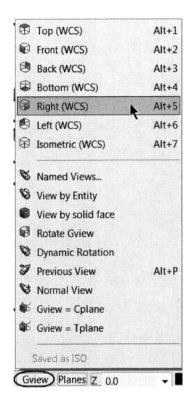

NOTE: This will allow you to view the part from the right side.

12.2 Create the Slot

Step Preview:

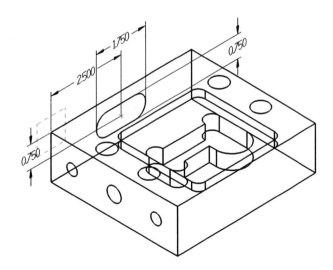

Create

- **Rectangular Shapes.**

- Enter a **Width** of **1.75** and a **Height** of **0.75**.
- Choose the **Obround Shape** and pick the option to anchor to center as shown in <u>Figure: 12.2.1</u>.

Figure: 12.2.1

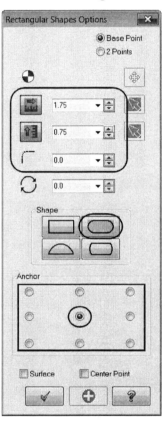

- Pick the **Fast Point** icon.
- Input the coordinates **2.5, -0.75** and hit **Enter** on your keyboard.

- Select the **OK** button to exit the **Rectangular Shapes Options**.

12.3 Change the Construction Mode to 3D

- From the **Status Bar**, select **2D** to change the mode to **3D** as shown.

- Choose the **Isometric** view.

◆ Your part will appear as shown once complete.

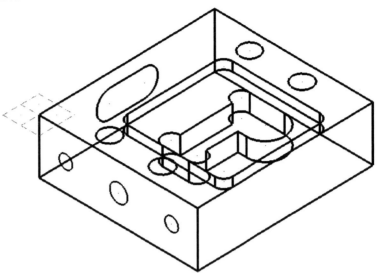

STEP 13: SAVE THE FILE

File

◆ 💾 **Save As.**
◆ File name: "**Your Name_6**".

TOOLPATH CREATION - SETUP 1

SUGGESTED FIXTURE:

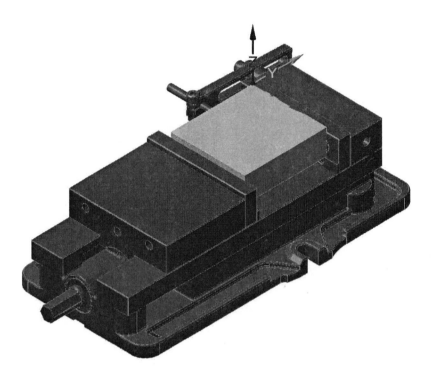

NOTE: In order to machine this part we will have 3 setups and output 3 NC files. To view the second setup see page 557 and to view the third setup see page 597.

SETUP SHEET:

TOOL LIST

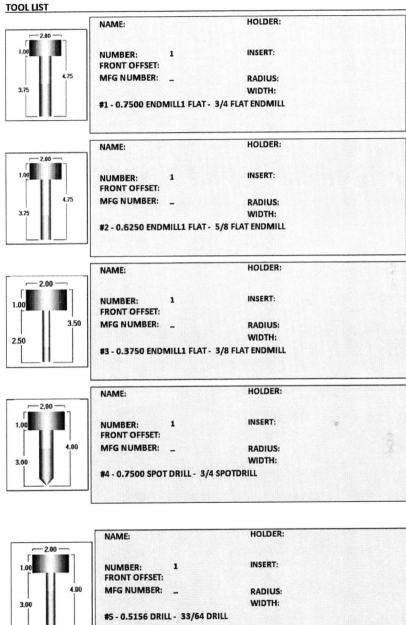

NAME:	HOLDER:
NUMBER: 1	INSERT:
FRONT OFFSET:	
MFG NUMBER: _	RADIUS:
	WIDTH:

#1 - 0.7500 ENDMILL1 FLAT - 3/4 FLAT ENDMILL

NAME:	HOLDER:
NUMBER: 1	INSERT:
FRONT OFFSET:	
MFG NUMBER: _	RADIUS:
	WIDTH:

#2 - 0.6250 ENDMILL1 FLAT - 5/8 FLAT ENDMILL

NAME:	HOLDER:
NUMBER: 1	INSERT:
FRONT OFFSET:	
MFG NUMBER: _	RADIUS:
	WIDTH:

#3 - 0.3750 ENDMILL1 FLAT - 3/8 FLAT ENDMILL

NAME:	HOLDER:
NUMBER: 1	INSERT:
FRONT OFFSET:	
MFG NUMBER: _	RADIUS:
	WIDTH:

#4 - 0.7500 SPOT DRILL - 3/4 SPOTDRILL

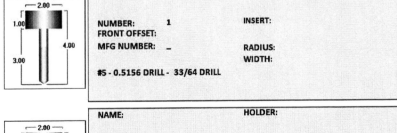

NAME:	HOLDER:
NUMBER: 1	INSERT:
FRONT OFFSET:	
MFG NUMBER: _	RADIUS:
	WIDTH:

#5 - 0.5156 DRILL - 33/64 DRILL

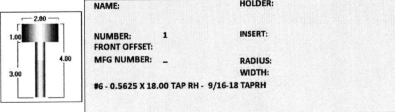

NAME:	HOLDER:
NUMBER: 1	INSERT:
FRONT OFFSET:	
MFG NUMBER: _	RADIUS:
	WIDTH:

#6 - 0.5625 X 18.00 TAP RH - 9/16-18 TAPRH

STEP 14: SELECT THE MACHINE AND SET UP THE STOCK

In Mastercam, you select a **Machine Definition** before creating any toolpaths. The **Machine Definition** is a model of your machines capabilities and features. It acts like a template for setting up your machine. The machine definition ties together three main components. The schematic model of your machines components, the control definition that models your control capabilities, and the post processor that will generate the required machine code (G-code). For a Mill Level 1 exercise (2D toolpaths) we need just a basic machine definition.

> **NOTE:** For the purpose of this tutorial, we will be using the Default milling machine.

• To display the **Operations Manager** press **Alt + O**.

• Use the **Fit** icon to fit the drawing to the screen.
Machine type
• **Mill.**
• **Default.**

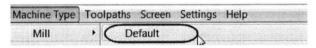

• Select the plus sign in front of **Properties** in the **Toolpaths Manager** to expand the **Toolpaths Group Properties.**

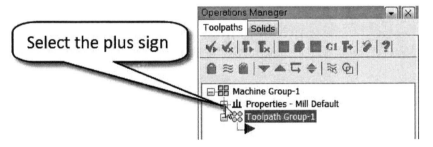

Select the plus sign

• Select **Tool Settings** to set the tool parameters.

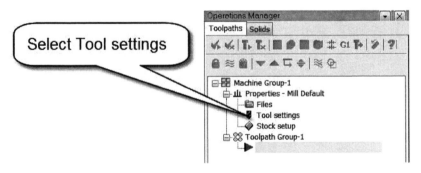

Select Tool settings

◆ Change the parameters to match the Figure: 14.0.1.

Figure: 14.0.1

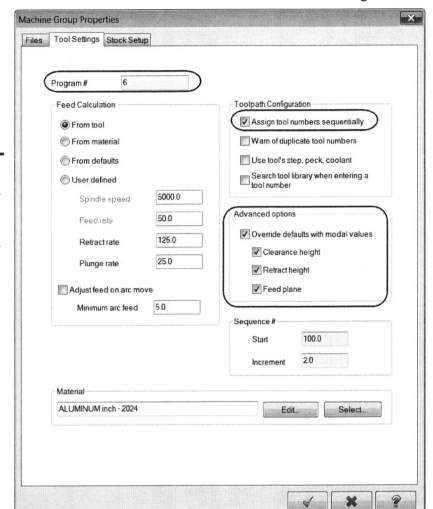

Program # is used to enter a number if your machine tool requires a number for a program name.

Assign tool numbers sequentially allows you to overwrite the tool number from the library with the next available tool number. (First operation tool number 1; Second operation tool number 2, etc.)

Warn of duplicate tool numbers allows you to get a warning if you enter two tools with the same number.

Override defaults with modal values enables the system to keep the values that you enter.

Feed Calculation set **From tool** uses feed rate, plunge rate, retract rate and spindle speed from the tool definition.

◆ Select the **Stock Setup** tab to define the stock.
◆ Pick the **Rectangular** shape option.

♦ Pick the **All Entities** button to define the stock size as shown in <u>Figure: 14.0.2</u>.

Figure: 14.0.2

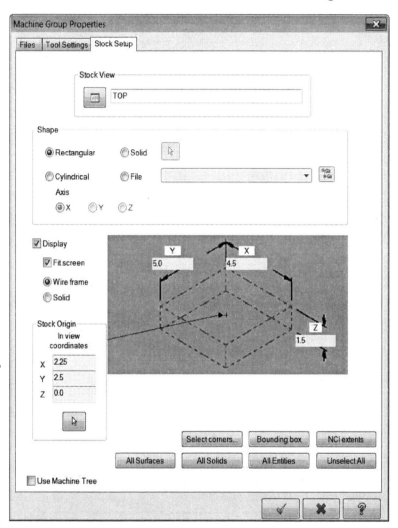

The **Stock Origin** values adjust the positioning of the stock, ensuring that you have equal amount of extra stock around the finished part.

Display options allow you to set the stock as **Wireframe** and to fit the stock to the screen. (Fit Screen)

NOTE: The **stock** model that you create can be displayed with the part geometry when viewing the file or the toolpaths, during backplot, or while verifying toolpaths. In the graphics, the plus shows you where the stock origin is. The default position is the middle of the stock.

♦ Select the **OK** button to exit **Machine Group Properties**.

♦ Select the **Isometric** view from the graphics view toolbar to see the stock.

♦ Use the **Fit** icon to fit the drawing to the screen.

◆ The stock model will appear as shown.

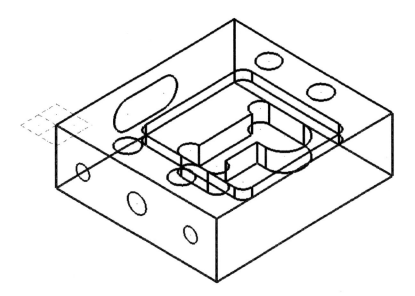

NOTE: You may not be able to see the stock very clearly due to the fact that the stock is the same size as the part. The stock is not geometry and can not be selected.

There will not be a facing toolpath because the stock is already to size.

STEP 15: 2D HIGH SPEED AREA MILL

2D High Speed Area Mill is used to machine pockets using a smooth clean motion. Helical entries and tangent stepovers create efficient motion for your machine. Cut parameters let you control smoothing to create the best toolpath, avoiding sharp corners or direction changes.

Toolpath Preview:

15.1 Chain Selection

Toolpaths
* **2D High Speed.**

* **Area.**

* When the new NC name dialog box appears select the **OK** button to accept the name.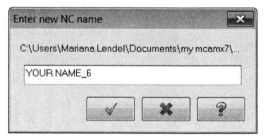

Mill Level 1 Training Tutorial *Mastercam.* X⁷

- When the chaining dialog box appears select **C-plane** as shown.
- Leave the chaining method set to **Chain** as shown in <u>Figure: 15.1.1</u>.

Figure: 15.1.1

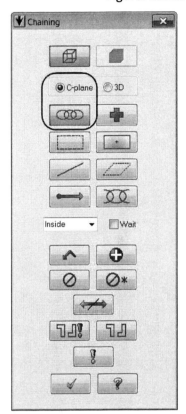

Cplane chains only the entities that are parallel to the current construction plane and at the same Z depth as the first entity you chain.

- Select the bottom of the pocket as shown in <u>Figure: 15.1.2</u>.

Figure: 15.1.2

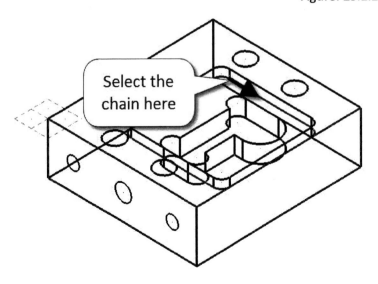

Select the chain here

• Select the **OK** button to exit the **Chaining** dialog box.

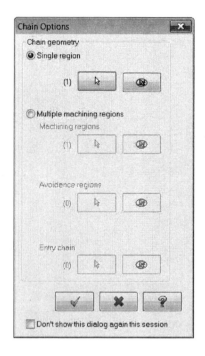

• Select the **OK** button to exit the **Chain Options**.
• In the **Toolpath Type** page, select **Area Mill.**

Core Mill   Peel Mill   Blend Mill   Area Mill   Rest Mill   Dynamic Area Mill

Dynamic Rest Mill   Dynamic Core Mill   Dynamic Contour

15.2 Select a 3/4" Flat endmill from the library and set the Tool parameters

• Select **Tool** from the **Tree view list**.

• Click on **Select library tool** button.
• Select the **Filter** button as shown.

Mill Level 1 Training Tutorial *Mastercam. X*⁷

- Select the **None** button and then under **Tool Types** choose the **Flat Endmill** icon.
- Under tool diameter pick **Equal** and input a value of **0.75** as shown in <u>Figure: 15.2.1</u>.

Figure: 15.2.1

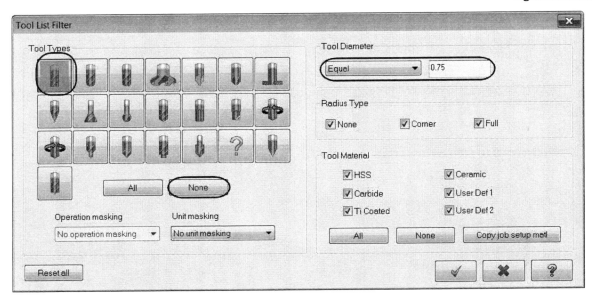

- Select the **OK** button to exit the **Tool List Filter**.
- In the **Tool Selection** dialog box you should only see a **3/4" Flat Endmill**.

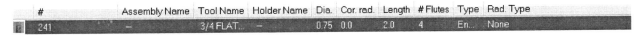

#	Assembly Name	Tool Name	Holder Name	Dia.	Cor. rad.	Length	# Flutes	Type	Rad. Type
241	—	3/4 FLAT..	—	0.75	0.0	2.0	4	En..	None

- Select the **3/4" Flat Endmill** in the **Tool Selection** page and then select the **OK** button to exit.

♦ Make all the necessary changes as shown in <u>Figure: 15.2.2</u>.

Figure: 15.2.2

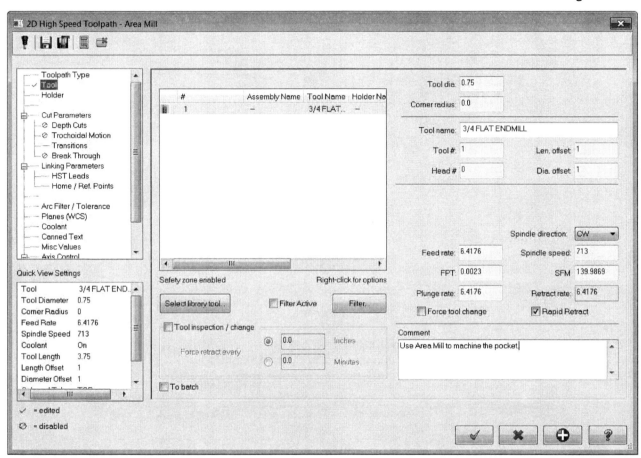

15.3 Set the Cut Parameters

- From the **Tree view list**, select **Cut Parameters**.
- Enable **Corner rounding** and ensure the settings appear as shown in <u>Figure: 15.3.1</u>.

Figure: 15.3.1

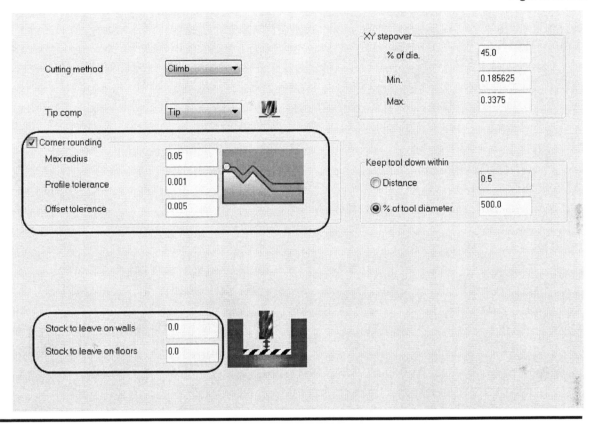

Corner rounding replaces sharp corners with arcs for faster and smoother transitions in tool direction.

Max radius inputs the radius of the largest arc that you will allow Mastercam to insert to replace a corner. Larger arcs will result in a smoother toolpath but with a greater deviatation from the part corner.

Profile tolerance represents the maximum distance that the outermost profile of a toolpath with corner rounding can deviate from the original toolpath.

Offset tolerance represents the maximum distance that a profile of a toolpath created with corner rounding can deviate from the original toolpath.

15.4 Set the Depth Cuts Parameters

◆ From the **Tree view list**, select the **Depth Cuts Parameters** and make sure it is disabled as shown in
Figure: 15.4.1.

Figure: 15.4.1

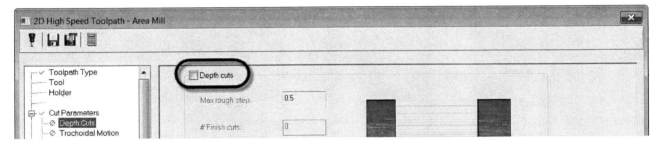

15.5 Set the Transitions

◆ Enable **Entry helix**, set the **Entry helix** to **0.500** and ensure the parameters are the same as shown in
Figure: 15.5.1.

Figure: 15.5.1

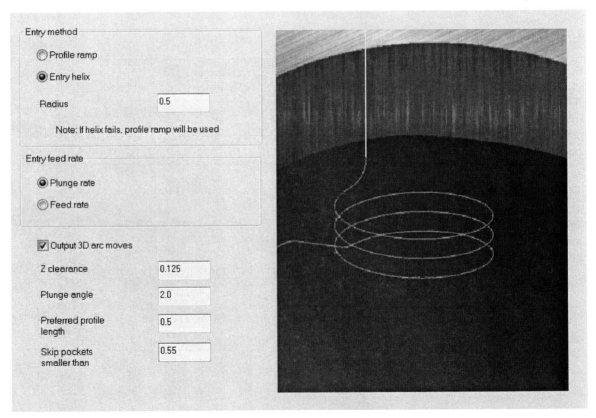

15.6 Set the Linking Parameters

♦ Select **Linking Parameters,** enable **Clearance** and input a value of **1.0.**
♦ You will notice the depth has been input based on the geometry we selected as shown in <u>Figure: 15.6.1</u>.

Figure: 15.6.1

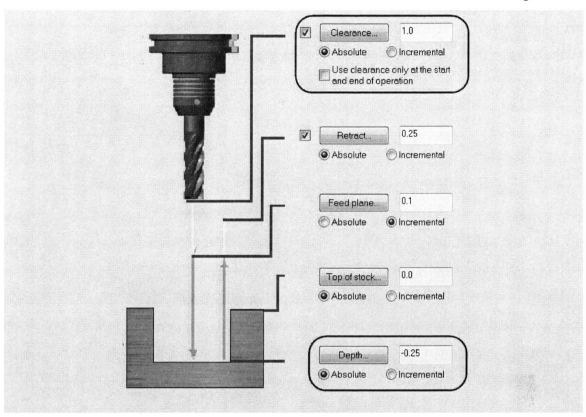

♦ Once complete pick the **OK** button to generate the toolpath.

STEP 16: BACKPLOT THE TOOLPATHS

Backplotting shows the path the tools take to cut the part. This display lets you spot errors in the program before you machine the part. As you backplot toolpaths, Mastercam displays additional information such as the X, Y, and Z coordinates, the path length , the minimum and maximum coordinates and the cycle time. It also shows any collisions between the workpiece and the tool.

- Make sure that the toolpath is selected (signified by the green check mark on the folder icon).
- Select the **Backplot selected operations** button.

- Select the **Backplot** tab and have the following settings enabled as shown.

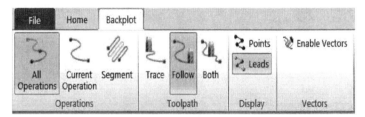

- Select the **Home** tab and make sure that you have the following settings on as shown.

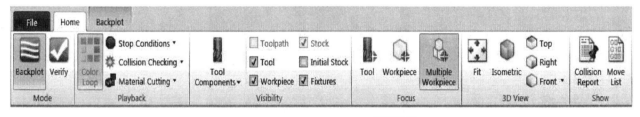

- To see the part from an **Isometric** view select the **Isometric** icon.

- To fit the workpiece to the screen, select the **Fit** icon.

- You can step through the **Backplot** by using the **Step forward** or **Step back** buttons.

- You can adjust the speed of the backplot.
- Select the **Play Simulation** button in the **VCR** bar to run **Backplot**.

◆ The toolpath should look as shown.

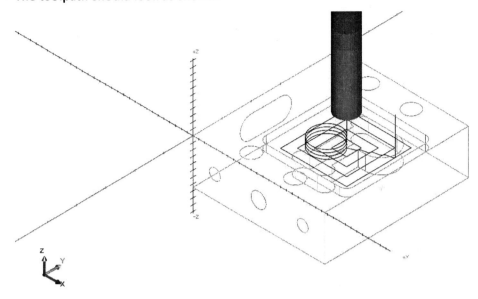

STEP 17: SIMULATE THE TOOLPATH IN VERIFY

Verify Mode shows the path the tools take to cut the part with material removal. This display lets you spot errors in the program before you machine the part. As you verify toolpaths, Mastercam displays additional information such as the X, Y, and Z coordinates, the path length , the minimum and maximum coordinates and the cycle time. It also shows any collisions between the workpiece and the tool.

◆ From **Mastercam Backplot Home** tab, switch to **Verify** and change the settings for the **Visibility** and **Focus** as shown in Figure: 17.0.1.

Figure: 17.0.1

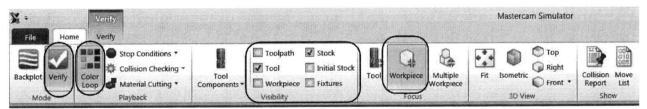

◆ Select the **Play Simulation** button in the **VCR** bar to run **Verify**.

◆ The part will appear as shown.

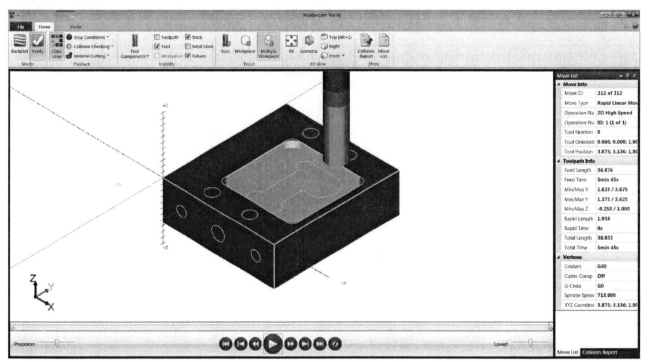

◆ To go back to Mastercam window, minimize **Verify** window as shown.

STEP 18: 2D HIGH SPEED AREA MILL

In this step you will learn how to copy a toolpath and reselect geometry. The main advantage of copying a toolpath is the parameters for the 1st toolpath remain intact for the second toolpath.

Toolpath Preview:

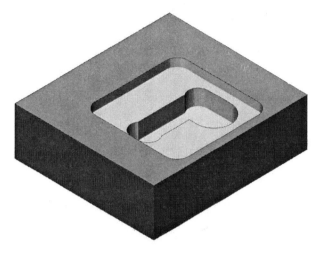

* To remove the toolpath display, from the **Toolpaths Operations Manager**, click on the **Toggle display on selected operations** or press **Alt + T**.

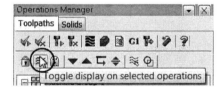

18.1 Copy the Previous Toolpath

* Select operation #1.

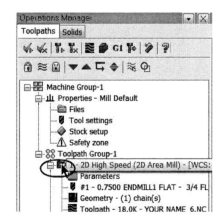

◆ Right click and hold the right mouse button down and drag the operation to a point below it as shown.

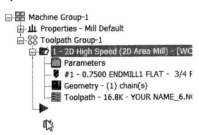

◆ Release the right mouse button and select the option **Copy After.**

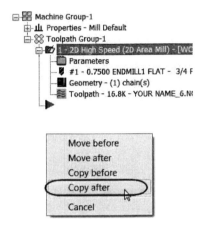

◆ Select the **Move insert arrow down one item** button to move the insert arrow down.

- The **Insert Arrow** should appear at the bottom of the list as shown in <u>Figure: 18.1.1</u>.

Figure: 18.1.1

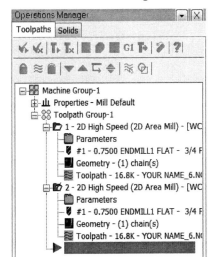

Insert Arrow controls where the new operation will be inserted.

18.2 Re-Chain the Geometry

- In Operation #2 pick the **Geometry** as shown.

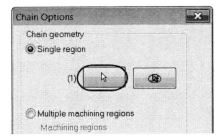

Select the Geometry

- Click on the **Select** button as shown.

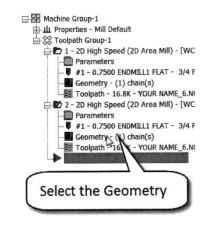

- When the **Chain Manager** appears select **Chain 1**.

• Right click and pick the option **Rechain all** as shown.

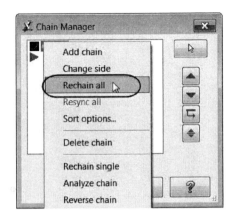

• When the **Chaining** dialog box appears select **C-plane.**

• Select the bottom of the pocket as shown in <u>Figure: 18.2.1</u>.

Figure: 18.2.1

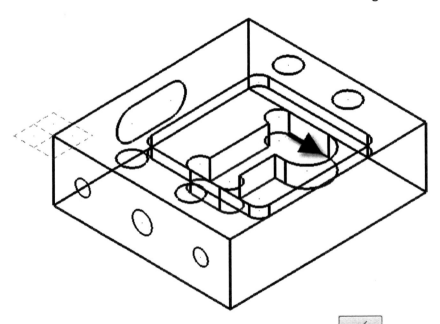

• Once the geometry has been selected choose the **OK** button to exit the **Chaining** dialog box.

• Pick the **OK** button to exit the **Chain Manager** box.

- Pick the **OK** button to exit the **Chain Options** box.

18.3 Select a 5/8" Flat Endmill from the Library and set the Tool Parameters

- Choose **Parameters** under Operation #2.

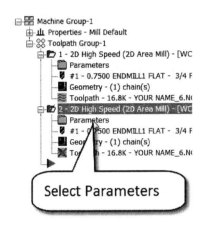

Select Parameters

- Select **Tool** from the **Tree view list**.

- Click on the **Select library tool** button.
- Select the **Filter** button.

- Select the **None** button and then under **Tool Types** choose the **Flat Endmill** icon.
- Under tool diameter pick **Equal** and input a value of **0.625** as shown in Figure: 18.3.1.

Figure: 18.3.1

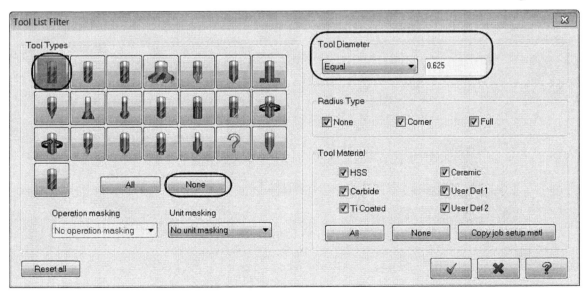

- Select the **OK** button to exit the **Tool List Filter.**
- In the **Tool Selection** dialog box you should only see a **5/8" Flat Endmill.**

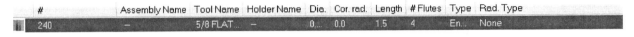

#	Assembly Name	Tool Name	Holder Name	Dia.	Cor. rad.	Length	# Flutes	Type	Rad. Type
240	–	5/8 FLAT...	–	0...	0.0	1.5	4	En...	None

- Select the **5/8" Flat Endmill** in the **Tool Selection** page and then select the **OK** button to exit.
- Make all the necessary changes as shown in Figure: 18.3.2.

Figure: 18.3.2

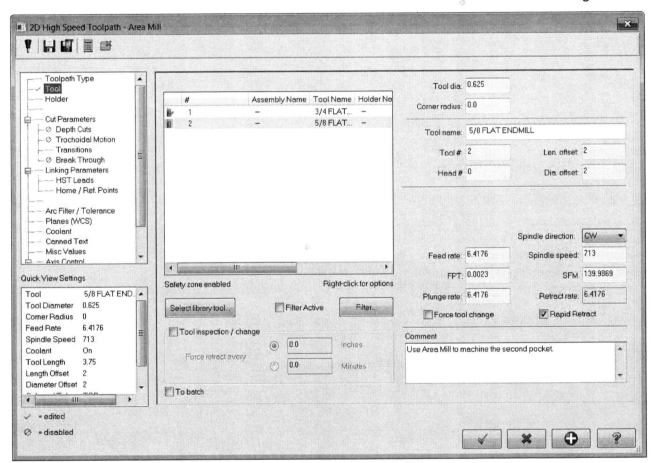

NOTE: Since this toolpath has been copied all the parameters remain the same. Therefore the only parameters shown are the ones we will be changing.

18.4 Set the Depth Cuts parameters

- From the **Tree view list**, select the **Depth Cuts** and enable **Depth Cuts**.
- Input a **Max rough step** of **0.25** as shown in Figure: 18.4.1.

Figure: 18.4.1

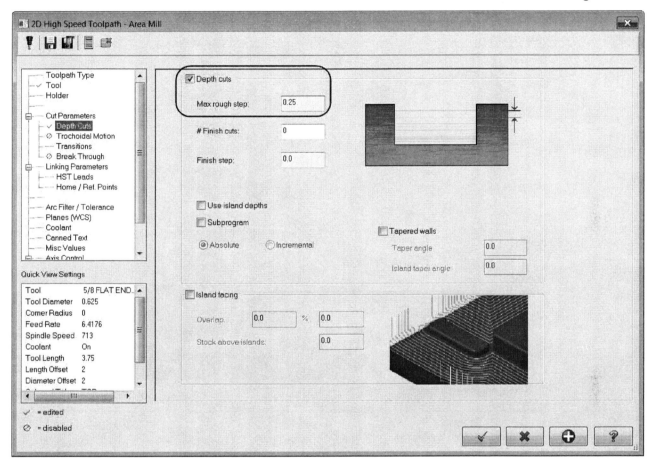

18.5 Set the Transitions

◆ Enable **Profile ramp** and enter a **Preferred Profile length** of **0.75** as shown in <u>Figure: 18.5.1</u>.

Figure: 18.5.1

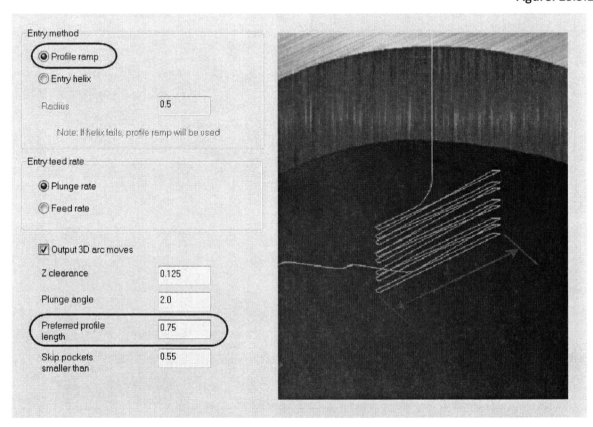

Profile Ramp creates a ramp motion to descend the tool.

Preferred profile length enters a minimum size for the profile in order for a ramp to be created.

18.6 Set the Linking Parameters

• Select **Linking Parameters** from the **Tree view list**.
• Select the **Top of Stock** button (this will return you to the graphics screen).

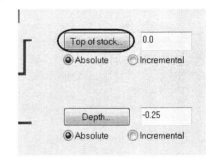

• Pick the line endpoint as shown in <u>Figure: 18.6.1</u>.

Figure: 18.6.1

• Choose the **Depth** button (this will return you to the graphics screen).
• Pick the line endpoint as shown in <u>Figure: 18.6.2</u>.

Figure: 18.6.2

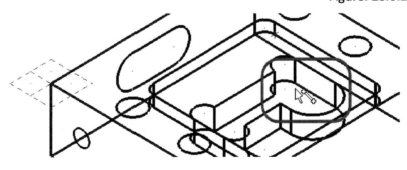

◆ **Top of Stock will be** set to **-0.25** and the **Depth** set to **-0.75** as shown in Figure: 18.6.3.

Figure: 18.6.3

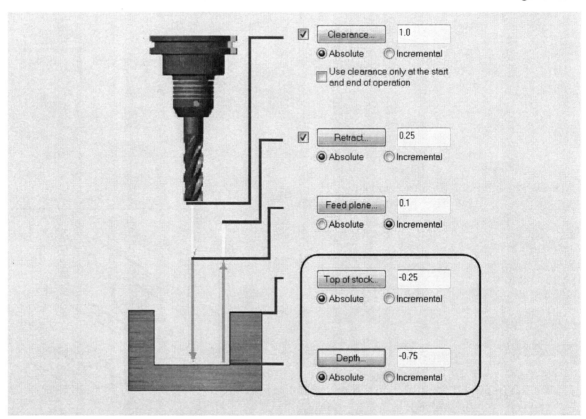

◆ Select the **OK** button to generate the **Area Mill** toolpath.
◆ Choose to **Regenerate all dirty operations**.

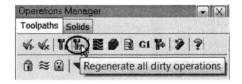

18.7 Backplot the toolpath

• Once the operation has been regenerated **Backplot** the toolpath. See page 512 to review these procedures.

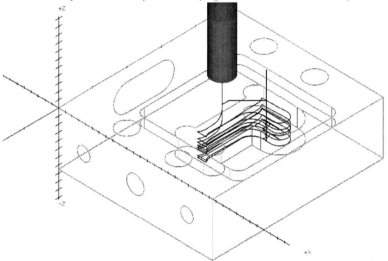

• To go back to Mastercam window, minimize **Backplot** window as shown.

18.8 Verify the toolpaths

• To verify all toolpaths, from the **Toolpaths Operations Manager**, choose the **Select all operations** icon.
• See page 513 to review these procedures.

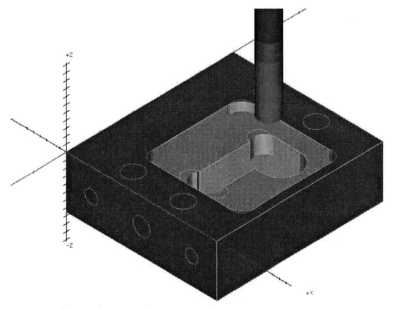

• To go back to Mastercam window, minimize **Verify** window as shown.

STEP 19: 2D HIGH SPEED REST MILL

2D High Speed Rest Mill toolpath targets material left behind by previous toolpaths.

Toolpath Preview:

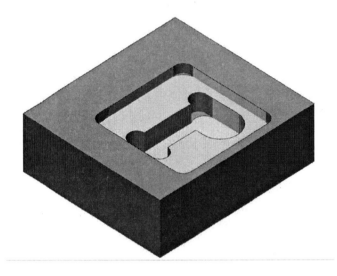

19.1 Copy the previous Toolpaths

• Pick the **Select all operations** button.

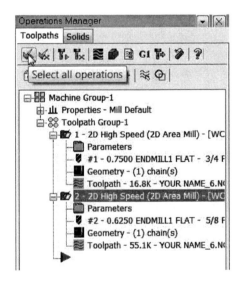

NOTE: Both toolpaths should be selected as shown.

◆ Right click and hold the right mouse button down and drag the operation to a point below it as shown in <u>Figure: 19.1.1</u>.

Figure: 19.1.1

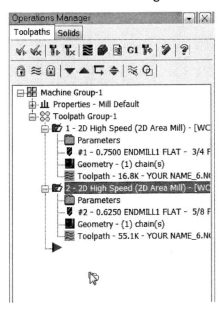

◆ Release the right mouse button and select the option **Copy After** as shown in <u>Figure: 19.1.2</u>.

Figure: 19.1.2

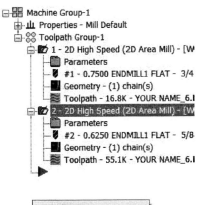

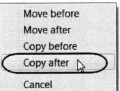

◆ Pick the button twice to move the insert arrow down as shown in <u>Figure: 19.1.3</u>.

Figure: 19.1.3

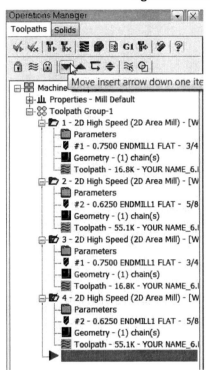

Insert Arrow controls where the new operation will be inserted.

19.2 2D High Speed Rest Mill

• Choose **Parameters** under operation #3.

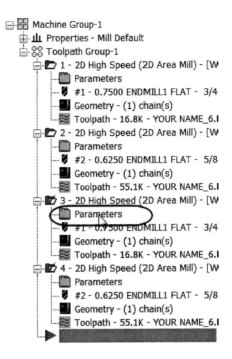

• Select **Toolpath Type** from the **Tree view list** and pick **Rest Mill.**

Core Mill   Peel Mill   Blend Mill   Area Mill   Rest Mill   Dynamic Area Mill

Dynamic Rest Mill   Dynamic Core Mill   Dynamic Contour

19.3 Select a 3/8" Flat Endmill from the Library and set the Tool parameters

◆ Select **Tool** from the **Tree view list**.

◆ Click on the **Select library tool** button.

◆ Select the **Filter** button.

◆ Select the **None** button and then under **Tool Types** choose the **Flat Endmill** Icon.

◆ Under tool diameter pick **Equal** and input a value of **0.375** as shown in Figure: 19.3.1.

Figure: 19.3.1

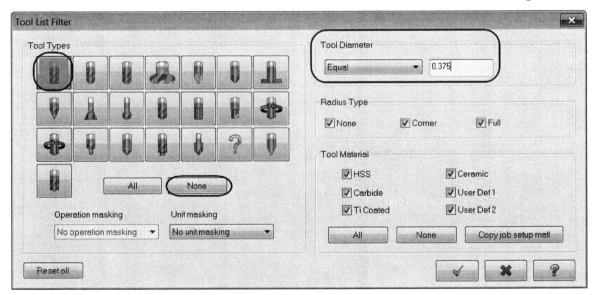

◆ Select the **OK** button to exit the **Tool List Filter.**

◆ In the **Tool Selection** dialog box you should only see a **3/8" Flat Endmill**.

#	Assembly Name	Tool Name	Holder Name	Dia.	Cor. rad.	Length	# Flutes	Type	Rad. Type
237	–	3/8 FLAT...	–	0...	0.0	0.75	4	En...	None

◆ Select the **3/8" Flat Endmill** in the **Tool Selection** page and then select the **OK** button to exit.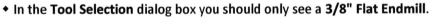

◆ Make the necessary changes as shown in <u>Figure: 19.3.2</u>.

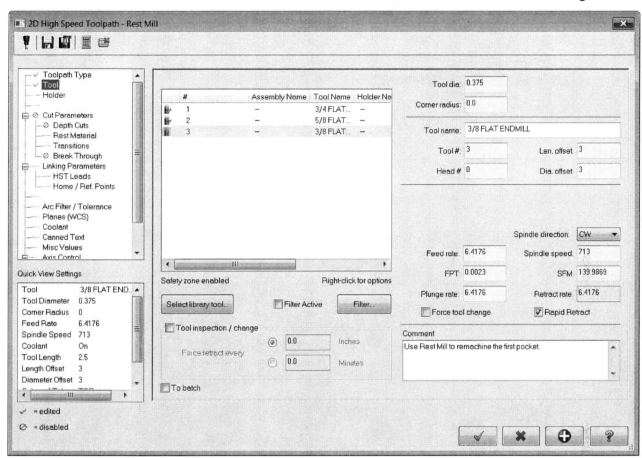

19.4 Set the Cut Parameters

♦ Ensure your parameters appear the same as shown in <u>Figure: 19.4.1</u>.

Figure: 19.4.1

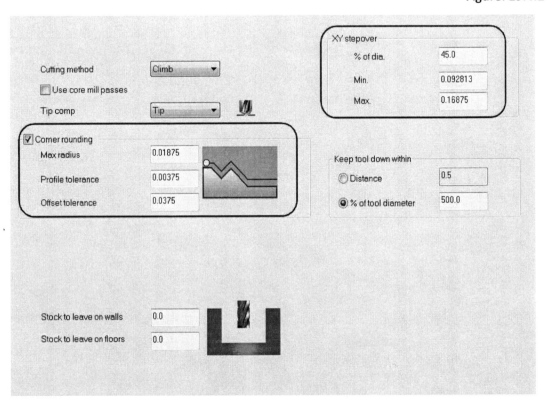

♦ Choose the **OK** button to generate the toolpath.

NOTE: Since this toolpath has been copied all the parameters remain the same. Therefore we do not have to view all the parameters.

19.5 Repeat the same steps for operation #4

♦ Regenerate the dirty operations.

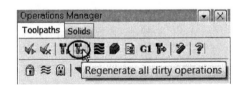

Mill Level 1 Training Tutorial

*Mastercam. X*⁷

19.6 Backplot and Verify the toolpaths

* To **Backplot** both toolpaths see page 512.
* To select both operations, hold down the **Ctrl** key.
* The toolpaths should look as shown.

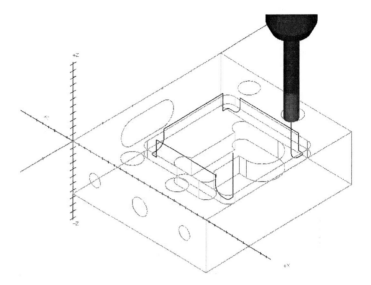

* To go back to Mastercam window, minimize **Backplot** window as shown.

* To **Verify** make sure that all toolpaths are selected by choosing the **Select all operations** icon.
* See page 513 for more information.

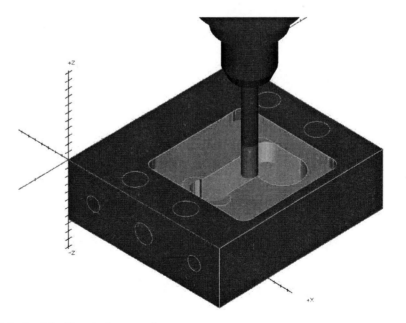

* To go back to Mastercam window, minimize **Verify** window as shown.

STEP 20: SPOT DRILL THE HOLE

Spot Drilling the holes allows you to start the hole. In this operation we will use the spot drill to chamfer the hole before drilling it.

Toolpath Preview:

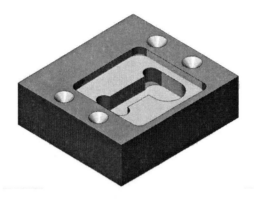

Toolpaths

• 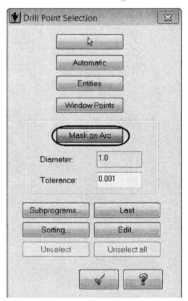 Drill.

• In the **Drill Point Selection** dialog box choose the option **Mask on Arc** as shown in Figure: 20.0.1.

Figure: 20.0.1

◆ Select the circle as shown in <u>Figure: 20.0.2</u>.

Figure: 20.0.2

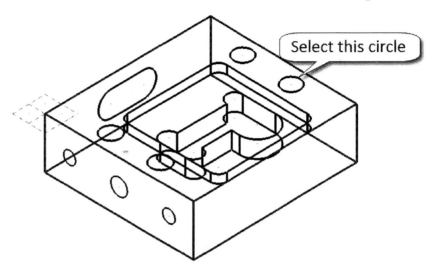

◆ Create a window around your part selecting all your entities as shown in <u>Figure: 20.0.3</u>.

Figure: 20.0.3

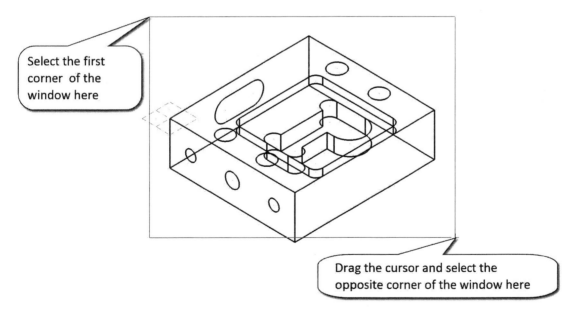

Select the first corner of the window here

Drag the cursor and select the opposite corner of the window here

◆ Hit **Enter** once the entities have been selected.

NOTE: Mask on Arc picks all the arcs on your screen but will only create a toolpath based on the first arc you selected, in our case being the **9/16"** diameter circle.

* In the **Drill Point Selection** dialog box pick the **Sorting** button.

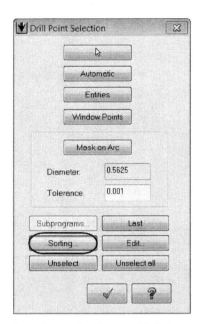

* When the **Sorting** dialog box appears choose the **Point to Point** sorting method as shown in <u>Figure: 20.0.4</u>.

Figure: 20.0.4

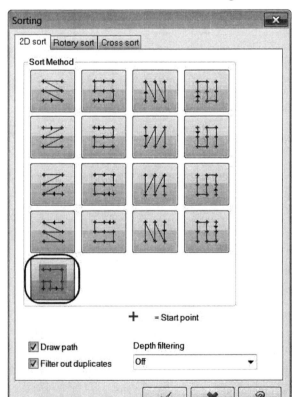

Sorting sets the drilling order for a set of points.

2D Sorting sorts points when distributed in a flat plane. The **Point to Point** option sorts points by the shortest distance from one point to the next.

Rotary sorting is used for circular patterns.

Cross sorting is used when points are wrapped around a cylinder. It will order the points based on an axis selection.

* Pick the **OK** button to exit the **Sorting** dialog box.

• [Select sorting start point]: Select the circle center point as shown in Figure: 20.0.5.

Figure: 20.0.5

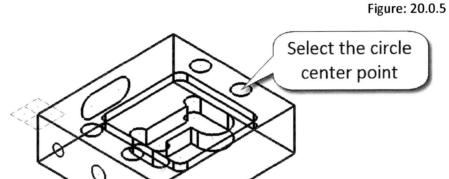

Select the circle center point

• Select the **OK** button in the **Drill Point Selection** dialog box once you have picked the arc.
• In the **Toolpath Type** page, the **Drill** toolpath will be selected.

Drill   Circle Mill   Point   Helix Bore   Thread Mill

20.1 Select a 3/4"Spot Drill from the Library and set the Tool Parameters

• Select **Tool** from the **Tree view list**.

• Click on the **Select library tool** button.
• To be able to see just the spot drill select the **Filter** button.

- Under **Tool Types** select the **None** button and then choose the **Spot drill** icon.
- Ensure the **Diameter** is set to **0.75** as shown in Figure: 20.1.1.

Figure: 20.1.1

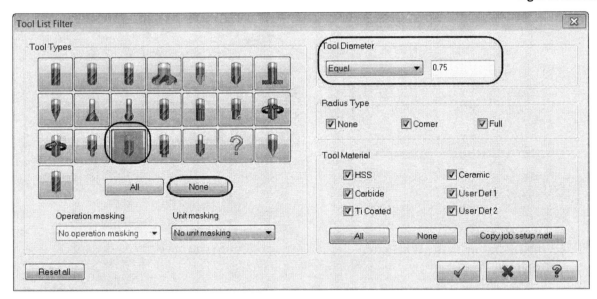

- Select the **OK** button to exit the **Tool List Filter** dialog box.
- Select the **3/4" Spot Drill**.

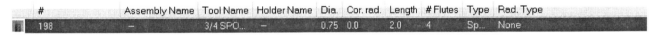

#	Assembly Name	Tool Name	Holder Name	Dia.	Cor. rad.	Length	# Flutes	Type	Rad. Type
198	–	3/4 SPO...	–	0.75	0.0	2.0	4	Sp...	None

- Select the tool in the **Tool Selection** page and then select the **OK** button to exit.

◆ Make the necessary changes to the **Tool** page as shown in Figure: 20.1.2.

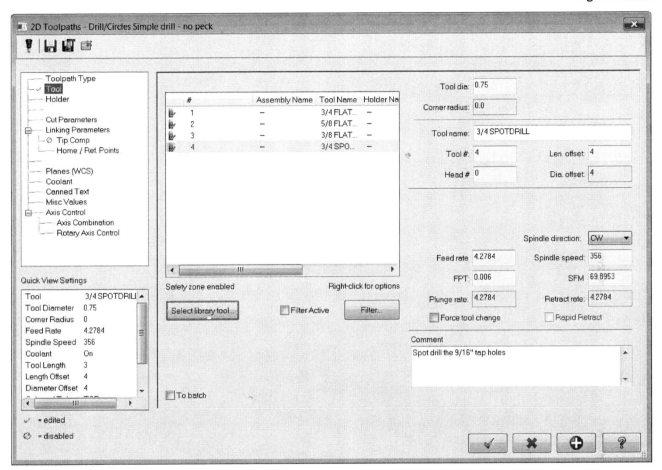

20.2 Set the Cut Parameters

◆ Select **Cut Parameters** and make the necessary changes as shown in <u>Figure: 20.2.1</u>.

Figure: 20.2.1

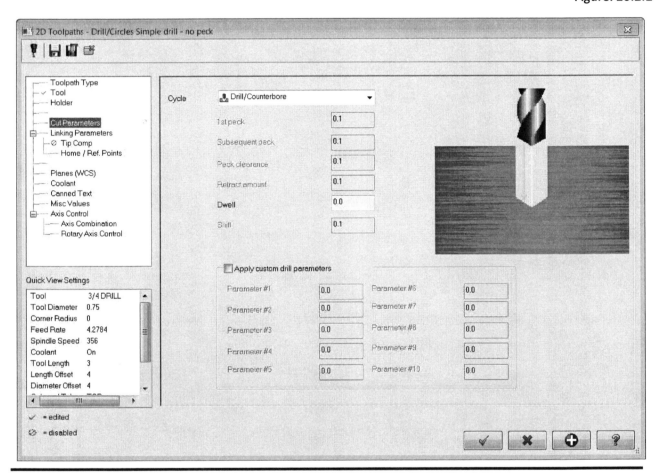

Drill/Counterbore is recommended for drilling holes with depths of less than three times the tools diameter.

Dwell sets the amount of time in seconds that the tool remains at the bottom of a drilled hole.

20.3 Set the Linking Parameters

◆ Choose **Linking Parameters**, ensure clearance is enabled and set the **Top of stock** and the **Depth** to **Absolute** and **0**.

◆ To input the depth select the **Calculator** icon.

◆ Input the following equation in the **Finish diameter** area: **9/16 + 0.05** as shown in <u>Figure: 20.3.1</u> and hit **Enter** to calculate the **Depth.**

Figure: 20.3.1

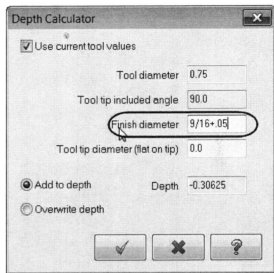

◆ Select the **OK** button to exit the **Depth Calculator.**

• You will now see the depth we calculated for the spot drilling operation set in the **Depth** field as shown in Figure: 20.3.2.

• This will chamfer the hole for the tapping operation.

Figure: 20.3.2

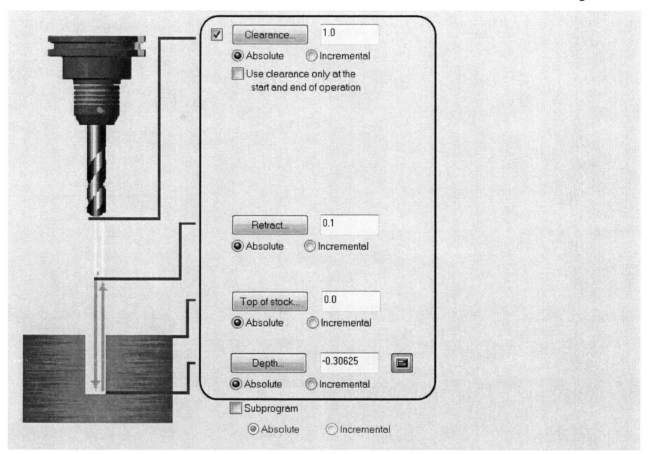

• Select the **OK** button to exit the **Drill/Counterbore** parameters.

20.4 Backplot and Verify the toolpaths

* To **Backplot** and **Verify** your toolpaths see page 512 and page 513.

* To verify all toolpaths, from the **Toolpaths Operations Manager**, choose the **Select all operations** icon.
* The part should look as shown.

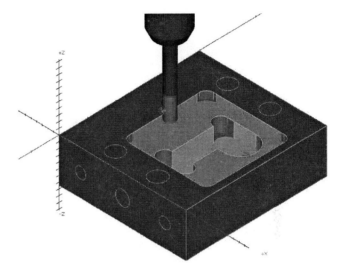

STEP 21: DRILL THE HOLES

In this example we will drill the holes through the part.

Toolpath Preview:

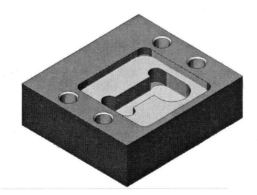

Toolpaths

♦ **Drill.**

♦ In the **Drill Point Selection** dialog box choose the option **Last**.

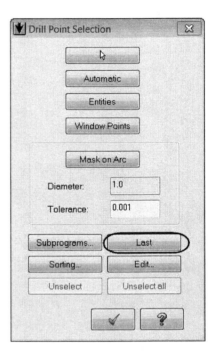

NOTE: This option will automatically select the hole for you based off the selection from the previous drill operation.

♦ Select the **OK** button in the **Drill Point Selection** dialog box to accept the 4 drill points.

♦ In the **Toolpath Type** page, the Drill toolpath will be selected.

Drill   Circle Mill   Point   Helix Bore   Thread Mill

21.1 Select a 33/64" Drill from the Library and set the Tool Parameters

♦ Select **Tool** from the **Tree view list**.

♦ Click on the **Select library tool** button. `Select library tool...`

♦ To be able to see just the spot drill select the **Filter** button.

Filter Active
367 of 367 tools

- Under **Tool Types** select the **None** button and then choose the **Drill** icon as shown in Figure: 21.1.1.
- Under **Tool Diameter** select **Equal** and enter the value **33/64** as shown in Figure: 21.1.1.

Figure: 21.1.1

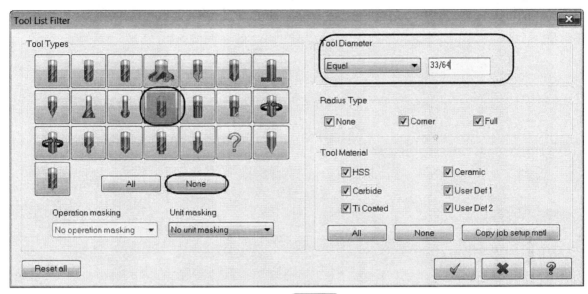

- Select the **OK** button to exit the **Tool List Filter** dialog box.
- At this point you should see only a **33/64"**drill.
- From that list select the **33/64" Drill** as shown in Figure: 21.1.2.

Figure: 21.1.2

#	Assembly Name	Tool Name	Holder Name	Dia.	Cor. rad.	Length	# Flutes	Type	Rad. Type
142	—	33/64 D...	—	0....	0.0	2.0	2	Drill	None

- Select the tool in the **Tool Selection** page and then choose the **OK** button to exit.

• Make the necessary changes to the **Tool** page as shown in Figure: 21.1.3.

Figure: 21.1.3

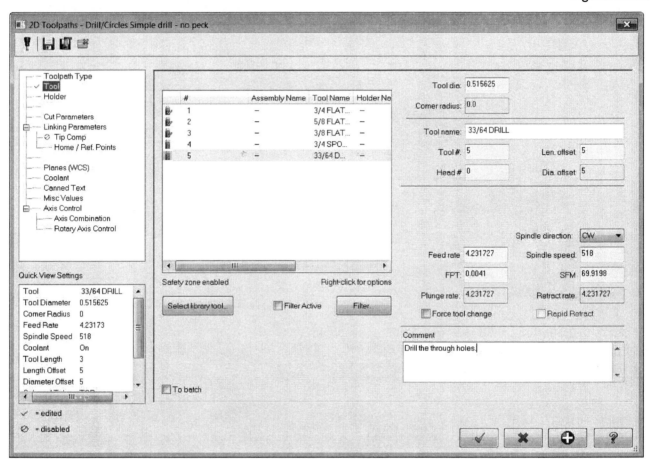

21.2 Set the Cut Parameters

- Select **Cut Parameters**, change the drill **Cycle** to **Peck Drill** and input a **1st peck** value of **0.25** as shown in Figure: 21.2.1.

Figure: 21.2.1

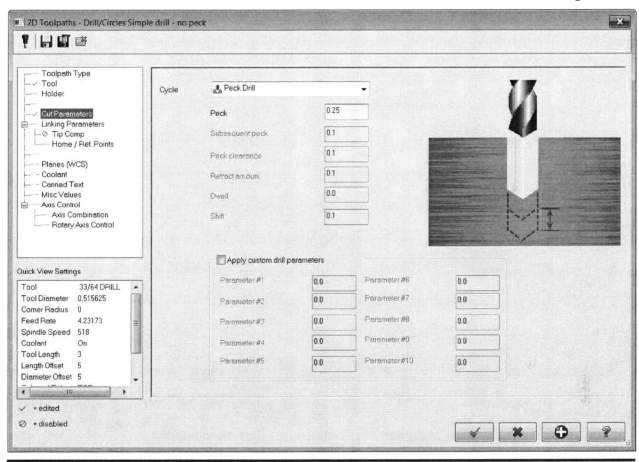

Peck Drill is recommended for drilling holes with depths of more than three times the tool diameter. The drill retracts fully out of the drilled hole to remove material.

Peck sets the depth for the peck move.

21.3 Set the Linking Parameters

• Choose **Linking Parameters** and input a **depth** value of **-1.5** as shown in <u>Figure: 21.3.1</u>.

Figure: 21.3.1

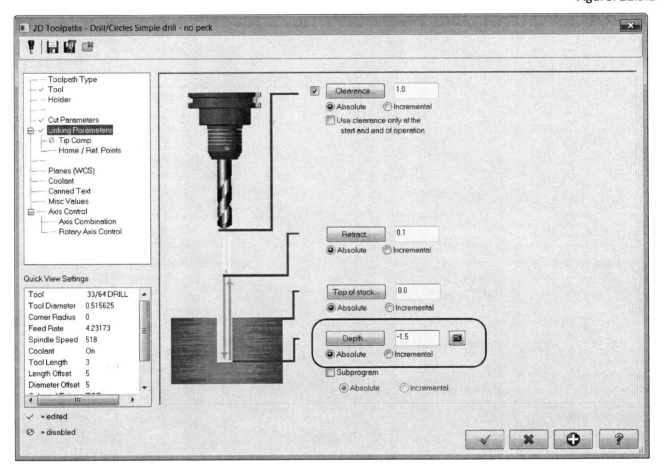

21.4 Set the Tip Comp Parameters

◆ Pick **Tip Comp** and enable this option. Input a **Breakthrough amount** of **0.1** as shown in <u>Figure: 21.4.1</u>.

Figure: 21.4.1

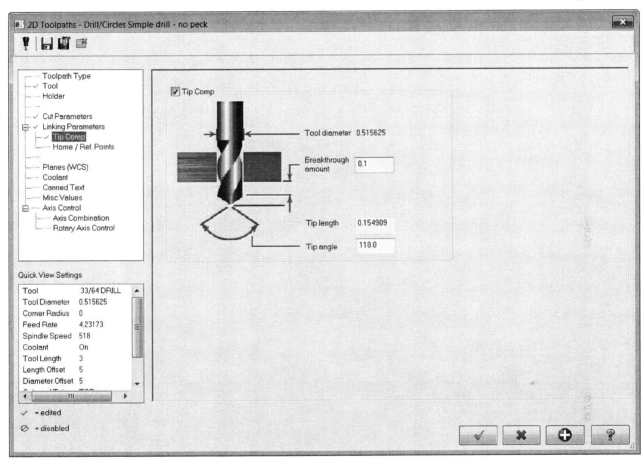

◆ Select the **OK** button to exit the **Drill/Counterbore** parameters.

21.5 Backplot and Verify

♦ To **Backplot** and **Verify** the toolpaths see page 512 and page 513.

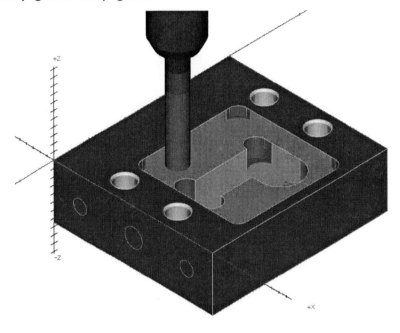

STEP 22: TAP THE HOLES

Tap cycle taps right or left internal threaded holes.

Toolpath Preview:

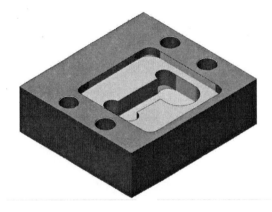

Toolpaths

- **Drill.**
- In the **Drill Point Selection** dialog box choose the option **Last**.

> **NOTE:** This option will automatically select the hole for you based off the selection from the previous drill operation.

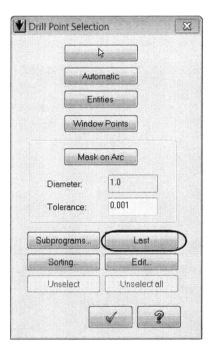

- Select the **OK** button in the **Drill Point Selection** dialog box to accept the 4 drill points.

- In the **Toolpath Type** page, the **Drill** toolpath will be selected.

Drill Circle Mill Point Helix Bore Thread Mill

22.1 Select a 9/16 - 18 RH Tap from the Library and set the Tool Parameters

- Select **Tool** from the **Tree view** list.

- Click on the **Select library tool** button.
- To be able to see just the spot drill select the **Filter** button.

- Under **Tool Types** select the **None** button and then choose the **Tap RH** icon. Under **Tool Diameter** select **Equal** and enter the value **9/16** as shown in Figure: 22.1.1.

Figure: 22.1.1

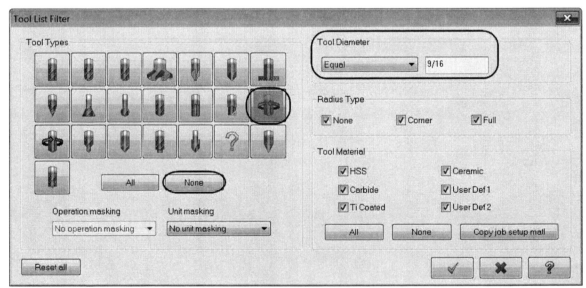

- Select **OK** button to exit the **Tool List Filter** dialog box.
- At this point you should see a list full of taps.
- From that list, select the **9/16 - 18 Tap RH** as shown.

#	Assembly Name	Tool Name	Holder Name	Dia.	Cor. rad.	Length	# Flutes	Type	Rad. Type
209	–	9/16-12 ...	–	0....	0.0	2.0	1	Ta...	None
210	–	9/16-18 ...	–	0....	0.0	2.0	1	Ta...	None

- Select the tool in the **Tool Selection** page and then choose the **OK** button to exit.

◆ Make the necessary changes to the **Tool** page as shown in <u>Figure: 22.1.2</u>.

Figure: 22.1.2

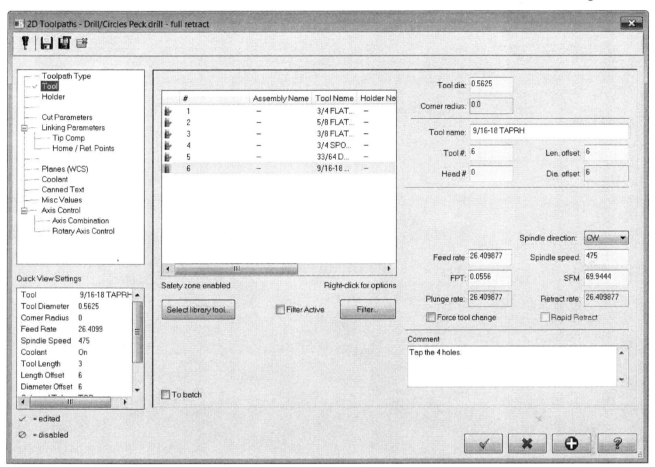

22.2 Set the Cut Parameters

♦ Select **Cut Parameters**, change the drill **Cycle** to **Tap** as shown in <u>Figure: 22.2.1</u>.

Figure: 22.2.1

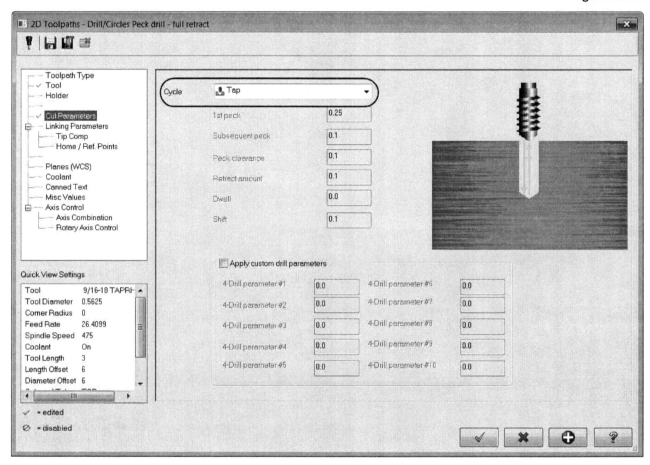

22.3 Set the Linking Parameters

◆ Choose **Linking Parameters** and input a **Depth** value of **-1.5** as shown in <u>Figure: 22.3.1</u>.

Figure: 22.3.1

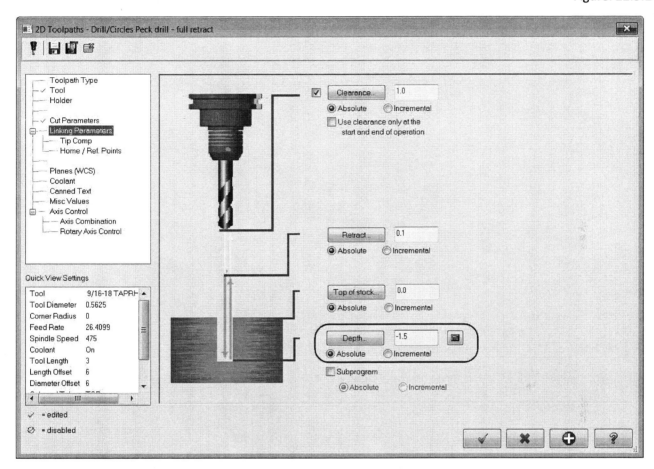

22.4 Set the Tip Comp Parameters

♦ Pick **Tip Comp** and enable this option.
♦ Input a **Break through amount** of **0.1** as shown in Figure: 22.4.1.

Figure: 22.4.1

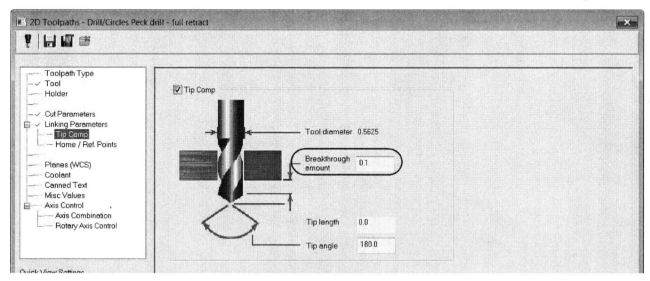

♦ Select the **OK** button to exit the **Drill/Counterbore** parameters.
♦ To **Backplot** and **Verify** the toolpaths see page 512 and page 513.

♦ To make sure that all toolpaths are selected, choose the **Select all operations** icon.

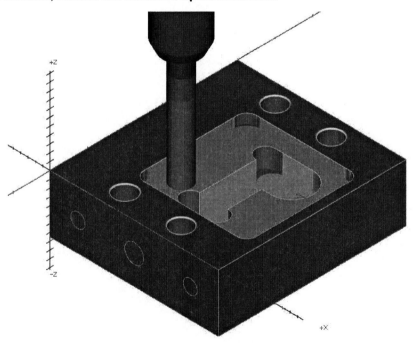

TOOLPATH CREATION - SETUP 2

SUGGESTED FIXTURE:

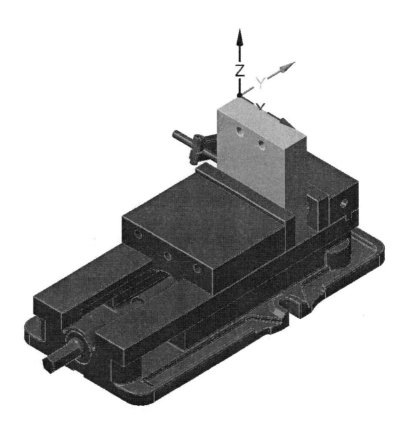

> **NOTE:** The part is now flipped over and we will machine the part from the **Front**.

SETUP SHEET:

TOOL LIST

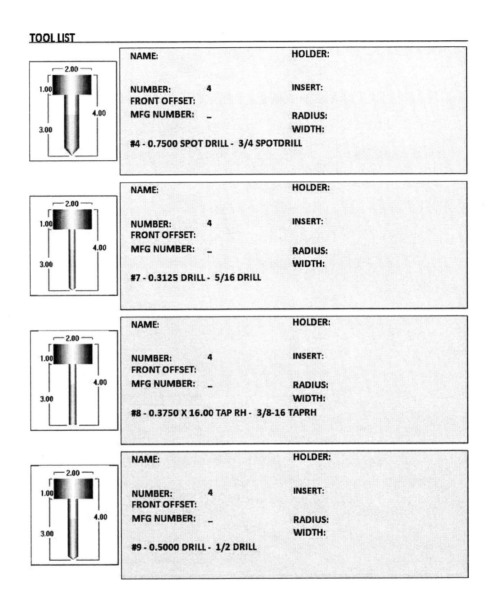

NAME: HOLDER:

NUMBER: 4   INSERT:
FRONT OFFSET:
MFG NUMBER: _   RADIUS:
                              WIDTH:

#4 - 0.7500 SPOT DRILL - 3/4 SPOTDRILL

NAME: HOLDER:

NUMBER: 4   INSERT:
FRONT OFFSET:
MFG NUMBER: _   RADIUS:
                              WIDTH:

#7 - 0.3125 DRILL - 5/16 DRILL

NAME: HOLDER:

NUMBER: 4   INSERT:
FRONT OFFSET:
MFG NUMBER: _   RADIUS:
                              WIDTH:

#8 - 0.3750 X 16.00 TAP RH - 3/8-16 TAPRH

NAME: HOLDER:

NUMBER: 4   INSERT:
FRONT OFFSET:
MFG NUMBER: _   RADIUS:
                              WIDTH:

#9 - 0.5000 DRILL - 1/2 DRILL

STEP 23: CREATING AND RENAMING TOOLPATH GROUPS

To machine the part in different setups, we will need to have separate programs. To be able to post the operations separate of each setup, we will create them under different toolpath groups with different NC names.

23.1 Rename the Current Toolpath Group - 1 and NC File

• Click on the Toolpath Group - 1 to highlight it and then click again to rename it "Setup #1."

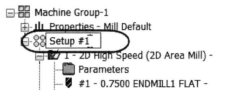

• Right mouse click on the toolpath group and select **Edit selected operations** and then, select **Change NC file name.**

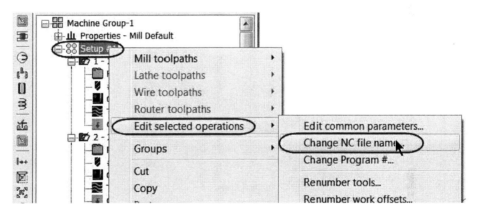

* Enter the new NC name: **"Setup #1."**

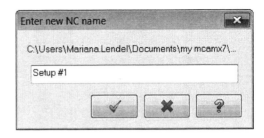

* Select the **OK** button to accept the new **NC name.**

23.2 Create a new Toolpath Group.

* Right mouse click on the **Machine Group 1.**
* From the list, select **Groups** and then **New Toolpath group** as shown.

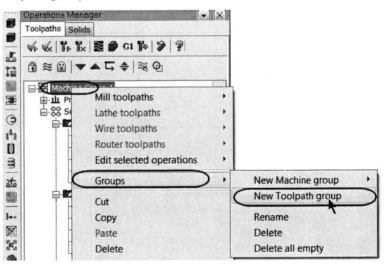

* Double click on the new **Toolpath Group 1** and rename it **"Setup #2 - Front."**

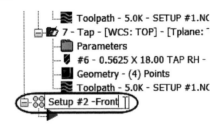

STEP 24: SET WCS TO FRONT

Work coordinate system (WCS) is the active coordinate system in use by Mastercam at any given time. The WCS contains the orientation of the X-Y-Z axes plus the location of the zero point (the origin). This tells Mastercam how your part is positioned or orientated in the machine.

◆ Select **WCS** located in the status bar.

◆ When the **WCS** menu appears select **"View Manager"** from it.

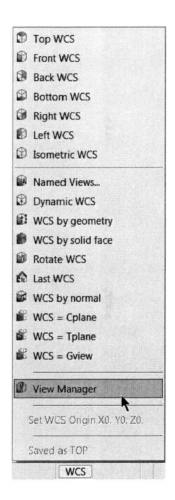

- When the **View Manager** dialog box appears pick **Front.**
- Set the **Work Coordinate System (WCS), Tool plane, Construction plane** to the **Front,** by selecting the equal icon as shown in Figure: 24.0.1.
- Enable and set the **Origin** as shown in Figure: 24.0.1.

Figure: 24.0.1

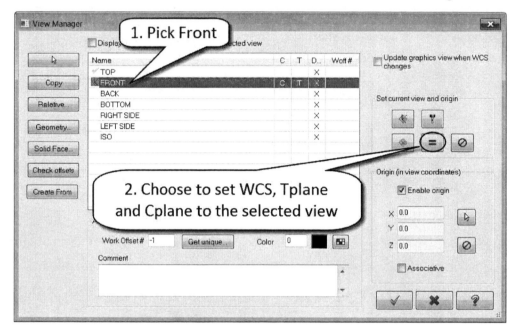

- Select the **OK** button to exit the **View Manager.**

- Pick the **Isometric graphics view** to see the part in its new orientation.
- Press **F9** on your keyboard to view the coordinate axes.

NOTE: The color of the coordinate axes remains the same because it is the same origin.

- Select the **Fit** icon.

◆ Your part should look as shown.

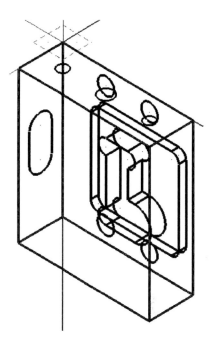

◆ Press **F9** again to remove the axes display.

STEP 25: SPOT DRILL ALL 3 HOLES

Toolpath Preview:

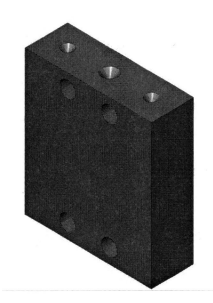

Toolpaths

◆ 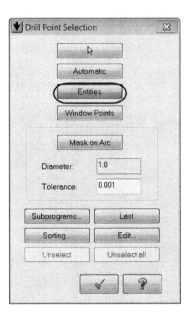**Drill.**

◆ In the **Drill Point Selection** dialog box choose the option **Entities** as shown.

◆ Select the 3 circles as shown in Figure: 25.0.1, then press **Enter**.

Figure: 25.0.1

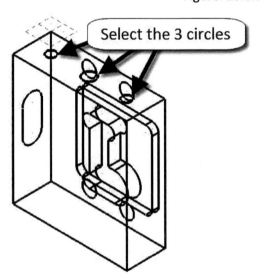

Select the 3 circles

◆ Press **Esc** to not have to select the sorting start point.

◆ Select the **OK** button in the **Drill Point Selection** dialog box once you have picked the arcs.

◆ In the **Toolpath Type** page, the **Drill** toolpath will be selected.

Drill

Circle Mill

Point

Helix Bore

Thread Mill

◆ Select the **3/4" Spot Drill** from the list.
◆ Make the necessary changes to the **Tool** page as shown in Figure: 25.0.2.

Figure: 25.0.2

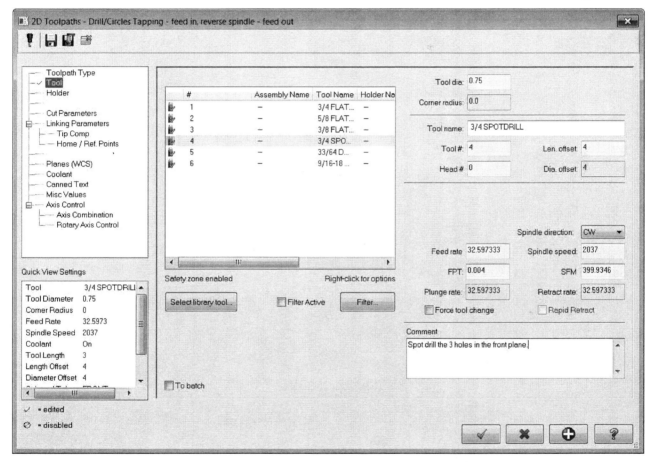

25.1 Set the Cut Parameters

♦ Select **Cut Parameters** and change the **Cycle** to **Drill/Counterbore** as shown in Figure: 25.1.1.

Figure: 25.1.1

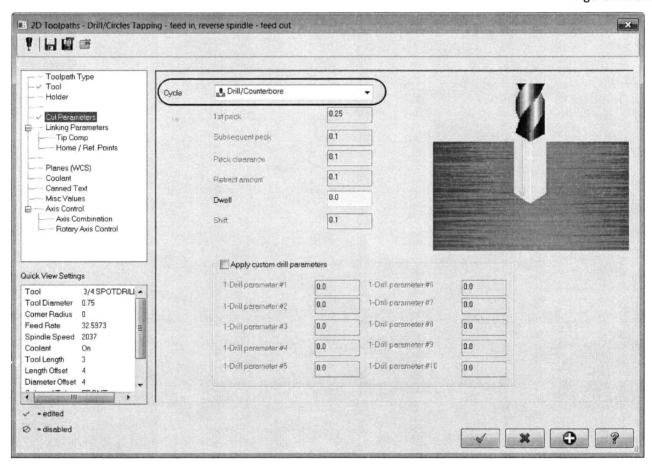

25.2 Set the Linking Parameters

- Choose **Linking Parameters**, ensure clearance is enabled and the **Top of stock** and **Depth** is set to **Absolute** and **0**.

- To input the **Depth** select the **Calculator** icon.
- Input the following equation in the **Finish diameter** area: **3/8+0.04** and hit **Enter** to calculate the **Depth** as shown in <u>Figure: 25.2.1</u>.

Figure: 25.2.1

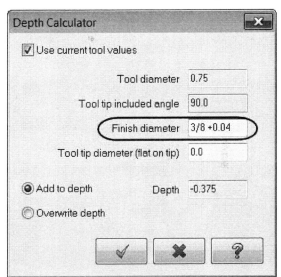

- Select the **OK** button to exit the **Depth Calculator**.

♦ You will now see the depth we calculated for the spot drilling operation set in the **Depth** field as shown in <u>Figure: 25.2.2</u>. This will chamfer the holes for the tapping operation.

Figure: 25.2.2

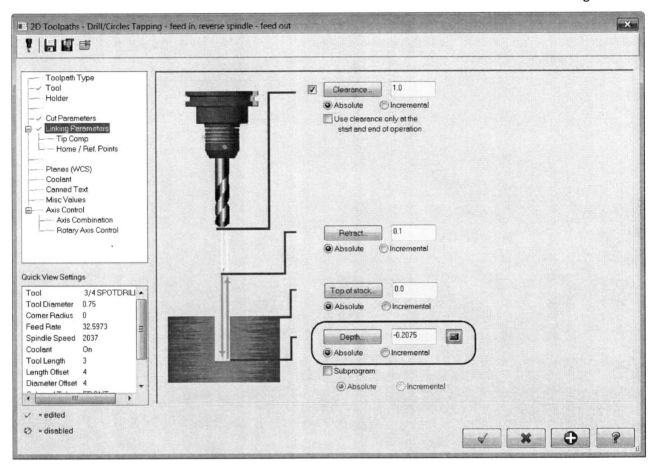

Mastercam X⁷

25.3 Set the Tip Comp

• Select **Tip Comp** and disable this option. If left enabled the holes would be drilled much deeper as shown in <u>Figure: 25.3.1</u>.

Figure: 25.3.1

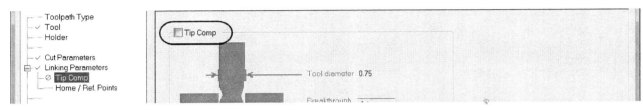

• Select the **OK** button to exit the **Drill/Counterbore** parameters and generate the toolpath.

> **NOTE:** All 3 holes are spot drilled to the same depth. The 0.5" diameter hole has to be drilled to a deeper depth.

25.4 Adjust the Depth of the Spot Drill

• Left click on **Geometry** in **Operation #8**.
• When the **Drill Point Manager** appears, select the point which represents the **0.5" diameter hole**.
• Click on the Point 2 to select it and then right click on it and pick the option to **Change at point** as shown in <u>Figure: 25.4.1</u>.

Figure: 25.4.1

◆ When the **Drill change at point** dialog box appears enable **Depth** and change the depth to **-0.27** as shown in <u>Figure: 25.4.2</u>.

Figure: 25.4.2

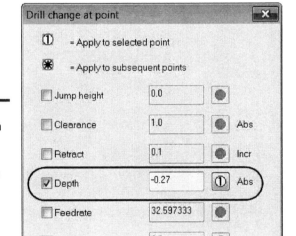

Drill Change At Point allows you to make point-specific changes to a drill toolpath.

Depth changes the hole depth at the selected point. The coordinate you enter here will be output as either an absolute or incremental value, depending on the original settings for the operation.

◆ Select the **OK** button to apply the changes and exit the dialog box.

◆ Choose the **OK** button to exit the **Drill Point Manager**.
◆ Pick the button **Regenerate all dirty operations**.

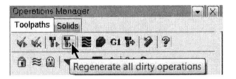

Mastercam X⁷

25.5 Backplot and Verify the toolpaths

◆ To **Backplot** and **Verify** your toolpaths see page 512 and page 513.

◆ To make sure that all toolpaths are selected, choose the **Select all operations** icon.

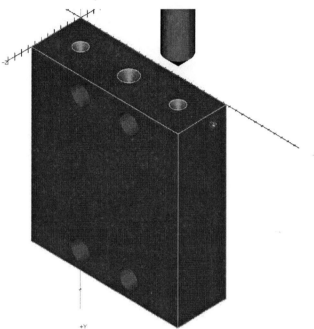

♦ When backplotting the toolpath, if you want to check the depth of the holes you can check the values in the **Move List** as shown in <u>Figure: 25.5.1</u>.

Figure: 25.5.1

NOTE: The depth value is the Y value 0.208 as the **Move Info** does not reflect the tool plane change. The Tool Orientation has the -1.000 which should be multiply with the 0.208 for a correct direction.

While backplotting the toolpath, in the **Move Info** section you will be able to see the coordinates of where the tool is located.

The **Toolpath Info** found under the **Move info** tab are related to cycle time and the distance the tool travels. The cycle time is based on your rapid rates and feed rates.

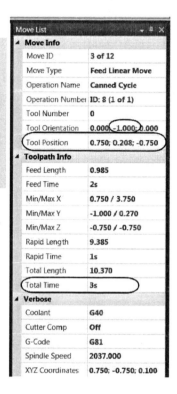

Move List	
◢ **Move Info**	
Move ID	**3 of 12**
Move Type	**Feed Linear Move**
Operation Name	**Canned Cycle**
Operation Number	**ID: 8 (1 of 1)**
Tool Number	**0**
Tool Orientation	**0.000; -1.000; 0.000**
Tool Position	**0.750; 0.208; -0.750**
◢ **Toolpath Info**	
Feed Length	**0.985**
Feed Time	**2s**
Min/Max X	**0.750 / 3.750**
Min/Max Y	**-1.000 / 0.270**
Min/Max Z	**-0.750 / -0.750**
Rapid Length	**9.385**
Rapid Time	**1s**
Total Length	**10.370**
Total Time	**3s**
◢ **Verbose**	
Coolant	**G40**
Cutter Comp	**Off**
G-Code	**G81**
Spindle Speed	**2037.000**
XYZ Coordinates	**0.750; -0.750; 0.100**

STEP 26: DRILL THE TWO 3/8" TAPPED HOLES

In this example we will drill the holes to a specific depth.

Toolpath Preview:

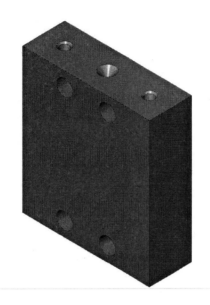

Toolpaths

• 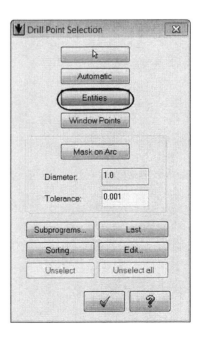 **Drill.**

• In the **Drill Point Selection** dialog box choose the option **Entities**.

NOTE: This option will let you select the arcs we wish to drill.

* Pick the arcs as shown in <u>Figure: 26.0.1</u>.

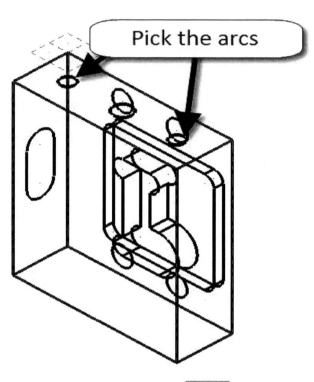

Pick the arcs

* Select the **OK** button in the **Drill Point Selection** dialog box to accept the 2 drill points.
* Press **Esc** to not have to select the sorting start point.
* In the **Toolpath Type** page, the **Drill** toolpath will be selected.

Drill   Circle Mill   Point   Helix Bore   Thread Mill

26.1 Select a 5/16" Drill from the Library and set the Tool Parameters

* Select **Tool** from the **Tree view list**.

* Click on the **Select library tool** button. Select library tool...
* To be able to see just the **5/16" Drill** select the **Filter** button.

Filter...
☐ Filter Active
367 of 367 tools

- Under **Tool Types** select the **None** button and then choose the **Drill** icon.
- Under **Tool Diameter** select **Equal** and enter the value **5/16** as shown in <u>Figure: 26.1.1</u>.

Figure: 26.1.1

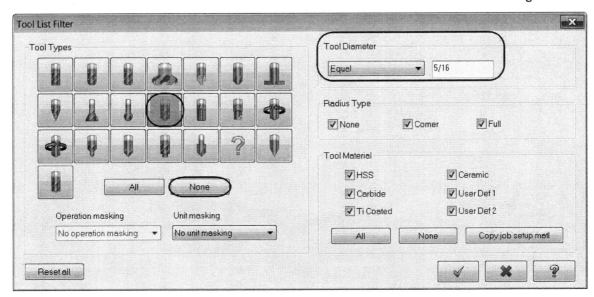

- Select the **OK** button to exit the **Tool List Filter** dialog box.
- At this point you should see only a **5/16" Drill**.
- Select the **5/16" Drill**.

#	Assembly Name	Tool Name	Holder Name	Dia.	Cor. rad.	Length	# Flutes	Type	Rad. Type
117	–	5/16 DRI...	–	0...	0.0	2.0	2	Drill	None

- Select the tool in the **Tool Selection** page and then choose the **OK** button to exit.

◆ Make the necessary changes to the **Tool** page as shown in Figure: 26.1.2.

Figure: 26.1.2

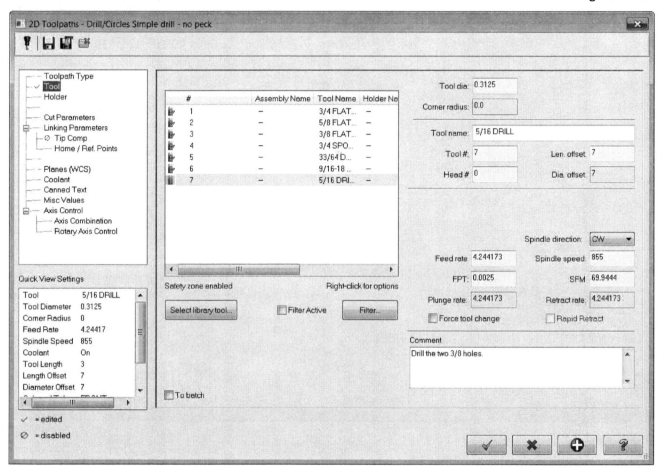

26.2 Set the Cut Parameters

◆ Select **Cut Parameters**, change the drill **Cycle** to **Peck Drill** and input a **1st peck** value of **0.25** as shown in
<u>Figure: 26.2.1</u>.

Figure: 26.2.1

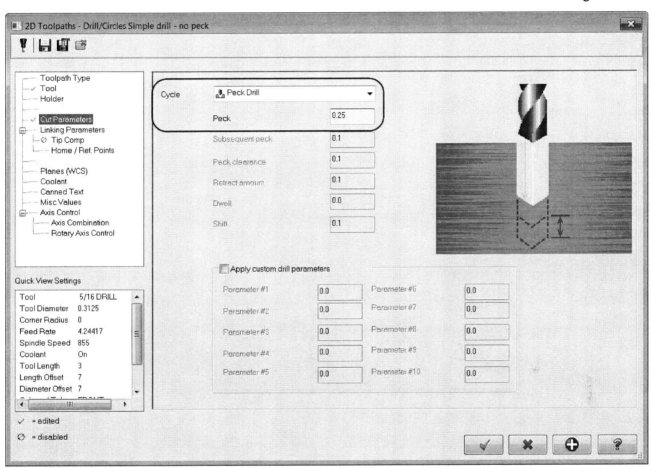

NOTE: For more information regarding the settings found on this page, see page 547.

26.3 Set the Linking Parameters

• Choose **Linking Parameters** and input a **Depth** value of **-1.25** as shown in <u>Figure: 26.3.1</u>.

Figure: 26.3.1

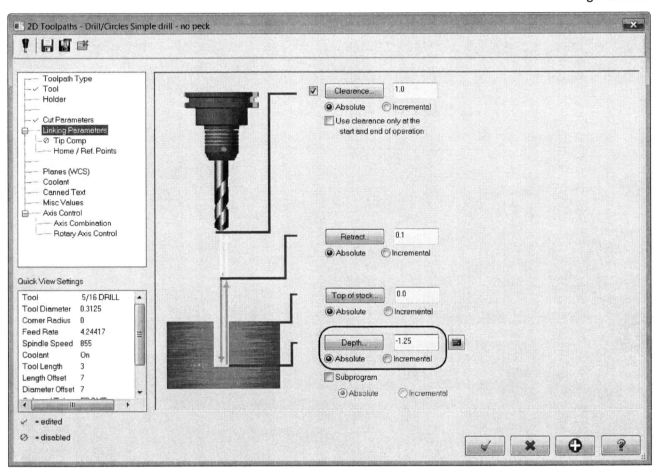

• Pick **Tip Comp** and ensure this option is disabled.

• Select the **OK** button to exit the **Peck Drill** parameters.

26.4 Backplot and Verify

♦ To **Backplot** and **Verify** the toolpaths see page 512 and page 513.

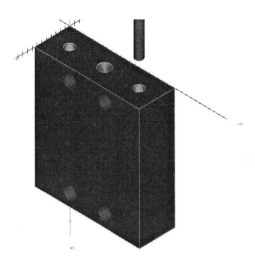

STEP 27: TAP THE TWO HOLES

Toolpath Preview:

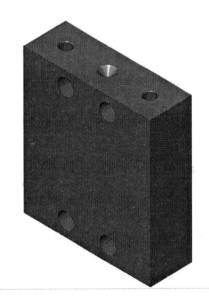

Toolpaths

* **Drill.**
* In the **Drill Point Selection** dialog box choose the option **Last.**

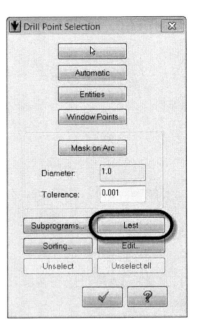

NOTE: This option will automatically select the hole for you based off the selection from the previous drill operation.

* Press **Esc** to not have to select the sorting start point.

* Select the **OK** button in the **Drill Point Selection** dialog box to accept the **2 drill points**.
* In the **Toolpath Type** page, the **Drill** toolpath will be selected.

Drill   Circle Mill   Point   Helix Bore   Thread Mill

27.1 Select a 3/8 - 16 RH Tap from the Library and set the Tool Parameters

* Select **Tool** from the **Tree view list**.

* Click on the **Select library tool** button.
* To be able to see just the spot drill select the **Filter** button.

Filter Active
367 of 367 tools

* Under **Tool Types** select the **None** button and then choose the **Tap RH** Icon. Under **Tool Diameter** make sure the the **Equal** option is selected and enter the diameter **3/8** as shown in Figure: 27.1.1.

Figure: 27.1.1

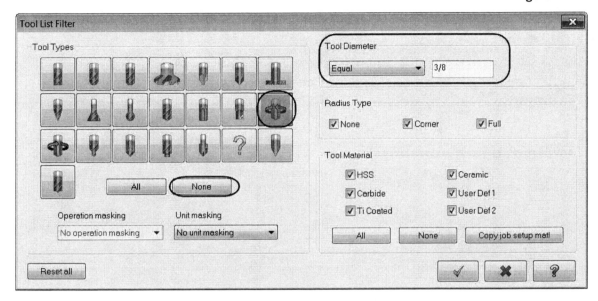

* Select **OK** button to exit the **Tool List Filter** dialog box.
* From the list select the **3/8 - 16 Tap RH** as shown in Figure: 27.1.2.

Figure: 27.1.2

#	Assembly Name	Tool Name	Holder Name	Dia.	Cor. rad.	Length	# Flutes	Type	Rad. Type
203	–	3/8-16 T...	–	0...	0.0	2.0	1	Ta...	None
204	–	3/8-24 T...	–	0....	0.0	2.0	1	Ta...	None

* Select the tool in the **Tool Selection** page and then choose the **OK** button to exit.

• Make the necessary changes to the **Tool** page as shown in <u>Figure: 27.1.3</u>.

Figure: 27.1.3

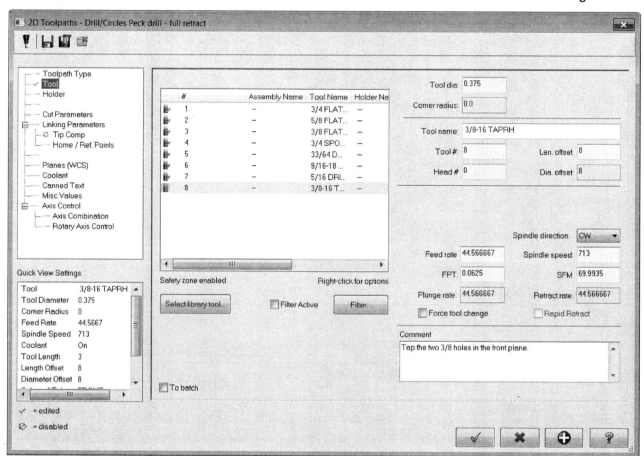

27.2 Set the Cut Parameters

• Select **Cut Parameters**, change the drill **Cycle** to **Tap** as shown in <u>Figure: 27.2.1</u>.

Figure: 27.2.1

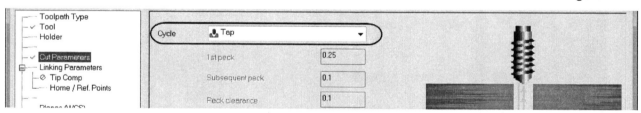

27.3 Set the Linking Parameters

◆ Choose **Linking Parameters** and input a **Depth** of **-1.0** as shown in <u>Figure: 27.3.1</u>.

Figure: 27.3.1

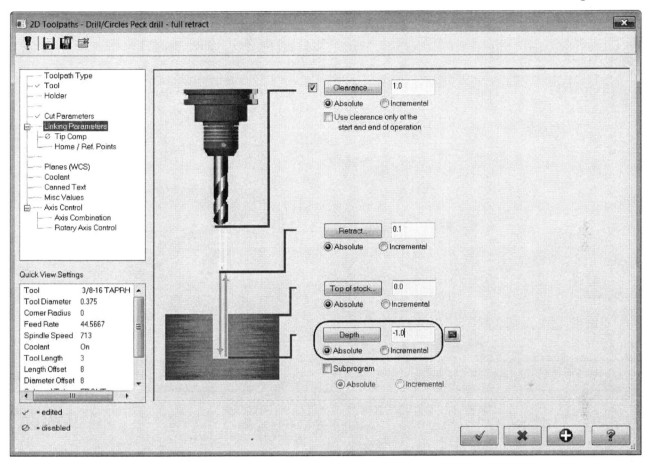

◆ Pick **Tip Comp** and ensure this option is disabled. The **Depth** set in the **Linking Parameters** page is as deep as we would like the tap to go.

◆ Select the **OK** button to exit the **Tap** parameters.

27.4 Backplot and Verify

◆ To **Backplot** and **Verify** the toolpaths see page 512 and page 513.

◆ To make sure that all toolpaths are selected, choose the **Select all operations** icon.

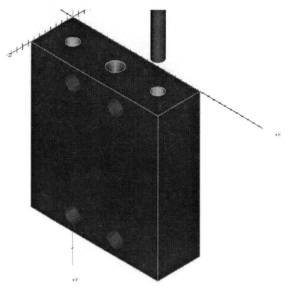

STEP 28: DRILL THE 1/2" HOLE

You will drill the holes to a specific depth.

Toolpath Preview:

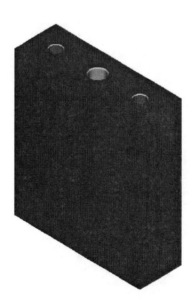

Toolpaths

• **Drill.**

• In the **Drill Point Selection** dialog box choose the option **Entities** as shown in <u>Figure: 28.0.1</u>.

Figure: 28.0.1

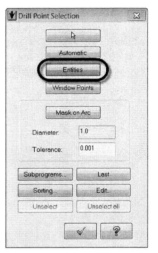

• This option will let you select the arcs we wish to drill. Pick the arc as shown in <u>Figure: 28.0.2</u>.

Figure: 28.0.2

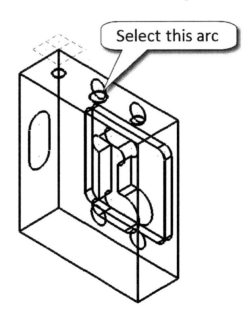

Select this arc

• Press **Enter**.

• Select the **OK** button in the **Drill Point Selection** dialog box to accept the 1 drill point.

- In the **Toolpath Type** page, the **Drill** toolpath will be selected.

Drill   Circle Mill   Point   Helix Bore   Thread Mill

28.1 Select a 1/2" Drill from the Library and set the Tool Parameters

- Select **Tool** from the **Tree view list**.

- Click on **Select library tool** button. [Select library tool...]
- To be able to see just the **1/2" Drill** select the **Filter** button.

- Under **Tool Types** select the **None** button and then choose the **drill** Icon. Under **Tool Diameter** select **Equal** and enter the value **0.5** as shown in Figure: 28.1.1.

Figure: 28.1.1

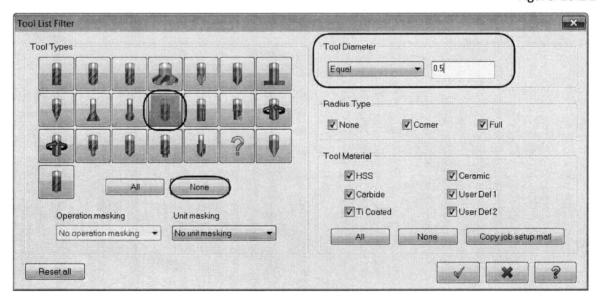

- Select the **OK** button to exit the **Tool List Filter** dialog box.
- Select the **1/2 Drill**.

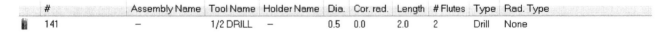

#	Assembly Name	Tool Name	Holder Name	Dia.	Cor. rad.	Length	# Flutes	Type	Rad. Type
141	–	1/2 DRILL	–	0.5	0.0	2.0	2	Drill	None

- Select the tool in the **Tool Selection** page and then choose the **OK** button to exit.

• Make the necessary changes to the **Tool** page as shown in <u>Figure: 28.1.2</u>.

Figure: 28.1.2

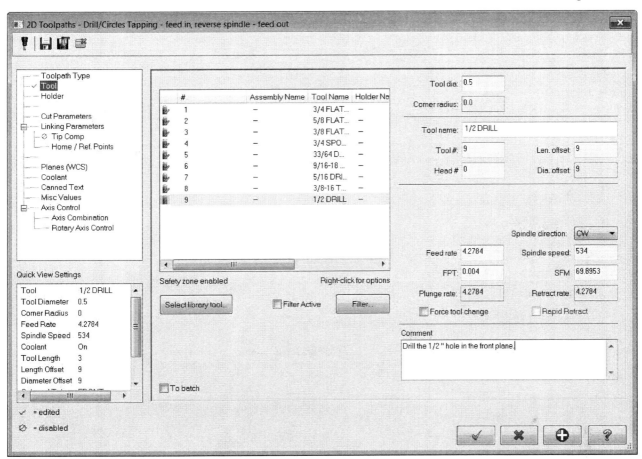

28.2 Set the Cut Parameters

◆ Select **Cut Parameters**, change the drill **Cycle** to **Chip Break** and input a **Peck** of **0.25** as shown in Figure: 28.2.1.

Figure: 28.2.1

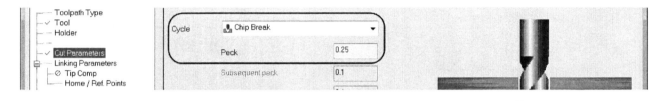

Chip Break retracts partially out of the drilled hole to break the material chips.

28.3 Set the Linking Parameters

◆ Choose **Linking Parameters** and input a **Depth** value of **-0.55** as shown in Figure: 28.3.1.

Figure: 28.3.1

◆ Pick **Tip Comp** and ensure this option is disabled.

◆ Select the **OK** button to exit the **Drill/Counterbore** parameters.

28.4 Backplot and Verify

♦ To **Backplot** and **Verify** the toolpaths see page 512 and page 513.

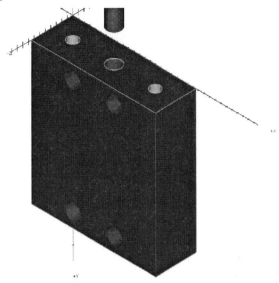

STEP 29: COUNTERBORE THE 1/2" HOLE

Counterbore hole in this example you will drill the holes to a specific depth using a 1/2 Flat endmill to give us a flat bottom hole.

Toolpath Preview:

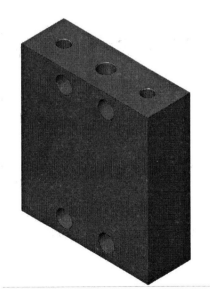

Toolpaths

♦ 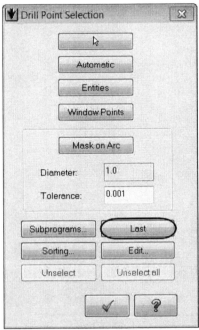 **Drill.**

♦ In the **Drill Point Selection** dialog box choose the option **Last** as shown in <u>Figure: 29.0.1</u>.

Figure: 29.0.1

♦ This option will automatically select the hole for you based off the selection from the previous drill operation.

♦ Select the **OK** button in the **Drill Point Selection** dialog box to accept the drill point.

♦ In the **Toolpath Type** page, the **Drill** toolpath will be selected.

Drill   Circle Mill   Point   Helix Bore   Thread Mill

29.1 Select a 1/2" Flat Endmill from the Library and set the Tool Parameters

♦ Select **Tool** from the **Tree view list**.

♦ Click on **Select library tool** button.

♦ To be able to see just the **flat endmill** select the **Filter** button.

Filter Active
367 of 367 tools

• Under **Tool Types** select the **None** button and then choose the **Flat Endmill** icon. Under **Tool Diameter** select **Equal** and enter the value **0.5** as shown in <u>Figure: 29.1.1</u>.

Figure: 29.1.1

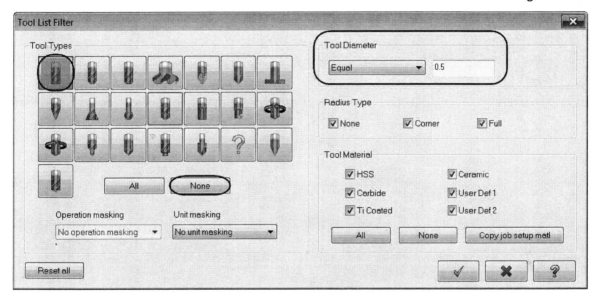

• Select the **OK** button to exit the **Tool List Filter** dialog box.
• Select the **1/2" Flat Endmill** as shown in <u>Figure: 29.1.2</u>.

Figure: 29.1.2

#	Assembly Name	Tool Name	Holder Name	Dia.	Cor. rad.	Length	# Flutes	Type	Rad. Type
239	—	1/2 FLAT...	—	0.5	0.0	1.0	4	En...	None

• Select the tool in the **Tool Selection** page and then choose the **OK** button to exit.

♦ Make the necessary changes to the **Tool** page as shown in <u>Figure: 29.1.3</u>.

Figure: 29.1.3

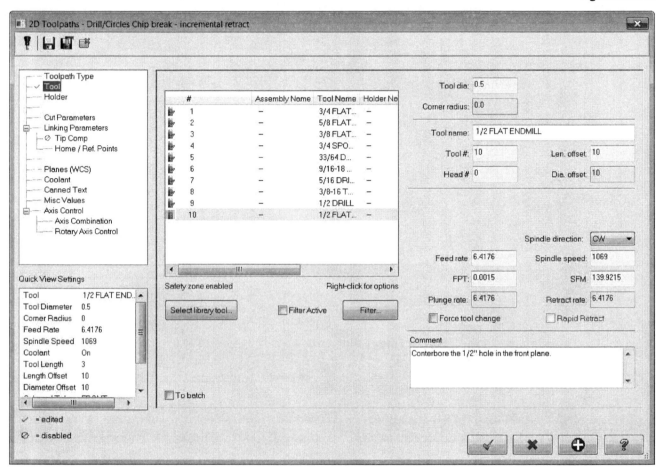

29.2 Set the Cut Parameters

◆ Select **Cut Parameters**, change the drill **Cycle** to **Drill/Counterbore** and input a **Dwell** of **1.0** second as shown in Figure: 29.2.1.

Figure: 29.2.1

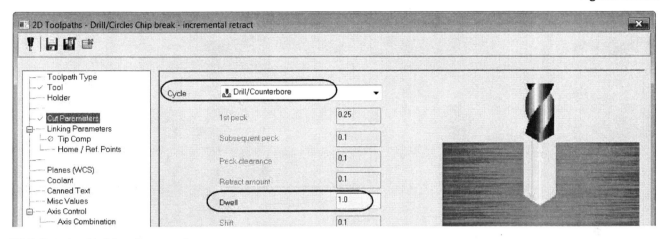

29.3 Set the Linking Parameters

◆ Choose **Linking Parameters** and input a **Depth** value of **-0.55** as shown in Figure: 29.3.1.

Figure: 29.3.1

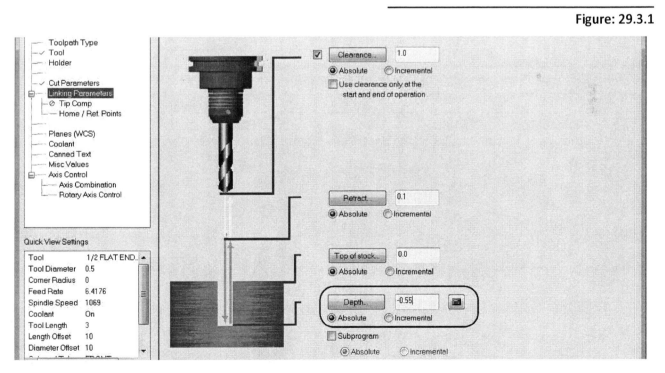

◆ Pick **Tip Comp** and ensure this option is disabled.

◆ Select the **OK** button to exit the **Drill/Counterbore** parameters and generate the toolpath.

29.4 Backplot and Verify

⬥ To **Backplot** and **Verify** the toolpaths see page 512 and page 513.

⬥ To make sure that all toolpaths are selected, choose the **Select all operations** icon.

⬥ The part should look as shown.

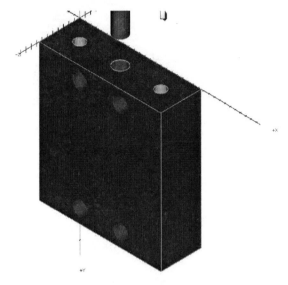

STEP 30: RENAME NC FILE

The Drilling and Tapping operations in "Setup #2 - Front" kept the NC name from Setup #1. We need to rename this operation so it will create a separate program for this setup.

⬥ Select "Setup #2 - Front" (make sure all the operations in setup #2 are selected).

- Right click on the group , choose the option **Edit selected operations** and then pick **Change NC file name**.

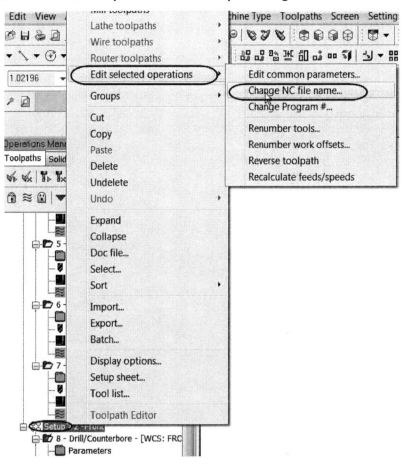

- When the **Enter new NC name** dialog box appears enter **"Setup #2 - Front"**.

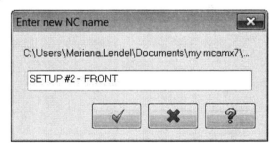

- Select the **OK** button to apply the changed NC name to all the operations in the second setup.

♦ The result you should see is **Setup #2 - Front.NC** in any of the operations in the second setup.

```
            ⋙ Toolpath - 5.0K - SETUP #1.NC - Progra
⊟ ⋇ Setup #2 -Front
   ⊟ 🗁 8 - Drill/Counterbore - [WCS: FRONT] - [Tp
      📁 Parameters
      ▯ #4 - 0.7500 SPOT DRILL - 3/4 SPOTDRI
      ▮ Geometry - (3) Points
      ⋙ Toolpath - 4.8K ⊂ SETUP #2 - FRONT ⊃ N
   ⊟ 🗁 9 - Peck Drill - [WCS: FRONT] - [Tplane: FF
      📁 Parameters
      ▯ #7 - 0.3125 DRILL - 5/16 DRILL
      ▮ Geometry - (2) Points
      ⋙ Toolpath - 4.6K ⊂ SETUP #2 - FRONT ⊃ N
   ⊟ 🗁 10 - Tap - [WCS: FRONT] - [Tplane: FRON
      📁 Parameters
      ▯ #8 - 0.3750 X 16.00 TAP RH - 3/8-16 T
      ▮ Geometry - (2) Points
      ⋙ Toolpath - 4.6K ⊂ SETUP #2 - FRONT ⊃ N
   ⊟ 🗁 11 - Chip Break - [WCS: FRONT] - [Tplane:
      📁 Parameters
      ▯ #9 - 0.5000 DRILL - 1/2 DRILL
      ▮ Geometry - (1) Points
      ⋙ Toolpath - 4.4K ⊂ SETUP #2 - FRONT ⊃ N
   ⊟ 🗁 12 - Drill/Counterbore - [WCS: FRONT] - [T
      📁 Parameters
      ▯ #10 - 0.5000 ENDMILL1 FLAT - 1/2 FLAT
      ▮ Geometry - (1) Points
      ⋙ Toolpath - 4.4K ⊂ SETUP #2 - FRONT ⊃ N
   ▶
```

Mastercam. X⁷

TOOLPATH CREATION - SETUP 3

SUGGESTED FIXTURE:

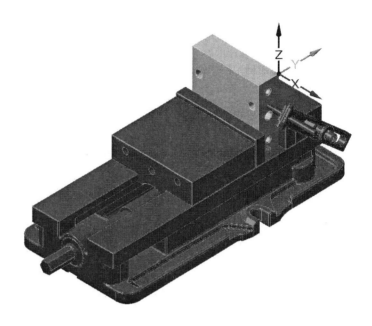

> **NOTE:** The part is now flipped and we will machine the part from the left side.

SETUP SHEET:

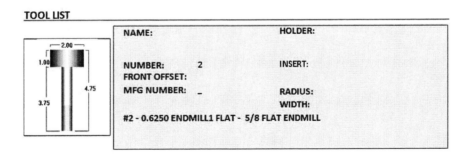

TOOL LIST

	NAME:		HOLDER:
	NUMBER:	2	INSERT:
	FRONT OFFSET:		
	MFG NUMBER:	_	RADIUS:
			WIDTH:

#2 - 0.6250 ENDMILL1 FLAT - 5/8 FLAT ENDMILL

STEP 31: CREATING AND RENAMING TOOLPATH GROUPS

To machine the part in different setups, we will need to have separate programs. To be able to post the operations separate of each setup, we will create them under different toolpath groups with different NC names.

31.1 Create Toolpath Group #3 (Setup #3 - Left)

* Right mouse click on the **"Machine Group-1**.
* Select **Groups** and then **New Toolpath Group** as shown in <u>Figure: 31.1.1</u>.

Figure: 31.1.1

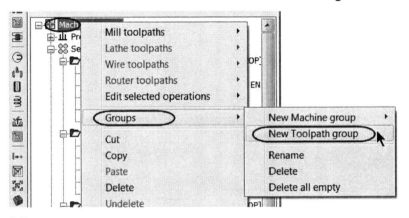

* Rename the toolpath group "**Setup #3 - Left.**"

Figure: 31.1.2

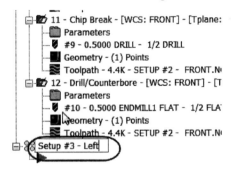

* Ensure the arrow is below "**Setup #3 - Left.**"

STEP 32: SET THE WCS TO LEFT

Work coordinate system (WCS) is the active coordinate system in use by Mastercam at any given time. The WCS contains the orientation of the X-Y-Z axes plus the location of the zero point (the origin). This tells Mastercam how your part is positioned or orientated in the machine.

◆ Select **WCS** located in the status bar.

◆ When the **WCS** menu appears select **"View Manager"** from it.

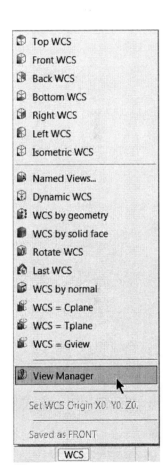

• When the **View Manager** dialog box appears pick **Left** and then choose to set the **Work Coordinate System (WCS), Tool plane, Construction plane**, and their origins, to the selected view as shown in <u>Figure: 32.0.1</u>.

Figure: 32.0.1

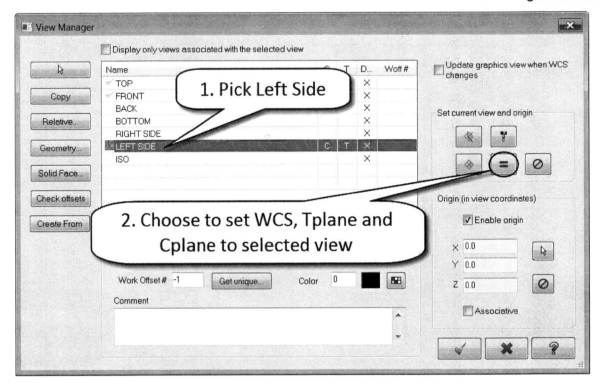

• Select the **OK** button to exit the **View Manager**.

• Pick the **Isometric** graphics view to see the part in its new orientation.

• Select the **Fit** icon.

• Press **F9** on your keyboard to view the coordinate axes.

> **NOTE:** The color of the coordinate axes remains the same because it is the same origin.

◆ Your part will appear as shown up to this point.

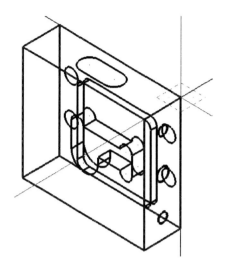

◆ Press **F9** to remove the axes display.

STEP 33: MACHINE THE SLOT

Slot Mill efficiently machines obround slots. This toolpath automatically calculates plunge, entry and exit points appropriate for slots.

Toolpath Preview:

Toolpaths

• **Circle Paths.**

• **Slot Mill.**

• When the chaining dialog box appears keep the default settings and select the slot as shown in <u>Figure: 33.0.1</u>.

Figure: 33.0.1

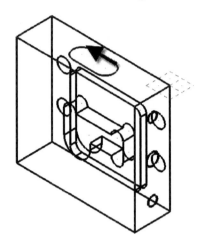

• Select the **OK** button in the chaining dialog box to continue.

• In the **Toolpath Type** page, the **Slot Mill** Toolpath will be selected as shown in <u>Figure: 33.0.2</u>.

Figure: 33.0.2

| Contour | Pocket | Facing | Slot Mill |

33.1 Select the 5/8" Flat Endmill from the Tool List

* Select **Tool** from the **Tree view list**.
* Pick the **5/8" Flat Endmill** tool from the list.
* Make the necessary changes to the **Tool** page as shown in Figure: 33.1.1.

Figure: 33.1.1

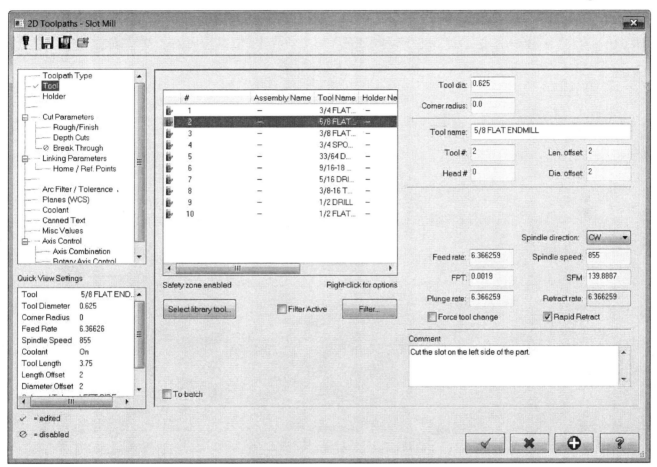

33.2 Set the Cut Parameters

◆ Select **Cut Parameters**, and add an overlap of **0.02** as shown in <u>Figure: 33.2.1</u>.

Figure: 33.2.1

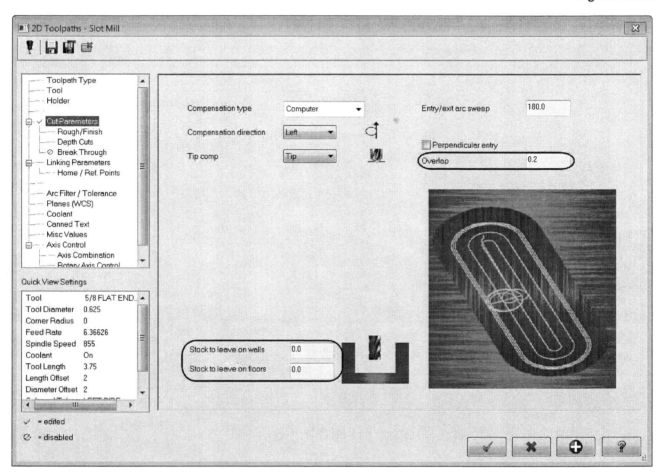

Entry/exit arc sweep sets the included angle of each entry and exit arc. If this value is set to less than 180 degrees a line will be created.

Overlap sets how far the tool goes past the end of the toolpath before exiting for a cleaner finish.

33.3 Set the Rough/Finish Parameters

♦ Choose **Rough/Finish Parameters** and ensure your settings appear as shown in <u>Figure: 33.3.1</u>.

Figure: 33.3.1

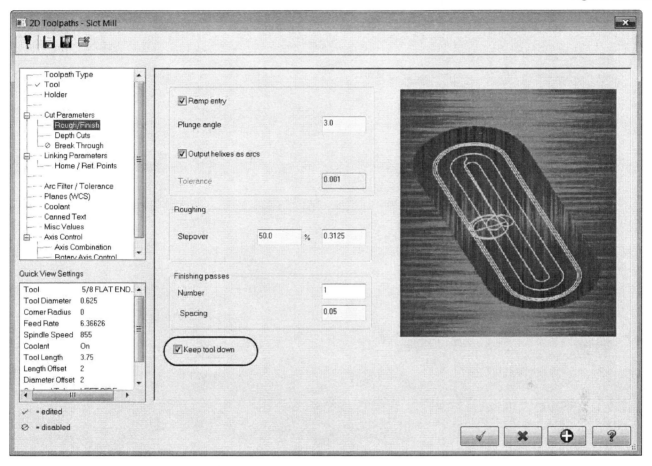

33.4 Set the Depth Cut Parameters

• Select **Depth Cuts**, input a **Max rough step** of **0.2** as shown in Figure: 33.4.1.
• Enter a **# of Finish Cuts** value of **1** and a **Finish step** of **0.1**.

NOTE: These settings instruct Mastercam to rough the slot leaving 0.1" and then create one lighter cut removing 0.1" of material for a finish pass.

Figure: 33.4.1

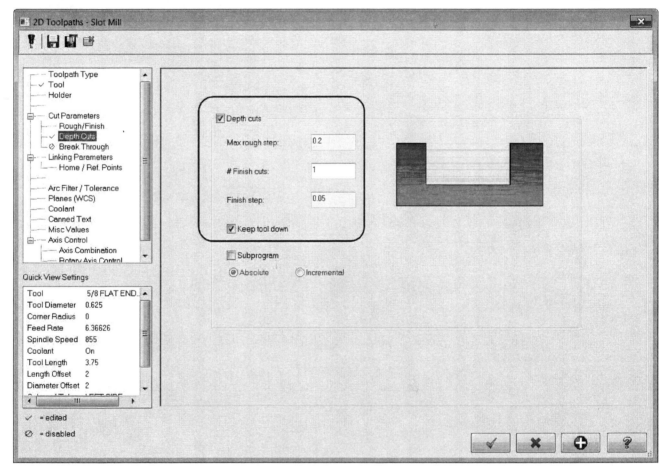

33.5 Set the Linking Parameters

◆ Select **Linking Parameters**, enable **Clearance** and set it to **1.0** and input a **Depth** of **-1.0** as shown in
  <u>Figure: 33.5.1</u>.

Figure: 33.5.1

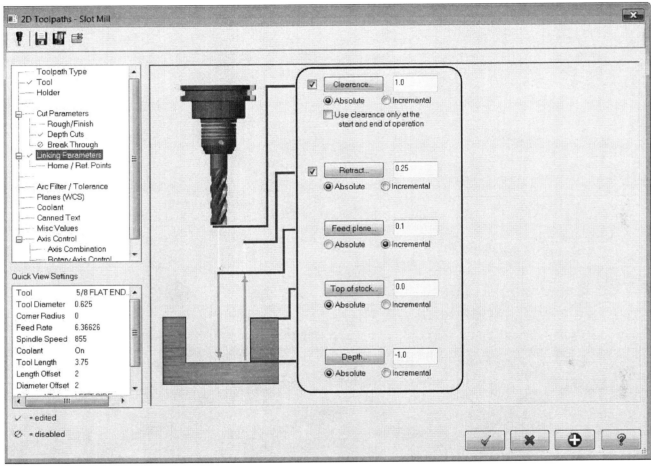

◆ Select the **OK** button to exit the **Slot Mill** parameters and generate the toolpath.

33.6 Backplot and Verify

- To **Backplot** and **Verify** the toolpaths see page 512 and page 513.
- Ensure all operations are selected, if they are not use the **Select all operations** icon from the **Operations Manager.**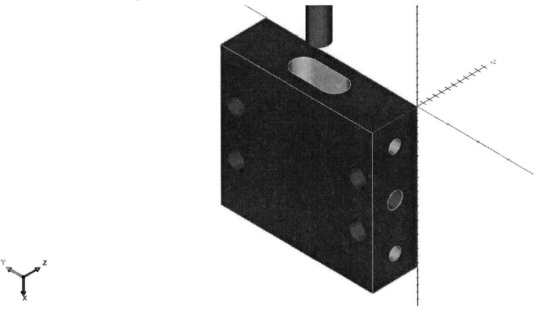
- Your part will appear as shown once complete.

- To rotate the part, pick a point in the center of the part with the mouse wheel and slowly move the cursor in the graphics window.

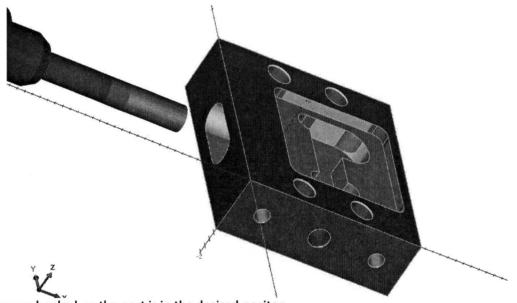

- Release the mouse wheel when the part is in the desired positon.

- To exit **Verify** click on the **Close** icon.

STEP 34: RENAME THE NC FILE

The Slot milling operation in "Setup #3 - Left" kept the NC name from Setup #2 _Front. We need to rename this operation so it will create a separate program for this setup.

- Select **"Setup #3 - Left"**, right click on the group (make sure all the operations in setup #3 are selected), choose the option **Edit selected operations** and then pick **Change NC file name** as shown in <u>Figure: 34.0.1</u>.

Figure: 34.0.1

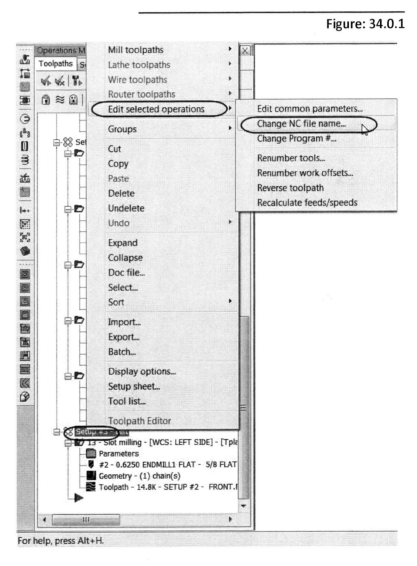

• When the **Enter new NC name** dialog box appears enter **"Setup #3 - Left"**.

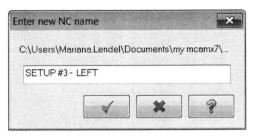

• Select the **OK** button to apply the changed NC name to all the operations in the second setup.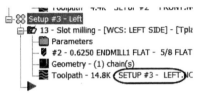
• The result you should see is **Setup #3 - Left.NC** in the last operation in the third setup as shown in Figure: 34.0.2.

Figure: 34.0.2

STEP 35: POST THE FILE

* Ensure all operations are selected, if they are not use the button **Select all operations** 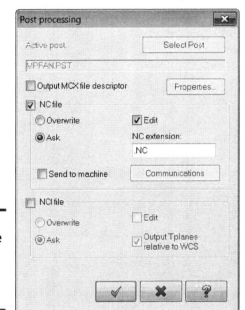 from the **Operations Manager.**
* Select the **Post selected operations** **G1** button from the **Operations Manager.**
* In the **Post processing** window make the necessary changes as shown in <u>Figure: 35.0.1</u>.

Figure: 35.0.1

NC File enabled allows you to keep the NC file and to assign the same name as the MCX file.

Edit enabled allows you to automatically launch the default editor.

* Select the **OK** button to continue.
* Save your file and name it Setup #1.NC.
* Save your file and name it Setup #2 - Front.NC.
* Save your file and name it Setup #3 - Left.NC.

• A window with Mastercam Code Expert will be lunched and the NC program will appear as shown in Figure: 35.0.2.

Figure: 35.0.2

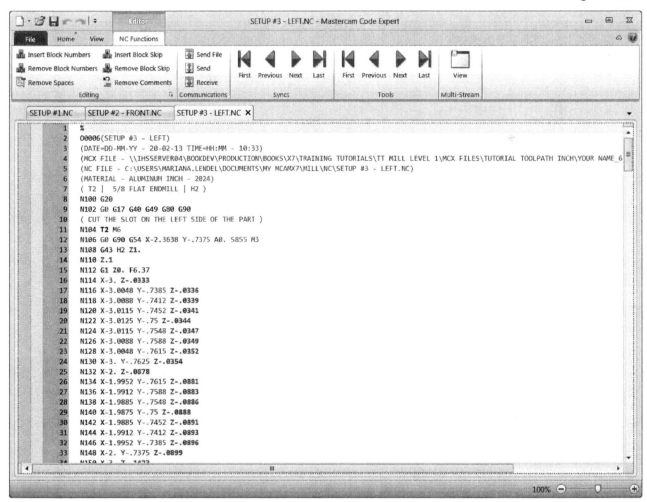

• Select the red "**X**" box at the upper right corner to exit the editor.

STEP 36: SAVE THE UPDATED MCX FILE

Mastercam X⁷

REVIEW EXERCISE -STUDENT PRACTICE

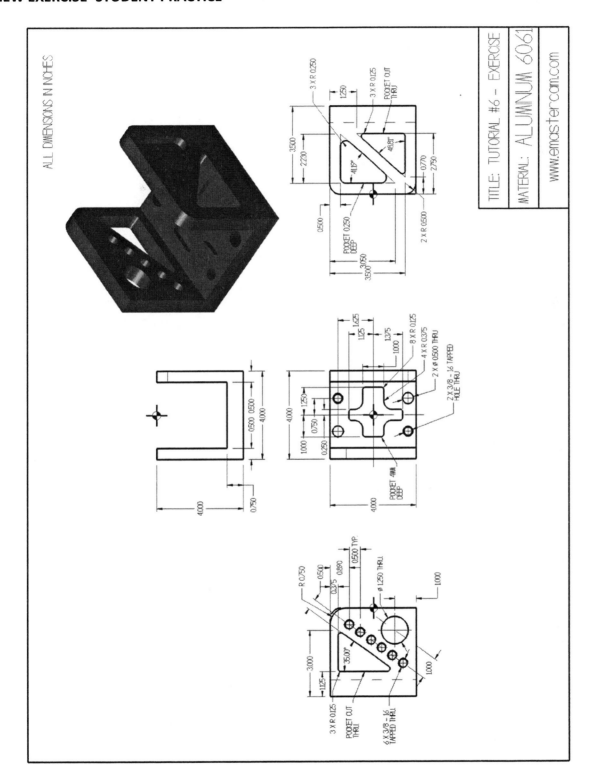

ALL DIMENSIONS IN INCHES

TITLE: TUTORIAL #6 — EXERCISE

MATERIAL: ALUMINUM 6061

www.emastercam.com

CREATE THE GEOMETRY FOR TUTORIAL #6

Use these commands to create the geometry.
Create the geometry in the top construction plane.

* Set the Construction depth and Construction mode.
* Create Rectangle.
* Create Line Endpoint.
* Create Fillet Entities.
* Create Arcs.
* Trim/Break/Extend.
* Break two Pieces.
* Delete entities.

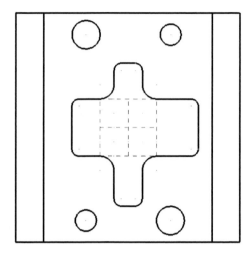

Create the geometry in the Right construction plane.

* Set the Construction depth.
* Create Rectangle.
* Create Line Parallel.
* Create Line Endpoint.
* Create Fillet Entities.
* Create Arcs.
* Trim/Break/Extend.
* Delete Entities.
* Create Fillet Entities.

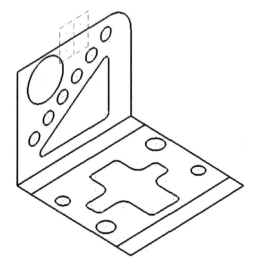

Create the geometry in the Right construction plane.

* Set the Construction depth.
* Create Rectangle.
* Create Line Parallel.
* Create Line Endpoint.
* Create Fillet Entities.
* Create Arcs.
* Trim/Break/Extend.
* Delete Entities.
* Create Fillet Entities.

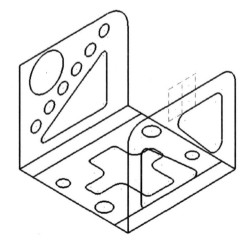

CREATE THE TOOLPATHS FOR TUTORIAL #6 EXERCISE

Create the Toolpaths for the Tutorial #6 Exercise as per the instructions below.

Set the machine properties including the stock setup.
◆ The stock will appear as shown.

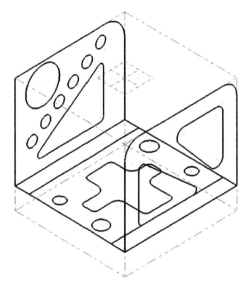

Modify the geometry for a toolpath.
◆ Create Line Parallel.
◆ Trim/Break/Extend.

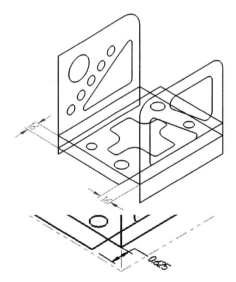

Remove the material in the center of the part Pocket.
* Use a **1" Flat Endmill**.
* Ensure the **Machining direction** is set to **Climb**.
* Select a desired cutting method.
* Choose an **Entry method**.
* Set the **Finish Parameters**.
* Enable **Lead In/Out**.
* Enable depth cuts and set the **Max depth cut** to **0.25"**.
* No **Break Through**.
* Set the depth according to the drawing.

Machine the Pocket.
* Use a **1/4" Flat Endmill**.
* Ensure the **Machining direction** is set to **Climb**.
* Select a desired cutting method.
* Choose an **Entry method**.
* Set the **Finish** parameters.
* Enable **Lead In/Out**.
* Disable **Depth Cuts**, and **Break Through**.
* Set **Depth** according to the drawing.

Spot Drill the holes.
* Use a **3/4" Spot Drill**.
* Set the **Drill cycle** to **Drill/Counterbore**.
* Set the top of stock according to the material.
* Set the depth to leave a **0.05" Chamfer** on all the holes.

Drill the 1/2" Holes.
- Use a **1/2" Drill**.
- Set the **Drill cycle** to **Drill/Counterbore**.
- Set the top of stock according to the material.
- Set the depth and include tip comp.

Drill the 3/8Tapped Holes.
- Use a **5/16" Drill**.
- Set the **Drill cycle** to **Drill/Counterbore**.
- Set the top of stock according to the material.
- Set the depth and include tip comp.

Tap the 3/8 - 16 Holes.
- Use a **3/8 - 16 NC Tap RH**.
- Set the **Drill Cycle** to **Tap**.
- Set the top of stock according to the material.
- Set the depth and include tip comp.

Set the WCS to Right and input an Origin Z value of 2.0".
Create a new Toolpath Group and rename the NC File name for the last toolpath group.

* **Pocket** the two triangles to the depths shown on the drawing.
* Use a **1/4" Flat Endmill.**

* Create a **Contour** toolpath around the two fillets.
* Use the **1/4" Flat Endmill.**
* Set the depth according to the drawing.

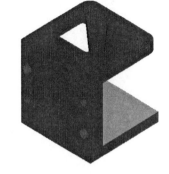

Set the WCS to Left and input an Origin Z value of 2.0".
Create a new Toolpath Group and rename the NC File name for the last toolpath group.

* Pocket the triangle to the depths shown on the drawing.
* Use a **1/4" Flat Endmill.**

* **Drill** the 6 Holes.
* Use the **5/16" Drill.**

* **Tap** the 6 Holes.
* Use the **3/8 - 16 Tap.**

* **Circle Mill** the Ø1.25" Hole.
* Use a **1/2" Flat Endmill.**
* Enable **Roughing**.
* Enable **Finishing** and set the **Finish Passes** to **2** with a spacing of **0.02".**
* Set the depth according to the drawing.

* Create a **Contour** operation to remove the material around the fillet.
* Use a **1/2" Flat Endmill.**

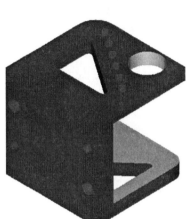

Once complete your part will appear as shown.

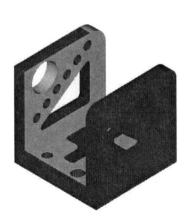

NOTES:

TUTORIAL #6 QUIZ

◆ What does the Translate join command do?

◆ What does a 2D High Speed Rest Mill Toolpath do?

◆ What is the use of WCS in Mastercam?

◆ After creating a new toolpath group why do you rename the NC file?

TUTORIAL #7

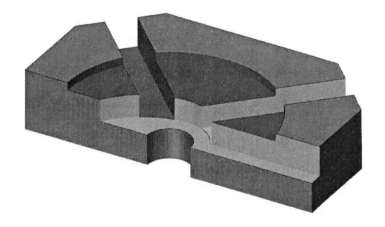

OVERVIEW OF STEPS TAKEN TO CREATE THE FINAL PART:

From Drawing to CAD Model:
* The student should examine the drawing on the following page to understand what part is being created in the tutorial.
* From the drawing we can decide how to go about creating the geometry in Mastercam.

Create the 2D CAD Model used to generate Toolpaths from:
* The student will create the Top 2D geometry needed to create the toolpaths.
* Geometry creation commands such as create rectangle, circle center point, line polar and line parallel will be used.
* The student will also learn how to clean up the geometry using the trimming functions.

Create the necessary Toolpaths to machine the part:
* The student will set up the stock size to be used and the clamping method used.
* A 2D High Speed Dynamic Core Mill toolpath will be created to remove the material outside of the step.
* A 2D High Speed Core Mill toolpath will be created to machine the step.
* A 2D High Speed Blend Mill toolpath will be created to machine the semi arc shape pocket.
* Two 2D High Speed Peel Mill toolpaths will be created to machine the two slots.

Backplot and Verify the file:
* The Backplot will be used to simulate a step by step process of the tool's movements.
* The Verify will be used to watch a tool machine the part out of a solid model.

Post Process the file to generate the G-code:
* The Student will then post process the file to obtain an NC file containing the necessary code for the machine.

 This tutorial takes approximately two hours to complete.

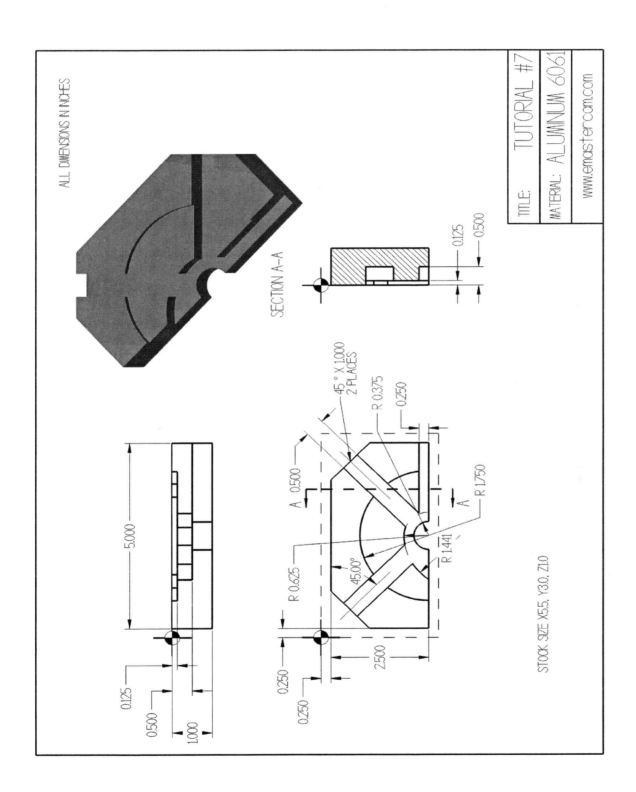

ALL DIMENSIONS IN INCHES

SECTION A-A

TITLE: TUTORIAL #7
MATERIAL: ALUMINUM 6061
www.emastercam.com

45° X 1.000 2 PLACES
R 0.375
0.250
R 1.750
R 1.441
45.00°
R 0.625
2.500
0.250
0.250
5.000
0.125
0.500
1.000
0.125
0.500

STOCK SIZE X5.5, Y3.0, Z1.0

GEOMETRY CREATION

STEP 1: SETTING UP THE GRAPHIC USER INTERFACE

Please refer to the **Getting Started** section to set up the graphics user interface.

STEP 2: CREATE RECTANGLES

In this step we will create rectangles using the rectangular command. The rectangle we create will be based off the origin.

Step Preview:

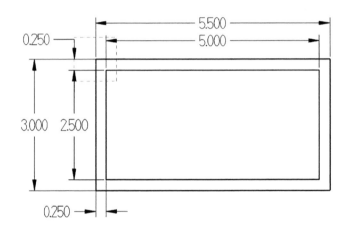

2.1 Create the 5.5" by 3.0" rectangle

Create

- **Rectangle.**
- [Select position of first corner]: Select the **Origin** as shown in Figure: 2.1.1.

Figure: 2.1.1

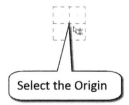

Select the Origin

- Make sure that when selecting the origin, the visual cue of the cursor changes as shown.

◆ [Select position of second corner]: Pick a point to right of the origin and below it as shown in <u>Figure: 2.1.2</u>.

Figure: 2.1.2

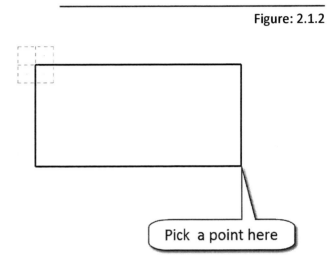

Pick a point here

NOTE: You can make this rectangle as small or as large as you want. The entities are still live therefore we can modify the values to get the size we want.

◆ Enter a **Width** 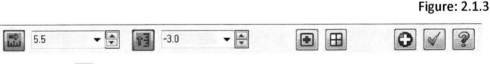 of **5.5** and a **Height** of **-3.0** as shown in <u>Figure: 2.1.3</u>.

Figure: 2.1.3

◆ Choose the **Apply** button to continue. ⊕

NOTE: During the geometry creation of this tutorial, if you make a mistake you can undo the last step using the **Undo** icon. 🔄 You can undo as many steps as needed. If you delete or undo a step by mistake, just use the **Redo** icon. 🔁 To delete unwanted geometry, select it first and then press **Delete** from the keyboard.

◆ Use the **Fit** icon to fit the drawing to the screen. ✛

2.2 Create the 5.0" by 2.5" rectangle

◆ [Select position of first corner]: Pick the **Fast Point** icon.
◆ Enter the coordinate values of **0.25, -0.25.**
◆ Hit **Enter** on your keyboard to set the first position of the corner.

◆ Enter a **Width** of **5.0** and a **Height** of **-2.5**.

◆ Choose the **OK** button to exit the command. ✓

STEP 3: CREATE CIRCLES AND ARC TANGENT

Create Circle Center Point lets you create circles knowing the center point and the radius or the diameter.
Create Arc Tangent 1 Entity lets you create an arc knowing the radius, the arc that is tangent too and the tangency point.

Step Preview:

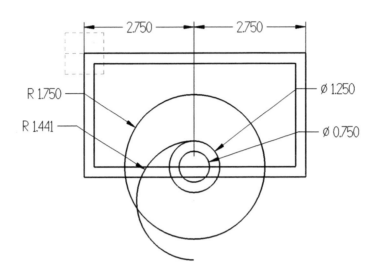

3.1 Create the Circles using Circle Center Point command

Create

♦ **Arc.**

♦ 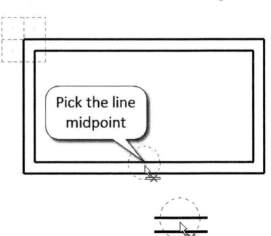 **Circle Center Point.**

♦ Enter a **Radius** ⊙ value of **0.375** and pick the line **Midpoint** as shown in <u>Figure: 3.1.1</u>.

Figure: 3.1.1

Pick the line
midpoint

♦ Make sure that when selecting the origin, the visual cue of the cursor changes as shown.

◆ Select the **Apply** button to continue. ⊕

◆ Enter a **Radius** ⊚ value of **0.625** and pick the same line midpoint.

◆ Select the **Apply** button to continue. ⊕

◆ Enter a **Radius** ⊚ value of **1.75** and pick the same line midpoint.

◆ Choose the **OK** button to exit the command. ☑

◆ The geometry should look as shown.

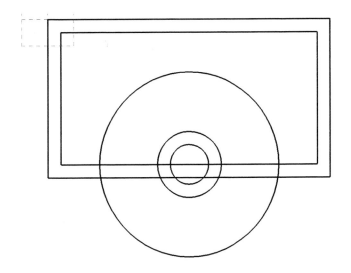

3.2 Create the Arc tangent to an entity

Create

◆ ◁ **Arc Tangent.**

◆ From the **Ribbon Bar** select the **Tangent 1 Entity** as shown.

◆ Enter a **Radius** ⊚ value of **1.441**.

- [Select the entity that the arc is to be tangent to]: Select the arc as shown in Figure: 3.2.1.

Figure: 3.2.1

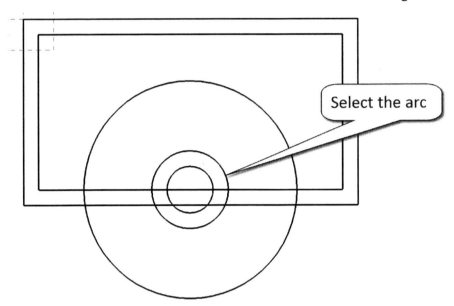

Select the arc

- [Specify the tangent point]: Select the **Quadrant** as shown in Figure: 3.2.2.

Figure: 3.2.2

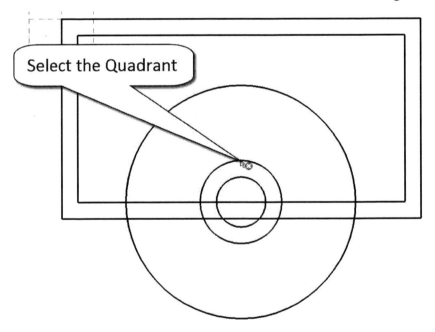

Select the Quadrant

• Select an arc]: Pick the arc as shown in <u>Figure: 3.2.3</u>.

Figure: 3.2.3

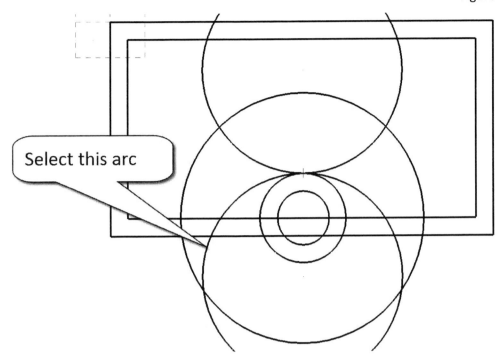

• Choose the **OK** button to exit the command.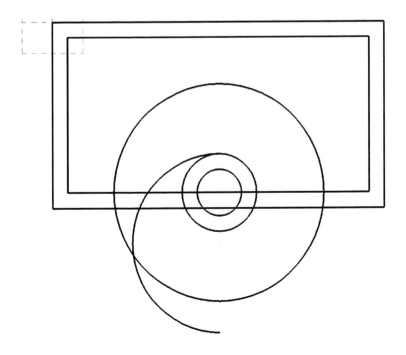

• Select the **Fit** icon.
• The geometry should look as shown.

STEP 4: TRIM THE ARCS

Trim to Point trims an entity to a point or any defined position in the graphics window. If the point you enter does not lie on the selected entity, Mastercam calculates the closest position on the entity and trims the entity to that point.

Step Preview:

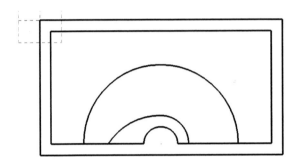

Edit
- ◆ **Trim/Break.**
- ◆ **Trim/Break/Extend.**

4.1 Trim the entities using Trim to Point command

- ◆ Select the **Trim to Point** icon in the ribbon bar.
- ◆ [Select the entity to trim/extend]: Select the arc as shown in <u>Figure: 4.1.1</u>.
- ◆ [Indicate the trim/extend location]: Select the Endpoint as shown in <u>Figure: 4.1.1</u>.

Figure: 4.1.1

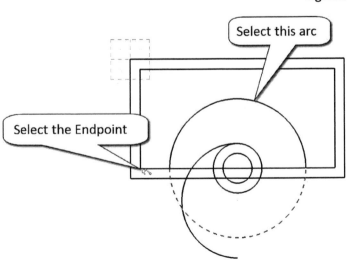

• [Select the entity to trim/extend]: Select the arc as shown in <u>Figure: 4.1.2</u>.
• [Indicate the trim/extend location]: Select the Intersection as shown in <u>Figure: 4.1.2</u>.

Figure: 4.1.2

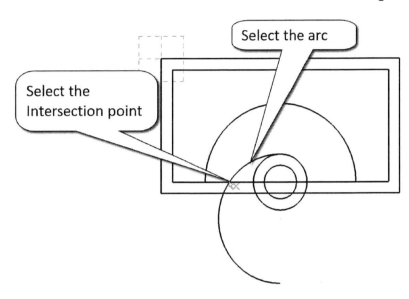

Select the arc

Select the
Intersection point

• [Select the entity to trim/extend]: Select the 0.375 radius circle as shown in <u>Figure: 4.1.3</u>.
• [Indicate the trim/extend location]: Select the Endpoint as shown in <u>Figure: 4.1.3</u>.

Figure: 4.1.3

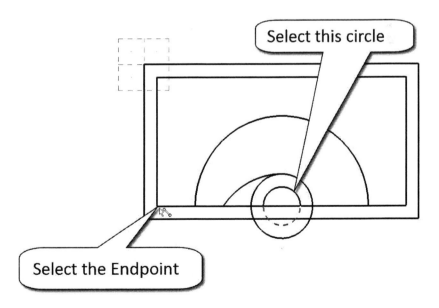

Select this circle

Select the Endpoint

4.2 Trim the entities using Trim two entities

♦ Choose the icon **Trim 2 Entity** from the ribbon bar.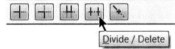
♦ [Select the entity to trim/extend]: Select Entity A as shown in <u>Figure: 4.2.1</u>.
♦ [Select the entity to trim/extend too]: Select Entity B as shown in <u>Figure: 4.2.1</u>.

Figure: 4.2.1

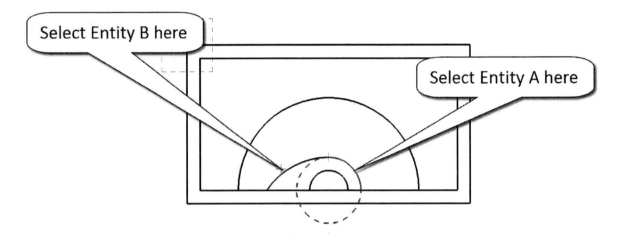

4.3 Trim Entities using Divide/Delete

♦ Select the command **Divide/Delete** from the ribbon bar.
♦ Pick the line in between the half circle endpoints as shown in <u>Figure: 4.3.1</u>.

Figure: 4.3.1

NOTE: Divide/Delete trims a line or arc to the intersection point between it.

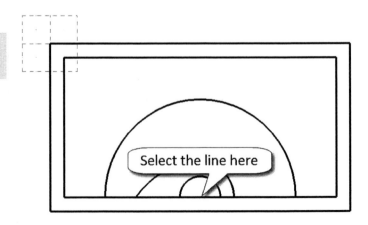

• Select the **OK** button to exit the **Trim/Break/Extend** command. ☑
• The part will appear as shown.

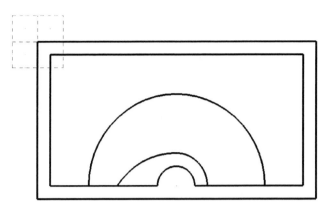

STEP 5: CREATE LINE PARALLEL

In this step you will learn how to create a line parallel knowing the distance and side to create the line on.

Step Preview:

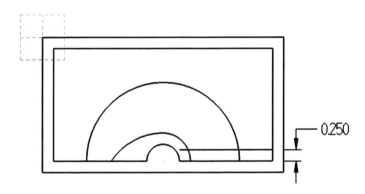

0.250

Create
• **Line.**

•  **Parallel.**

- [Select a line]: Select the line as shown in Figure: 5.0.1.

Figure: 5.0.1

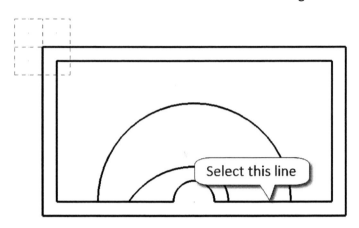

- [Select the point to place a parallel line through]: Pick a point above that line as shown in Figure: 5.0.2.

Figure: 5.0.2

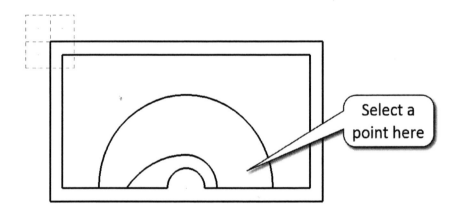

- In the **Ribbon bar** change the **Distance** [+] to **0.25**.
- Choose the **OK** button to exit the command. ✓

STEP 6: CREATE CHAMFERS

In this step you will learn how to create a chamfer on two corners of the part. You will create this chamfer knowing the width and angle.

Step Preview:

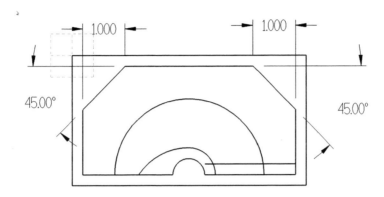

Create
* **Chamfer.**

* 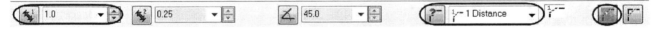 **Entities.**

* In the **Ribbon bar** make sure the **Chamfer Style** is set to **1 Distance**, the **Width** is set to **1.0** and ensure **Trim** is enabled.

* Pick the vertical line and then the horizontal line as shown in Figure: 6.0.1.

Figure: 6.0.1

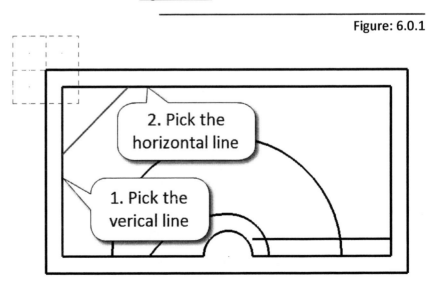

* Repeat the step for the opposite corner.

* Choose the **OK** button to exit the command.

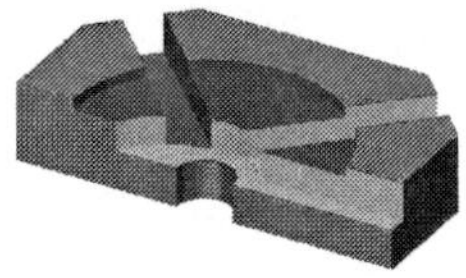

STEP 7: CREATE POLAR LINES

In this step you will learn how to create a line knowing one endpoint and angle.

Step Preview:

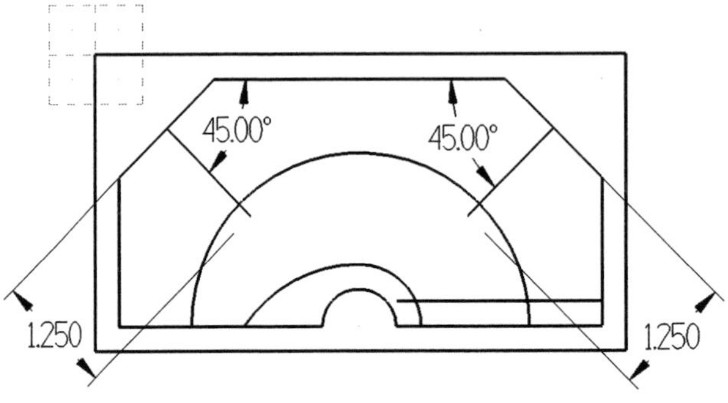

Create
- **Line.**
- 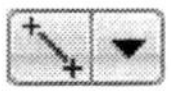 **Endpoint.**
- [Specify the first endpoint]: Pick the **Midpoint** of the left chamfer.
- Ensure the **AutoCursor** icon has changed to represent the line midpoint. 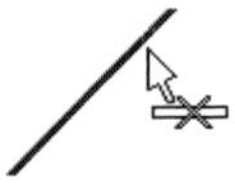
- [Specify the second endpoint]: Sketch a line at any angle and any length as shown in Figure: 7.0.1.

Figure: 7.0.1

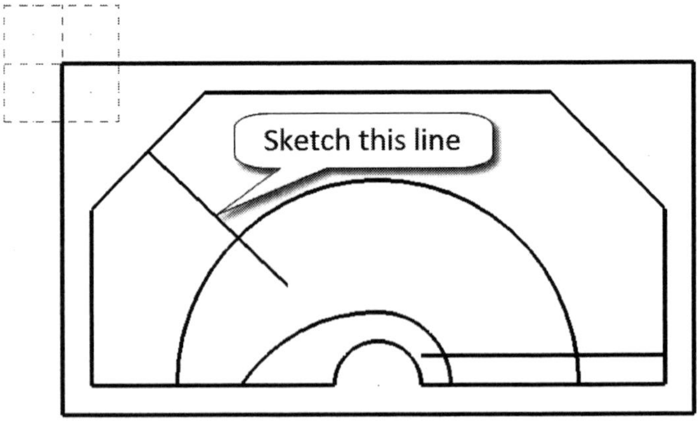

NOTE: At this point the line is still live and can be modified to any angle or length we desire.

- Enter a **Length**  of **1.25** and an **Angle**  of **-45.0** Degrees.
- Hit **Enter** on your keyboard to preview the line.

• Select the **Apply** button to continue.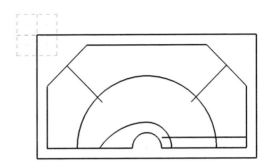
• Pick the midpoint of the opposite chamfer and sketch a line.

• Enter a **Length** 📐 of **1.25** and an **Angle** 📐 of **270-45.0** degrees.

• Select the **OK** button to exit the create line endpoint command. ✓
• The geometry should look as shown.

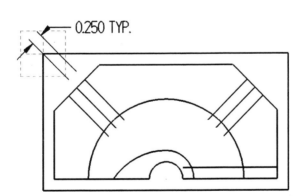

STEP 8: CREATE LINE PARALLEL

In this step you will learn how to create a line parallel knowing the distance and side to create the line on.

Step Preview:

Create
• **Line.**

• ↘️▼ **Parallel.**

• Select the line as shown in <u>Figure: 8.0.1</u>.

Figure: 8.0.1

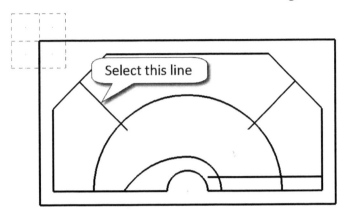

• Pick a point on either side of this line.

• Input a **Distance** 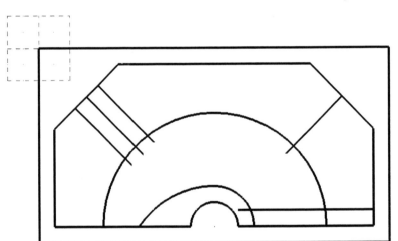 of **0.25**and hit **Enter** your keyboard.

• Select the **Flip** button twice.
• This will position lines on either side of the originally selected entity as shown in <u>Figure: 8.0.2</u>.

Figure: 8.0.2

• Repeat the step for the opposite side of the part.

• The geometry should look as shown.

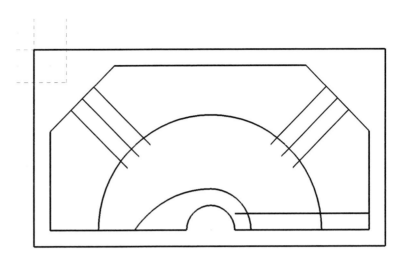

• Select the **OK** button to exit the create line parallel command.

STEP 9: DELETE ENTITIES

Step Preview:

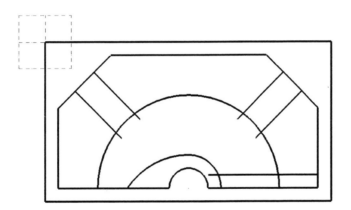

Edit
• **Delete.**

•  **Delete Entities.**

◆ Select the entities as shown in <u>Figure: 9.0.1</u>.

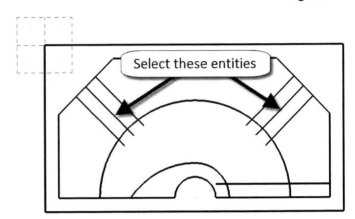

Select these entities

◆ Pick the **End Selection** button.

STEP 10: TRIM ENTITIES

To **Trim 1 Entity** select the entity you wish to trim, then select the entity you wish to trim to.

Step Preview:

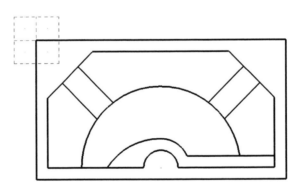

10.1 Trim entities using Trim 1 Entity command

Edit
◆ **Trim/Break.**

◆ 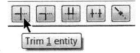 **Trim/Break/Extend.**

Trim 1 entity

◆ Select the **Trim 1 Entity** icon in the ribbon bar.

Mastercam. X⁷

- ◆ [Select the entity to trim]: Select the line as shown in <u>Figure: 10.1.1</u>.
- ◆ [Select the entity to trim to]: Choose the line and then pick the arc as shown in <u>Figure: 10.1.1</u>.

Figure: 10.1.1

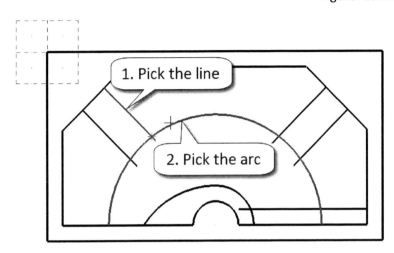

- ◆ Repeat the step for the other 4 lines.
- ◆ Your part should look as shown.

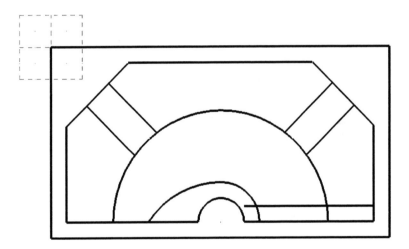

● Select the half circle and then pick the line as shown in Figure: 10.1.2.

Figure: 10.1.2

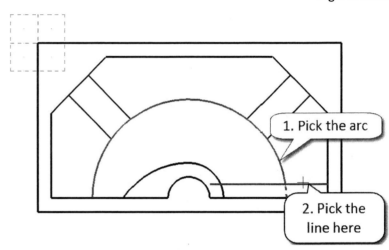

1. Pick the arc

2. Pick the line here

10.2 Trim entities using Trim 2 Entities

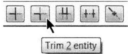

Trim 2 entity

● Select the **Trim 2 Entities** icon in the ribbon bar.
● Select the line and arc as shown in Figure: 10.2.1.

Figure: 10.2.1

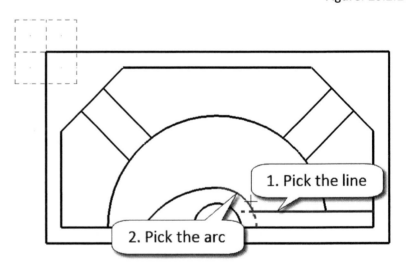

1. Pick the line

2. Pick the arc

● Pick the **OK** button to exit the **Trim/Break/Extend** command. ☑

• The part will appear as shown once complete.

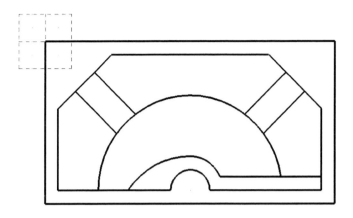

STEP 11: SAVE THE FILE

File

• ⊞ **Save As.**
• File name: "Your Name_7".

TOOLPATH CREATION

SUGGESTED FIXTURE:

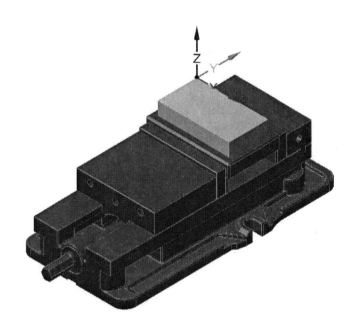

SETUP SHEET:

TOOL LIST

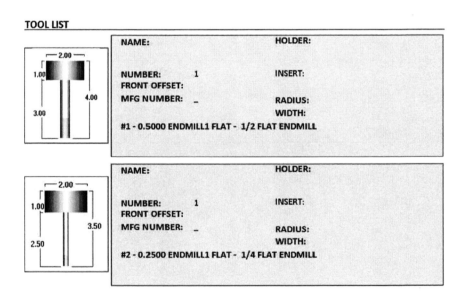

	NAME:	HOLDER:
	NUMBER: 1	INSERT:
	FRONT OFFSET:	
	MFG NUMBER: _	RADIUS:
		WIDTH:

#1 - 0.5000 ENDMILL1 FLAT - 1/2 FLAT ENDMILL

	NAME:	HOLDER:
	NUMBER: 1	INSERT:
	FRONT OFFSET:	
	MFG NUMBER: _	RADIUS:
		WIDTH:

#2 - 0.2500 ENDMILL1 FLAT - 1/4 FLAT ENDMILL

STEP 12: SELECT THE MACHINE AND SET UP THE STOCK

In Mastercam, you select a **Machine Definition** before creating any toolpaths. The **Machine Definition** is a model of your machines capabilities and features. It acts like a template for setting up your machine. The machine definition ties together three main components. The schematic model of your machines components, the control definition that models your control capabilities, and the post processor that will generate the required machine code (G-code). For a Mill Level 1 exercise (2D toolpaths) we need just a basic machine definition.

> **NOTE:** For the purpose of this tutorial, we will be using the Default milling machine.

• To display the **Operations Manager** press **Alt + O**.

• Use the **Fit** icon to fit the drawing to the screen.

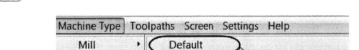

Machine type
• **Mill.**
• **Default.**
• Select the plus sign in front of **Properties** in the **Toolpaths Manager** to expand the **Toolpaths Group Properties.**

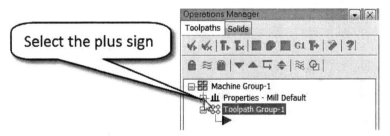

• Select **Tool Settings** to set the tool parameters.

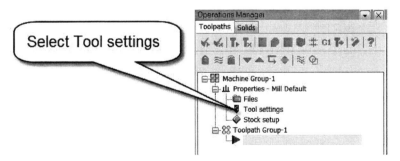

♦ Change the parameters to match the screen shot as shown in Figure: 12.0.1.

Figure: 12.0.1

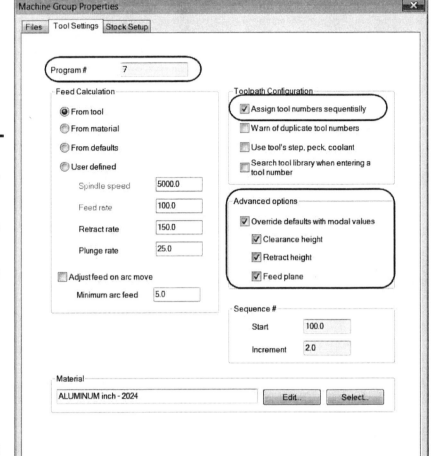

Program # is used to enter a number if your machine tool requires a number for a program name.

Assign tool numbers sequentially allows you to overwrite the tool number from the library with the next available tool number. (First operation tool number 1; Second operation tool number 2, etc.)

Warn of duplicate tool numbers allows you to get a warning if you enter two tools with the same number.

Override defaults with modal values enables the system to keep the values that you enter.

Feed Calculation set From tool uses feed rate, plunge rate, retract rate and spindle speed from the tool definition.

- Select the **Stock setup** tab to define the stock.
- Pick the **Rectangular** shape option.
- Pick the **All Entities** button and input a **Z** value of **1.0** as shown in Figure: 12.0.2.

Figure: 12.0.2

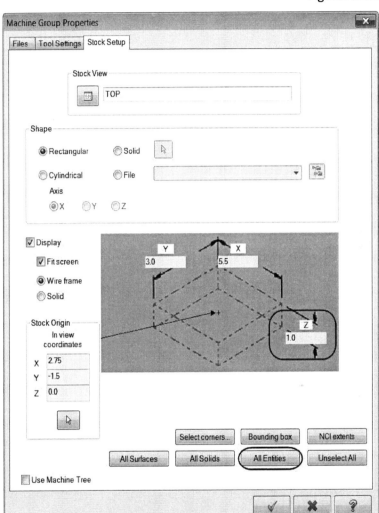

The **Stock Origin** values adjust the positioning of the stock, ensuring that you have equal amount of extra stock around the finished part.

Display options allow you to set the stock as Wireframe and to fit the stock to the screen. (Fit Screen)

NOTE: The **stock** model that you create can be displayed with the part geometry when viewing the file or the toolpaths, during backplot, or while verifying toolpaths. In the graphics, the plus shows you where the stock origin is. The default position is the middle of the stock.

- Select the **OK** button to exit **Machine Group Properties**.

- Select the **Isometric** view from the graphics view toolbar to see the stock.

- Use the **Fit** icon to fit the drawing to the screen.

• The stock model should appear as shown in <u>Figure: 12.0.3</u>.

Figure: 12.0.3

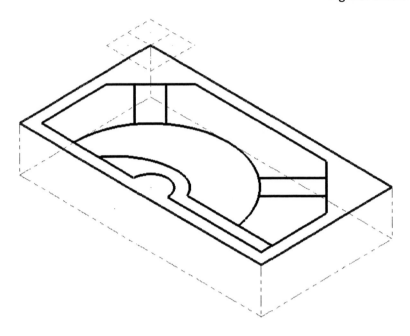

NOTE: You may not be able to see the stock clearly due to the fact that the stock is the same size as the part. The stock is not geometry and can not be selected.

There will not be a facing toolpath because the stock is already to size.

STEP 13: 2D HIGH SPEED DYNAMIC CORE

2D High Speed Dynamic Core Mill utilizes the entire flute length of their cutting tools to produce the smoothest, most efficient tool motion for high speed pocketing and core milling. The **Dynamic Core** toolpath machines open pocket shapes or standing core shapes using the outmost chain as the stock boundary. The tool moves freely outside of this area; the inner chain defines the limit of the toolpath.

Toolpath Preview:

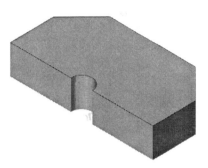

13.1 Break Lines prior to Chaining

Edit
- **Trim/Break.**
- 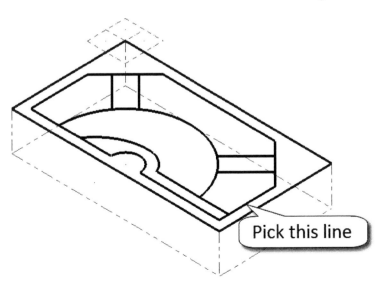 **Break Two Pieces.**
- [Select an entity to break]: Select the line as shown in Figure: 13.1.1.

Figure: 13.1.1

Pick this line

* [Indicate the break position]: Pick the line endpoint or point which is where we want to break the line as shown in Figure: 13.1.2.

Figure: 13.1.2

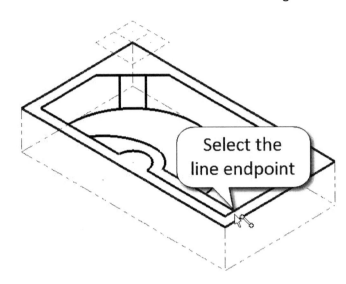

* [Select an entity to break]: Select the line as shown in Figure: 13.1.3.
* [Indicate the break position]: Select the endpoint as shown in Figure: 13.1.3.

Figure: 13.1.3

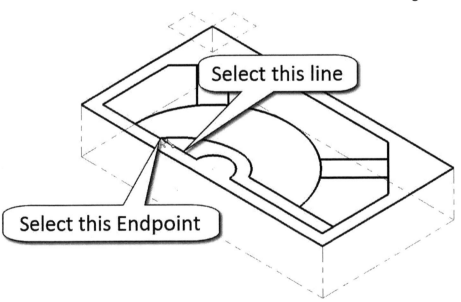

* Select the **OK** button to exit the command.

13.2 Chain Selection

Toolpaths
- **2D High Speed.**

 Dynamic Core.

- When the new **NC name** dialog box appears select the **OK** button to accept the name.

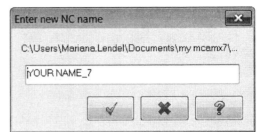

- When the chaining dialog box appears leave the default settings.
- Select the rectangle as shown in <u>Figure: 13.2.1</u>.

Figure: 13.2.1

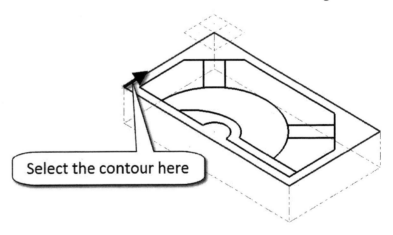

Select the contour here

• Select the outer profile of the part as shown. The chain will stop at the break point. Pick the line past that point to continue the chain as shown in <u>Figure: 13.2.2</u>.

Figure: 13.2.2

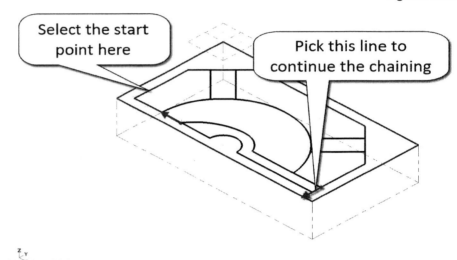

Select the start point here

Pick this line to continue the chaining

Z Y
Gview:ISO WCS:TOP T/Cplane:TOP

• Select the **OK** button to exit the **Chaining** dialog box.

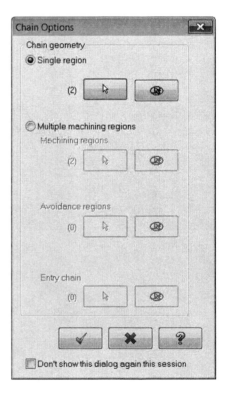

• Select the **OK** button to exit the **Chain Options** dialog box.

• In the toolpath type page **Dynamic Core Mill** should be already selected.

13.3 Select a 0.5" Flat Endmill from the Library and set the Tool Parameters

• Select **Tool** from the **Tree view list**.

• Click on the **Select library tool** button.   Select library tool...
• Select the **Filter** button as shown.

• Select the **None** button and then under **Tool Types** choose the **Flat Endmill** icon.
• Under tool diameter pick **Equal** and input a value of **0.5** as shown in Figure: 13.3.1.

Figure: 13.3.1

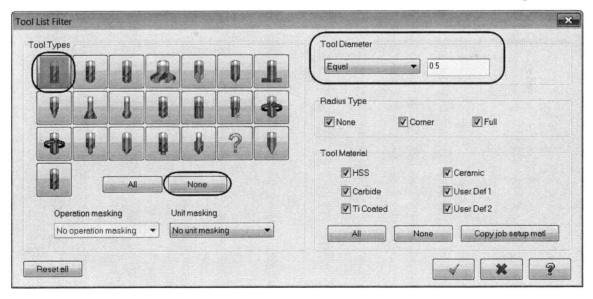

• Select the **OK** button to exit the **Tool List Filter.**

- In the **Tool Selection** dialog box you should only see a **1/2" Flat Endmill**.

#	Assembly Name	Tool Name	Holder Name	Dia.	Cor. rad.	Length	# Flutes	Type	Rad. Type
239	–	1/2 FLAT...	–	0.5	0.0	1.0	4	En...	None

- Select the **1/2" Flat Endmill** in the **Tool Selection** page and then select the **OK** button to exit.
- Make all the necessary changes as shown in Figure: 13.3.2.

Figure: 13.3.2

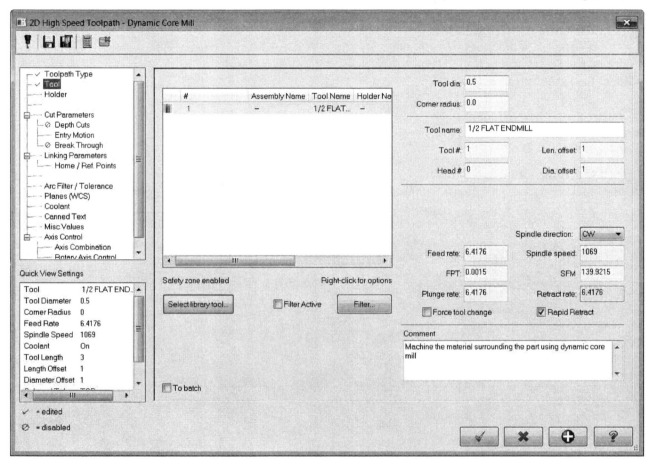

13.4 Set the Cut Parameters

♦ From the **Tree view list**, select **Cut Parameters** and ensure the parameters appear the same as shown in
  <u>Figure: 13.4.1</u>.

Figure: 13.4.1

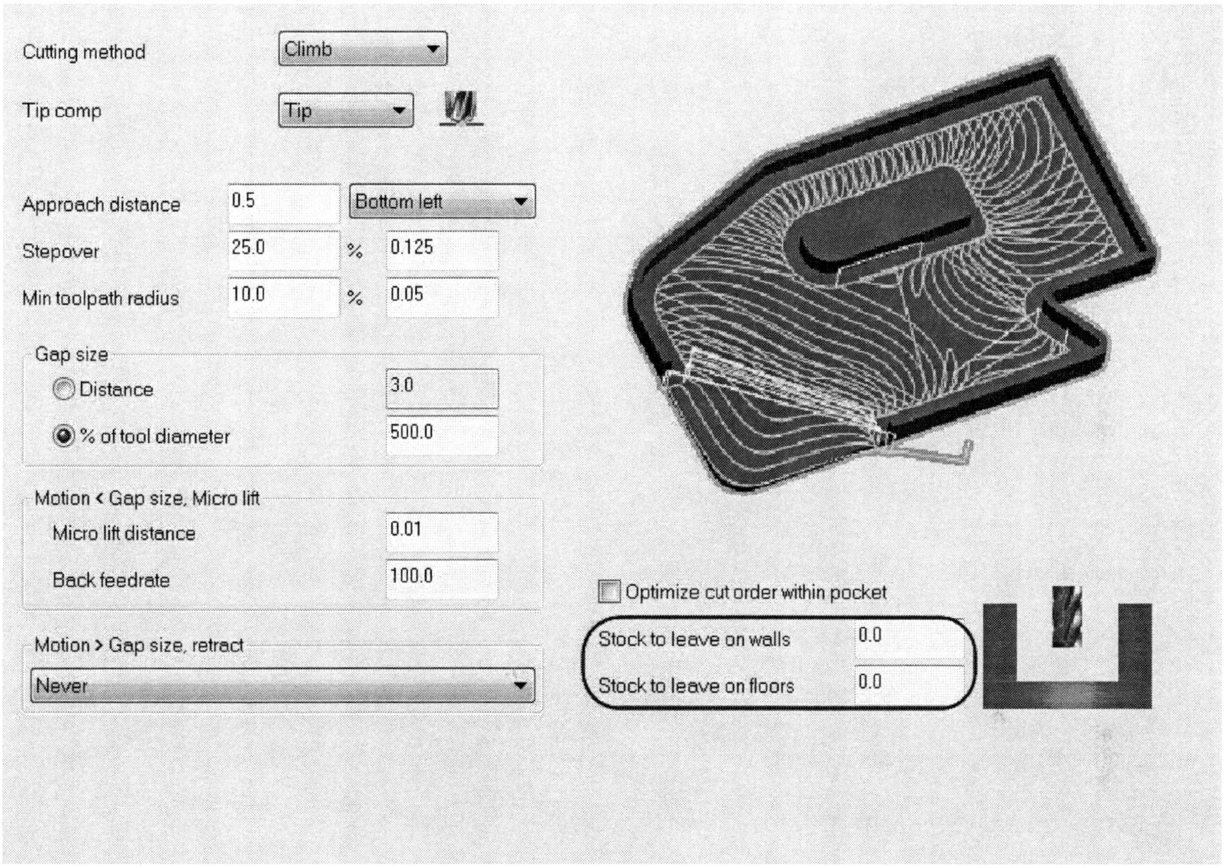

Cutting method	Climb ▼
Tip comp	Tip ▼

Approach distance	0.5		Bottom left ▼
Stepover	25.0	%	0.125
Min toolpath radius	10.0	%	0.05

Gap size
- ○ Distance   3.0
- ◉ % of tool diameter   500.0

Motion < Gap size, Micro lift
Micro lift distance	0.01
Back feedrate	100.0

Motion > Gap size, retract
Never ▼

☐ Optimize cut order within pocket

Stock to leave on walls   0.0
Stock to leave on floors   0.0

13.5 Set the Depth Cuts Parameters

• From the **Tree view list**, select the **Depth Cuts Parameters** and disable **Depth Cuts** as shown in Figure: 13.5.1.

Figure: 13.5.1

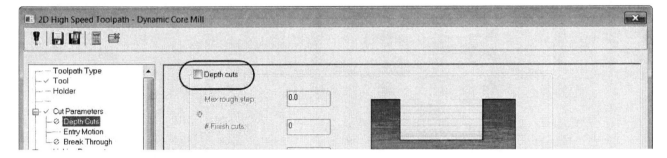

13.6 Set the Entry Motion

• Set the **Entry Method to helix only**. Input a **Z clearance** value of **0.05** and a **Plunge angle** of **2.0** degrees as shown in Figure: 13.6.1.

Figure: 13.6.1

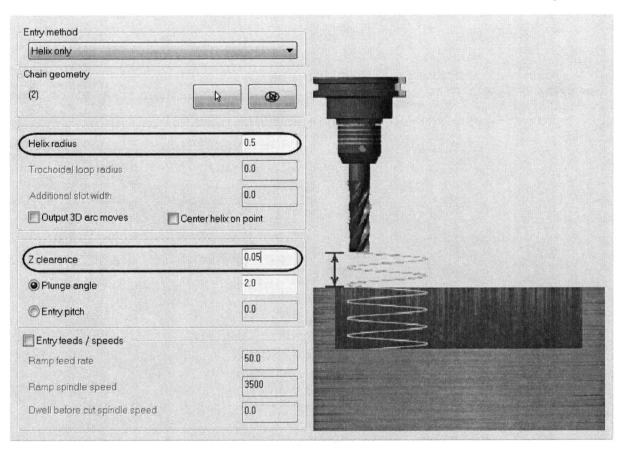

13.7 Set the Linking Parameters

♦ Select **Linking Parameters,** enable **Clearance**, input a value of **1.0** and input a **Depth** value of **-1.0** as shown in <u>Figure: 13.7.1</u>.

Figure: 13.7.1

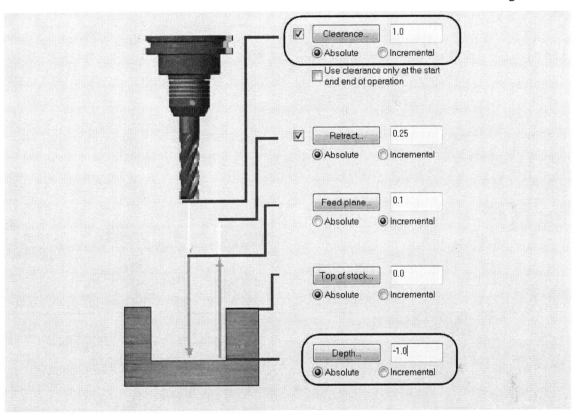

♦ Select the **OK** button to generate the toolpath.

STEP 14: BACKPLOT THE TOOLPATHS

Backplotting shows the path the tools take to cut the part. This display lets you spot errors in the program before you machine the part. As you backplot toolpaths, Mastercam displays additional information such as the X, Y, and Z coordinates, the path length, the minimum and maximum coordinates and the cycle time. It also shows any collisions between the workpiece and the tool.

◆ Make sure that the toolpath is selected (signified by the green check mark on the folder icon). If all operations

are not selected choose the **Select All Operations** icon.

◆ Select the **Backplot selected operations** icon.

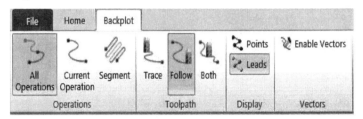

◆ Select the **Backplot** tab and have the following settings enabled as shown.

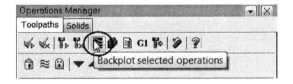

◆ Select the **Home** tab and make sure that you have the following settings on as shown.

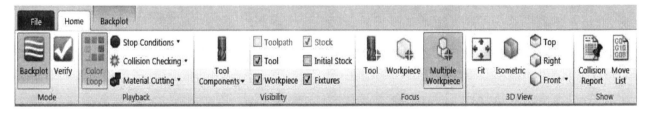

◆ To see the part from an **Isometric** view select the **Isometric** icon.

◆ To fit the workpiece to the screen, select the **Fit** icon.

◆ You can step through the **Backplot** by using the **Step forward** or **Step back** buttons.

◆ You can adjust the speed of the backplot.

◆ Select the **Play Simulation** button in the VCR bar to run **Backplot**.

◆ The toolpath should look as shown.

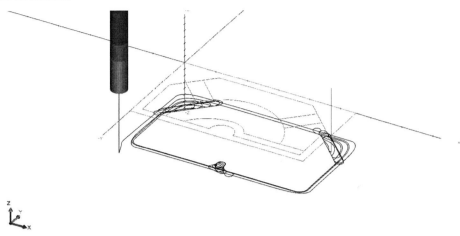

STEP 15: SIMULATE THE TOOLPATH IN VERIFY

Verify Mode shows the path the tools take to cut the part with material removal. This display lets you spot errors in the program before you machine the part. As you verify toolpaths, Mastercam displays additional information such as the X, Y, and Z coordinates, the path length , the minimum and maximum coordinates and the cycle time. It also shows any collisions between the workpiece and the tool.

◆ From **Mastercam Backplot Home** tab, switch to **Verify** and change the settings for the **Visibility** and **Focus** as shown in Figure: 15.0.1.

Figure: 15.0.1

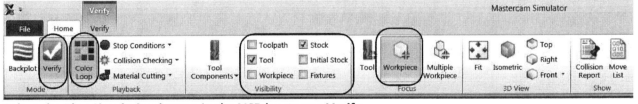

◆ Select the **Play Simulation** button in the VCR bar to run **Verify**.

◆ The part should appear as shown.

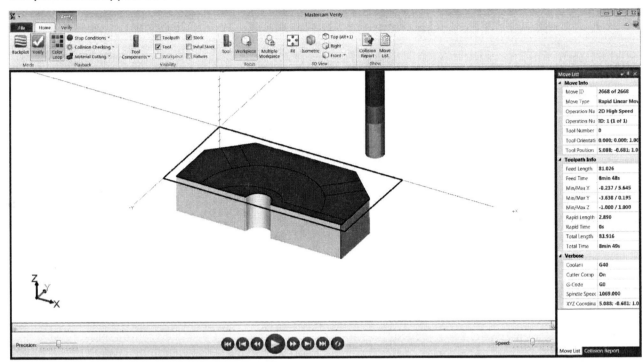

◆ To go back to Mastercam window, minimize **Verify** window as shown.

STEP 16: 2D HIGH SPEED CORE MILL

2D High Speed Core Mill toolpath generates the free flowing motion needed to machine features such as standing bosses and cores in a single operation. We need to chain the outer boundary of the part to define the stock and then machine the inner boundary which will be defined as an island and will not be machined.

Toolpath Preview:

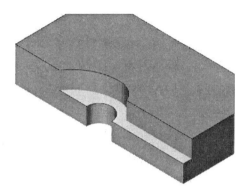

16.1 Chain the Entities

♦ Press **Alt** + **T** to remove the toolpath display.

Toolpaths
♦ **2D High speed.**

♦ 🔲 **Core.**

♦ When the **Chaining** dialog box appears leave the default settings.

♦ Select the outer profile of the part as shown in <u>Figure: 16.1.1</u>.

Figure: 16.1.1

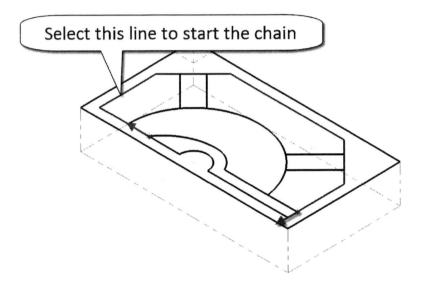

♦ Select the line as shown in <u>Figure: 16.1.2</u> to continue the selection.

Figure: 16.1.2

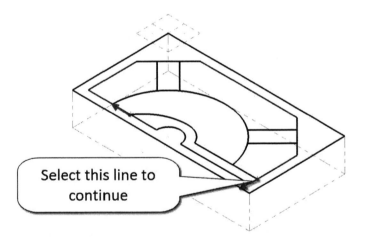

♦ Pick the **End** button from the **Chaining** dialog box to complete the first chain.

♦ Select the second profile of the part starting as shown in <u>Figure: 16.1.3</u>.

Figure: 16.1.3

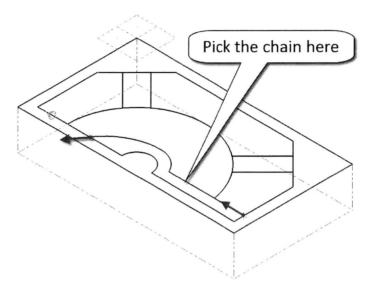

Pick the chain here

♦ Select the line as shown in <u>Figure: 16.1.4</u> to finish the chain.

Figure: 16.1.4

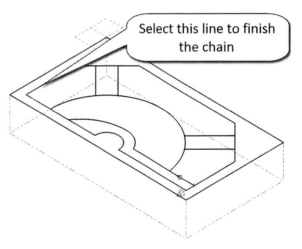

Select this line to finish the chain

♦ Pick the **End** button from the **Chaining** dialog box to complete the second chain.

• Select the **OK** button to exit the **Chaining** dialog box.

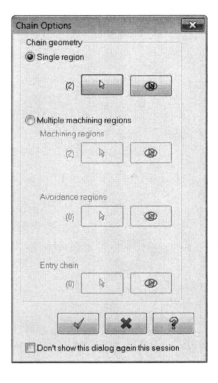

• Select the **OK** button to exit the **Chain Options** dialog box.
• In the toolpath type page choose **Core Mill.**

Core Mill   Peel Mill   Blend Mill   Area Mill   Rest Mill   Dynamic Area Mill

Dynamic Rest Mill   Dynamic Core Mill   Dynamic Contour

- Select the **Tool** page and make all the necessary changes as shown in <u>Figure: 16.1.5</u>.
- Select the **1/2" Flat Endmill** from the list.

Figure: 16.1.5

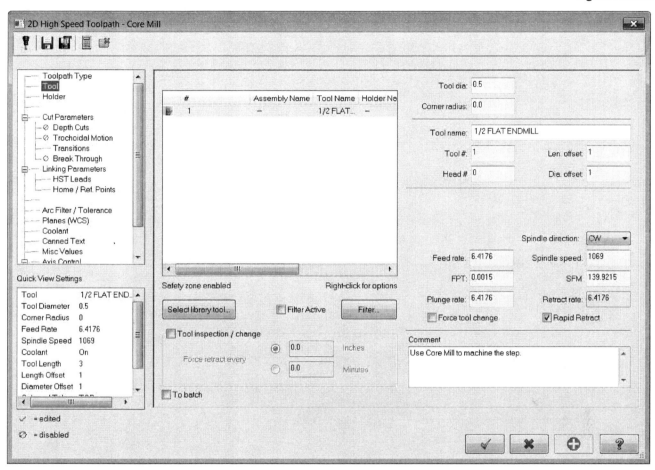

16.2 Set the Cut Parameters

◆ Choose **Cut Parameters** and enable **Smoothing** as shown in <u>Figure: 16.2.1</u>.

Figure: 16.2.1

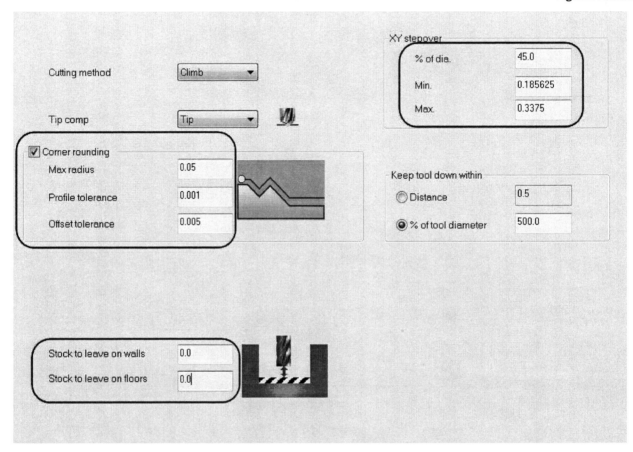

16.3 Set the Depth Cuts Parameters

• From the **Tree view list**, select the **Depth Cuts Parameters** and enable **Depth Cuts** as shown in Figure: 16.3.1.

Figure: 16.3.1

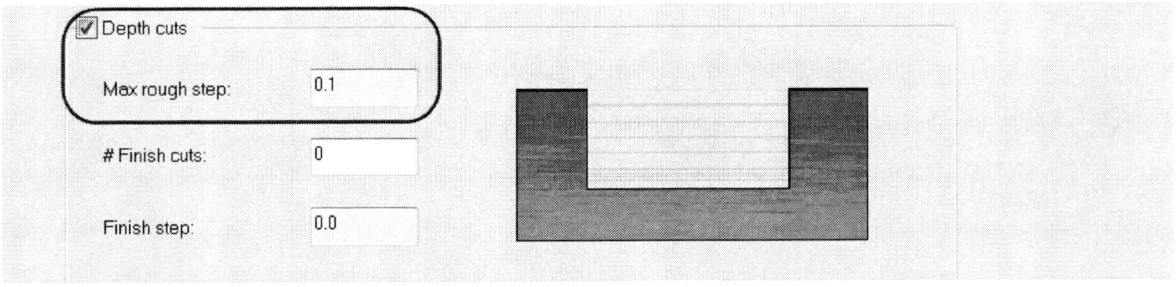

☑ Depth cuts	
Max rough step:	0.1
# Finish cuts:	0
Finish step:	0.0

16.4 Set the Transitions

• Select transitions and enable **Entry helix** and enter a **Radius** of **0.475**. Enable **Output 3D arc moves** as shown in Figure: 16.4.1.

Figure: 16.4.1

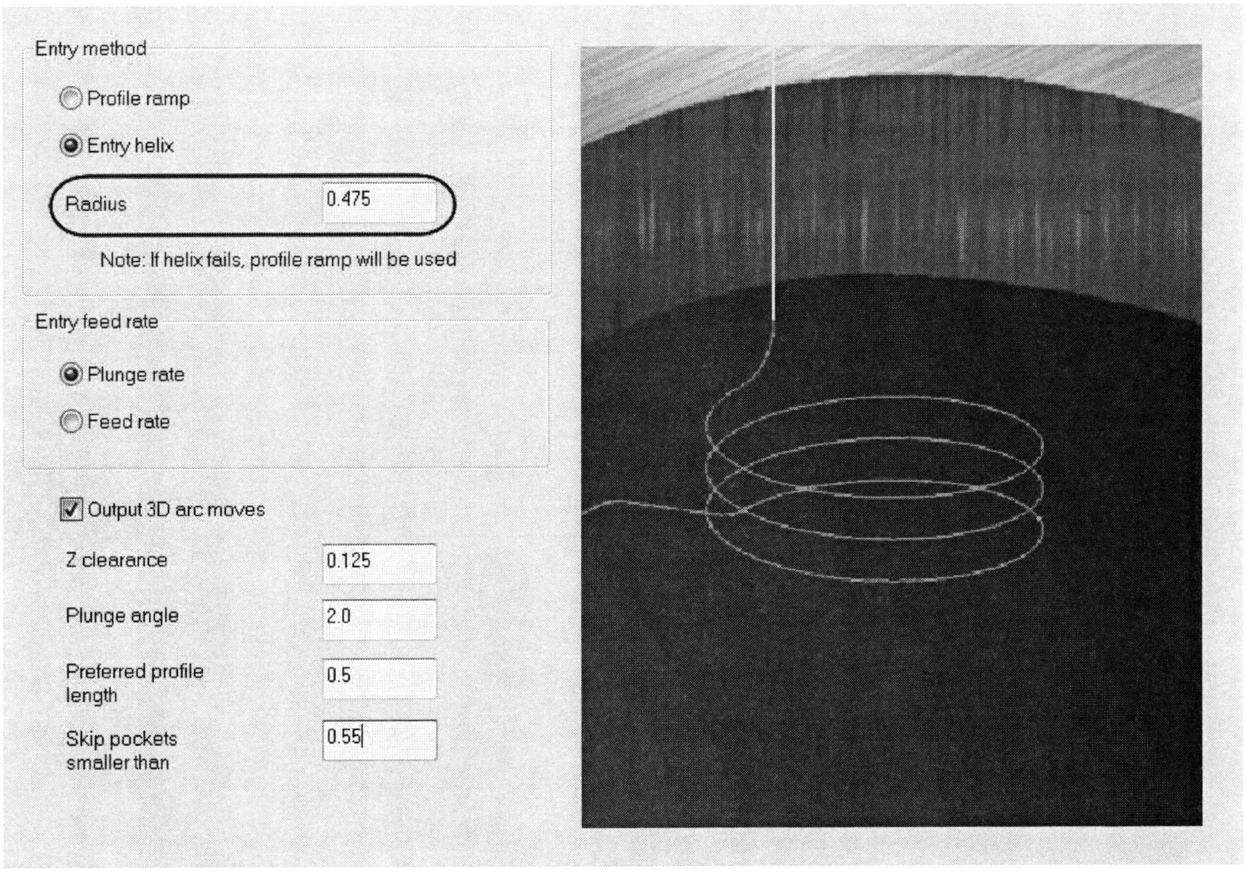

Entry method
- ○ Profile ramp
- ● Entry helix
  - Radius   0.475
  - Note: If helix fails, profile ramp will be used

Entry feed rate
- ● Plunge rate
- ○ Feed rate

☑ Output 3D arc moves

Z clearance	0.125
Plunge angle	2.0
Preferred profile length	0.5
Skip pockets smaller than	0.55

16.5 Set the Linking Parameters

♦ Select **Linking Parameters** and input a **Depth of -0.5** as shown in <u>Figure: 16.5.1</u>.

Figure: 16.5.1

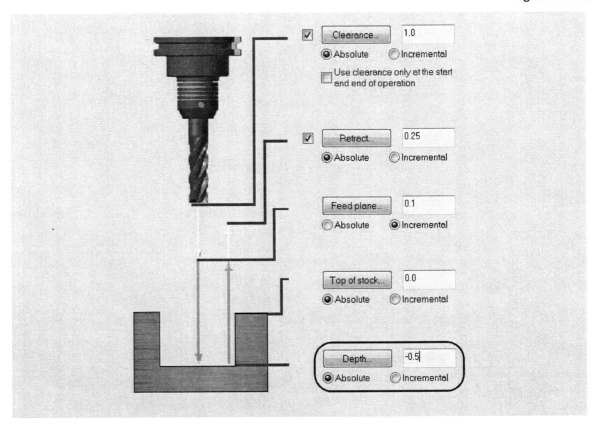

♦ Select the **OK** button to exit the **Area Mill** parameters.

16.6 Backplot the toolpath

◆ See page 658 to review Backplot procedure.

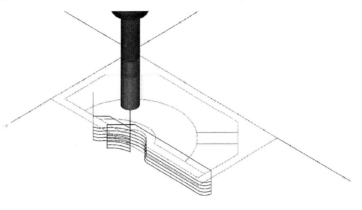

◆ To go back to Mastercam window, minimize **Backplot** window as shown.

16.7 Verify both toolpaths

◆ See page 659 for more info.

◆ To verify all toolpaths, from the **Toolpaths Operations Manager**, choose the **Select all operations** icon.

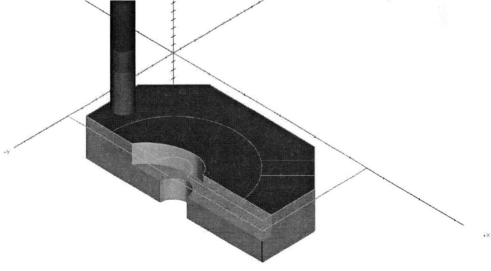

◆ To go back to Mastercam minimize **Verify** window.

STEP 17: 2D HIGH SPEED BLEND MILL

2D High Speed Blend Mill toolpath morphs smoothly between two open chains. You can create the toolpath along or across the selected chains. This machining strategy supports the full depth of cutting, utilizing more of the cutters flute length and resulting in less cycle time and tool wear.

Toolpath Preview:

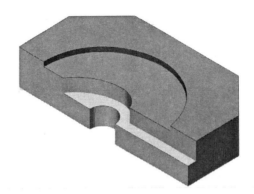

17.1 Chain the Entities

Toolpaths
* **2D High speed.**

* 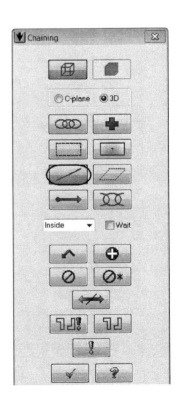 **Blend.**
* When the **Chaining** dialog box appears select the **Single** button.

Mill Level 1 Training Tutorial

• Select the arc as shown in <u>Figure: 17.1.1</u>.

Figure: 17.1.1

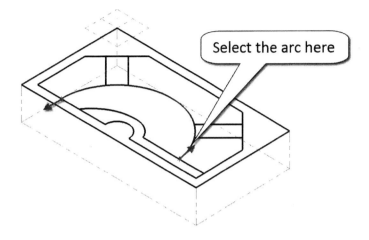

Select the arc here

• To chain the second arc choose the **Partial** chaining method as shown in <u>Figure: 17.1.2</u>.

Figure: 17.1.2

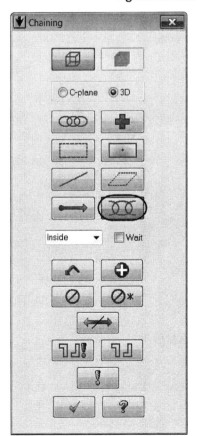

* Select the two entities as shown in <u>Figure: 17.1.3</u>.

Figure: 17.1.3

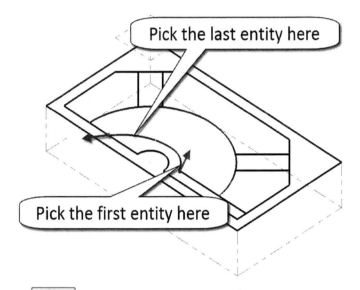

Pick the last entity here

Pick the first entity here

* Choose the **OK** button to exit the chaining dialog box.
* Select **Toolpath Type** from the **Tree view list** and pick **Blend Mill.**

Core Mill   Peel Mill   Blend Mill   Area Mill   Rest Mill   Dynamic Area
                                                                 Mill

Dynamic Rest   Dynamic Core   Dynamic
    Mill   Mill   Contour

17.2 Select a 1/4" Flat Endmill from the Library and set the Tool Parameters

* Select **Tool** from the **Tree view list**.

* Click on the **Select library tool** button.
* Select the **Filter** button as shown.

* Select the **None** button and then under **Tool Types** choose the **Flat Endmill** Icon.

◆ Under tool diameter pick **Equal** and input a value **0.25** as shown in <u>Figure: 17.2.1</u>.

Figure: 17.2.1

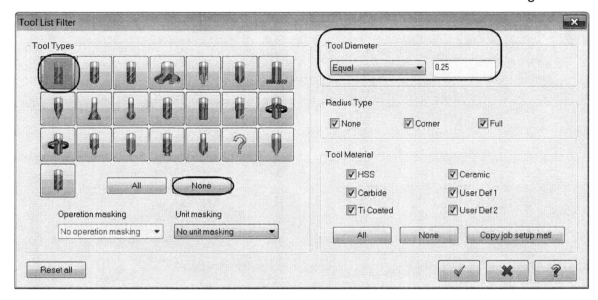

◆ Select the **OK** button to exit the **Tool List Filter.**
◆ In the **Tool Selection** dialog box you should only see a **1/4"** Flat Endmill.

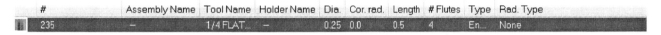

#	Assembly Name	Tool Name	Holder Name	Dia.	Cor. rad.	Length	# Flutes	Type	Rad. Type
235	–	1/4 FLAT...	–	0.25	0.0	0.5	4	En...	None

◆ Select the **1/4" Flat Endmill** in the **Tool Selection** page and then select the **OK** button to exit.

• Make the necessary changes as shown in <u>Figure: 17.2.2</u>.

Figure: 17.2.2

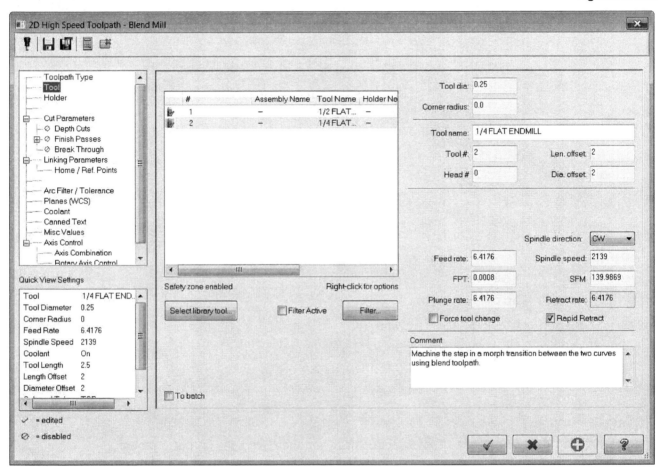

17.3 Set the Cut Parameters

- Set the **Cutting method** to **Zigzag** and **Along** as shown in <u>Figure: 17.3.1</u>. This will morph start the cut along the first chain and then morph it towards the second chain.

Figure: 17.3.1

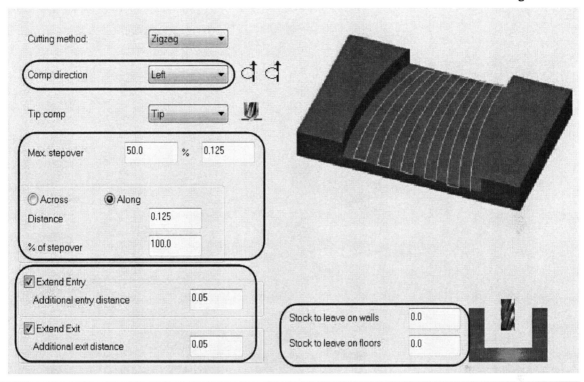

Along cuts in the along direction, stepping over in the across direction.

Max Stepover sets the distance between adjacent passes.

Distance/% of stepover sets the spacing between the temporary across moves. These moves are used to generate the final toolpath but are not included in the final toolpath.

17.4 Set Depth Cuts

• Ensure **Depth cuts** is off.

17.5 Set the Linking Parameters

• Enter a **Depth** of **-0.125** as shown in Figure: 17.5.1.

Figure: 17.5.1

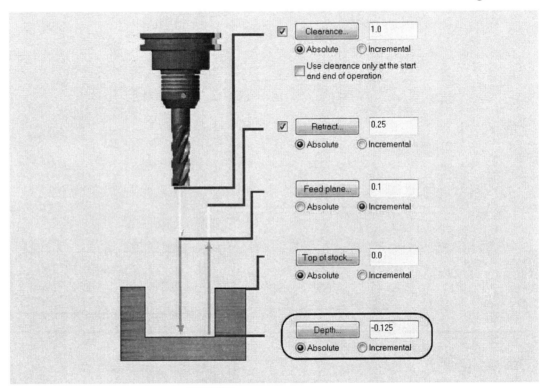

• Choose the **OK** button to generate the toolpath.

17.6 Backplot the toolpath

◆ **Backplot** the toolpath page 658 for more information.

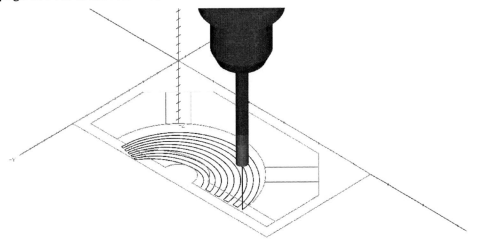

◆ To go back to Mastercam minimize **Backplot** window.

17.7 Verify the toolpaths

◆ To **Verify** the toolpaths see page 659 for more information.

◆ To verify all toolpaths, from the **Toolpaths Operations Manager**, choose the **Select all operations** icon.

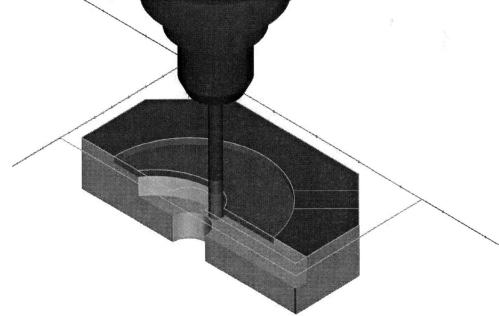

◆ To go back to Mastercam minimize **Verify** window.

STEP 18: 2D HIGH SPEED PEEL MILL

2D High Speed Peel Mill toolpath allows for efficient constant climb milling between two selected contours or along a single contour. It uses a trochodial style of motion to cut the slot. For single chains, you need to define the width of the cut. Otherwise the width is defined by the area between the two contours.

Toolpath Preview:

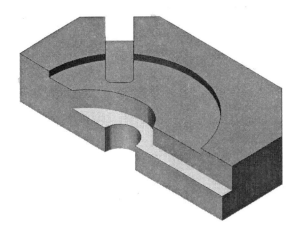

Toolpaths
- **2D High Speed.**
- **Peel.**
- Leave the default chaining method and select the lines as shown. Ensure both chains go in the same direction as shown in in <u>Figure: 18.0.1</u>.

Figure: 18.0.1

NOTE: To change the direction of chaining if needed, click on the **Reverse** button from the **Chaining** dialog box. ⟷

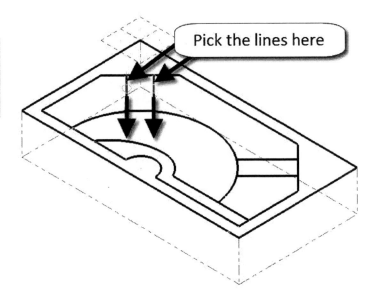

Pick the lines here

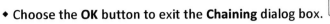

- Choose the **OK** button to exit the **Chaining** dialog box.
- In the **Toolpath Type**, **Peel Mill** is already selected.

Core Mill   Peel Mill   Blend Mill   Area Mill   Rest Mill   Dynamic Area Mill

- Select the **Tool** page from the **Tree view list** and select the **1/4" Flat Endmill** from the list of tools.
- Make any necessary changes as shown in Figure: 18.0.2.

Figure: 18.0.2

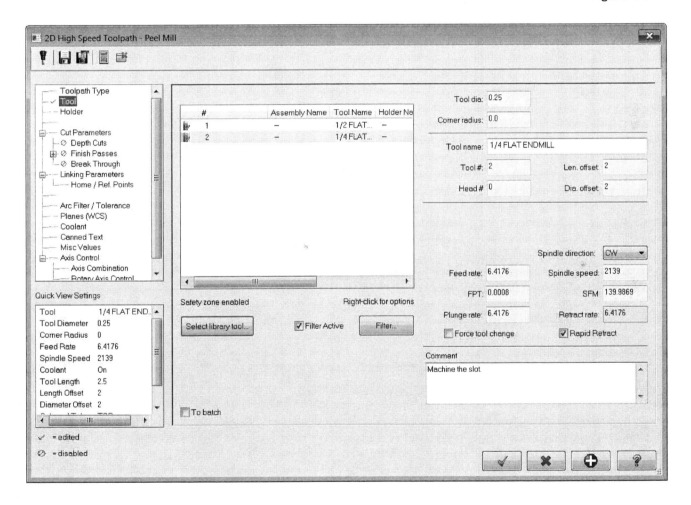

18.1 Set the Cut Parameters

◆ Select **Cut Parameters** and enter a **Min toolpath radius** of **2.5%** and a **Stepover** amount of **0.05** as shown in Figure: 18.1.1.

◆ Enable the **Extend entry** option and **Extend Exit**. Input a value to extend the entry by **0.5** and to extend the exit by **1.25** as shown in Figure: 18.1.1.

Figure: 18.1.1

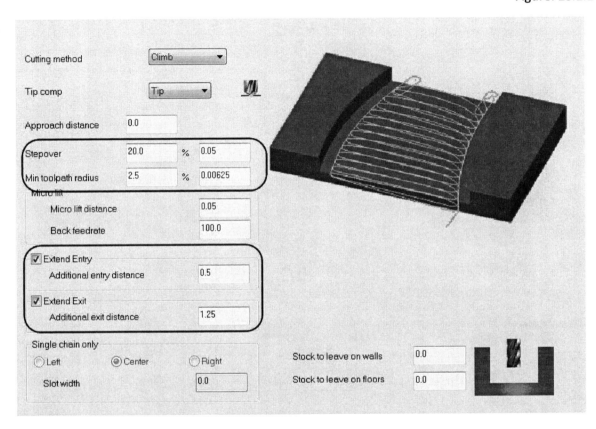

Stepover sets the distance between adjacent cuts of the toolpath.

Min toolpath radius defines the radius of the arc that the tool follows along its semi-circular path. This value must be greater than the stepover amount.

Micro lift distance enter the distance the tool lifts off of the part on back moves. Micro lifts are slight lifts that help clear chips and minimize excessive tool heating.

Back feedrate controls the speed (inches per minute or millimeters per minute) of the backfeed movement of the tool. This allows 3D arcs between cuts to have a different feed rate than the rest of the toolpath, which can help reduce cycle time.

Extend Entry/Exit allows you to adjust the initial and final tool engagement with the material.

18.2 Set the Depth Cuts

◆ Ensure the **Depth Cuts** are disabled.

18.3 Set the Finish Pass Parameters

◆ Ensure **Finish passes, Machine Finish passes only at final depth** and **Keep tool down** are enabled as shown in Figure: 18.3.1.

Figure: 18.3.1

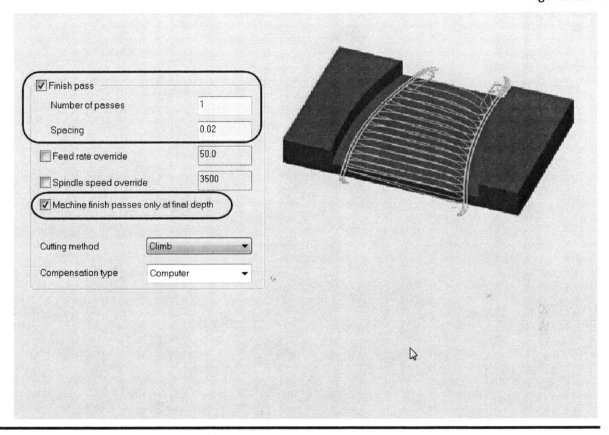

Finish Pass performs a high speed finish pass along the walls of the slot.

Machine finish passes only at final depth performs the finish passes at the final cutting depth only.

Keep tool down determines whether or not to retract the tool between depth cuts/multi-passes.

18.4 Set the Linking Parameters

◆ Set the **Depth** to **-0.5** as shown in <u>Figure: 18.4.1</u>.

Figure: 18.4.1

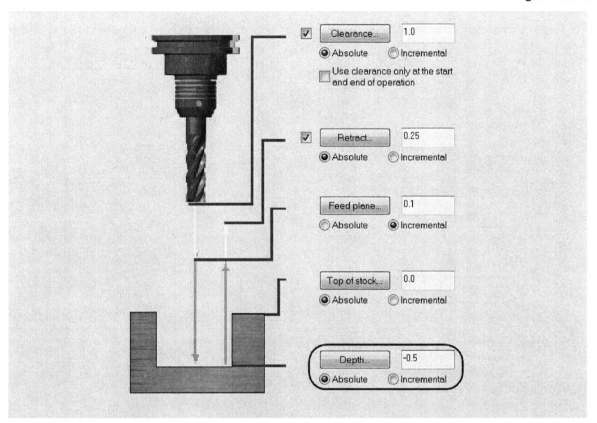

◆ Choose the **OK** button to generate the toolpath.

18.5 Backplot the toolpath

◆ See page 658 for more information.

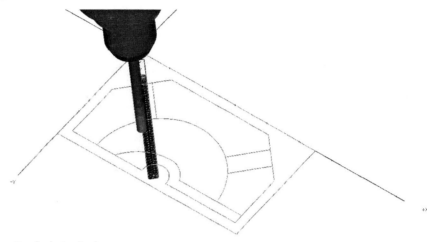

◆ To go back to Mastercam minimize **Backplot** window.

18.6 Verify all toolpaths

◆ See page 659 for more information.

◆ To verify all toolpaths, from the **Toolpaths Operations Manager**, choose the **Select all operations** icon.

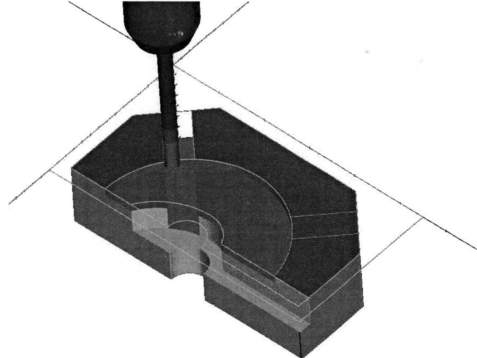

◆ To go back to Mastercam minimize **Verify** window.

STEP 19: 2D HIGH SPEED PEEL MILL

In this step you will learn how to copy an existing toolpath in the Toolpaths Operations Manager. You will also learn how to rechain the geometry used in the toolpath.

Toolpath Preview:

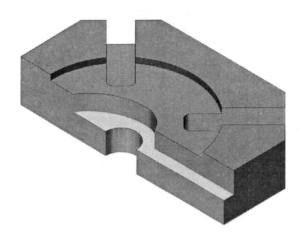

19.1 Copy the Previous Toolpath

• From the **Toolpaths Operations Manager**, select only operation #4 (the peel mill toolpath).

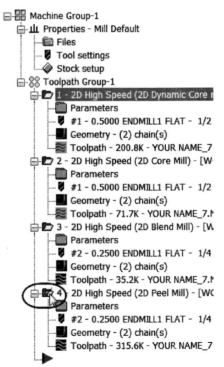

Mill Level 1 Training Tutorial

Mastercam. **X**⁷

♦ Right click and hold the right mouse button down and drag the operation to a point below it as shown in
Figure: 19.1.1.

Figure: 19.1.1

Geometry - (2) chain(s)
Toolpath - 35.2K - YOUR NAME_7.I
4 - 2D High Speed (2D Peel Mill) - [W(
Parameters
#2 - 0.2500 ENDMILL1 FLAT - 1/4
Geometry - (2) chain(s)
Toolpath - 315.6K - YOUR NAME_7

♦ Release the right mouse button and select the option **Copy After** as shown in Figure: 19.1.2.

Figure: 19.1.2

Geometry - (2) chain(s)
Toolpath - 35.2K - YOUR NAME_7.I
4 - 2D High Speed (2D Peel Mill) - [W(
Parameters
#2 - 0.2500 ENDMILL1 FLAT - 1/4
Geometry - (2) chain(s)
Toolpath - 315.6K - YOUR NAME_7

Move before
Move after
Copy before
Copy after
Cancel

• Make sure that the insert arrow is below the last toolpath as shown in <u>Figure: 19.1.3</u>; otherwise, pick the icon to move the insert arrow down.

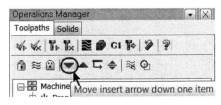

Figure: 19.1.3

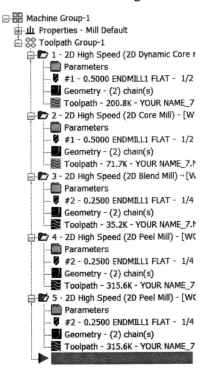

19.2 Re-Chain the Geometry

• In the operation #5, pick **Geometry**.

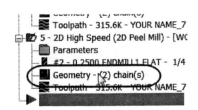

Mastercam. X⁷

• From the **Chain Options**, click on the **Unselect** button to remove the existing chains.

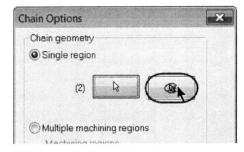

• Click on the **Select** button.

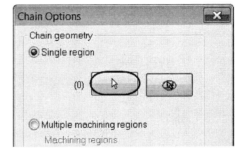

• When the chaining dialog box appears leave the default settings and choose the line as shown in <u>Figure: 19.2.1</u> (this time we will chain one entity only to create the toolpath).

Figure: 19.2.1

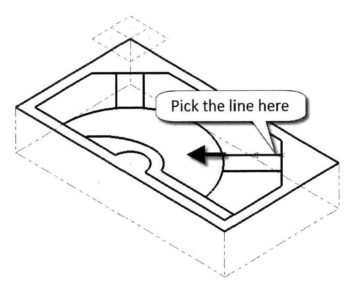

• Once the geometry has been selected choose the **OK** button to exit the **Chaining** dialog box.

• Choose the **OK** button again to exit the **Chain Options**.

• Pick **Parameters** in **Operation #5.**

19.3 Set the Cut Parameters

• Select **Cut Parameters** and change **Single chain** only to **Left** and enter a **Slot width** of **0.5** as shown in Figure: 19.3.1.

Figure: 19.3.1

Mastercam. X⁷

19.4 Set the Linking Parameters

• Select **Linking Parameters** and make sure that the **Depth** is set to **-0.5** as shown in  .

Figure: 19.4.1

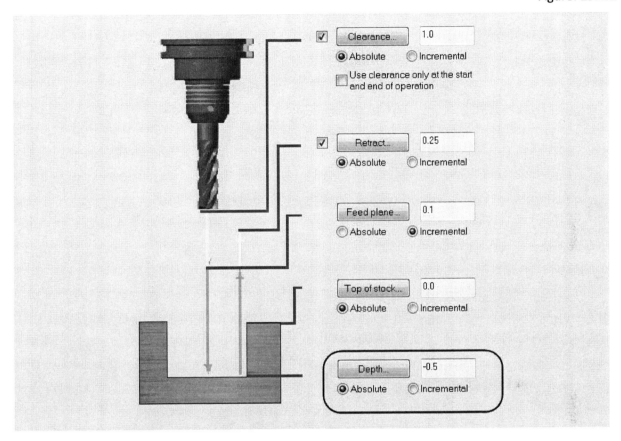

• Choose the **OK** button to exit the toolpath parameters.

• Pick the button to **Regenerate all dirty operations**.

19.5 Backplot the toolpath

• To **Backplot** the toolpath see page 658 for more information.

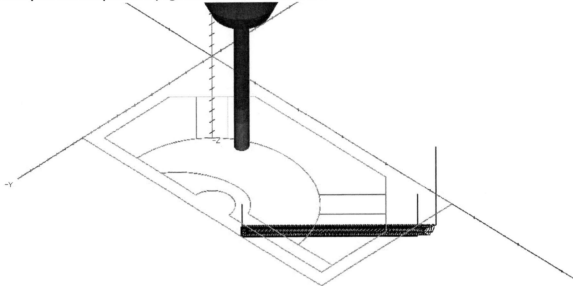

• To go back to Mastercam minimize **Backplot** window.

19.6 Verify all toolpaths

• To Verify the toolpaths see page 659 for more information.

• To verify all toolpaths, from the **Toolpaths Operations Manager**, choose the **Select all operations** icon.

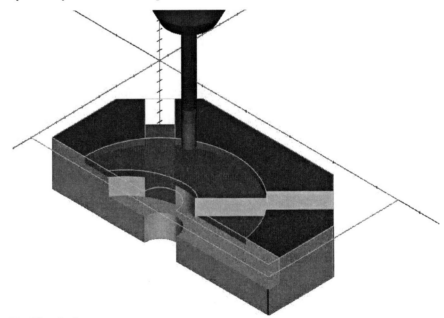

• To go back to Mastercam minimize **Verify** window.

STEP 20: POST THE FILE

♦ Ensure all operations are selected; if they are not, use the **Select all operations** button in the **Operations Manager.**

♦ Select the **Post selected operations** button from the **Operations Manager.** G1

♦ In the **Post processing** window make the necessary changes as shown in <u>Figure: 20.0.1</u>.

Figure: 20.0.1

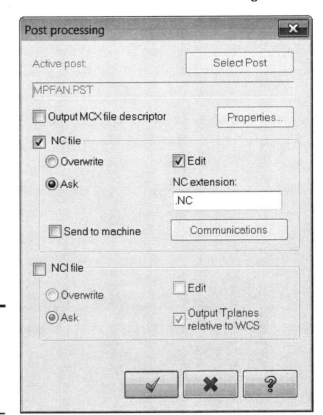

NC File enabled allows you to keep the NC file and to assign the same name as the MCX file.

Edit enabled allows you to automatically launch the default editor.

♦ Select the **OK** button to continue.

♦ Save your file and name it **YOUR NAME_7.NC**.

- A window with Mastercam Code Expert will be lunched and the NC program will appear as shown.

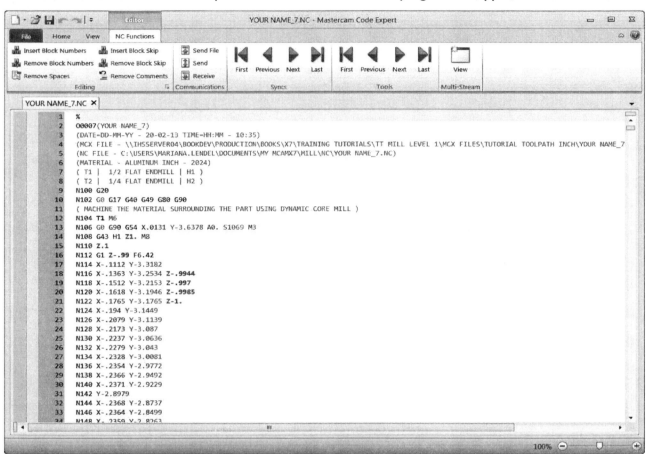

- Select the red "**X**" box at the upper right corner to exit the editor.

STEP 21: SAVE THE UPDATED MCX FILE

REVIEW EXERCISE - STUDENT PRACTICE

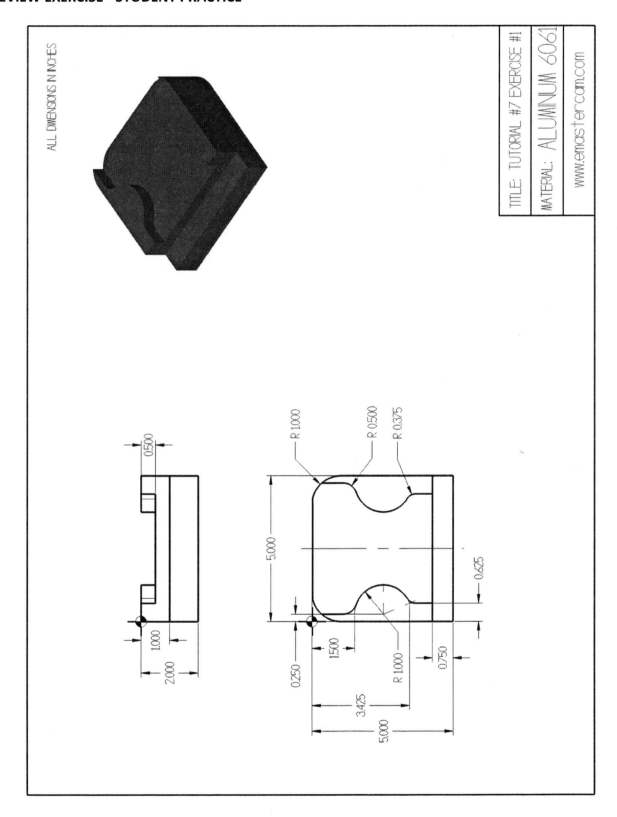

ALL DIMENSIONS IN INCHES

TITLE: TUTORIAL #7 EXERCISE #1

MATERIAL: ALUMINUM 6061

www.emastercam.com

R 1.000
R 0.500
R 0.375
0.625
R 1.000
0.750
0.250
1.500
3.425
5.000
5.000
0.500
1.000
2.000

CREATE THE GEOMETRY FOR TUTORIAL #7 EXERCISE

Use these commands to create the geometry:
- Create Rectangle.
- Create Line Endpoint.
- Create Arc Polar.
- Create Fillet Entities.

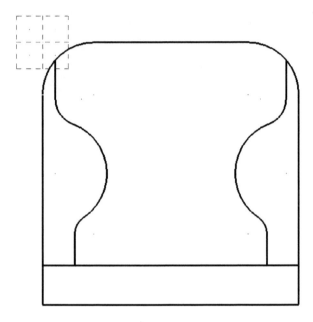

CREATE THE TOOLPATHS FOR TUTORIAL #7 EXERCISE

Create the Toolpaths for Tutorial #7 Exercise as per the instructions below.

Set the machine properties including the Stock Setup.
Remove the material on the step Contour (2D).

* Use a **7/8"Flat Endmill**.
* Based on your chaining direction ensure the **Compensation direction** is set correct.
* Enable **Depth Cuts**.
* **Lead In/Out**, ensure the arc radius is set to zero.
* No **Break Through**, **Multi Passes**.
* Set the depth according to the drawing.

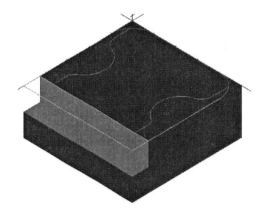

Remove the material around the fillets using Contour (2D).

* Use the **7/8" Flat Endmill**.
* Based on your chaining direction ensure the **Compensation direction** is set correct.
* Enable **Depth Cuts**.
* Set a **Lead In/Out** and **Break Through**.
* No **Multi Passes**.
* Set the depth according to the drawing.

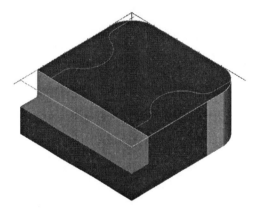

Create a 2D High Speed Blend Mill toolpath to remove the material in the center of the part.

* Select the two chains.
* Use a **1/2" Flat Endmill**.
* Select along for the tool cutting direction.
* Set the **Compensation** direction to **Inside**.
* **Extend Exit 0.5"**
* Disable **Depth Cuts** and **Break Through**.
* Set the depth according to the drawing.
* Your part will appear as shown.

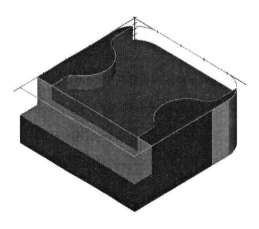

NOTES:

TUTORIAL #7 QUIZ

◆ What is the advantage of Dynamic Mill?

◆ What features does Core Mill Machine have?

◆ What entities need to be chained to utilize Core Milling?

◆ How does a Blend Mill toolpath work?

TUTORIAL #8

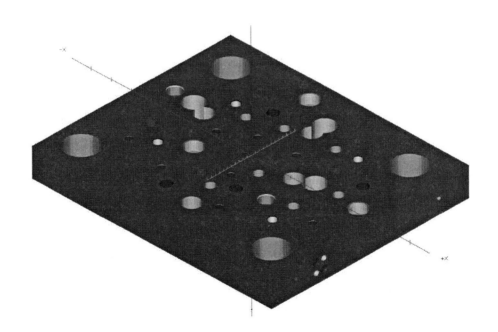

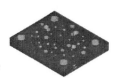

OVERVIEW OF STEPS TAKEN TO CREATE THE FINAL PART:

Import the 3D SolidWorks file (CAD Model) used to generate Toolpaths from:
- The student will download the file from emastercam.com.
- The student will open the SolidWorks file without importing the solid history.
- The student will use the WCS to rotate the part.

Create the necessary Toolpaths to machine the part:
- The student will set up the stock size to be used and the clamping method used.
- The Feature Based Drilling toolpath will be used to machine all the holes.

Backplot and Verify the file:
- The Backplot will be used to simulate a step by step process of the tool's movements.
- The Verify will be used to watch the tool's machine the part out of a solid model.

Post Process the file to generate the G-code:
- The Student will then post process the file to obtain an NC file containing the necessary code for the machine.

 This tutorial takes approximately one hour to complete.

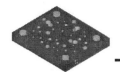

GEOMETRY CREATION

STEP 1: SETTING UP THE GRAPHIC USER INTERFACE

Please refer to the **Getting Started** section to set up the graphics user interface.

STEP 2: DOWNLOAD THE FILE

You will require an internet connection to download this file.

Resources - Download the file from **www.emastercam.com/files/**
* Find the Tutorial #8 file.
* Pick a place which is easy to remember to save the file, example desktop, and save the file there.

> **NOTE:** You will need to extract the .zip file before you can open the solidworks file.

STEP 3: OPEN THE SOLID WITH NO SW HISTORY

If you do not have SolidWorks installed on your computer this is how you go about opening the solid.

* With Mastercam open.

File
* 📂 **Open.**
* Click on the **All Mastercam X Files** button as shown in Figure: 3.0.1.

Figure: 3.0.1

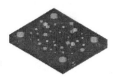

◆ In the list that opens select **SolidWorks Files (*.SLDPRT; *.SLDASM)** as shown in <u>Figure: 3.0.2</u>.

Figure: 3.0.2

All Mastercam X Files (*.MCX-7;*.MCX-6;*.MCX-5;*.M
Mastercam X7 Files (*.MCX-7)
Mastercam X6 Files (*.MCX-6)
Mastercam X5 Files (*.MCX-5)
Mastercam pre-X5 Files (*.MCX)
Mastercam Educ X7 Files (*.EMCX-7)
Mastercam Educ X6 Files (*.EMCX-6)
Mastercam Educ X5 Files (*.EMCX-5)
Mastercam Educ pre-X5 Files (*.EMCX)
Mastercam V9 Files (*.MC9)
Mastercam V8 Files (*.MC8)
All Mastercam Files (*.MCX-7;*.MCX-6;*.MCX-5;*.MC
IGES Files (*.IGS;*.IGES)
AutoCAD Files (*.DWG;*.DXF;*.DWF;*.DWFx)
Parasolid Files (*.X_T;*.X_B;*.XMT_TXT)
ProE/Creo Files (*.PRT;*.ASM;*.PRT.*;*.ASM.*)
ACIS Kernel SAT Files (*.SAT;*.SAB)
STEP Files (*.STP;*.STEP)
VDA Files (*.VDA)
Rhino 3D Files (*.3DM)
SolidWorks Files (*.SLDPRT;*.SLDASM)
SolidWorks Drawing Files (*.SLDDRW)
Solid Edge Files (*.PAR;*.PSM;*.ASM)
Autodesk Inventor Files (*.IPT;*.IAM)
Autodesk Inventor Drawing Files (*.IDW)
KeyCreator Files (*.CKD)
Unigraphics/NX Files (*.PRT)
ASCII Files (*.TXT;*.CSV;*.DOC)
StereoLithography Files (*.STL)
Catia V4 Files (*.MODEL;*.EXP)

◆ Find the file in the location it was placed i.e. the desktop.
◆ Select the file **Tutorial #8.SLDPRT** and pick **Options**.
◆ Make sure that both **Import Solids History** and **Import MCX Toolpaths from SolidWorks file** are disabled as shown in <u>Figure: 3.0.3</u>.

Figure: 3.0.3

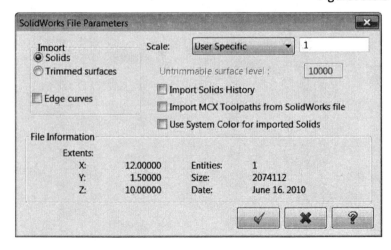

◆ Select the **OK** button to exit the **SolidWorks File Parameters** dialog box.

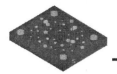

- Pick the **Open** button to open the file.
- Press **Alt** + **S** to shade the solid if needed.

> **NOTE:** By pressing **Alt+S** to shade/unshade the part.

- The file will appear as shown in the top view as shown in <u>Figure: 3.0.4</u>.

Figure: 3.0.4

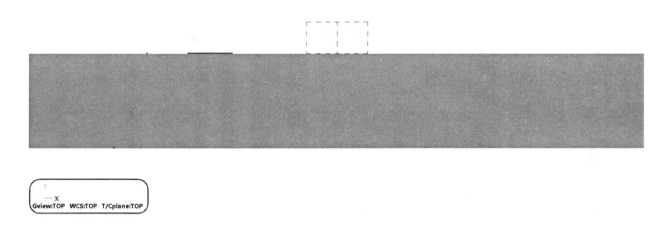

STEP 4: VIEW THE SOLIDS HISTORY

The Solids history shows you the history of the solid, which is a list of operations that were performed to construct the solid. In this case we will only see a solid body because the file is not associated with SolidWorks.

- In the **Operations Manager** choose the **Solids**.

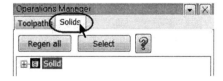

- Select the plus next to **Solid** to see the history.

> **NOTE:** No solid history was imported in this case.

STEP 5: SET THE WCS

If you do not have the solids adon and cannot manipulate the solid part, setting the wcs will allow you to manipulate the part into the proper orientation.

* From the **Status Bar** select **WCS**.
* Pick **View Manager**.

* Select **Back** and then pick the button to set the current **WCS**, **Construction plane** and **Tool plane** with the origins to the selected view as shown in Figure: 5.0.1.

Figure: 5.0.1

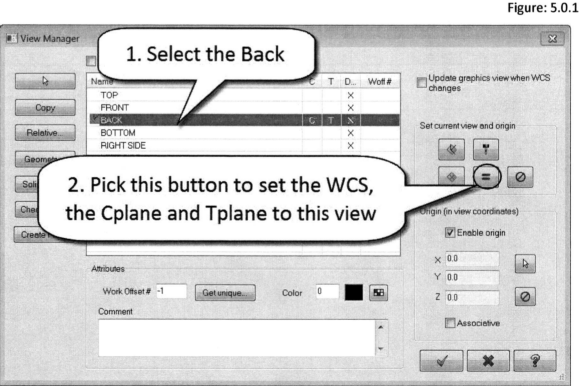

* Choose the **OK** button to exit the **View Manager** dialog box.

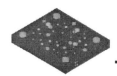

◆ Select the **Top Graphics** view.

◆ Select the **Fit** icon to fit geometry to the graphics window.

◆ Your part will appear as shown.

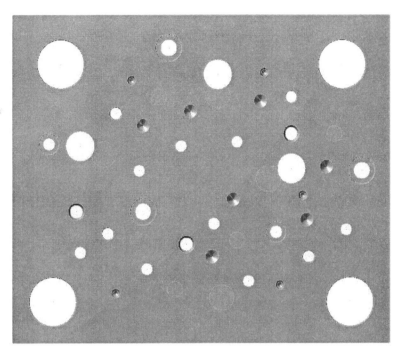

Z
X
Gview:BACK (TOP)   WCS:BACK   T/Cplane:BACK (TOP)

NOTE: Press **Alt+S** to shade/unshade the part.

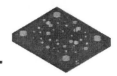

TOOLPATH CREATION

SUGGESTED FIXTURE:

NOTE: In this tutorial we will drill holes on 3 sides of this part. This will require 3 separate setups.

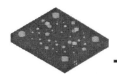

STEP 6: SELECT THE MACHINE AND SET UP THE STOCK

In Mastercam, you select a **Machine Definition** before creating any toolpaths. The **Machine Definition** is a model of your machines capabilities and features. It acts like a template for setting up your machine. The machine definition ties together three main components. The schematic model of your machines components, the control definition that models your control capabilities, and the post processor that will generate the required machine code (G-code). For a Mill Level 1 exercise (2D toolpaths) we need just a basic machine definition.

> **NOTE:** For the purpose of this tutorial, we will be using the Default milling machine.

Machine type

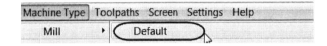

* **Mill.**
* **Default.**
* Select the plus sign in front of **Properties** in the **Toolpaths Manager** to expand the **Toolpaths Group Properties.**

* Select **Tool Settings** to set the tool parameters.

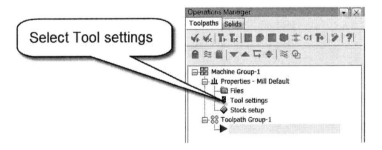

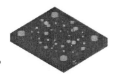

♦ Change the parameters to match the screen shot as shown in Figure: 6.0.1.

Figure: 6.0.1

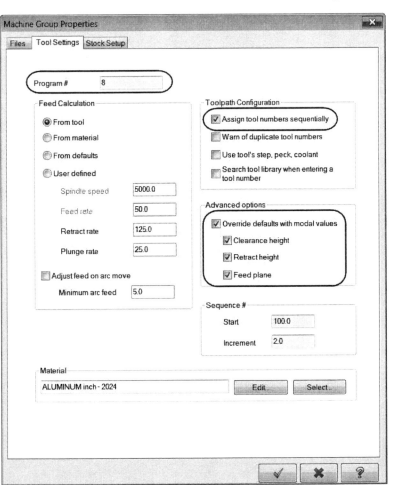

Program # is used to enter a number if your machine tool requires a number for a program name.

Assign tool numbers sequentially allows you to overwrite the tool number from the library with the next available tool number. (First operation tool number 1; Second operation tool number 2, etc.)

Warn of duplicate tool numbers allows you to get a warning if you enter two tools with the same number.

Override defaults with modal values enables the system to keep the values that you enter.

Feed Calculation set **From tool** uses feed rate, plunge rate, retract rate and spindle speed from the tool definition.

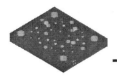
- Select the **Stock Setup** tab to define the stock.
- Make sure that the **Stock View** is set to **BACK** and pick the **Rectangular** shape option as shown in Figure: 6.0.2.
- Choose the **All Solids** button and the stock size will be input.

Figure: 6.0.2

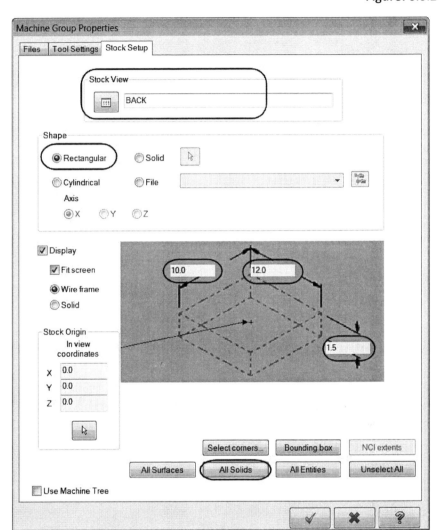

The **Stock Origin** values adjust the positioning of the stock, ensuring that you have equal amount of extra stock around the finished part.

Display options allow you to set the stock as **Wireframe** and to fit the stock to the screen. (Fit Screen)

NOTE: The **Stock** model that you create can be displayed with the part geometry when viewing the file or the toolpaths, during backplot, or while verifying toolpaths. In the graphics, the plus shows you where the stock origin is. The default position is the middle of the stock.

- Select the **OK** button to exit **Machine Group Properties**.

- Select the **Isometric** view from the graphics view toolbar to see the stock.

- Use the **Fit** icon to fit the drawing to the screen.

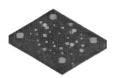

◆ The stock model should appear as shown in <u>Figure: 6.0.3</u>.

Figure: 6.0.3

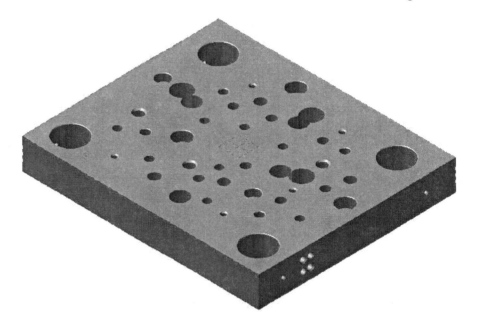

NOTE: You may not be able to see the stock very clear due to the fact that the stock is the same size as the part. The stock is not geometry and can not be selected.
We will only be demonstrating **Feature Based Drilling**. Therefore there will not be any facing or milling toolpaths.

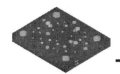
STEP 7: HOLE MAKING OPERATIONS

Several hole-making operations exists, each using a different type of cutting tool and forming a different type of hole.

Drilling: a drill bit enters the workpiece and cuts a blind hole or a through hole with a diameter equal to that of the tool. A drill bit typically has a pointed end to aid it in entering the work piece. A twist drill is the most commonly used, but other types of drill bits, such as a center drill, spot drill, or tap drill can be used to start a hole that will be completed by another operation.

Reaming: a reamer enters the workpiece and enlarges an existing hole to the diamter of the tool. A reamer is a multi point tool that has many flutes, which may be straight or in a helix. Reaming removes a minimal amount of material and is often performed after drilling to obtain a more accurate diameter and a smoother finish.

Tapping: a tap enters the workpiece and cuts threads into an exiting hole. The existing hole is typically drilled by the required tap drill size that will accommodate the desired tap. Threads may be cut to a specified depth inside the hole (bottom tap) or the complete depth of a through hole (through tap).

Boring: a boring tool enters the workpiece and cuts along the internal surface of an existing hole to enlarge the diameter or obtain more precise dimensions. The boring tool is a single point cutting tool, which can be set to cut the desired diameter.

Counterboring: a counterbore tool enters the workpiece and enlarges the top portion of an existing hole to the diameter of the tool. Counterboring is often performed after drilling to provide space for the head of a fastener, such as a bolt to sit flush with the workpiece surface. The counterboring tool has a pilot on the end to guide it straight into the existing hole.

Countersinking: a countersink tool enters the workpiece and enlarges the top portion of an existing hole to a cone shaped opening. Countersinking is often performed after drilling to provide space for the head of a fastener, such as a screw to sit flush with the workpiece surface.

NOTE: We will machine this part using FBM Drill. It will be shown in 4 steps, each step demonstrating features.

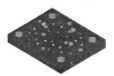

STEP 8: FBM DRILLING

FBM Drill automatically detects holes in a solid based on your specific criteria and to generate a complete series of drilling and chamfering. FBM drill also generates circle mill or helix bore operations for large-hole features when you activate these settings.

Toolpath Preview:

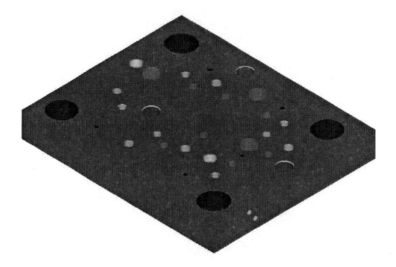

Toolpaths

◆ **FBM Drill.**

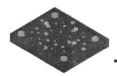
- When the **FBM Toolpaths - Setup** page appears, enable **Automatic initial hole detection.**
- Change the **Grouping** to **Plane** to group the operations by the plane in which the holes lie as shown in
  <u>Figure: 8.0.1</u>.

Figure: 8.0.1

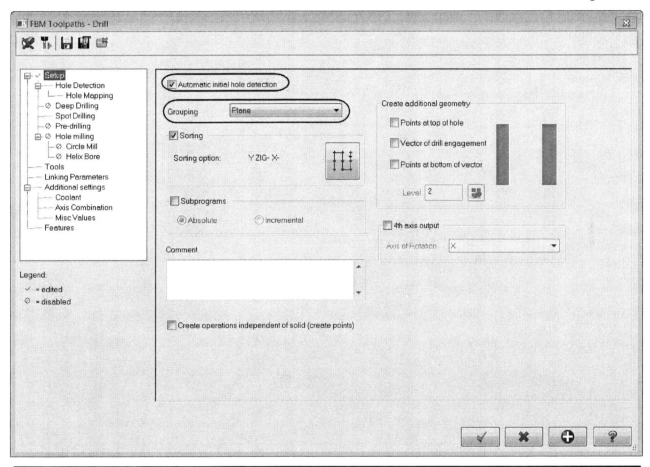

Automatic initial hole/feature detection when selected, Mastercam automatically detects features when you choose the FBM operation. If you save the settings to your toolpath .DEFAULTS file and use that final in the active machine group, Mastercam automatically detects features everytime you choose the FBM operation.

Grouping controls how the drill cycles that FBM Drill creates are organized in the Toolpath Manager. Mastercam orders operations within groups into subgroups by operation type.

Plane groups all operations based on the plane of the hole.

Create additional geometry select one or more options to create geometry for detected hole features without generating toolpaths. The geometry is saved to a level you choose in this section and is non associative.

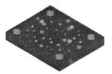

8.1 Hole Detection

♦ Choose **Hole Detection** to control the types of holes **FBM Drill** detects. Enable/disable the options as shown in Figure: 8.1.1.

♦ Ensure the **Maximum diameter** is set to **2.0**. This is done so **FBM Drill** will detect all the holes in the part.

Figure: 8.1.1

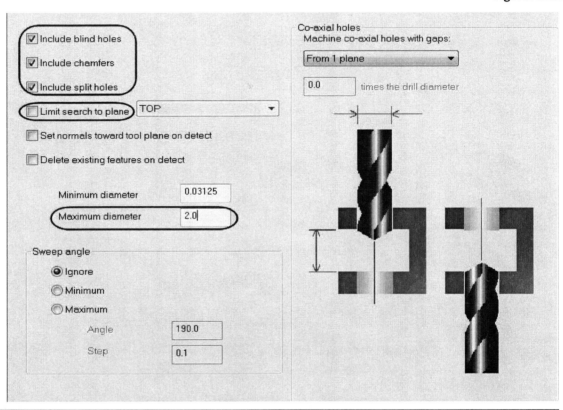

Include blind holes will search your part for blind holes (holes that do not go through the entire solid).

Include chamfers searches for holes with chamfers.

Include split holes searches the part for holes that are incomplete.

Limit search to plane detects features that can only be machined in the selected plane.

Minimum diameter finds holes which are equal to or greater than this value.

Maximum diameter finds holes which are equal to or less than this value.

Sweep angle lets you set a tolerance for how complete holes needs to be in terms of its included angle to be detected by and included in the FBM Drill operation.

Machine co-axial holes with gaps determines whether Mastercam treats multiple holes that share a common axis as a single hole, or as multiple holes from different planes.

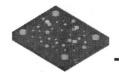

8.2 Spot Drilling

- Select **Spot Drilling** to activate and define the spot drilling toolpaths for the **FBM Drill** operation.
- Enable the option **Use this tool for all spot drill** operations as shown in <u>Figure: 8.2.1</u>.

> **NOTE:** It takes couple of minutes to enable the **Use this tool for all spot drill**.

Figure: 8.2.1

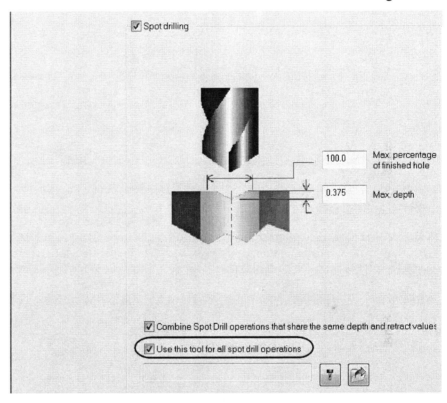

Use this tool for all spot drill operations allows you to choose a specific spot drill cycle generated by the FBM Drill operation.

- Pick the button **Select tool from library.**
- This will let you choose a tool from the current tool library.
- Find and select the **1.0" Spotdrill** from the list (312).

#	Assembly Name	Tool Name	Holder Name	Dia.	Cor. rad.	Length	# Flutes	Type	Rad. Type
311	–	13/16 FL	–	0	0.0	2.0	4	En	None
312	–	1. SPOT...	–	1.0	0.0	2.0	4	Sp...	None
313	–	1-3/16 FL...	–	1....	0.0	2.0	4	En...	None
314	–	3/8 SPO...	–	0....	0.0	2.0	4	Sp...	None
315	–	1-1/16 D	–	1	0.0	2.5	2	Drill	None

- Select the **OK** button and the **Spot drill** will appear in the box to the left of the buttons.

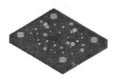

8.3 Pre-Drilling

♦ This page defines pre-drilling cycles that rough out the drilled holes before the finish drill cycle. Select Pre-drill pilot holes only as shown in <u>Figure: 8.3.1</u>.

Figure: 8.3.1

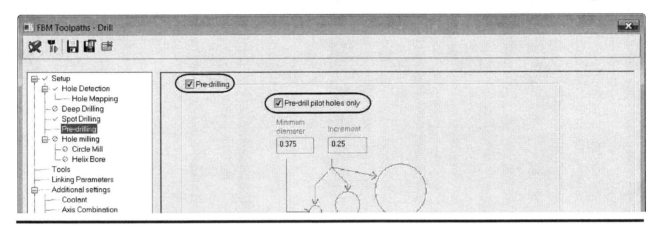

Pre-drilling Mastercam creates pre-drilling operations that rough out the detected holes before creating any finished drill and chamfer operations.

Pre-drill pilot holes only Select to deactivate all pre-drill roughing cycles except for assigned pilot holes cycles. This also deactivates the parameters for minimum diameter, increment and stock to leave on the page because they are not applicable. FBM Drill generates only pilot holes pre-drill cycles followed by finish hole cycles.

Minimum pre-drill diameter sets the smallest tool size that can be used from the tool library for the pre-drill operations.

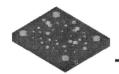

8.4 Tools

♦ This page controls the tools Mastercam selects for the drill cycles that the **FBM Drill** operation creates.
♦ From the **Tool creation**, disable first the **Create only standard sizes**, then enable **Consider flute length** and leave the rest of the parameters as shown in <u>Figure: 8.4.1</u>.

Figure: 8.4.1

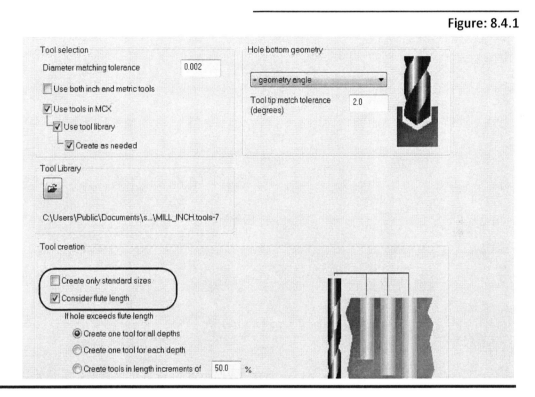

Diameter matching tolerance Mastercam uses this value to determine how closely the diameter of the tool and the hole must match before selecting an appropriate tool.

Tool Selection lets you pick one or more of the following options to tell Mastercam where to locate tools for the FBM-generated toolpaths.

Use tools in MCX looks in the current Mastercam file for an appropriate tool. The tools do not have to be used in previous operations to be available to the FBM operations.

Use tool library searches the selected tool library for the necessary tools.

Create as needed creates the necessary tools using the tool creation parameters you define.

Hole Bottom Geometry defines the realationship of the bottom hole geometry to the tool tip geometry.

= geometry angle the tool tip angle must match the hole bottom geometry within the specified tool tip match tolerance.

> geometry angle the tool tip must be greater than the floor angle geometry.

< geometry angle the tool tip angle must be smaller than the floor angle.

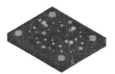

8.5 Linking Parameters

This page defines how **FBM Drill** calculates clearance height and retract height for the drilling cycles.

◆ Set the parameters as shown in <u>Figure: 8.5.1</u>.

Figure: 8.5.1

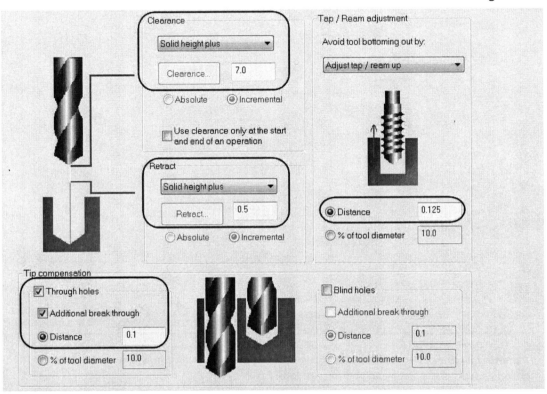

Clearance is the height at which the tool moves to and from the part. There are several options available from where the height is measured:

> **Solid height plus** adds a fixed height above the highest point of the solid model.
>
> **Stock model plus** adds a specified height above the stock model.
>
> **Top of hole plus** adds clearance distance above the top of each hole.
>
> **Top of Coaxial holes plus** for holes that share the same axis, it sets the clearance above the highest hole on the shared axis.
>
> **Manual** allows you to set the clearance using all options in any combination.

Retract is the height at which the tool moves before the next tool pass. The same options are available as for **Clearance height.**

Tap/Ream adjustment determines whether tapped and reamed holes are fully finished.

Tip compensation compensates for the tool tip.

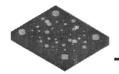

8.6 Features

This page allows you to manage the list of hole features that FBM Drill detects in the solid model.

- Choose the button to **Detect the Features** for Mastercam to detect the holes as shown in <u>Figure: 8.6.1</u>.
- Click on **State** to organize the features better, and scroll down to check for any unassigned tools as shown in <u>Figure: 8.6.1</u>.

Figure: 8.6.1

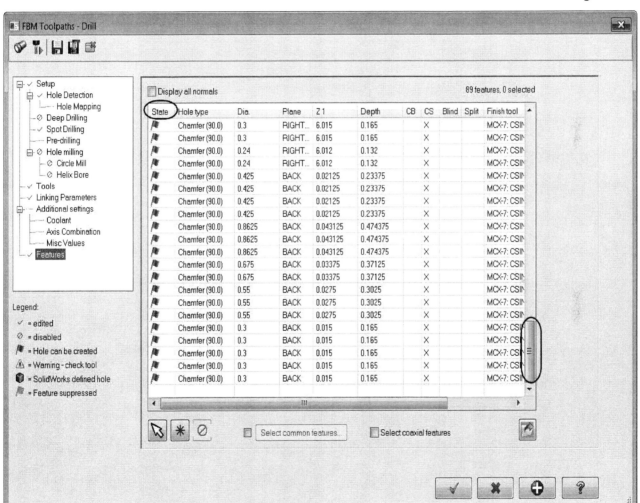

NOTE: No unassigned tools are listed because in the **Tools** page the **Create as needed** option was enabled. This enable Mastercam to automatically create any required tools to machine the part.

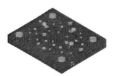

8.7 Assign a tap tool to the 0.5312 diameter drilled hole

♦ To select all holes with the same diameter and hole type, enable **Select common features** as shown.In

♦ To organize the holes based on their type, click on the **Hole type** as shown.

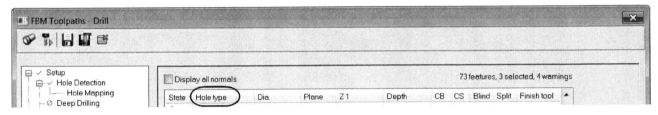

• Scroll down to the right side of the screen until you find the **0.5312** drill .
• In the **Finish Tool** column, click where it says **Unassigned** to select all holes with the same diameter.
• Right mouse click on the **Unassigned** and choose **Finish tool** and pick the **Tap RH, 5/8-11 UNC,** from the fly out menu as shown in <u>Figure: 8.7.1</u>.

Figure: 8.7.1

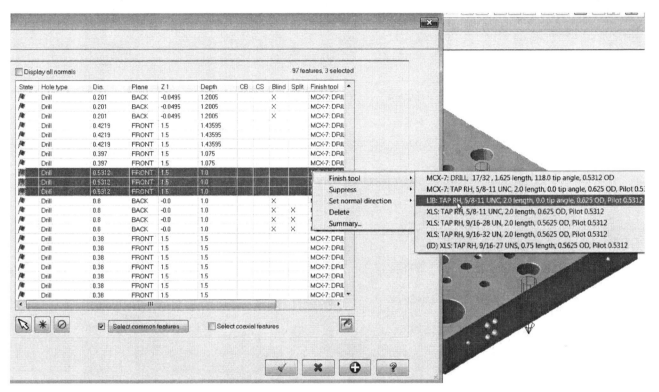

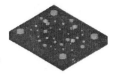

8.8 Assigning a 1/4 -20 Tap to the 0.201Drill

♦ Select one of the **Drill** with the diameter **0.201,** as shown in Figure: 8.8.1.

Figure: 8.8.1

State	Hole type	Dia.	Plane	Z1	Depth	CB	CS	Blind	Split	Finish tool
	Counter bore	0.625	BACK	-0.025	0.4	X		X		MCX-7: END
	Counter bore	0.625	BACK	-0.025	0.4	X		X		MCX-7: END
	Counter bore	0.8125	BACK	-0.025	0.475	X		X		MCX-7: END
	Counter bore	0.8125	BACK	-0.025	0.475	X		X		MCX-7: END
	Counter bore	0.8125	BACK	-0.025	0.475	X		X		MCX-7: END
	Drill	1.5	FRONT	1.5	1.475					MCX-7: DRIL
	Drill	1.5	FRONT	1.5	1.475					MCX-7: DRIL
	Drill	1.5	FRONT	1.5	1.475					MCX-7: DRIL
	Drill	1.5	FRONT	1.5	1.475					MCX-7: DRIL
	Drill	0.201	BACK	-0.0495	1.2005			X		MCX-7: DRIL
	Drill	0.201	BACK	-0.0495	1.2005			X		MCX-7: DRIL
	Drill	0.201	BACK	-0.0495	1.2005			X		MCX-7: DRIL
	Drill	0.201	BACK	-0.0495	1.2005			X		MCX-7: DRIL
	Drill	0.201	BACK	-0.0495	1.2005			X		MCX-7: DRIL
	Drill	0.4219	FRONT	1.5	1.43595					MCX-7: DRIL
	Drill	0.4219	FRONT	1.5	1.43595					MCX-7: DRIL
	Drill	0.4219	FRONT	1.5	1.43595					MCX-7: DRIL
	Drill	0.397	FRONT	1.5	1.075					MCX-7: DRIL
	Drill	0.397	FRONT	1.5	1.075					MCX-7: DRIL
	Tap RH	0.5312	FRONT	1.5	1.0					MCX-7: TAP
	Tap RH	0.5312	FRONT	1.5	1.0					MCX-7: TAP
	Tap RH	0.5312	FRONT	1.5	1.0					MCX-7: TAP

Display all normals   97 features, 5 selected

☑ Select common features...   ☐ Select coaxial features

♦ To change the hole type, **Right** mouse click in the **Finish tool** column.

• Select the **Finish tool** and from the list sselect the **Tap RH, 1/4 - 10 UNC** as shown in Figure: 8.8.2.

Figure: 8.8.2

	Counter bore	0.8125	BACK	-0.025	0.475			MCX-7: ENE
	Counter bore	0.8125	BACK	-0.025	0.475	X	X	MCX-7: ENE
	Counter bore	0.8125	BACK	-0.025	0.475	X	X	MCX-7: ENE
	Drill	1.5	FRONT	1.5	1.475			MCX-7: DRIL
	Drill	1.5	FRONT	1.5	1.475			MCX-7: DRIL
	Drill	1.5	FRONT	1.5	1.475			MCX-7: DRIL
	Drill	1.5	FRONT	1.5	1.475			MCX-7: DRIL
	Drill	0.201	BACK	-0.0495	1.2005		X	MCX-7: DRIL
	Drill	0.201	BACK	-0.0495	1.2005		X	MC
	Drill	0.201	BACK	-0.0495	1.2005		X	MC
	Drill	0.201	BACK	-0.0495	1.2005		X	MC
	Drill	0.201	BACK	-0.0495	1.2005		X	MC
	Drill	0.4219	FRONT	1.5	1.43595			MC
	Drill	0.4219	FRONT	1.5	1.43595			MC
	Drill	0.4219	FRONT	1.5	1.43595			MCX-7: DRIL
	Drill	0.397	FRONT	1.5	1.075			MCX-7: DRIL
	Drill	0.397	FRONT	1.5	1.075			MCX-7: DRIL
	Tap RH	0.5312	FRONT	1.5	1.0			MCX-7: TAP
	Tap RH	0.5312	FRONT	1.5	1.0			MCX-7: TAP

Finish tool ▶
Suppress ▶
Set normal direction ▶
Delete
Summary...

MCX-7: DRILL, #7, 2.0 length, 118.0 tip angle, 0.201 OD
MCX-7: TAP RH, 1/4-20 UNC, 2.0 length, 0.0 tip angle, 0.25 OD, Pilot 0.201
LIB: DRILL, #7, 2.0 length, 118.0 tip angle, 0.201 OD
LIB: DRILL, #8, 2.0 length, 118.0 tip angle, 0.199 OD
LIB: TAP RH, 1/4-20 UNC, 2.0 length, 0.0 tip angle, 0.25 OD, Pilot 0.201
XLS: DRILL, #7, 2.0 length, 0.201 OD
XLS: DRILL, #8, 2.0 length, 0.199 OD
XLS: TAP RH, 1/4-20 UNC, 2.0 length, 0.25 OD, Pilot 0.201

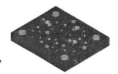

♦ The **Tap RH 1/4 - 20 UNC** will be automatically added as shown in <u>Figure: 8.8.3</u>.

Figure: 8.8.3

State	Hole type	Dia.	Plane	Z 1	Depth	CB	CS	Blind	Split	Finish tool
⚑	Counter bore	0.625	BACK	-0.025	0.4	X		X		MCX-7: END
⚑	Counter bore	0.625	BACK	-0.025	0.4	X		X		MCX-7: END
⚑	Counter bore	0.8125	BACK	-0.025	0.475	X		X		MCX-7: END
⚑	Counter bore	0.8125	BACK	-0.025	0.475	X		X		MCX-7: END
⚑	Counter bore	0.8125	BACK	-0.025	0.475	X		X		MCX-7: END
⚑	Drill	1.5	FRONT	1.5	1.475					MCX-7: DRIL
⚑	Drill	1.5	FRONT	1.5	1.475					MCX-7: DRIL
⚑	Drill	1.5	FRONT	1.5	1.475					MCX-7: DRIL
⚑	Drill	1.5	FRONT	1.5	1.475					MCX-7: DRIL
⚑	Tap RH	0.201	BACK	-0.0495	1.2005			X		MCX-7: TAP
⚑	Tap RH	0.201	BACK	-0.0495	1.2005			X		MCX-7: TAP
⚑	Tap RH	0.201	BACK	-0.0495	1.2005			X		MCX-7: TAP
⚑	Tap RH	0.201	BACK	-0.0495	1.2005			X		MCX-7: TAP
⚑	Tap RH	0.201	BACK	-0.0495	1.2005			X		MCX-7: TAP
⚑	Drill	0.4219	FRONT	1.5	1.43595					MCX-7: DRIL
⚑	Drill	0.4219	FRONT	1.5	1.43595					MCX-7: DRIL
⚑	Drill	0.4219	FRONT	1.5	1.43595					MCX-7: DRIL
⚑	Drill	0.397	FRONT	1.5	1.075					MCX-7: DRIL
⚑	Drill	0.397	FRONT	1.5	1.075					MCX-7: DRIL
⚑	Tap RH	0.5312	FRONT	1.5	1.0					MCX-7: TAP
⚑	Tap RH	0.5312	FRONT	1.5	1.0					MCX-7: TAP
⚑	Tap RH	0.5312	FRONT	1.5	1.0					MCX-7: TAP

☐ Display all normals   97 features, 5 selected

☑ Select common features...   ☐ Select coaxial features

NOTE: All the 0.201 diameter holes will be first drill with a #7 drill, then tap with a **1/4 - 20 RH Tap**. When assigning as a finish tool a tap Mastercam looks in the library if a tap with the same diameter exists and it will assign it as the finish tool. If the diameter can not be found in the library, Mastercam will assign the tap required considering the pilot diameter the original diameter.

♦ Choose the **OK** button to generate the **FBM Drill Toolpath**.

♦ Enter the new **NC name** when the dialog box appears, **YOUR NAME_8** and then choose the **OK** button.

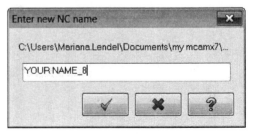

Enter new NC name

C:\Users\Mariana.Lendel\Documents\my mcamx7\...

YOUR NAME_8|

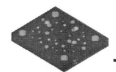

STEP 9: SIMULATE THE TOOLPATH IN VERIFY

Verify Mode shows the path the tools take to cut the part with material removal. This display lets you spot errors in the program before you machine the part. As you verify toolpaths, Mastercam displays additional information such as the X, Y, and Z coordinates, the path length , the minimum and maximum coordinates and the cycle time. It also shows any collisions between the workpiece and the tool.

◆ Make sure that the toolpath is selected (signified by the green check mark on the folder icon). If all operations

are not selected choose the **Select All Operations** icon.

◆ Select the **Verify selected operations** icon.

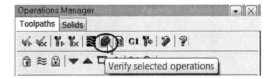

> **NOTE:** Mastercam lunches a new window that allows you to check the part usind **Backplot** or **Verify**.

◆ Select the **Verify** tab and have the following settings enabled as shown.

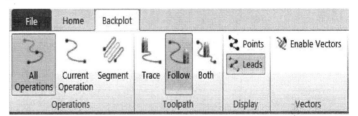

◆ Select the **Home** tab and make sure that you have the following settings on as shown.

◆ To fit the workpiece to the screen, select the **Fit** icon. Fit

◆ You can step through the **Backplot** by using the **Step forward** or **Step back** buttons.

◆ You can adjust the speed of the backplot. Speed:

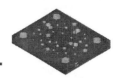

♦ Select the **Play Simulation** button in the **VCR** bar to run **Verify**.

♦ The part should look as shown.

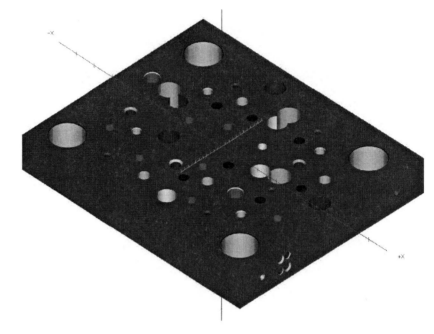

♦ To go back to Mastercam window, minimize **Verify** window as shown.

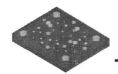

STEP 10: HOLE MILLING

You can include Circle mill or Helix bore toolpaths with the drill cycles that FBM Drill generates for detected features. Adding circle mill or helix bore toolpaths to your FBM drill operation lets Mastercam switch from drilling to milling when machining holes that are significantly larger than drills, or require flat bottoms.

Toolpath Preview:

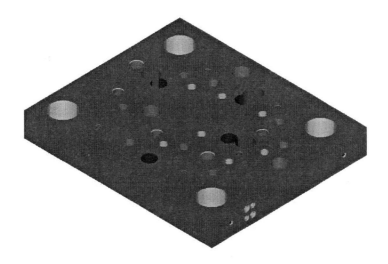

10.1 Hole Milling

◆ Select **Parameters** under **FBM Drill Operation #1**.

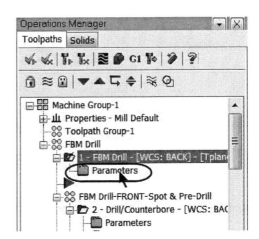

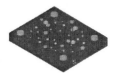

- From the **Tree view list** choose **Hole Milling.**
- Enable the options to use hole milling for **Counter bores**, **Through holes**, and **Blind flat-bottom holes** as shown in Figure: 10.1.1.
- Once those options have been selected you can choose to use either **Circle Mill** or **Helix bore**.
- Select the **Circle Mill**.
- Change the values as shown in Figure: 10.1.1.

Figure: 10.1.1

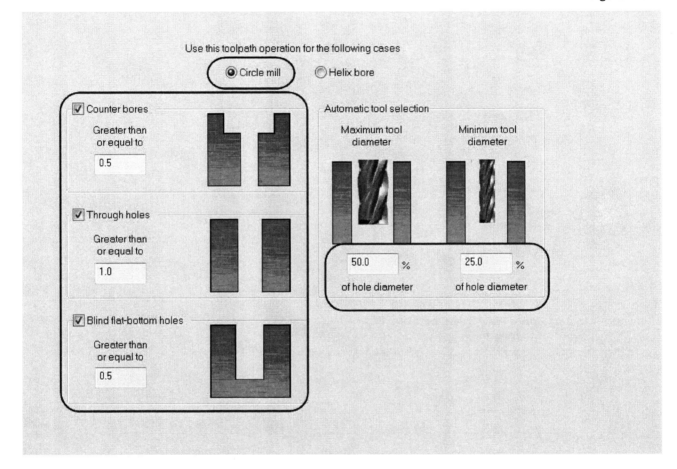

Mill Level 1 Training Tutorial *Mastercam.* X⁷

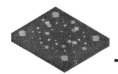
- Select **Circle Mill** from the **Tree view list**.
- Change the parameters as shown in <u>Figure: 10.1.2</u>.

Figure: 10.1.2

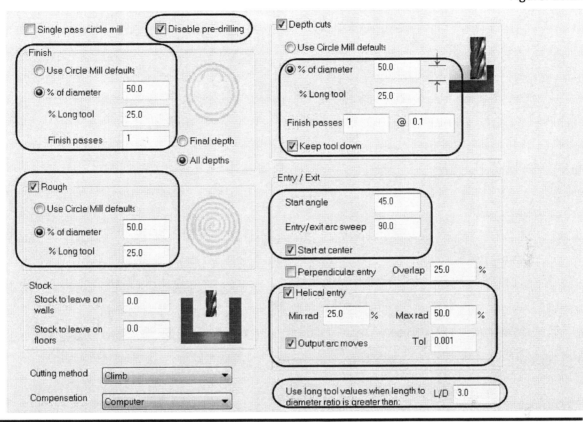

Use Circle Mill defaults uses default parameters for this setting, either from values in the FBM-generated operation's .DEFAULTS file or from the tool definitions when this option is enabled.

% of diameter determines the maximum depth and number of cuts made in the FBM-generated toolpath by multiplying the diameter of the tool by the diameter percentage you enter in this field.

Long tool reduces the stress on long tools by using separate depth cuts or an XY stepover calculation for them. Long tools are defined by the length to diameter ratio you define in the **L/D** field.

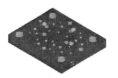

10.2 Features

♦ In the **Features**, take note of the **0.8** diameter holes, they do not have a tool defined to machine them as shown in Figure: 10.2.1.

Figure: 10.2.1

State	Hole type	Dia.	Plane	Z 1	Depth	CB	CS	Blind	Split	Finish tool
🚩	Drill	0.4375	BACK	0.0	0.88			×		MCX-7: DRIL
🚩	Drill	0.4375	BACK	0.0	0.88			×		MCX-7: DRIL
🚩	Drill	0.4375	BACK	0.0	0.88			×		MCX-7: DRIL
🚩	Drill	0.4375	BACK	0.0	0.88			×		MCX-7: DRIL
🚩	Drill	0.505	BACK	0.0	1.125			×		MCX-7: DRIL
🚩	Drill	0.505	BACK	0.0	1.125			×		MCX-7: DRIL
🚩	Drill	0.505	BACK	0.0	1.125			×		MCX-7: DRIL
🚩	Drill	0.505	BACK	0.0	1.125			×		MCX-7: DRIL
🚩	Counter bore	0.625	BACK	-0.025	0.4	×		×		MCX-7: ENC
🚩	Counter bore	0.625	BACK	-0.025	0.4	×		×		MCX-7: ENC
	Drill	0.8	BACK	-0.0	1.0			×		MCX-7: DRIL
🚩	Drill	0.8	BACK	-0.0	1.0			×	×	MCX-7: DRII
🚩	Drill	0.8	BACK	-0.0	1.0			×	×	MCX-7: DRII
🚩	Drill	0.8	BACK	-0.0	1.0			×	×	MCX-7: DRIL
🚩	Counter bore	0.8125	BACK	-0.025	0.475	×		×		MCX-7: ENC
🚩	Counter bore	0.8125	BACK	-0.025	0.475	×		×		MCX-7: ENC
🚩	Counter bore	0.8125	BACK	-0.025	0.475	×		×		MCX-7: ENC
🚩	Drill	0.375	FRONT	1.5	1.475					MCX-7: DRIL
🚩	Drill	0.375	FRONT	1.5	1.475					MCX-7: DRIL
🚩	Drill	0.375	FRONT	1.5	1.475					MCX-7: DRIL
🚩	Drill	0.375	FRONT	1.5	1.475					MCX-7: DRIL
🚩	Drill	0.38	FRONT	1.5	1.5					MCX-7: DRIL

Mastercam. X⁷

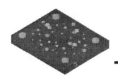

• Choose the button to **Detect features**.
• Find the **0.8** diameter holes and notice the **Hole type** has been changed to **Circle mill** as shown in
  Figure: 10.2.2.

Figure: 10.2.2

State	Hole type	Dia.	Plane	Z 1	Depth	CB	CS	Blind	Split	Finish tool
	Drill	0.4219	FRONT	1.5	1.43595					MCX-7: DRIL
	Drill	0.4219	FRONT	1.5	1.43595					MCX-7: DRIL
	Drill	0.397	FRONT	1.5	1.075					MCX-7: DRIL
	Circle mill	0.625	BACK	-0.025	0.4	X	X			MCX-7: ENC
	Drill	0.397	FRONT	1.5	1.075					MCX-7: DRIL
	Circle mill	0.625	BACK	-0.025	0.4	X	X			MCX-7: ENC
	Tap RH	0.5312	FRONT	1.5	1.0					MCX-7: TAP
	Circle mill	0.8125	BACK	-0.025	0.475	X	X			MCX-7: ENC
	Tap RH	0.5312	FRONT	1.5	1.0					MCX-7: TAP
	Circle mill	0.8125	BACK	-0.025	0.475	X	X			MCX-7: ENC
	Tap RH	0.5312	FRONT	1.5	1.0					MCX-7: TAP
	Circle mill	0.8125	BACK	-0.025	0.475	X	X			MCX-7: ENC
	Circle mill	0.8	BACK	-0.0	1.0	X	X			MCX-7: ENC
	Circle mill	0.8	BACK	-0.0	1.0	X	X	X		MCX-7: ENC
	Circle mill	0.8	BACK	-0.0	1.0	X	X	X		MCX-7: ENC
	Circle mill	0.8	BACK	-0.0	1.0	X	X	X		MCX-7: ENC
	Drill	0.38	FRONT	1.5	1.5					MCX-7: DRIL
	Drill	0.38	FRONT	1.5	1.5					MCX-7: DRIL
	Drill	0.38	FRONT	1.5	1.5					MCX-7: DRIL
	Drill	0.38	FRONT	1.5	1.5					MCX-7: DRIL
	Drill	0.38	FRONT	1.5	1.5					MCX-7: DRIL
	Drill	0.38	FRONT	1.5	1.5					MCX-7: DRIL

• Select the **OK** to exit and generate the toolpaths.
• Pick the **Regenerate all dirty operations** icon found in the **Operations Manager**.

• Select the **OK** button to accept the nc file name.

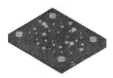

◆ The toolpath will look as shown.

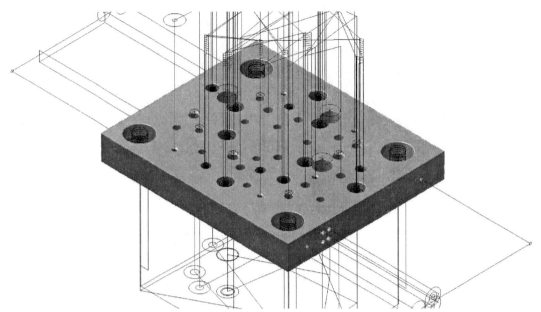

Mastercam. X^7

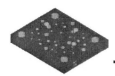
STEP 11: CREATE CUSTOM TOOLING

In this step we will create custom tools so we can machine the holes with the diameters of 0.38", and 0.505". This step is critical when using FBM if you have holes which are not typical sizes.

11.1 Create a Custom Tool

Toolpaths

* 🔧 **Tool Manager.**
* In the top half of the tool manager are the tools used to machine this part.
* In the bottom half of the page is the tool library listing all of the tools.
* Select the **Filter** button as shown in Figure: 11.1.1.

Figure: 11.1.1

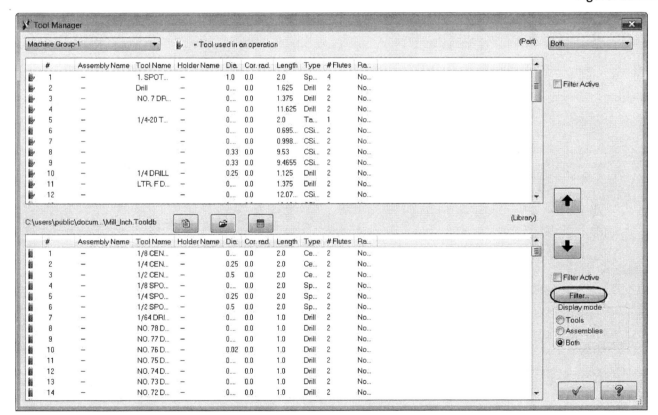

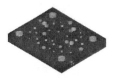

• Choose the **None** button and then the **Reamer** icon as shown.

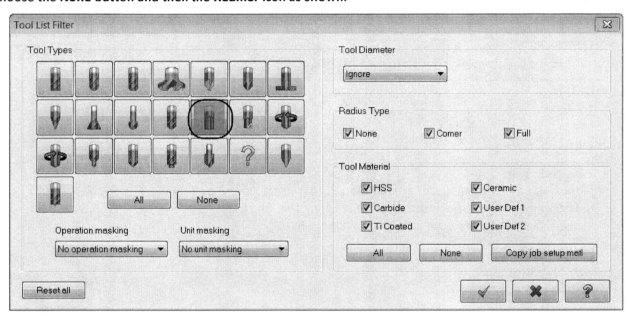

• Select the **OK** button.
• Enable **Filter Active** as shown.

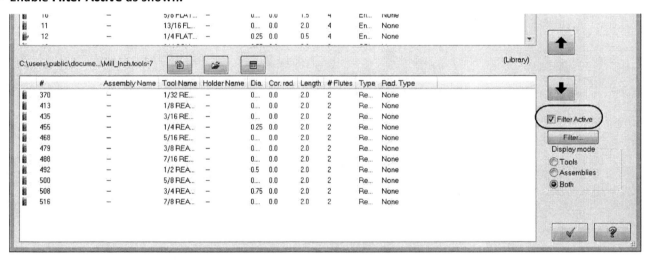

◆ Right click in the white dialog box (below the listed tools) and choose **Create new tool** as shown in Figure: 11.1.2.

Figure: 11.1.2

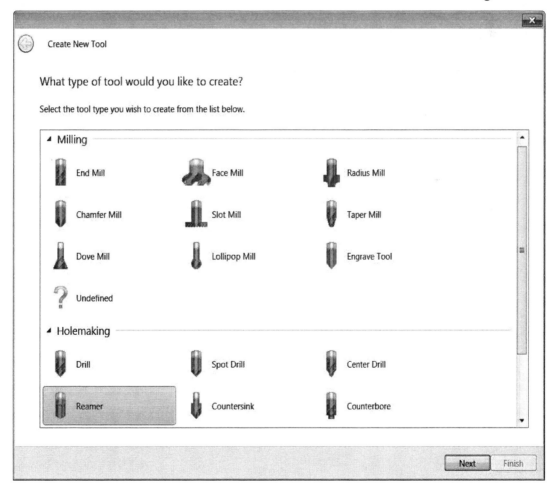

◆ Select the **Reamer** from the tools and click on the **Next** button as shown in Figure: 11.1.3.

Figure: 11.1.3

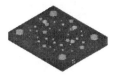

* Make changes to the **Overall Length** and **Cutting Length** as shown in <u>Figure: 11.1.4</u>.
* Change the diameter to **0.38** as shown.

Figure: 11.1.4

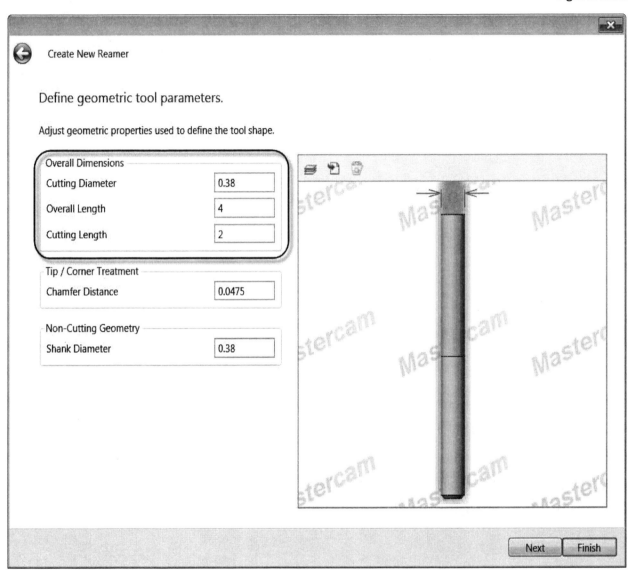

* Select the **Next** button.

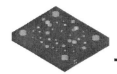

• In the **Operation** field change the parameters as shown in <u>Figure: 11.1.5</u>.

Figure: 11.1.5

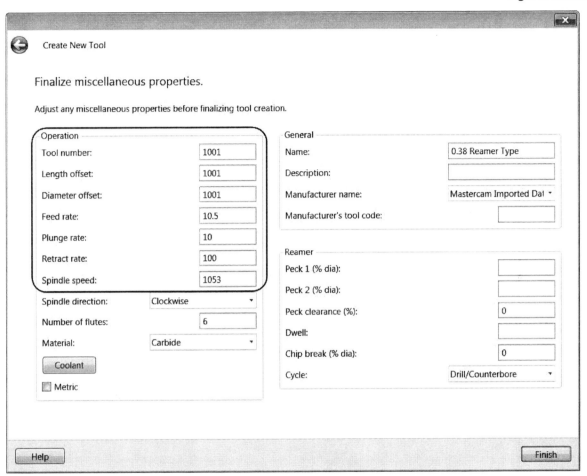

• Select the **Finish** button.

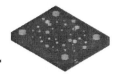

- Select the **Reamer** we just created as shown in Figure: 11.1.6.
- Hold the left mouse button down and drag the tools to the list at the top of the page as shown in Figure: 11.1.6.
- Once there let go of the left mouse button as shown in Figure: 11.1.6.

Figure: 11.1.6

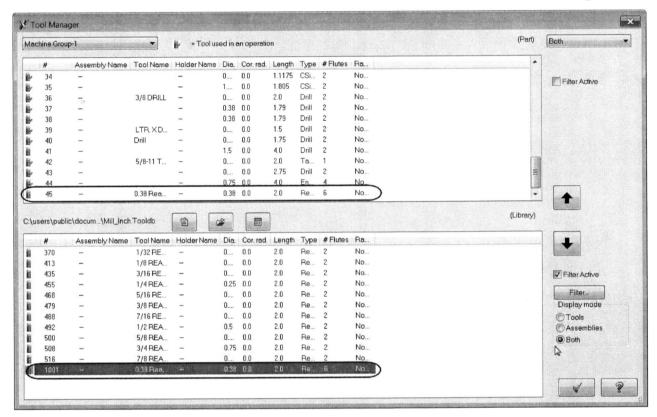

- Select the **OK** button to exit the tool manager.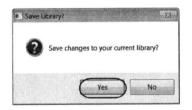
- Choose the **YES** button to **Save the changes to the current library**.

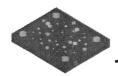

11.2 Selecting the Custom Tooling

◆ Select **Parameters** under **FBM Drill Operation #1**.

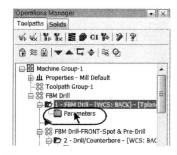

◆ A Warning might appear on the screen that the pilot hole diameter is not defined in tool definition.

◆ Select the **OK** button to continue.

◆ In the **Tree view list** select **Features,** scroll down the list of holes and find the **0.38** dia holes.

◆ Enable **Select common features** and pick one of the holes. This will pick all of them and allow us to modify them all at once.

◆ In the **Finish tool** column right click and pick **Finish Tool** and then select the **MCX REAMER, 0.38 dia** as shown in Figure: 11.2.1.

Figure: 11.2.1

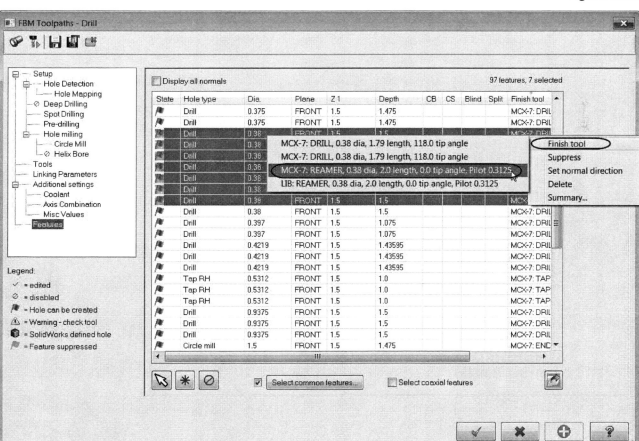

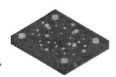

♦ The tool will automatically be entered in the **Finish tool** column as shown in <u>Figure: 11.2.2</u>.

Figure: 11.2.2

State	Hole type	Dia.	Plane	Z 1	Depth	CB	CS	Blind	Split	Finish tool
▶	Circle mill	0.8	BACK	-0.0	1.0	X		X	X	MCX-7: END
▶	Circle mill	0.8	BACK	-0.0	1.0	X		X	X	MCX-7: END
▶	Circle mill	0.8	BACK	-0.0	1.0	X		X	X	MCX-7: END
▶	Circle mill	0.8125	BACK	-0.025	0.475	X		X		MCX-7: END
▶	Circle mill	0.8125	BACK	-0.025	0.475	X		X		MCX-7: END
▶	Circle mill	0.8125	BACK	-0.025	0.475	X		X		MCX-7: END
▶	Drill	0.375	FRONT	1.5	1.475					MCX-7: DRIL
▶	Drill	0.375	FRONT	1.5	1.475					MCX-7: DRIL
▶	Drill	0.375	FRONT	1.5	1.475					MCX-7: DRIL
▶	Drill	0.375	FRONT	1.5	1.475					MCX-7: DRIL
▶	Ream	0.38	FRONT	1.5	1.5					MCX-7: REA
▶	Ream	0.38	FRONT	1.5	1.5					MCX-7: REA
▶	Ream	0.38	FRONT	1.5	1.5					MCX-7: REA
▶	Ream	0.38	FRONT	1.5	1.5					MCX-7: REA
▶	Ream	0.38	FRONT	1.5	1.5					MCX-7: REA
▶	Ream	0.38	FRONT	1.5	1.5					MCX-7: REA
▶	Ream	0.38	FRONT	1.5	1.5					MCX-7: REA
▶	Ream	0.38	FRONT	1.5	1.5					MCX-7: REA
▶	Drill	0.397	FRONT	1.5	1.075					MCX-7: DRIL
▶	Drill	0.397	FRONT	1.5	1.075					MCX-7: DRIL
▶	Drill	0.4219	FRONT	1.5	1.43595					MCX-7: DRIL
▶	Drill	0.4219	FRONT	1.5	1.43595					MCX-7: DRIL

♦ All the features in the list will now be able to be created.

♦ Select the **OK** button to exit the toolpath.

♦ Pick the **Regenerate All Dirty Operations** icon found in the **Operations Manager** as shown.

♦ A Warning might appear on the screen that the pilot hole diameter is not defined in tool definition.

♦ Select the **OK** button to continue.

♦ Select the **OK** button in the NC name dialog box.

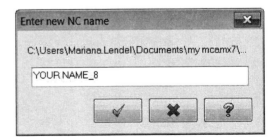

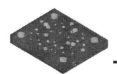
♦ Moving down the list of toolpaths you will be able to locate the Peck drill operation with the 0.3125 Drill as shown in <u>Figure: 11.2.3</u>.

Figure: 11.2.3

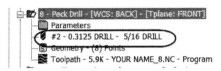

NOTE: Although you had the warning that the pilot hole diameter is not defined in tool definition, the operation was generated.

♦ Moving down the list of toolpaths you will be able to locate the reaming operations using the custom tools we just created as shown in <u>Figure: 11.2.4</u>.

Figure: 11.2.4

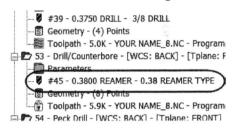

♦ Once the operation has been regenerated **Backplot** and **Verify** your toolpath.
♦ The part will appear as shown.

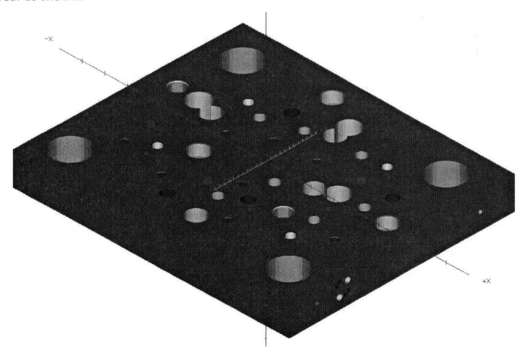

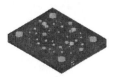

STEP 12: POST THE FILE

• Ensure all operations are selected, if they are not use the button **Select all operations** in the **Operations Manager.**

• Select the **Post selected operations** button from the **Operations Manager.** G1

• In the **Post processing** window make the necessary changes as shown in Figure: 12.0.1.

Figure: 12.0.1

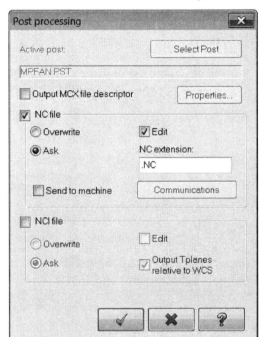

NC File enabled allows you to keep the NC file and to assign the same name as the MCX file.

Edit enabled allows you to automatically launch the default editor.

• Select the **OK** button to continue.

• Save the NC file.

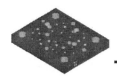

• A window with Mastercam Code Expert will be lunched and the NC program will appear as shown in <u>Figure: 12.0.2</u>.

Figure: 12.0.2

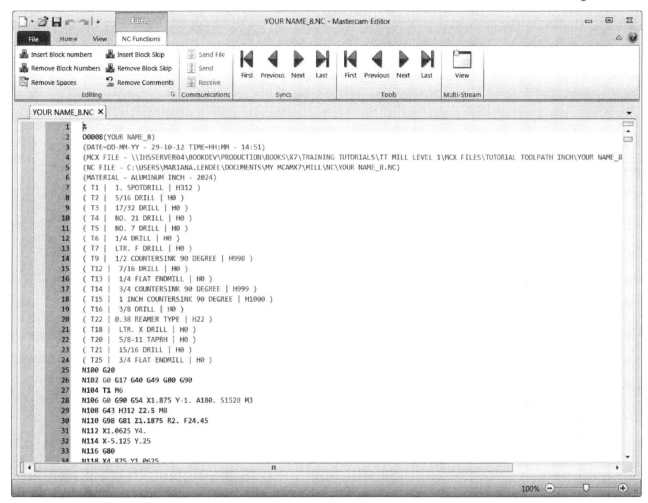

• Select the red **"X"** box at the upper right corner to exit the editor.

STEP 13: SAVE THE UPDATED MCX FILE

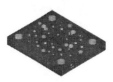

CREATE THE TOOLPATHS FOR TUTORIAL #8 EXERCISE

Create the **Toolpaths** for the **Tutorial #8 Exercise** as per the instructions below.

+ Download the **SolidWorks** part from **www.emastercam.com**.
+ Import the part into Mastercam.
+ **Xform Translate 3D. Move** the part to the top view.
+ Setup the **Tool Settings** and **Stock Setup**.

FBM Drill

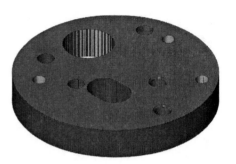

+ Enable **Automatic initial hole detection**.
+ Enable the option to **Include Split Holes**.
+ Disable the option **Limit search to plane**.
+ Enable **Spot drilling** and **Enable use this tool for all spot drilling operations**.
+ Select a **1" Spotdrill** from the library.
+ Enable **Hole Milling** and change the diameter to machine through holes to **0.5"** for all the features.
+ Select a cutting method and set the parameters.
+ **Tools**, enable **Use tools in MCX** and **use tool library**.
+ Set the **Linking Parameters**.
+ **Detect the features**.
+ Modify any tools to ensure the whole part will be machined.
+ Your part will appear as shown.

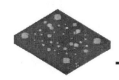

NOTES:

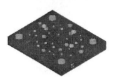

TUTORIAL #8 QUIZ

• What does FBM Drill do?

• What is the purpose of Predrilling?

• What does Hole Mapping do?

• What does Circle Milling allow you to do?

TUTORIAL #9

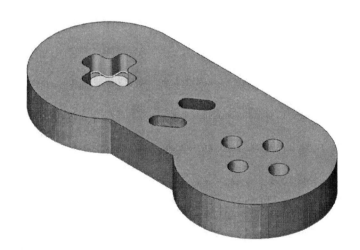

OVERVIEW OF STEPS TAKEN TO CREATE THE FINAL PART:

From Drawing to CAD Model:
- The student should examine the drawing on the following page to understand what part is being created in the tutorial.
- From the drawing we can decide how to go about creating the geometry in Mastercam.

Create the 2D CAD Model used to generate Toolpaths from:
- The student will create the Top 2D geometry needed to create the toolpaths.
- Geometry creation commands such as circle center point, line tangent, line parallel, rectangular shapes and change attributes will be used.
- The student will also learn how to clean up the geometry using the trimming functions such as trim 3 entities and trim divide.
- The student will use solids extrude to create a solid.

Create the necessary Toolpaths to machine the part:
- The student will set up the stock size to be used and the clamping method used.
- The **Feature Based Mill** toolpath will be used to machine the entire part.
- The **Feature Based Drill** toolpath will be used to machine the four holes.

Backplot and Verify the file:
- The Backplot will be used to simulate a step by step process of the tool's movements.
- The Verify will be used to watch a tool machine the part out of a solid model.

Post Process the file to generate the G-code:
- The Student will then post process the file to obtain an NC file containing the necessary code for the machine.

 This tutorial takes approximately one hour to complete.

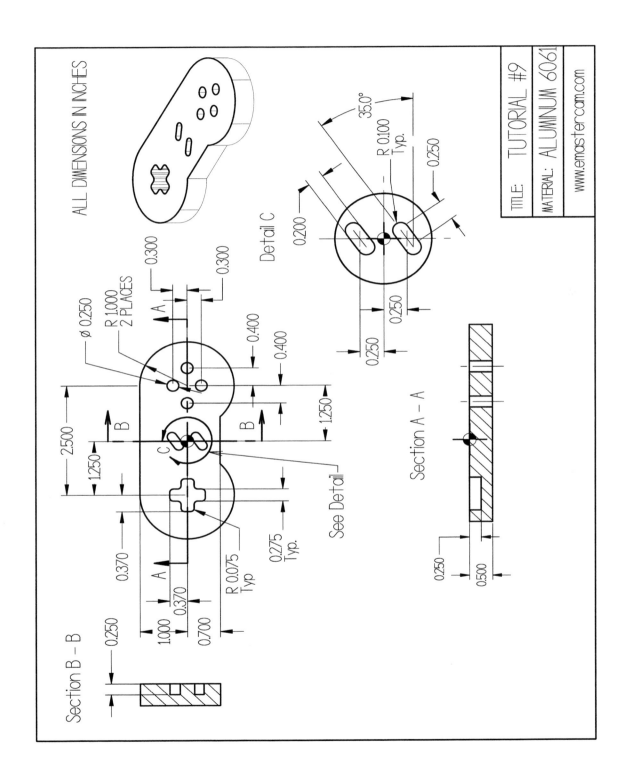

ALL DIMENSIONS IN INCHES

Detail C

35.0°

R 0.100
Typ.

0.200

0.250

0.250

0.250

TITLE: TUTORIAL #9

MATERIAL: ALUMINUM 6061

www.emastercam.com

Ø 0.250

R 1.000
2 PLACES

0.300

0.300

A

0.400

0.400

B

B

2.500

1.250

1.250

C

See Detail

0.370

A

R 0.075
Typ

0.275
Typ.

1.000

0.370

0.700

0.250

Section B – B

Section A – A

0.250

0.500

GEOMETRY CREATION

STEP 1: SETTING UP THE GRAPHIC USER INTERFACE

Please refer to the **Getting Started** section to set up the graphics user interface.

NOTE: The part is symmetric about the X-axis and the Y-axis. We are going to create a quarter of the geometry and then mirror it about both axes.

STEP 2: CREATE CIRCLE CENTER POINT

Create Circle Center Point lets you create circles knowing the center point and the radius or the diameter.

Step Preview:

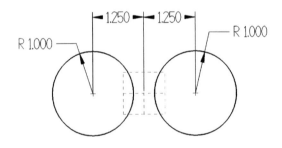

Create
* **Arc.**

*  **Circle Center Point.**

* In the **Ribbon Bar**, enter the **Radius** ⊙ value of **1.0** and click on the radius icon to lock it as shown.

* Choose the **Fast Point** icon to enter coordinates for the center point as shown.

| -1.25, 0.0 |

* Select the **Apply** button to continue. ⊕
* Use the **Fit** icon to fit the geometry to the screen. ✛

♦ Choose the **Fast Point** 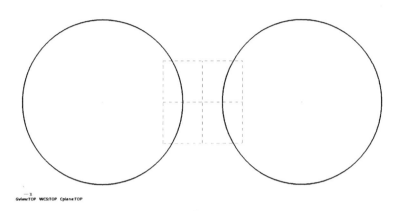 icon to enter coordinates for the center point as shown.

```
1.25,0.0|
```

♦ Choose the **OK** button to exit the command. ☑

♦ Use the **Fit** icon to fit the geometry to the screen. ✦

♦ The geometry should look as shown.

—X
Gview:TOP WCS:TOP Cplane:TOP

> **NOTE:** During the geometry creation of this tutorial, if you make a mistake you can undo the last step using the **Undo** icon. ↺ You can undo as many steps as needed. If you delete or undo a step by mistake, just use the **Redo** icon. ↻ To delete unwanted geometry, select it first and then press **Delete** from the keyboard.

STEP 3: CREATE LINE TANGENT

You will create a line tangent to two arcs. You will use Create Line Endpoint command with tangent icon enabled.

Step Preview:

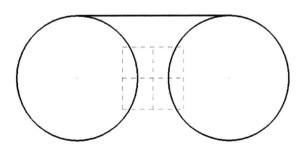

Create
- **Line.**

-  **Endpoint.**
- In the **Ribbon Bar**, make sure that only the **Tangent** icon is enabled as shown.

> **NOTE:** Make sure that you are not select the quadrant points while selecting the circles.

- [Select the first endpoint]: Select Entity A as shown in <u>Figure: 3.0.1</u>.
- [Select the second endpoint]: Select Entity B as shown in <u>Figure: 3.0.1</u>.

Figure: 3.0.1

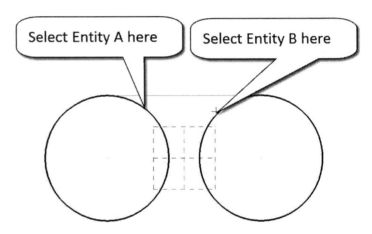

Select Entity A here

Select Entity B here

- Choose the **OK** button to exit the command.
- The geometry should look as shown.

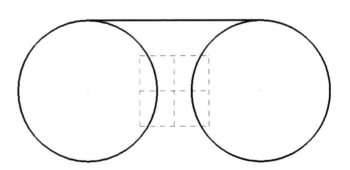

STEP 4: CREATE A LINE PARALLEL

Create a Line Parallel command knowing the distance between the lines.

Step Preview:

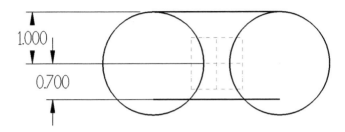

Create
+ **Line.**

+ 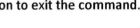 **Parallel.**
+ [Select a line]: Select the line as shown in <u>Figure: 4.0.1</u>.

Figure: 4.0.1

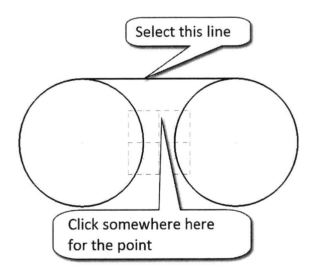

+ [Select the point to place a parallel line through]: Click somewhere below the line.

+ In the **Ribbon Bar**, change the **Distance** ⊢⊣ to **1.7**.

+ Select the **OK** button to exit the command. ☑

♦ The geometry should look as shown.

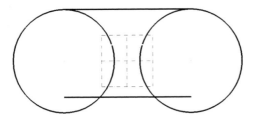

STEP 5: TRIM THE ENTITIES

You will trim the entities using Trim 3 entities command. The first two entities that you select are trimmed to the third, which acts as a trimming curve. The third entity is then trimmed to the first two.

Step Preview:

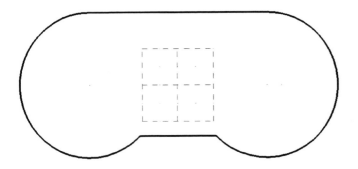

Edit
♦ **Trim/Break.**

♦ 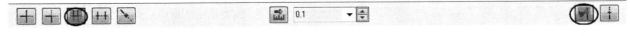 **Trim/Break/Extend.**

♦ Select the **Trim 3 Entity** icon and make sure that the **Trim** icon is enabled in the Ribbon Bar as shown.

- [Select the first entity to trim/extend]: Select Entity A as shown in <u>Figure: 5.0.1</u>.
- [Select the second entity to trim/extend]: Select Entity B as shown in <u>Figure: 5.0.1</u>.
- [Select the entity to trim/extend to]: Select Entity C as shown in <u>Figure: 5.0.1</u>.

Figure: 5.0.1

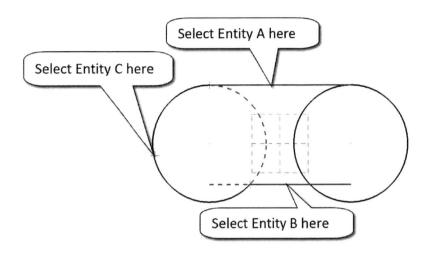

- [Select the first entity to trim/extend]: Select Entity A as shown in <u>Figure: 5.0.2</u>.
- [Select the second entity to trim/extend]: Select Entity B as shown in <u>Figure: 5.0.2</u>.
- [Select the entity to trim/extend to]: Select Entity C as shown in <u>Figure: 5.0.2</u>.

Figure: 5.0.2

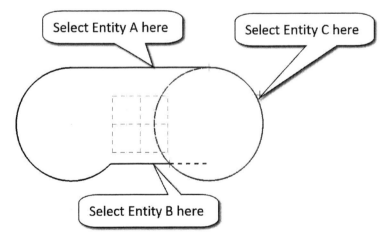

- Select the **OK** button to exit the command.

• The geometry should look as shown.

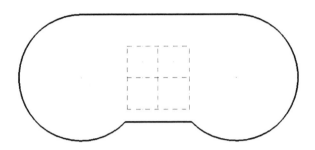

STEP 6: CREATE RECTANGULAR SHAPE

In this step you will create two rectangles using Create Rectangular Shapes.

Step Preview:

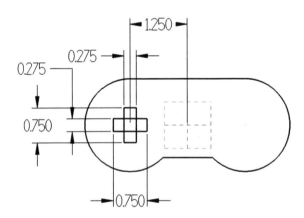

Create

•  **Rectangular Shapes.**

◆ Enter the **Width**, the **Height** and enable the **Anchor** location as shown in the Figure: 6.0.1.

Figure: 6.0.1

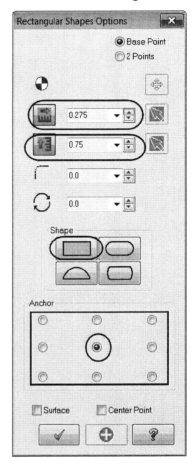

◆ [Select position for base point]: Select the circle center point as shown in Figure: 6.0.2.

Figure: 6.0.2

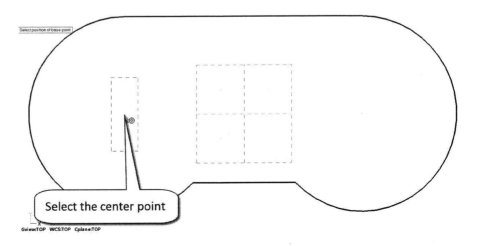

Select the center point

NOTE: Make sure that the center point icon appear while selecting the point.

* Select the **Apply** button to continue in the same command. ⊕
* In the Rectangular Shapes Options dialog box, click on the icons in front of the **Width** and **Height** to lock the rectangle values and enter **90** in the **Rotation** field as shown in Figure: 6.0.3.

Figure: 6.0.3

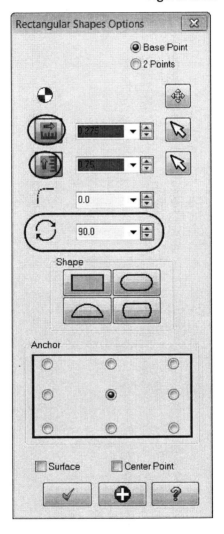

• [Select position for base point]: Select the same center point as shown in <u>Figure: 6.0.4</u>.

Figure: 6.0.4

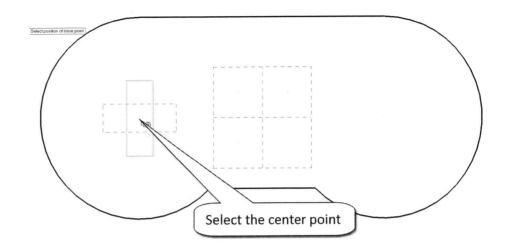

Select the center point

• Selected the **OK** button to exit the command.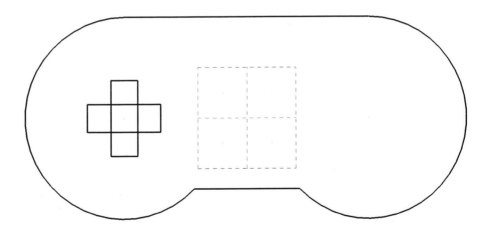
• The geometry should look as shown.

STEP 7: TRIM DIVIDE

In this step you will trimthe entities using divide which trims a line, arc, or spline into two disjointed segments by removing the segment that lies between two dividing intersections. When you choose the Divide/Delete function and select an entity in the graphics window, Mastercam uses the nearest two intersections on each end to divide the entity.

If only one intersection exists, the selected entity is trimmed to the single intersection. If no intersection is found on the selected entity, or the point of intersection is an endpoint of the selected entity, the entity is deleted.

Step Preview:

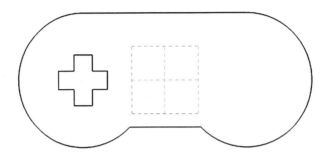

Edit

♦ **Trim/Break.**

♦ **Trim/Break/Extend.**

♦ Select the **Divide** icon as shown.

♦ [Select the entity to trim/extend]: Select the line as shown in Figure: 7.0.1.

Figure: 7.0.1

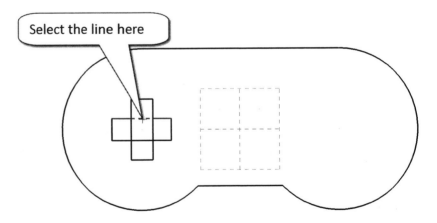

Select the line here

◆ Select the rest of the lines as shown in <u>Figure: 7.0.2</u>.

Figure: 7.0.2

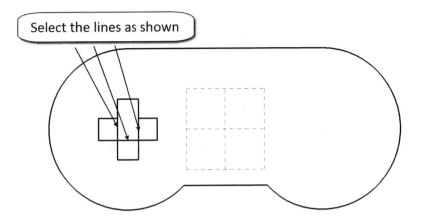

Select the lines as shown

◆ Select the **OK** button to exit the command. ☑
◆ The geometry should look as shown.

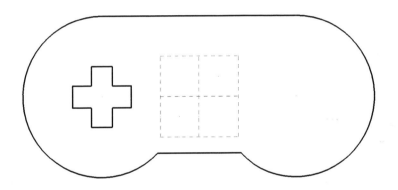

STEP 8: FILLET CHAIN

In this step we will fillet all the sharp edges of the shape using Fillet Chain command.

Step Preview:

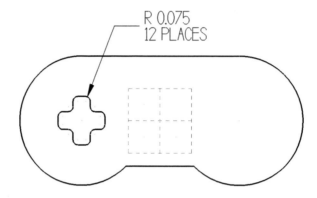

R 0.075
12 PLACES

Create
• **Fillet.**

• 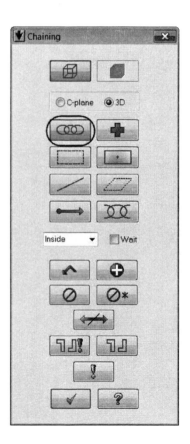 **Chains.**

• Leave the **Chain** button enabled in the **Chaining** as shown.

• Select the chain as shown.

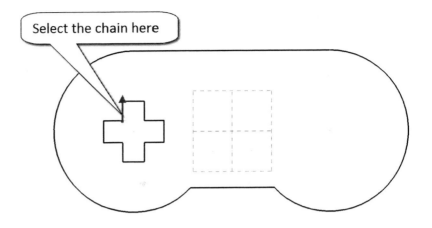

Select the chain here

• Select the **OK** button to exit **Chaining** dialog box.
• Change thee **Radius** and make sure the **Trim** icon is enabled in the **Ribbon Bar** as shown.

• Press **Enter** to apply the radius.

• Select the **OK** button to exit the **Fillet Chain** command.
• The geometry should looks as shown.

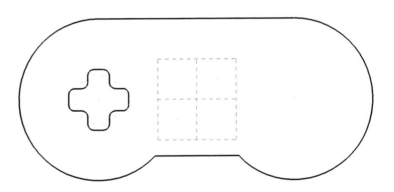

STEP 9: CREATE THE OBROUND SHAPES

In this step you will create the two Obround shapes using Rectangular Shapes command.

Step Preview:

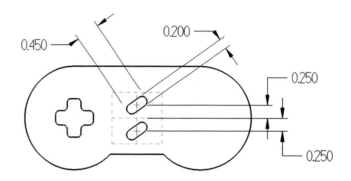

Create

* 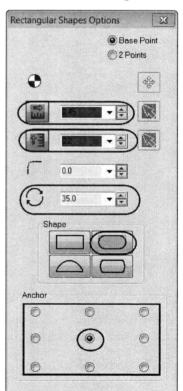 **Rectangular Shapes.**
* Enter the **Width**, the **Height**, **Angle** and enable the **Obround** shape and make sure that the **Anchor** location is in the center as shown in the <u>Figure: 9.0.1</u>.

Figure: 9.0.1

◆ [Select position for base point]: Select the **Fast point**  icon and enter the coordinates as shown.

0, 0.25

◆ Press **Enter**.

◆ Select the **Apply** button to continue in the same command. ⊕

◆ [Select position for base point]: Select the **Fast point** icon and enter the coordinates as shown.

0,-0.25

◆ Press **Enter**.

◆ Selected the **OK** button to exit the **Rectangular Shapes Options** command. ✓

◆ The geometry should look as shown.

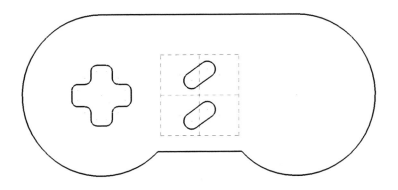

STEP 10: CREATE CIRCLE CENTER POINT

In the step you will create the four 0.25" diameter holes knowing the diameter and the center points.

Step Preview:

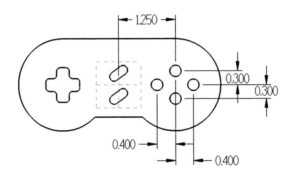

Create

* **Arc.**

*  **Circle Center Point.**

* In the **Ribbon Bar**, enter the **Diameter** value of **0.25** and make sure that the value is locked as shown.

* Choose the **Fast Point** icon to enter coordinates for the center point **1.25-0.4, 0** as shown.

1.25-0.4, 0

* Press **Enter**.

> **NOTE:** Mastercam lets you perform basic mathematical operations such as addition, substraction, multiplication or division.

* Select the **Apply** button to continue.

* Choose the **Fast Point** icon to enter coordinates for the center point **1.25+0.4, 0** as shown.

1.25+0.4, 0

* Press **Enter**.

* Select the **Apply** button to continue.

• Choose the **Fast Point** icon to enter coordinates for the center point **1.25, 0.3** as shown.

• Press **Enter**.

• Select the **Apply** button to continue. ⊕

• Choose the **Fast Point** icon to enter coordinates for the center point **1.25, -0.3** as shown.

• Press **Enter**.

• Choose the **OK** button to exit the command. ☑

• Use the **Fit** icon to fit the geometry to the screen. ✛

• The geometry should look as shown.

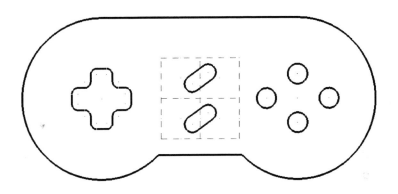

STEP 11: CHANGE ATTRIBUTES

In this step we will change the system color and level which the solid will be created on. This will be done to allow us to view our part easier.

- Left click on **System Color.**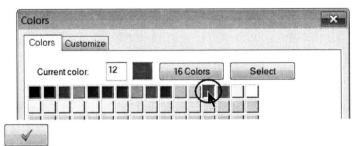
- When the **Color** dialog box appears choose color number **12** or the color **Red.**

- Select the **OK** button to exit the Color dialog box.

- Left click on **Level.**
- When the **Level Manager** appears below **Number** input "**2**" and enter the name **"Solid"** as shown in
  Figure: 11.0.1.

Figure: 11.0.1

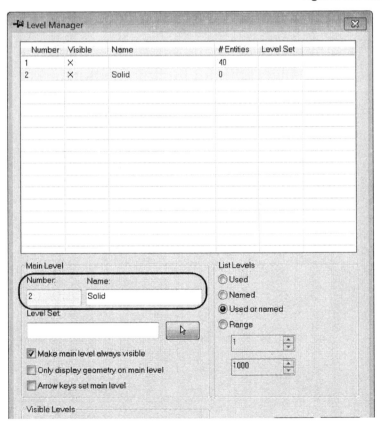

♦ Select the **OK** button to exit the **Level Manager.**

NOTE: All the entities you will create will be on Level #2.

♦ In the **Status bar** you should see the **System Color** is set to color number **12** and the **Level** will be set to **2**.

STEP 12: EXTRUDE THE BASE OF THE SOLID

Extruded function lets you extrude geometry to create one or more solid bodies, cuts on an exisiting body or create bosses on an existing body.

Step Preview:

12.1 Create the body and the four holes

Solids

♦ **Extrude.**

♦ When the chaining dialog appears leave the default settings.

♦ Change the **Graphics view** to **Isometric.**

* Start the chain on the outside profile of the part and the four holesin the clockwise direction as shown in <u>Figure: 12.1.1</u>.

Figure: 12.1.1

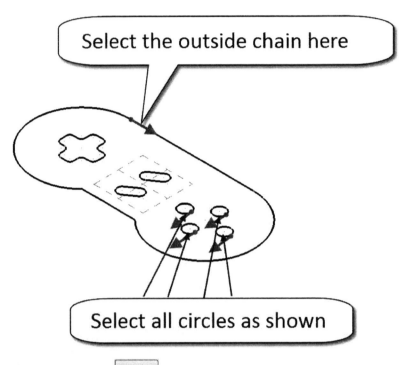

Select the outside chain here

Select all circles as shown

* Once the geometry has been chained select the **OK** button.
* Ensure that all the arrows are pointing in a negative or downward direction as shown in <u>Figure: 12.1.2</u>.

NOTE: To change an arrow direction, click on the chain close to the respective arrow.

Figure: 12.1.2

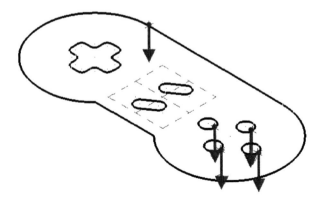

- In the **Extrude Chain** dialog box ensure **Create Body** is enabled and input **0.5** to **Extend by specified distance** as shown in Figure: 12.1.3.

Figure: 12.1.3

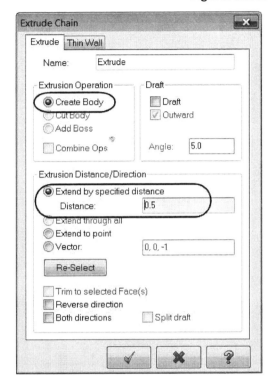

- Select the **OK** button to create the solid.

- Use the the icons found in the toolbars to **Shade** or **Unshade** (view the wireframe) the solid, or press **Alt + S** on your keyboard.

- Your part will appear as shown.

* Unshade the solid.

* Change the **Graphics view** to **Top**.

12.2 Cut the shapes

Solids

* **Extrude.**
* When the chaining dialog appears leave the default settings.
* Select the three chains in the clockwise directions as shown in <u>Figure: 12.2.1</u>.

Figure: 12.2.1

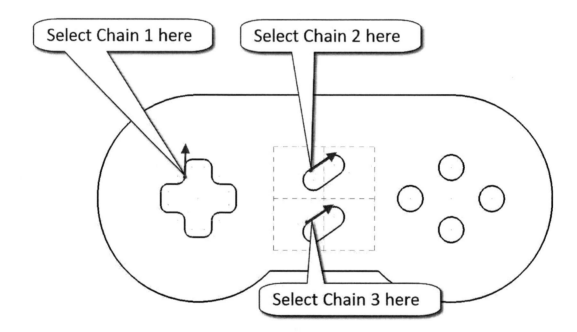

* Select the **OK** button in the **Chaining** dialog box.

* Select the **Isometric** view from the graphics view toolbar.

◆ Make sure that all three arrows are pointing downwards as shown in <u>Figure: 12.2.2</u>.

Figure: 12.2.2

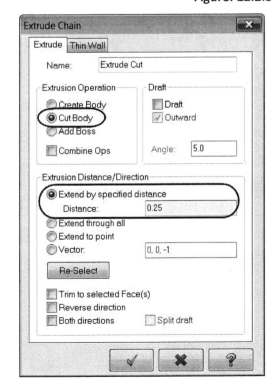

NOTE: To change the arrow direction, click on the chain close to the respective arrow.

◆ In the **Extrude Chain** dialog box enable **Cut Body** and input a **Distance** of **0.25** as shown in <u>Figure: 12.2.3</u>.

Figure: 12.2.3

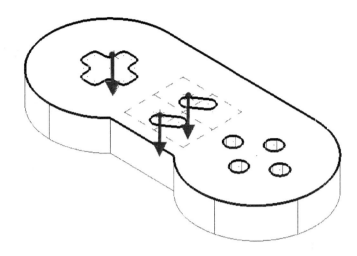

- Select the **OK** button and the steps will be cut from the solid.
- Press **Alt + S** to shade the solid. The part will appear as shown.

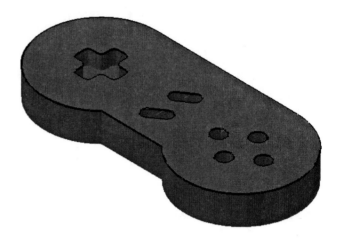

12.3 Make Level 1 Invisible

This will hide the 2D wireframe on your screen.

- Left click on **Level** in the **Status bar**.
- When the **Level Manager** appears left click in the **Visible** column and remove the "**X**" as shown in
  Figure: 12.3.1.

Figure: 12.3.1

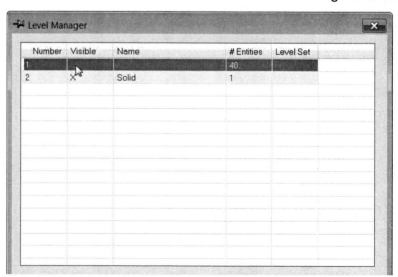

• Select the **OK** button to exit the **Level Manager**.
• The part will appear as shown.

STEP 13: SAVE THE FILE

File

• Save As.
• File name: "Your Name_9."

TOOLPATH CREATION

SUGGESTED FIXTURE:

STEP 14:   SELECT THE MACHINE AND SET UP THE STOCK

In Mastercam, you select a **Machine Definition** before creating any toolpaths. The **Machine Definition** is a model of your machines capabilities and features. It acts like a template for setting up your machine. The machine definition ties together three main components. The schematic model of your machines components. The control definition that models your control capabilities and the post processor that will generate the required machine code (G-code). For a Mill Level 1 exercise (2D toolpaths) we need just a basic machine definition.

> **NOTE:** For the purpose of this tutorial, we will be using the Default milling machine.

◆ To display the **Operations Manager** press **Alt + O**.

◆ Use the **Fit** icon to fit the drawing to the screen.

Machine type
◆ **Mill.**
◆ **Default.**

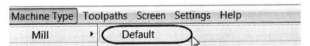

◆ Select the plus sign in front of **Properties** in the **Toolpaths Manager** to expand the **Toolpaths Group Properties.**

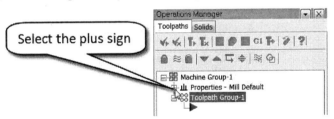

◆ Select **Tool Settings** to set the tool parameters.

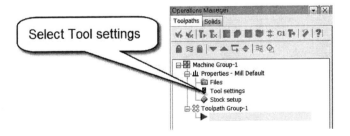

♦ Change the parameters to match the screen shot as shown in Figure: 14.0.1.

Figure: 14.0.1

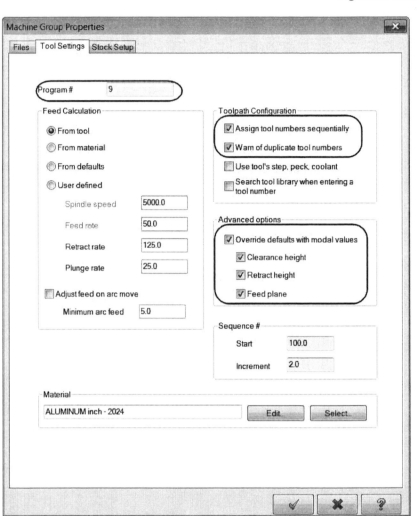

Program # is used to enter a number if your machine tool requires a number for a program name.

Assign tool numbers sequentially allows you to overwrite the tool number from the library with the next available tool number. (First operation tool number 1; Second operation tool number 2, etc.)

Warn of duplicate tool numbers allows you to get a warning if you enter two tools with the same number.

Override defaults with modal values enables the system to keep the values that you enter.

Feed Calculation set **From tool** uses feed rate, plunge rate, retract rate and spindle speed from the tool definition.

- Select the **Stock setup** tab to define the stock.
- Pick the **Rectangular** shape option.
- Choose the **All Solids** button and the stock size will be input as shown in Figure: 14.0.2.

Figure: 14.0.2

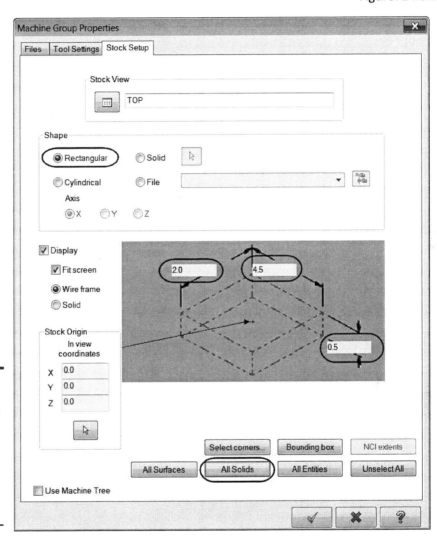

The **Stock Origin** values adjust the positioning of the stock, ensuring that you have equal amount of extra stock around the finished part.

Display options allow you to set the stock as **Wireframe** and to fit the stock to the screen. (Fit Screen)

NOTE: The **stock** model that you create can be displayed with the part geometry when viewing the file or the toolpaths, during backplot, or while verifying toolpaths. In the graphics, the plus shows you where the stock origin is. The default position is the middle of the stock.

- Select the **OK** button to exit **Machine Group Properties**.

- Select the **Isometric** view from the graphics view toolbar to see the stock.

- Use the **Fit** icon to fit the drawing to the screen.

◆ The stock model should appear as shown.

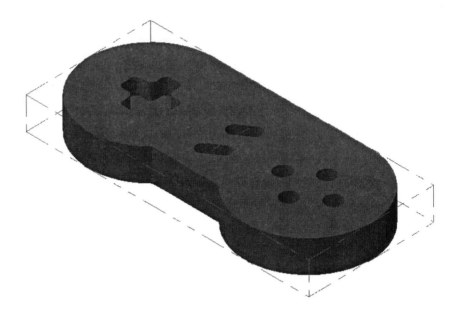

NOTE: You may not be able to see the stock very clearly due to the fact that the stock is the same size as the part. The stock is not geometry and can not be selected.
We will be demonstrating **Feature Based Milling**. There will not be a facing operation because the stock is the same size as the part.

STEP 15: FBM MILL

FBM Mill is a powerful feature based machining strategy available with Mastercam Mill. With a single operation Mastercam analyzes a solid part, detects all machining features in a specified plane and automatically generates all of the 2D milling toolpaths necessary to completely machine the selected features.

Toolpath Preview:

Toolpaths

◆  **FBM Mill.**

• Enable **Automatic initial feature detection,** and **Use tools in MCX** as shown in <u>Figure: 15.0.1</u>.

Figure: 15.0.1

☑ Automatic initial feature detection	Search plane TOP
☐ Recognize tapered features	Group by Feature & Zone
Tool selection	Outside of part
☐ Preferred tooling	☐ Rough outside of part
☑ Use tools in MCX	☐ Finish outside of part
— Automatic tool selection	Adjust depth 0.0
☑ Use tool library	
☐ Create as needed	

Tool library

🗁

C:\Documents and Settings\All ...\MILL_INCH.TOOLS-6

Comment

Tool creation

If feature depth exceeds tool length

◉ Create one tool for all depths

○ Create one tool for each depth

○ Create tools in length increments of   75.0   %

Automatic initial hole/feature detection when selected, Mastercam automatically detects features when you choose the FBM operation. If you save the settings to your toolpath, DEFAULTS file and use that final in the active machine group, Mastercam automatically detects features everytime you choose the FBM operation.

Recognize tapered features allows wall and boss features with consistant tapers to be machined.

Tool selection tells Mastercam where to locate tools for the FBM-generated toolpaths.

Preferred tooling searches the preferred tools list defined in the Facing tools, Roughing tools, Restmill tools and Finish tools pages to find an appropriate tool for the operation. Mastercam searches the preferred tool list from the largest to smallest tool and steps at the first tool small enough to machine the fearure.

Use tools in MCX looks in the current Mastercam file for an appropriate tool.

Use tool library searches the selected tool library for the necessary tools.

Create as needed creates the necessary tools using the Tool creation parameters you define.

Search Plane detects only features that can be machined in the selected plane.

Group by controls the organization of FBM Mill generated toolpaths.

Feature & Zone Mastercam creates a separate subgroup in the Toolpath Manager for each zone.

Minimize tool changes Mastercam sorts the toolpaths into subgroups.

15.1 Feature Detection

◆ Change the **Through features** to **Additional break through** and add **0.1** as shown in <u>Figure: 15.1.1</u>.

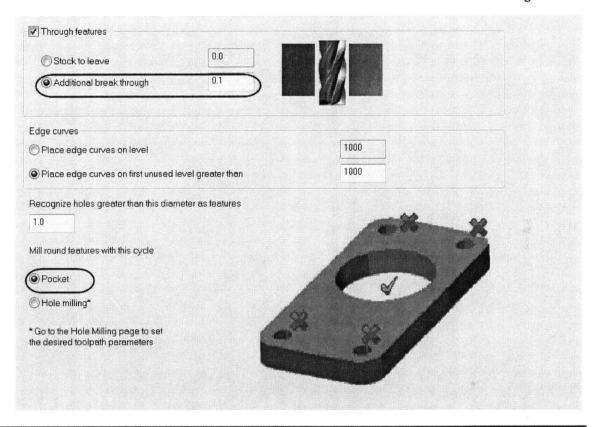

Through features select to allow FBM Mill to detect and include pockets that extend through the whole model.

Stock to leave sets the amount of material to leave at the bottom of the stock.

Additional break through sets the depth of the cut beyond the bottom of the part.

Edge Curves Mastercam creates the edge curve geometry that is required by the FBM-generated toolpaths to machine detected features.

Recognize holes greater than this diameter as features eliminates from detection any through holes that are not through pockets, for example drilled holes. All holes which are equal to or smaller than the entered diameter will be excluded from detection.

Mill round feature with this cycle Choose one of the following strategies for machining the round hole features that FBM Mill detects in your solid model.

Pocket generates pocketing toolpaths for round hole features, allowing you to output separate rough, rest and finish toolpaths.

15.2 Facing Tools

◆ This is where you setup the tools for a facing operation as shown in <u>Figure: 15.2.1</u>. You will not be setting up a facing toolpath for this part.

Figure: 15.2.1

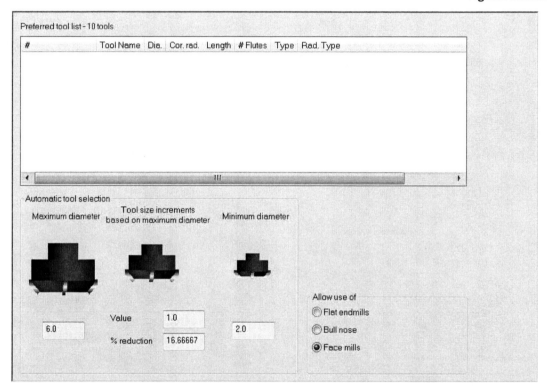

Preferred tool list Mastercam searches your preferred tools list from the largest to smallest tool to find an appropriate tool for each FBM-generated toolpath.

Automatic tool selection applies only when tool selection options **use tool library** or **Create as needed** are selected in the setup page.

Maximum diameter enter the maximum tool diameter for automatic tool library selection or tool creation.

Minimum diameter enter the minimum tool diameter for automatic tool library selection or tool creation.

Tool size increments based on maximum diameter defines the size gap between tools that Mastercam uses to find or create the next available tool size.

Allow use of select the tool type Mastercam should choose or create for the operation type.

15.3 Roughing Tools

◆ This is where you setup the tools for a roughing operation as shown in <u>Figure: 15.3.1</u>.

Figure: 15.3.1

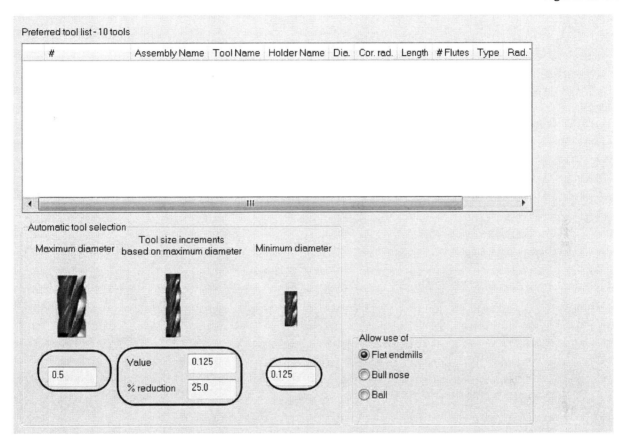

15.4 Restmill Tools

◆ This is where you setup the tools for a remachining operation as shown in <u>Figure: 15.4.1</u>.

Figure: 15.4.1

15.5 Finish Tools

♦ This is where you setup the tools for finish operations as shown in <u>Figure: 15.5.1</u>.

Figure: 15.5.1

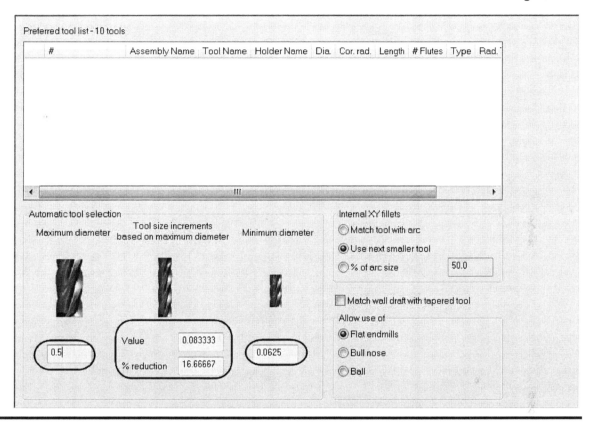

Internal XY fillets choose a strategy for selecting or creating tools to machine internal fillets in the XY axes. This strategy applies only when the minimum tool diameter is less than or equal to the fillet.

Match tool with arc selecting or creating the tool, Mastercam uses the fillet size plus the stock to leave value you defined in the floor finish and wall finish cut parameters.

Use next smaller tool selects a tool that is the next size smaller based on your automatic tool selection settings. If Mastercam must create the tool, it creates a tool the next small standard size for the tool type.

% of arc size selects or creates a tool no larger than the percentage of the arc you specify.

15.6 Facing

♦ We do not need to face the part. Make sure that facing is disabled as shown in <u>Figure: 15.6.1</u>.

Figure: 15.6.1

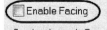

15.7 Roughing

This page allows you to add roughing toolpaths to the FBM Mill operations and to define their cutting passes. Mastercam will create the roughing toolpaths before any restmill or finish toolpaths.

♦ Change the **XY Stepover** and **Depth cuts** to **% of diameter**. Input the values as shown in Figure: 15.7.1.

Figure: 15.7.1

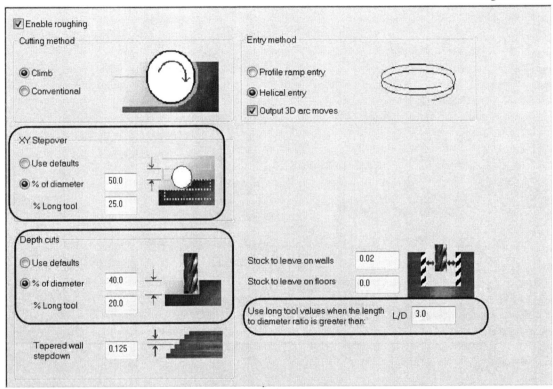

Cutting method allows you to set the direction which the tool travels in.

XY Stepover sets the spacing between passes in the X and Y axis for the FBM generated toolpath type.

Use defaults uses the XY stepover defaults defined for the FBM-generated toolpath type either from toolpath .DEFAULTS file or from defaults in the tool definition.

% of diameter calculates the XY stepover as a percentage of the tool diameter.

% Long tool reduces the stress on long tools by using separate depth cuts or an XY stepover calculation for them. Long tools are defined by the length of diameter ratio you define in the **L/D** field.

Tapered wall stepdown set the stepdown value to be used on tapered walls.

Use long tool values when the length to diameter ratio is greater than (L/D) defines long tools using the length to diameter ratio you enter.

Mill Level 1 Training Tutorial

Mastercam. X⁷

15.8 Restmill

This page allows you to add restmill toolpaths to the FBM Mill operation and to define their cutting passes. Mastercam creates the restmill toolpaths after roughing operations and before finish passes.

* Restmill toolpaths are roughing operations that remove remaining stock based on a previous roughing toolpath or based on a roughing tool as shown in <u>Figure: 15.8.1</u>.

Figure: 15.8.1

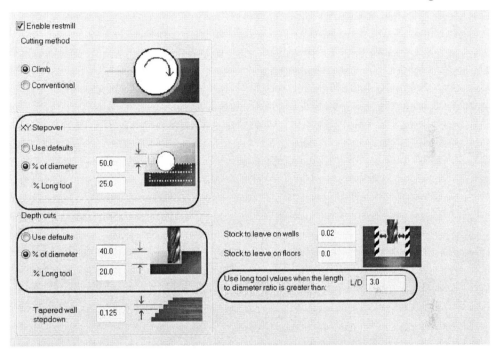

NOTE: The parameters found on this page are the same as the previous page minus entry method. Entry method is not necessary because the rough material would be removed before a restmill toolpath.

15.9 Floor Finish

This page allows you to add finish passes for the floor of each pocket feature in the FBM Mill operations. When this option is deselected Mastercam creates only roughing and restmill operations for pocket floors.

* We will disable **Floor finish** because we didn't leave any stock on the floors as shown in <u>Figure: 15.9.1</u>.

Figure: 15.9.1

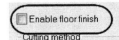

15.10 Wall Finish

With this option enabled Mastercam will add finish passes for the walls of each pocket feature included in the FBM Mill operation. When this option is deselected, Mastercam creates only roughing and restmill operations for pocket walls.

♦ Make sure this option is enabled and set the **Finish passes** to **Number** with a value of **1**. Set the **Depth cuts** to **# of cuts** with a value of **1** as shown in Figure: 15.10.1.

Figure: 15.10.1

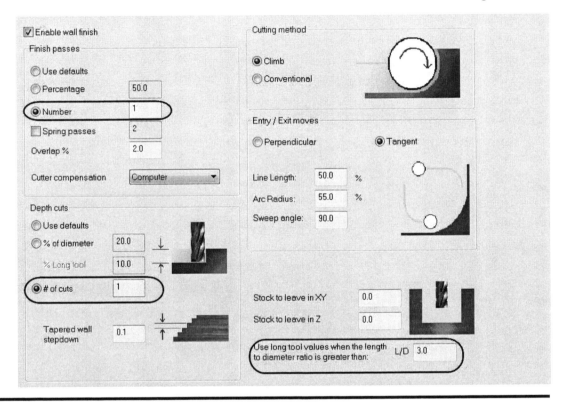

Finish passes defines how many passes the tool will step down the part.

Number lets you enter the number of wall finish passes.

Depth cuts defines how Mastercam divides the total depth cuts for the FBM-generated toolpath type into multiple depth cuts.

# of cuts enter the number of passes you want Mastercam to create in the FBM-generated toolpath.

Entry / Exit moves will define the tool moves Mastercam uses when entering and exiting the finish cut pass.

15.11 Linking Parameters

* The linking parameters allows you to set the clearance and the retract heights for the 2D toolpaths as shown in <u>Figure: 15.11.1</u>.

<u>Figure: 15.11.1</u>

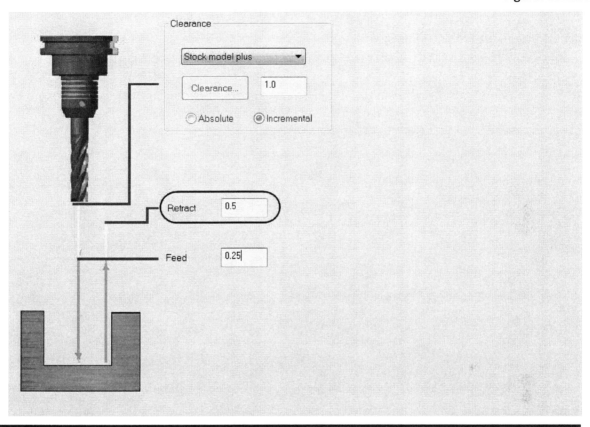

Clearance is the height at which the tool moves to and from the part.

Stock model plus adds a specified height above the stock model and automatcially selects incremental.

Retract enters a distance you want the tool to retract every time it makes a move.

Feed Plane sets the incremental height that the tool rapids to before changing to the plunge rate to enter the part.

15.12 Features

This page manages the list of features that FBM Mill detects in the solid model. The features and machining information in the list are based on the parameters you set in other FBM Mill pages.

- Select the **Detect Feature** button.
- A list of features will be generated on your features page as shown in <u>Figure: 15.12.1</u>.

NOTE: You should see a grey flag next to the outside profile. This is because the feature is surpressed. It is surpressed because on the Setup page we did not enable the options to machine the outside of the part due to the fact that the stock was made to the size of the part.

Figure: 15.12.1

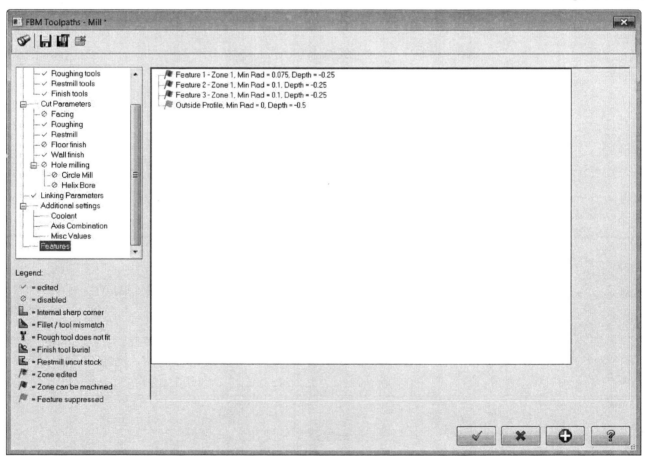

- Select the **OK** button to generate the toolpaths.

• Choose **OK** to the **NC name** dialog box.

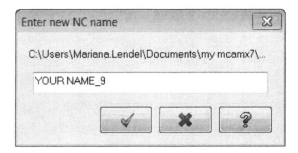

STEP 16: BACKPLOT THE TOOLPATHS

Backplotting shows the path the tools take to cut the part. This display lets you spot errors in the program before you machine the part. As you backplot toolpaths, Mastercam displays additional information such as the X, Y, and Z coordinates, the path length , the minimum and maximum coordinates and the cycle time. It also shows any collisions between the workpiece and the tool.

• Make sure that the toolpaths are selected (signified by the green check mark on the folder icon). If both

operations are not selected choose the **Select All Operations** icon.
• Select the **Backplot selected operations** button.

• Select the **Backplot** tab and have the following settings enabled as shown.

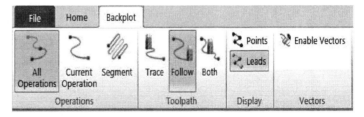

• Select the **Home** tab and make sure that you have the following settings on as shown.

- To see the part from an **Isometric** view select the **Isometric** icon.

- To fit the workpiece to the screen, select the **Fit** icon.

- You can step through the **Backplot** by using the **Step forward** or **Step back** buttons.

- You can adjust the speed of the backplot.
- Select the **Play Simulation** button in the **VCR** bar to run **Backplot**.

- The toolpath should look as shown.

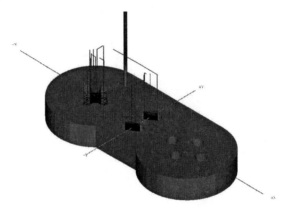

STEP 17: SIMULATE THE TOOLPATH IN VERIFY

Verify Mode shows the path the tools take to cut the part with material removal. This display lets you spot errors in the program before you machine the part. As you verify toolpaths, Mastercam displays additional information such as the X, Y, and Z coordinates, the path length , the minimum and maximum coordinates and the cycle time. It also shows any collisions between the workpiece and the tool.

- From **Mastercam Backplot Home** tab, switch to **Verify** and change the settings for the **Visibility** and **Focus** as shown in Figure: 17.0.1.

Figure: 17.0.1

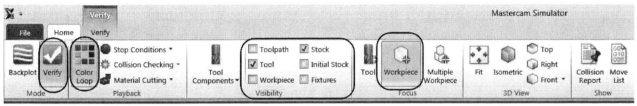

- Select the **Play Simulation** button in the **VCR** bar to run **Verify**.

- The part should appear as shown.

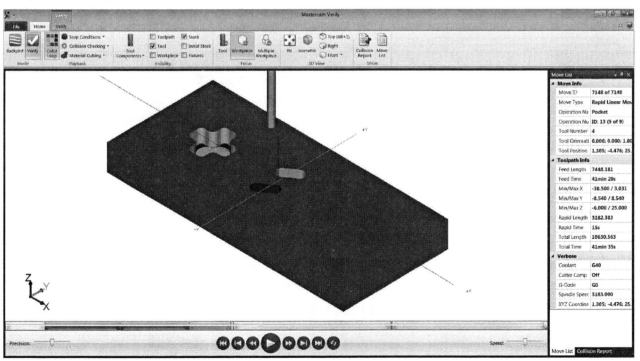

- To go back to Mastercam window, minimize **Verify** window as shown.

STEP 18: ENABLE MACHINE THE OUTSIDE OF THE PART

The part was not complete because the option to machine the outside of the part was not enabled.

♦ Under the 1st operation **FBM Mill** select **Parameters**.

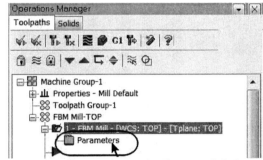

♦ When the **FBM Toolpath** dialog box appears pick **Setup** from the **Tree view list** as shown in <u>Figure: 18.0.1</u>.
♦ Under **Outside of part** enable the option to **Rough the Outside of the part** and to **Finish the outside of the part** as shown in <u>Figure: 18.0.1</u>.

Figure: 18.0.1

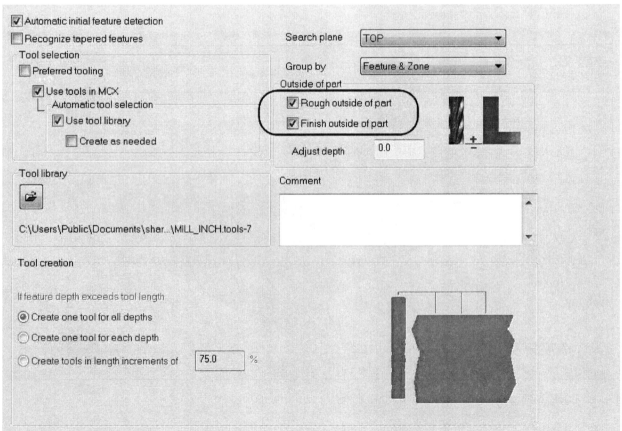

◆ Return to **Features** and ensure the outside profile can now be machined as shown in Figure: 18.0.2.

Figure: 18.0.2

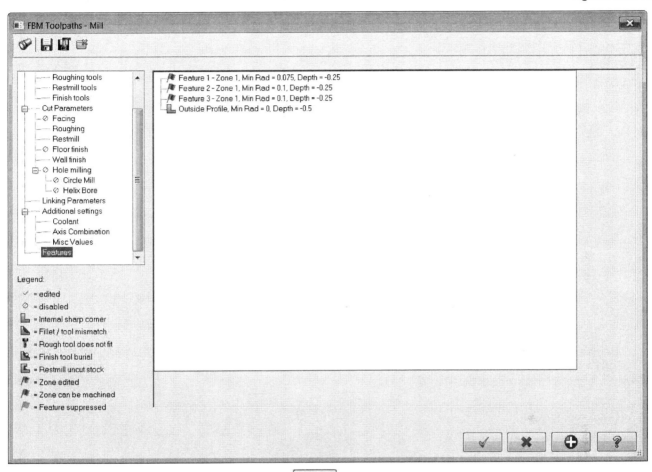

◆ Select the **OK** button to generate the toolpaths.

◆ Pick the **Regenerate All Dirty Operations** button in the operations manager.

18.1 Backplot the toolpaths

◆ To **Backplot** the toolpaths see page 793 to review the procedure.

◆ Click on the **Select all operations** icon in the **Operatoins Manager.**

◆ The toolpaths should look as shown.

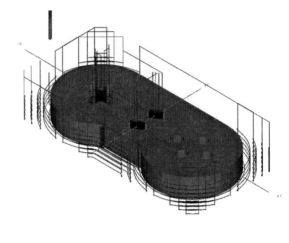

18.2 Verify the toolpaths

◆ To **Verify** the toolpaths see page 795 to review the procedure.

◆ The part should look as shown.

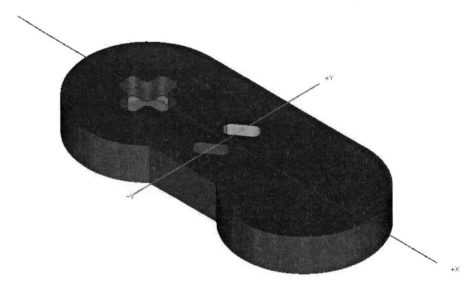

STEP 19: DRILL THE HOLES USING FBM DRILL

FBM Drill automatically detects holes in a solid based on your specific criteria and to generate a complete series of drilling and chamfering. FBM drill also generates circle mill or helix bore operations for large-hole features when you activate these settings.

Toolpath Preview:

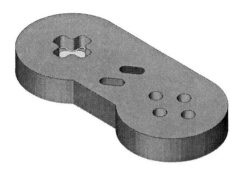

- In the **Toolpaths Operations Manager**, move the **Insert arrow** below all the toolpaths using **Move insert arrow down one item** icon.

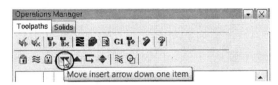

- The arrow should be below all the toolpaths as shown.

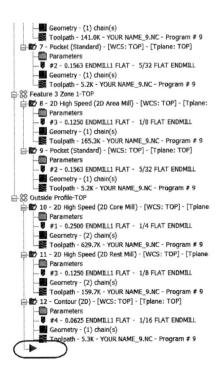

Toolpaths

- ◆ ▣ **FBM Drill.**
- ◆ When the **FBM Toolpaths - Setup page** appears, enable **Automatic initial hole detection.**
- ◆ Change the **Grouping** to **Plane** to group the operations by the plane in which the holes lie as shown in
  <u>Figure: 19.0.1</u>.

Figure: 19.0.1

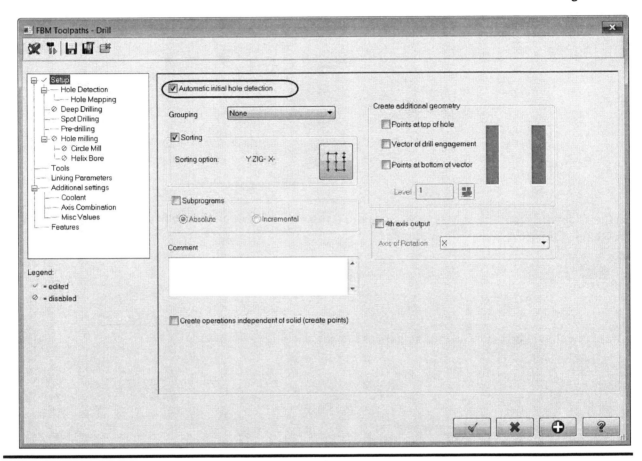

Automatic initial hole/feature detection when selected, Mastercam automatically detects features when you choose the FBM operation. If you save the settings to your toolpath .DEFAULTS file and use that final in the active machine group, Mastercam automatically detects features everytime you choose the FBM operation.

Grouping controls how the drill cycles that FBM Drill creates are organized in the Toolpath Manager. Mastercam orders operations within groups into subgroups by operation type.

Plane groups all operations based on the plane of the hole.

Create additional geometry select one or more options to create geometry for detected hole features without generating toolpaths. The geometry is saved to a level you choose in this section and is non associative.

19.1 Hole Detection

◆ Choose **Hole Detection** to control the types of holes **FBM Drill** detects. Enable/disable the options as shown in <u>Figure: 19.1.1</u>.

Figure: 19.1.1

Include blind holes will search your part for blind holes (holes that do not go through the entire solid).

Include chamfers searches for holes with chamfers.

Include split holes searches the part for holes that are incomplete.

Limit search to plane detects features that can only be machined in the selected plane.

Minimum diameter finds holes which are equal to or greater than this value.

Maximum diameter finds holes which are equal to or less than this value.

Sweep angle lets you set a tolerance for how complete holes needs to be in terms of its included angle to be detected by and included in the FBM Drill operation.

Machine co-axial holes with gaps determines whether Mastercam treats multiple holes that share a common axis as a single hole, or as multiple holes from different planes.

19.2 Spot Drilling

♦ Select **Spot Drilling** to activate and define the spot drilling toolpaths for the **FBM Drill** operation.
♦ Enable the option **Use this tool for all spot drill** operations as shown in Figure: 19.2.1.

NOTE: It takes couple of minutes to enable the **Use this tool for all spot drill**.

Figure: 19.2.1

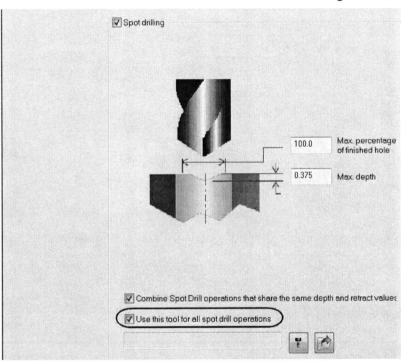

Use this tool for all spot drill operations allows you to choose a specific spot drill cycle generated by the FBM Drill operation.

♦ Pick the button **Select tool from library.**
♦ This will let you choose a tool from the current tool library.
♦ Find and select the **1/2" Spotdrill** from the list (6).

#	Assembly Name	Tool Name	Holder Name	Dia.	Cor. rad.	Length	# Flut...	Ra...	Type
1	–	1/8 CEN...	–	0....	0.0	2.0	2	No...	Ce...
2	–	1/4 CEN...	–	0.25	0.0	2.0	2	No...	Ce...
3	–	1/2 CEN...	–	0.5	0.0	2.0	2	No...	Ce...
4	–	1/8 SPO...	–	0....	0.0	2.0	2	No...	Sp...
5	–	1/4 SPO...	–	0.25	0.0	2.0	2	No...	Sp...
6	–	1/2 SPO...	–	0.5	0.0	2.0	2	No...	Sp...
7	–	1/64 DRI...	–	0....	0.0	1.0	2	No...	Drill

♦ Select the **OK** button and the **Spot drill** will appear in the box to the left of the buttons.

19.3 Pre-Drilling

◆ This page defines pre-drilling cycles that rough out the drilled holes before the finish drill cycle. Disable **Pre-drilling** as shown in <u>Figure: 19.3.1</u>.

Figure: 19.3.1

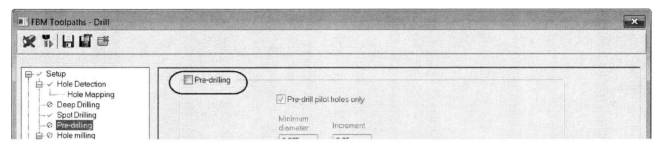

Pre-drilling Mastercam creates pre-drilling operations that rough out the detected holes before creating any finished drill and chamfer operations.

Pre-drill pilot holes only Select to deactivate all pre-drill roughing cycles except for assigned pilot holes cycles. This also deactivates the parameters for minimum diameter, increment and stock to leave on the page because they are not applicable. FBM Drill generates only pilot holes pre-drill cycles followed by finish hole cycles.

Minimum pre-drill diameter sets the smallest tool size that can be used from the tool library for the pre-drill operations.

19.4 Tools

♦ This page controls the tools Mastercam selects for the drill cycles that the **FBM Drill** operation creates.
♦ Enable/disable the parameters as shown in Figure: 19.4.1.

Figure: 19.4.1

Diameter matching tolerance Mastercam uses this value to determine how closely the diameter of the tool and the hole must match before selecting an appropriate tool.

Tool Selection lets you pick one or more of the following options to tell Mastercam where to locate tools for the FBM-generated toolpaths.

Use tools in MCX looks in the current Mastercam file for an appropriate tool. The tools do not have to be used in previous operations to be available to the FBM operations.

Use tool library searches the selected tool library for the necessary tools.

Create as needed creates the necessary tools using the tool creation parameters you define.

Hole Bottom Geometry defines the realationship of the bottom hole geometry to the tool tip geometry.

= geometry angle the tool tip angle must match the hole bottom geometry within the specified tool tip match tolerance.

> geometry angle the tool tip must be greater than the floor angle geometry.

< geometry angle the tool tip angle must be smaller than the floor angle.

19.5 Linking Parameters

This page defines how **FBM Drill** calculates clearance height and retract height for the drilling cycles.

• Set the parameters as shown in <u>Figure: 19.5.1</u>.

Figure: 19.5.1

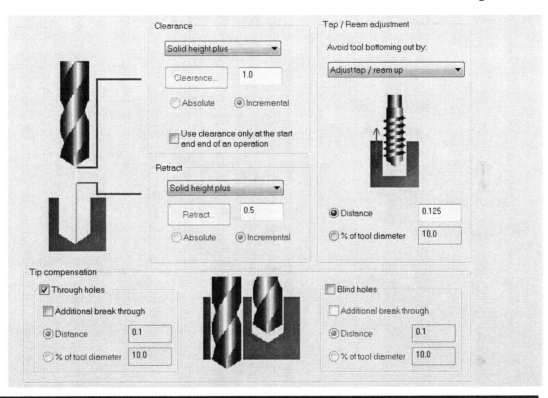

Clearance is the height at which the tool moves to and from the part. There are several options available from where the height is measured:

Solid height plus adds a fixed height above the highest point of the solid model.

Stock model plus adds a specified height above the stock model.

Top of hole plus adds clearance distance above the top of each hole.

Top of Coaxial holes plus for holes that share the same axis, it sets the clearance above the highest hole on the shared axis.

Manual allows you to set the clearance using all options in any combination.

Retract is the height at which the tool moves before the next tool pass. The same options are available as for **Clearance height**.

Tap/Ream adjustment determines whether tapped and reamed holes are fully finished.

Tip compensation compensates for the tool tip.

19.6 Features

This page allows you to manage the list of hole features that FBM Drill detects in the solid model.

---

* Choose the button to **Detect the Features** for Mastercam to detect the holes as shown in Figure: 19.6.1.
* Click on **State** to organize the features better, and scroll down until you reach the unassigned areas as shown in Figure: 19.6.1.

Figure: 19.6.1

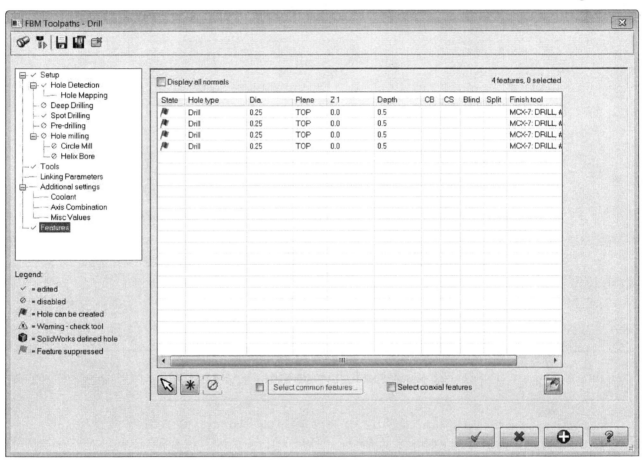

* Choose the **OK** button to generate the **FBM Drill Toolpath**.

19.7 Backplot the toolpaths

◆ To **Backplot** the toolpaths see page 793 to review the procedure.

◆ Click on the **Select all operations** icon in the **Operatoins Manager.**
◆ The toolpaths should look as shown.

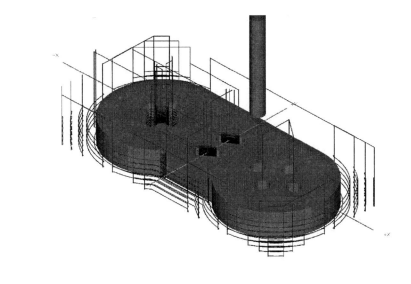

19.8 Verify the toolpaths

◆ To **Verify** the toolpaths see page 795 to review te procedure.
◆ The part should look as shown.

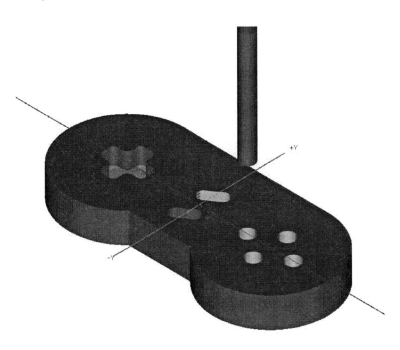

STEP 20: POST THE FILE

♦ Ensure all operations are slected, if they are not use the button **Select all operations** in the **Operatoins**

Manager.

♦ Select the **Post selected operations** button from the **Operations Manager.** G1
♦ In the **Post processing** window make the necessary changes as shown in Figure: 20.0.1.

Figure: 20.0.1

NC File enabled allows you to keep the NC file and to assign the same name as the MCX file.

Edit enabled allows you to automatically launch the default editor.

♦ Select the **OK** button to continue.

♦ Save "Your Name_9.NC" file.

♦ A window with the NC programs will appear as shown in <u>Figure: 20.0.2</u>.

Figure: 20.0.2

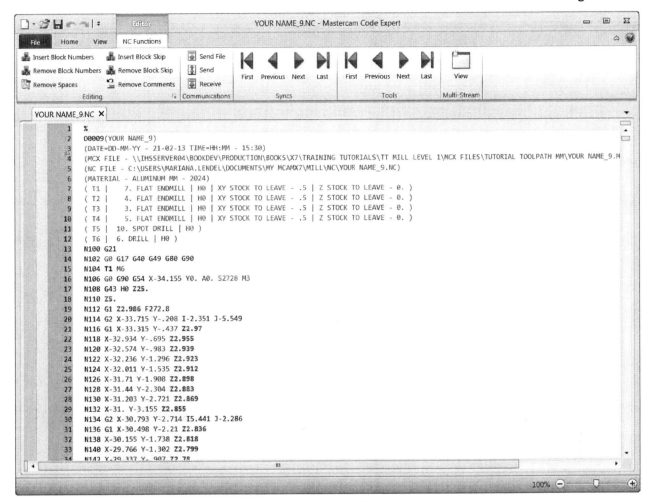

♦ Select the red **"X"** box at the upper right corner to exit the editor.

STEP 21: SAVE THE UPDATED MCX FILE

REVIEW EXERCISE -STUDENT PRACTICE

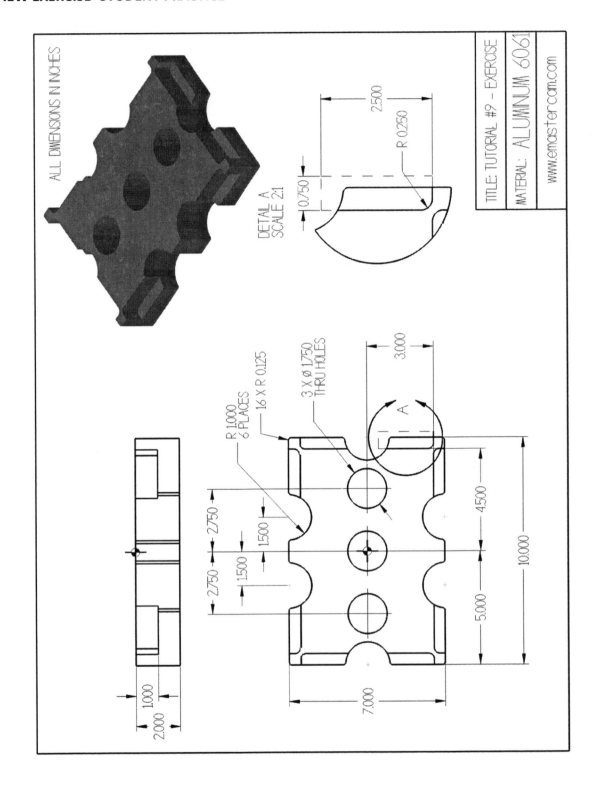

ALL DIMENSIONS IN INCHES

DETAIL A
SCALE 2:1

2.500

R 0.250

0.750

TITLE: TUTORIAL #9 – EXERCISE

MATERIAL: ALUMINUM 6061

www.emastercam.com

R 1.000
6 PLACES

16 X R 0.125

3 X ⌀ 1.750
THRU HOLES

2.750

2.750

1.500

1.500

3.000

A

4.500

10.000

5.000

7.000

2.000

1.000

CREATE THE GEOMETRY FOR TUTORIAL #9 EXERCISE

Use these commands to create the geometry:
- Create 1/4 of the geometry.
- Create Rectangle.
- Create Arc Polar.
- Create Fillet Entities.
- Edit Break Two Pieces.
- Trim and Delete Entities.
- Xform Mirror.
- Edit Join Entities.
- Change Attributes.
- Solid Extrude.

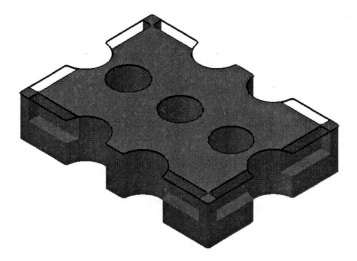

CREATE THE TOOLPATHS FOR TUTORIAL #9 EXERCISE

Create the Toolpaths for Tutorial #9 Exercise as per the instructions below.

Set the machine properties including the Stock.
FBM Mill

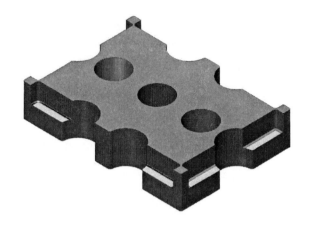

* Enable Automatic initial feature detection.
* Enable Use tools in MCX and disable the option to create as needed.
* Enable the option to Rough and Finish the outside of the part.
* Roughing tools enter the minimum diameter of 0.25".
* Restmill tools enter the minimum diameter of 0.125".
* Finish tools enter the minimum diameter of 0.0625".
* Disable facing.
* Roughing XY Stepover and Depth cuts use % of diameter.
* Enter 50% of diameter and 25% Long tool.
* Use the same values for Restmill.
* Wall finish enable number and enter 1.
* Use the # of cuts set to 1 as the option in the depth cuts.
* Enable Hole milling and Circle mill.
* Set the Finish passes to 1 at All depths.
* Set the Rough to 50% of the tool diameter and leave the rest of the default parameters.
* Check the Linking Parameters.
* Detect the features.

NOTES:

TUTORIAL #9 QUIZ

◆ What does FBM Mill allow you to do?

◆ What does automatic tool selection do?

◆ What does % Long tool do in the roughing and restmill parameters?

◆ What does Hole Milling allow you to do?

Mill Level 1 Training Tutorial *Mastercam.* X⁷

TUTORIAL #10

OVERVIEW OF STEPS TAKEN TO CREATE THE FINAL PART:

Open an existing 2D CAD Model:
- The student will download the file with the 2D geometry from emastercam.com.
- The student will open the file in Mastercam.
- The student will position the part in the correct orientation like it is setup on the Vertical CNC machine.
- The student will clean the geometry to be able to properly select it for machining.

Create the necessary Toolpaths to machine the part:
- The student will set up the stock size to be used and the clamping method to be used. For this part two setups will be used.
- A 2D High Speed Dynamic Area Mill toolpath will be created to remove material inside of the pockets.
- A 2D High Speed Dynamic Rest Mill toolpath will be created to remove the remaining material inside of the pockets.
- A 2D High Speed Dynamic Core Mill toolpath will be created to remove the material outside of the profile.
- A 2D High Speed Dynamic Contour Mill toolpath will be created to remove the remaining material outside of the profile.
- Use High Efficiency Machining (HEM) Iscar tools with the dynamic toolpaths.

Backplot and Verify the file:
- The Backplot will be used to simulate a step by step process of the tool's movements.
- The Verify will be used to watch a tool machine the part out of a solid model.

Post Process the file to generate the G-code:
- The Student will then post process the file to obtain an NC file containing the necessary code for the machine.

 This tutorial takes approximately one hour and half to complete.

GEOMETRY CREATION

STEP 1: SETTING UP THE GRAPHIC USER INTERFACE

Please refer to the **Getting Started** section to set up the graphic user interface accordingly.

DOWNLOAD THE FILE

You will require an internet connection to download this file.

Resources - Download the file from **www.emastercam.com/files/**
* Go to www.emastercam.com/files/.
* Select Tutorial #10.
* Minimize or close the internet explorer.
* The part should look as shown.

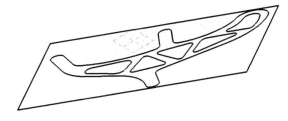

Gview:ISO WCS:TOP T/Cplane:TOP

NOTE: The plane in which the part was created is not one of the standard planes. In order to machine the part you will have to rotate it to match the way in which is fixtured on the machine. In the next step you will create the view in which the part was brought in.

STEP 2: CREATING A NEW VIEW

In this step you will learn how to create a new view from flat part geometry. To define a plane you can select two intersecting lines, a 2D entity such as an arc or a flat surface, or you can select 3 points.

• From the **Ribbon Bar**, select **Planes** and then **Planes by geometry** as shown.

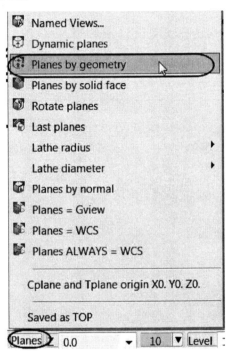

• Select the two intersecting lines as shown.

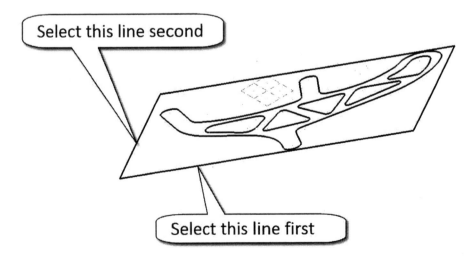

- The axes orientation should be as shown in Figure: 2.0.1.
- Otherwise, from the **Select view** select the **Next** button until the axes are matching.

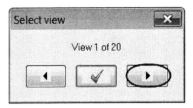

Figure: 2.0.1

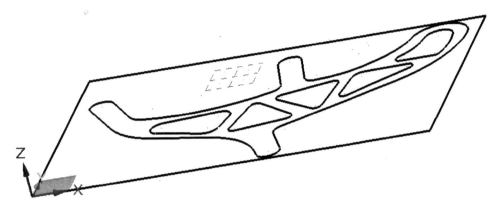

- In the **New View**, change the **Name** to **Toolpath View** and leave the other parameters as shown in Figure: 2.0.2.

Figure: 2.0.2

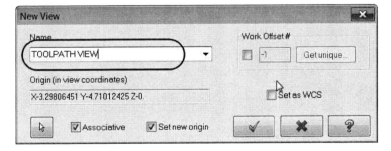

- Select the **OK** button to finish.

NOTE: The **Grid** shows you the new plane.

STEP 3: USE TRANSLATE 3D TO MOVE THE PART IN THE TOP VIEW

In this step you will use Translate 3D to rotate the part from the current "Toolpath view" into the Top view.

Xform

* 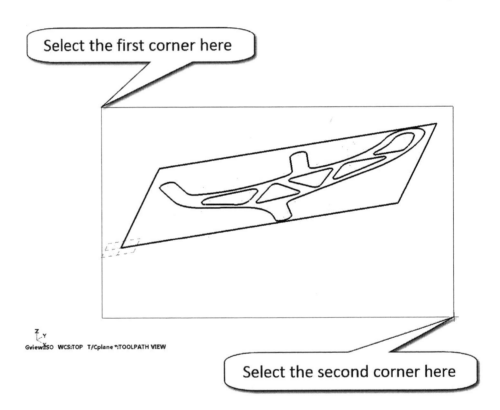 **Translate 3D.**
* [Translate: select entities to translate]: Make a window around the entire part as shown in Figure: 3.0.1.

> **NOTE:** To make a window to select all entities inside of it, click on the upper right corner outside the geometry and holding down the left mouse drag it to the opposite corner.

Figure: 3.0.1

Select the first corner here

Select the second corner here

Gview:ISO   WCS:TOP   T/Cplane *:TOOLPATH VIEW

* Press **Enter** or click on the **End Selection** button.

End Selection

◆ In the **Translate 3D** enable **Move** and change the **Source View** to **Toolpath View** and the **Destination View** to **Top** as shown in Figure: 3.0.2.

Figure: 3.0.2

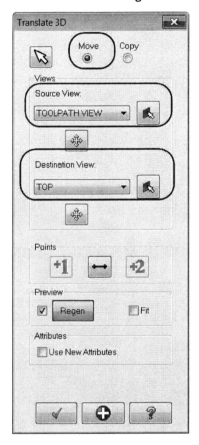

◆ Select the **OK** button to exit the command.

◆ Select the **Fit** icon.

◆ Select the **Clear colors** to remove the result color (magenta) and go back to the original color.

NOTE: When performing a transform function (Xform), Mastercam creates a temporary group from the originals (red) and a result (purple) from the transformed entities.

◆ The geometry should look as shown.

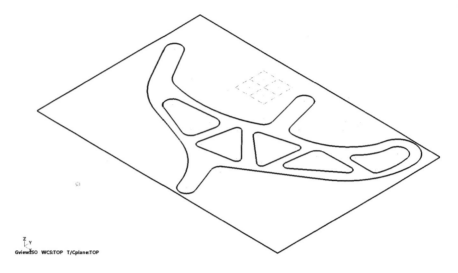

STEP 4: MOVE THE GEOMETRY TO SET A NEW ORIGIN

In this step you will use **Move to Origin** to set the **Origin** to the upper left corner.

Xform

◆ 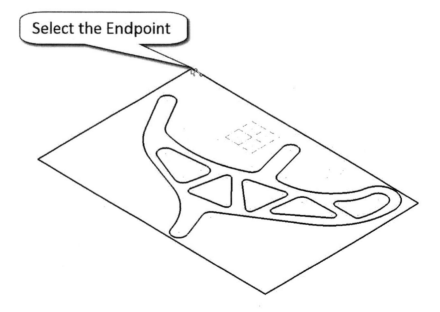 **Move to Origin.**

◆ [Select the point to translate from]: Select the Endpoint as shown in <u>Figure: 4.0.1</u>.

Figure: 4.0.1

- Select the **Fit** icon.
- Select the **Clear colors** to remove the result color (magenta) and go back to the original color.

- Change the **Graphic view** to **Isometric** as shown.
- The geometry should look as shown.

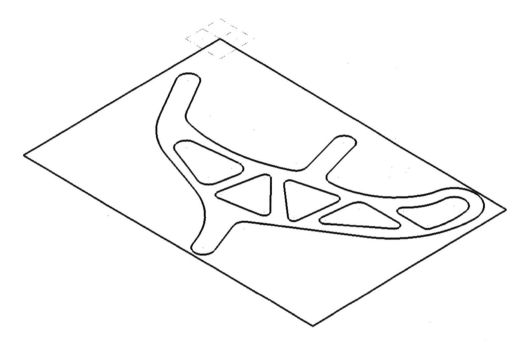

Z
Y
X
Gview:ISO WCS:TOP T/Cplane:TOP

NOTE: For Mastercam to create proper toolpaths, the geometry has to be chained. You will have to select chains of entities which consist of one or more entities linked together in order and direction. Problems such as overllaping entities, duplicate entities and untrimmed entities can result in gouges or unmachined areas. In the next step you will learn how to clean up the chains.

STEP 5: CLEANING UP THE GEOMETRY

In this step you will learn how to remove duplicate entities and to trim entities to fix the geometry that has to be chained. To quick check if there are any problems in the geometry you will have to select the chain by holding down the Shift key and selecting one entity of a chain. As you chain the geometry, Mastercam highlights the entities in the same color as selected entities (yellow is the default). If not all entities of the chain are highlighted that tells you that you encounter a problem in the geometry.

* Change the **Graphic view** to **Top** as shown.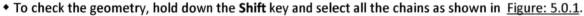
* To check the geometry, hold down the **Shift** key and select all the chains as shown in <u>Figure: 5.0.1</u>.

Figure: 5.0.1

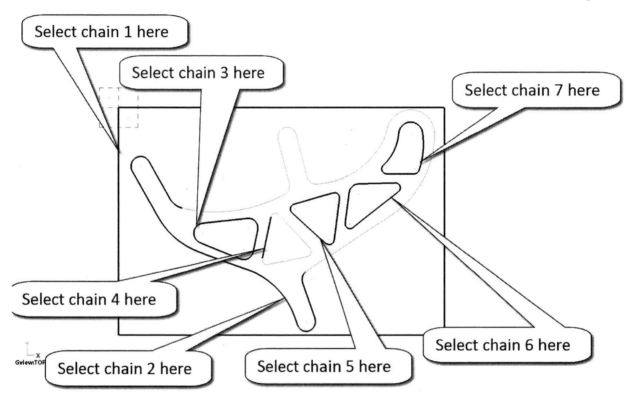

5.1 Cleaning duplicate entities

Duplicate entities are identical entities. To remove them you can use Delete duplicates command. For Mastercam to automatically remove all the duplicate entities from the current file make sure that no entities are selected.

♦ Make sure that you unselect all the entities by clicking in the **General Selection** toolbar on the **UnSelect All** button as shown.

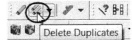

♦ Select **Delete Duplicates** icon.
♦ This message should appear on the screen.

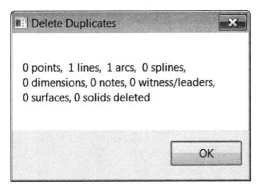

♦ Mastercam automatically removes all the duplicate entities.
♦ Holding down the **Shift** key and reselect all chains as shown before.

5.2 Use Analyze chain to check the chains

In this step you will use **Analyze chain** to check the chains and fix the them using Trim 2 entities.

Analyze
- **Chain.**
- Leave the **Chaining** dialog box set to **Chain** selection as shown.

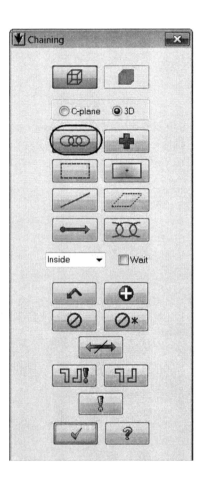

◆ Select the outside profile as shown in <u>Figure: 5.2.1</u>.

Figure: 5.2.1

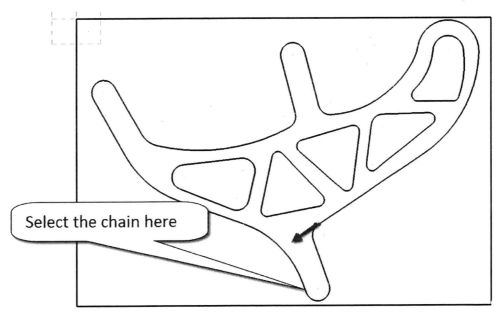

Select the chain here

NOTE: The two arrows that appear when you select the chain. You should only see one arrow (green) at the start of the chain. This means that the chain is not closed and that the entities at that location are not trimmed.

◆ Move the cursor close to the arrows and scroll up the mouse wheel to zoom in as shown in <u>Figure: 5.2.2</u>.

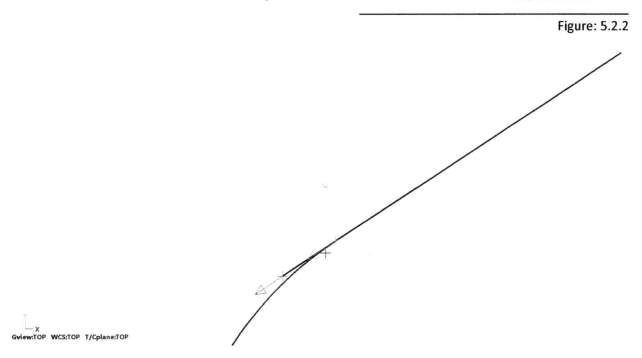

Gview:TOP   WCS:TOP   T/Cplane:TOP

◆ Press **Esc** key to exit the **Chaining** dialog box.

5.3 Use Trim Two Entities to fix the chain

Edit
◆ **Trim/Break.**

◆  **Trim/Break/Extend.**

◆ Choose the icon **Trim 2 Entity** from the ribbon bar.

◆ [Select the entity to trim/extend]: Select Entity A as shown in <u>Figure: 5.3.1</u>.
◆ [Select the entity to trim/extend too]: Select Entity B as shown in <u>Figure: 5.3.1</u>.

Figure: 5.3.1

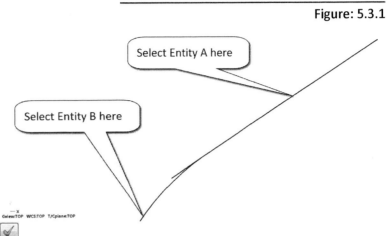

Select Entity A here

Select Entity B here

◆ Select the **OK** button to exit the command.

◆ Select the **Fit** icon.

Analyze
◆ **Chain.**
◆ Reselect the chain as shown in <u>Figure: 5.3.2</u>.

Figure: 5.3.2

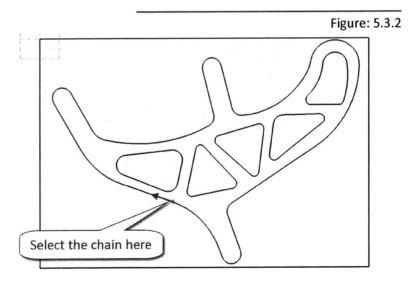

Select the chain here

◆ Check the rest of the chains.
◆ Press **Esc** to exit **Analyze Chain**.

STEP 6: SAVE THE FILE

File
◆ Save As.
◆ File name: "Your Name_10".
◆ Save your file.

TOOLPATH CREATION - SETUP 1

SUGGESTED FIXTURE:

SETUP SHEET:

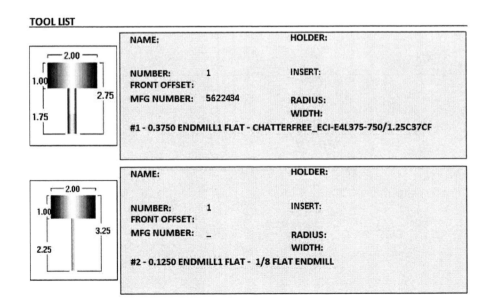

STEP 7: SELECT THE MACHINE AND SET UP THE STOCK

In Mastercam, you select a **Machine Definition** before creating any toolpaths. The **Machine Definition** is a model of your machines capabilities and features. It acts like a template for setting up your machine. The machine definition ties together three main components. The schematic model of your machines components, the control definition that models your control capabilities and the post processor that will generate the required machine code (G-code). For a Mill Level 1 exercise (2D toolpaths) we need just a basic machine definition.

> **NOTE:** For the purpose of this tutorial, we will be using the Default milling machine.

◆ To display the **Operations Manager** press **Alt + O**.

◆ Use the **Fit** icon to fit the drawing to the screen.

Machine type
◆ **Mill.**
◆ **Default.**

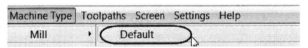

◆ Select the plus sign in front of **Properties** in the **Toolpaths Manager** to expand the **Toolpaths Group Properties.**

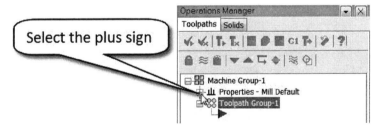

◆ Select **Tool Settings** to set the tool parameters.

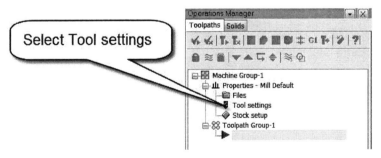

◆ Change the parameters to match the screen shot as shown in Figure: 7.0.1.

Figure: 7.0.1

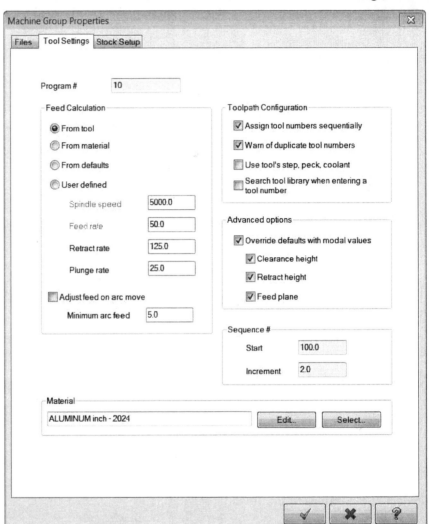

Program # is used to enter a number if your machine tool requires a number for a program name.

Assign tool numbers sequentially allows you to overwrite the tool number from the library with the next available tool number. (First operation tool number 1; Second operation tool number 2, etc.)

Warn of duplicate tool numbers allows you to get a warning if you enter two tools with the same number.

Override defaults with modal values enables the system to keep the values that you enter.

Feed Calculation set From tool uses feed rate, plunge rate, retract rate and spindle speed from the tool definition.

◆ Select the **Stock setup** tab to define the stock.
◆ Pick the **Rectangular** shape option.
◆ Choose the **All Entities** button and the stock size will be input as shown in Figure: 7.0.2.

Figure: 7.0.2

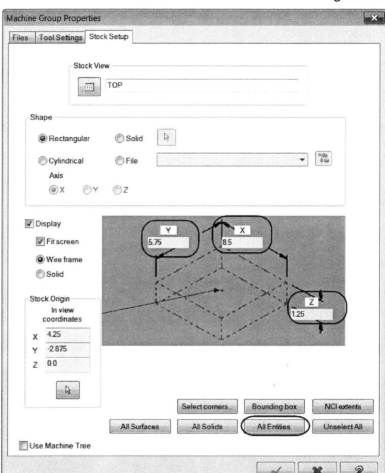

The **Stock Origin** values adjust the positioning of the stock, ensuring that you have equal amount of extra stock around the finished part.

Display options allow you to set the stock as Wireframe and to fit the stock to the screen. (Fit Screen)

NOTE: The **stock** model that you create can be displayed with the part geometry when viewing the file or the toolpaths, during backplot, or while verifying toolpaths. In the graphics, the plus shows you where the stock origin is. The default position is the middle of the stock. Click on the corner of the part to set it as the stock origin.

◆ Select the **OK** button to exit **Machine Group Properties**.

◆ Select the **Isometric** view from the graphics view toolbar to see the stock.

◆ Use the **Fit** icon to fit the drawing to the screen.

◆ The stock model will appear as shown.

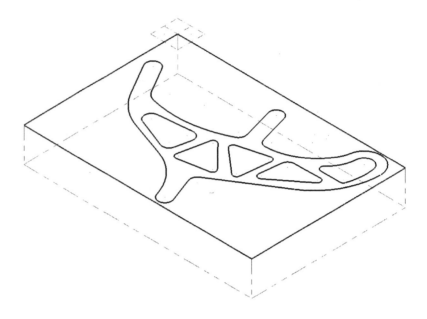

STEP 8: 2D HIGH SPEED DYNAMIC AREA MILL

This toolpath is used to machine pockets using a smooth clean motion. 2D high speed dynamic milling toolpaths utilize the entire flute length of their cutting tools to achieve efficiency in milling. They are designed to maximize material removal while minimizing tool wear. You are going to use ISCAR HEM (High Efficiency Machining) tools.

Toolpath Preview:

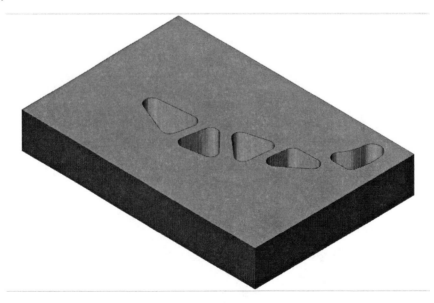

8.1 Chain Selection

Toolpaths
- **2D High Speed.**

- **Dynamic Area.**

- Select the **OK** button to accept the default **NC name**.

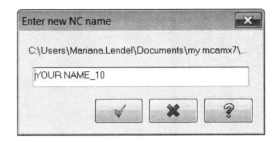

- Change the **Graphic view** to **Top** if needed.
- Leave the default setting in the chaining dialog box and pick the chains in the same direction as shown in
  Figure: 8.1.1.

Figure: 8.1.1

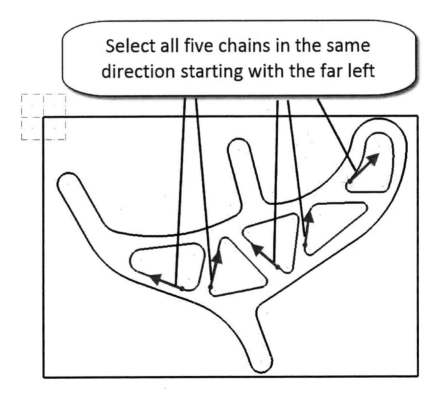

Select all five chains in the same direction starting with the far left

- Select the **OK** button to exit the chaining dialog box.

• In the **Chain Options** dialog box enable **Multiple machining regions** to instruct Mastercam to machine all the chains.

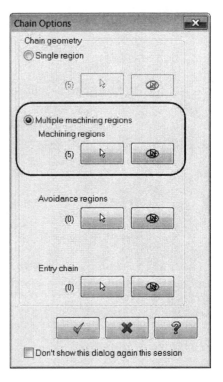

• Select the **OK** button to exit the **Chain Options** dialog box.
• In the **Toolpath Type** page, select **Dynamic Area Mill.**

Core Mill   Peel Mill   Blend Mill   Area Mill   Rest Mill   Dynamic Area Mill

Dynamic Rest Mill   Dynamic Core Mill   Dynamic Contour

8.2 Select a 3/8" ChatterFree Endmill from the Library and set the Tool Parameters

- Select **Tool** from the **Tree view list**.

- Click on the **Select library tool** button. [Select library tool...]

- Select the **New library** button as shown.

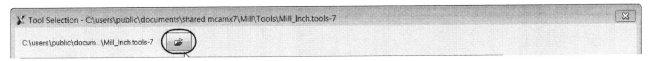

- Select the **ISCAR HEM - IN.TOOLDB** from the list as shown.

Name	Date modified	Type	Size
BIG_Inch.TOOLS-7	22/10/2012 11:37 ...	MastercamX7 Tool...	5,080 KB
BIG_MM.TOOLS-7	22/10/2012 11:37 ...	MastercamX7 Tool...	3,009 KB
BIGMM_INCH.TOOLS-7	22/10/2012 11:37 ...	MastercamX7 Tool...	5,371 KB
CBore library-Inch.TOOLS-7	22/10/2012 11:37 ...	MastercamX7 Tool...	314 KB
CBore library-metric.TOOLS-7	22/10/2012 11:37 ...	MastercamX7 Tool...	314 KB
DM-ALUM.TOOLS-7	22/10/2012 11:37 ...	MastercamX7 Tool...	1,069 KB
DM-SS.TOOLS-7	22/10/2012 11:37 ...	MastercamX7 Tool...	954 KB
HOLDERS.TOOLDB	22/10/2012 11:37 ...	TOOLDB File	1,232 KB
ISCAR HEM -IN.TOOLDB	22/10/2012 11:37 ...	TOOLDB File	217 KB
ISCAR HEM -MM.tooldb	22/10/2012 11:37 ...	TOOLDB File	435 KB
METRICST52.TOOLS-7	22/10/2012 11:37	MastercamX7 Tool	844 KB

- Open the library.
- Select the **Filter** button.

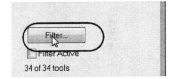

* Under tool diameter pick **Equal** and input a value **0.375** as shown in <u>Figure: 8.2.1</u>.

Figure: 8.2.1

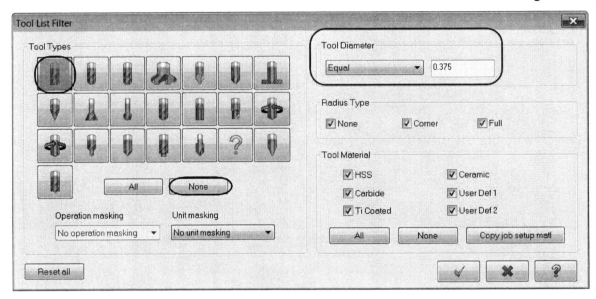

* Select the **OK** button to exit the **Tool List Filter**.
* Select the first **ChatterFree 3/8" Endmill** in the **Tool Selection** page as shown.

#	Assembly Name	Tool Name	Holder Name	Dia.	Cor. rad.	Length	# Flutes	Type	Rad. Type
17	–	CHATTE...	–	0....	0.0	0.75	4	En...	None
18	–	CHATTE...	–	0....	0.0	0.75	4	En...	None
29	–	CHATTE...	–	0....	0.0	0.94	5	En...	None
30	–	CHATTE...	–	0....	0.0	0.94	5	En...	None

* Select the **OK** button to continue.
* Enable **Iscar HEM** as shown.

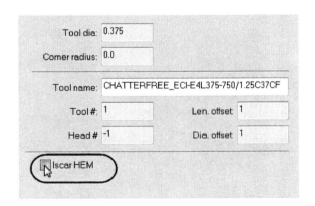

◆ Change the **HEM Factor** as shown.

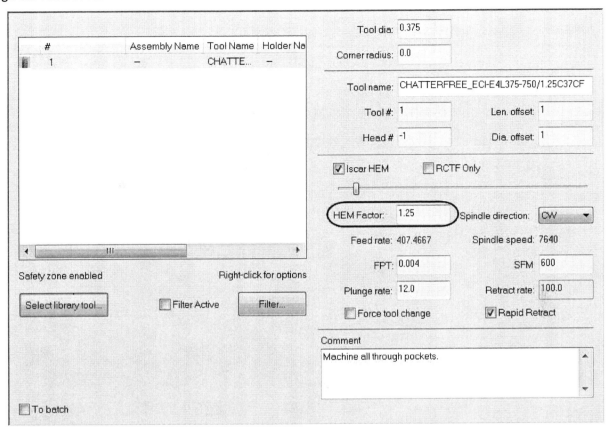

HEM Factor adjusts the ISCAR tool's feed rate and spindle speed values to achieve maximum speed and efficiency. Enter a value in the field or use the slider positioned directly above the field to adjust it. You can enter a value from 1 up to 5, depending on the selected machine and tool configuration. Mastercam displays the corresponding feed rate and spindle speed values below the field.

8.3 Set the Cut Parameters

♦ This page allows you to enter values for different cutting parameters and compensation options for dynamic area milling toolpaths.
♦ Make all the necessary changes as shown in <u>Figure: 8.3.1</u>.

Figure: 8.3.1

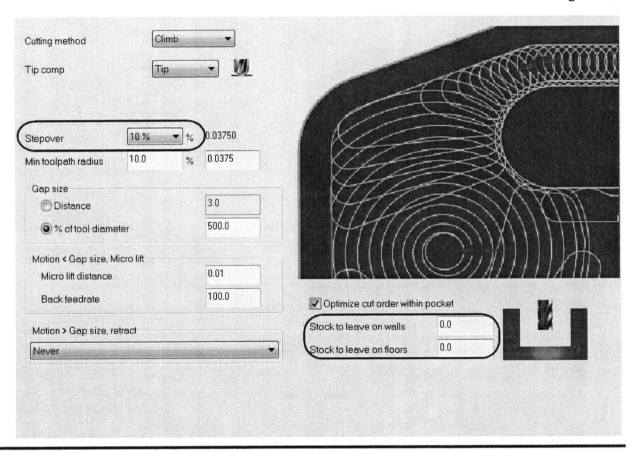

Stepover sets the distance between cutting passes in the X and Y axes. While using the HEM Iscar tools the stepover can be set up as a 5%, 7% or 10% of the tool diameter.

Motion > Gap size, retract controls retracts in the toolpath when making a non-cutting move within an area where the tool can be kept down or microlifted.

Never eliminates retracts from the toolpath for these types of tool moves.

Optimize cut order defines the cut order Mastercam applies to different cutting passes in the toolpath.

8.4 Set the Depth Cuts

♦ Enable **Depth cuts** and enter a **Max rough step** of **0.75** as shown in <u>Figure: 8.4.1</u>.

Figure: 8.4.1

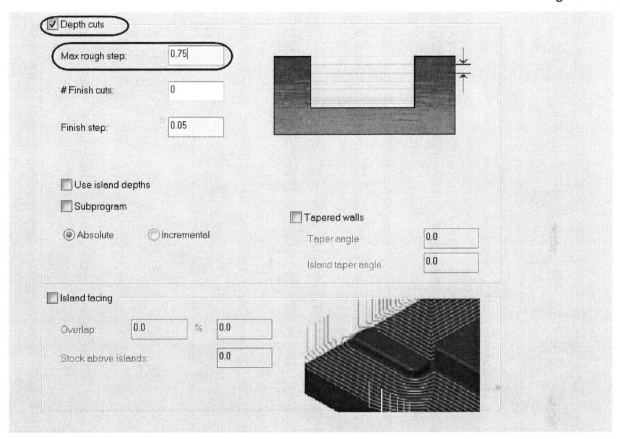

8.5 Entry Motion

+ Set the **Entry method** to **Profile.**
+ Input a **Z clearance** value of **0.125** and a **Plunge angle** of **2.0** degrees as shown in Figure: 8.5.1.

Figure: 8.5.1

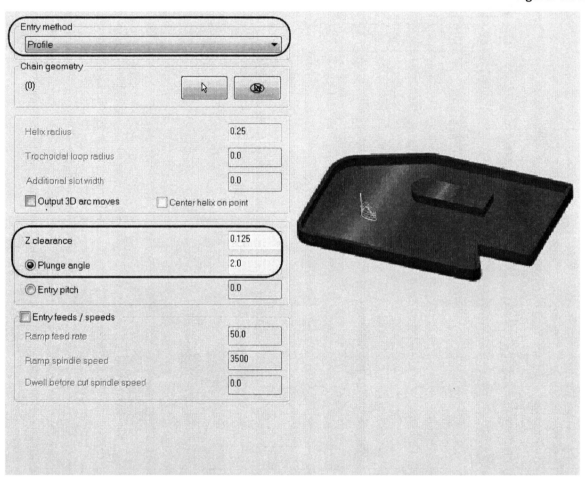

Profile creates a follow boundary ramp entry based on the shape of the offset pocket. The slot is cleared by taking lighter cuts in the Z axis. Subsequent cuts are properly engaged at the full cut depth.

8.6 Break Through

- Enable **Break through.**
- Input a **Break through amount** of **0.1** as shown in Figure: 8.6.1.

Figure: 8.6.1

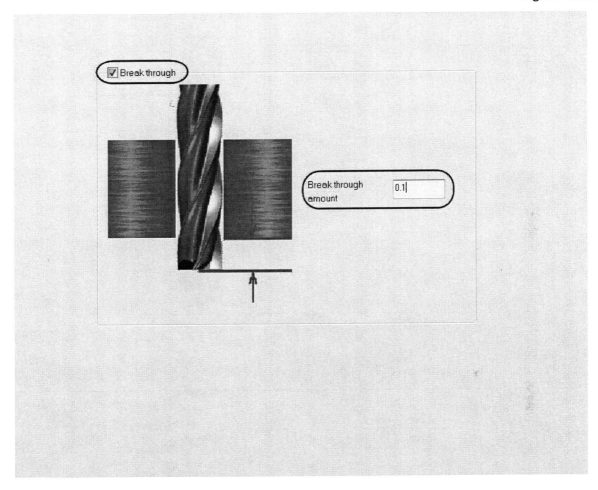

8.7 Linking Parameters

* Enable **Clearance** and set it to **1.0**.
* Input a **Depth** value of **-1.25** as shown in <u>Figure: 8.7.1</u>.

Figure: 8.7.1

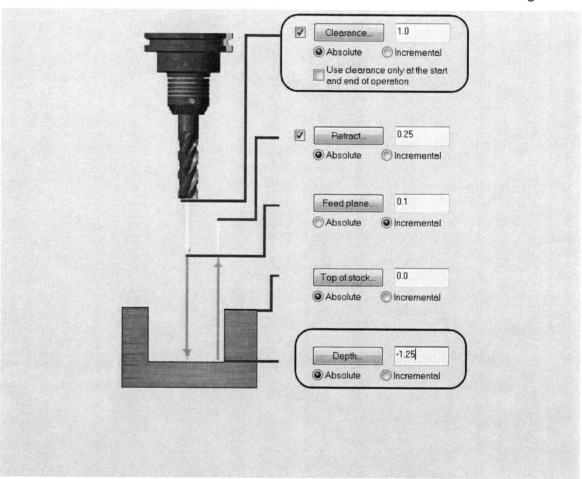

* Once the parameters have been entered select the **OK** button to generate the **Dynamic Area Mill** toolpath.

STEP 9: BACKPLOT THE TOOLPATHS

Backplotting shows the path the tools take to cut the part. This display lets you spot errors in the program before you machine the part. As you backplot toolpaths, Mastercam displays additional information such as the X, Y, and Z coordinates, the path length , the minimum and maximum coordinates and the cycle time. It also shows any collisions between the workpiece and the tool.

* Make sure that the toolpaths are selected (signified by the green check mark on the folder icon). If the

   operation is not selected choose the **Select All Operations** icon.
* Select the **Backplot Selected Operations** icon.

* Select the **Backplot** tab and have the following settings enabled as shown.

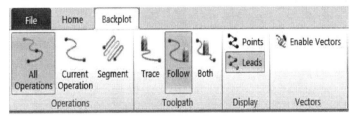

* Select the **Home** tab and make sure that you have the following settings on as shown.

* To see the part from an **Isometric** view select the **Isometric** icon.

* To fit the workpiece to the screen, select the **Fit** icon.

* You can step through the **Backplot** by using the **Step forward** or **Step back** buttons.

* You can adjust the speed of the backplot.
* Select the **Play Simulation** button in the VCR bar to run **Backplot**.

* The toolpath should look as shown.

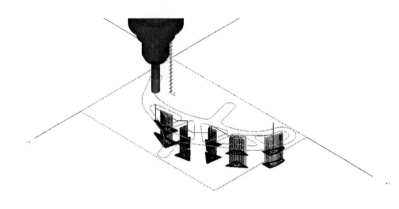

STEP 10: SIMULATE THE TOOLPATH IN VERIFY

Verify Mode shows the path the tools take to cut the part with material removal. This display lets you spot errors in the program before you machine the part. As you verify toolpaths, Mastercam displays additional information such as the X, Y, and Z coordinates, the path length , the minimum and maximum coordinates and the cycle time. It also shows any collisions between the workpiece and the tool.

* From **Mastercam Backplot Home** tab, switch to **Verify** and change the settings for the **Visibility** and **Focus** as shown in Figure: 10.0.1.

Figure: 10.0.1

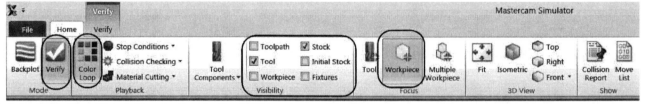

* Select the **Play Simulation** button in the **VCR** bar to run **Verify**.

- The part should appear as shown.

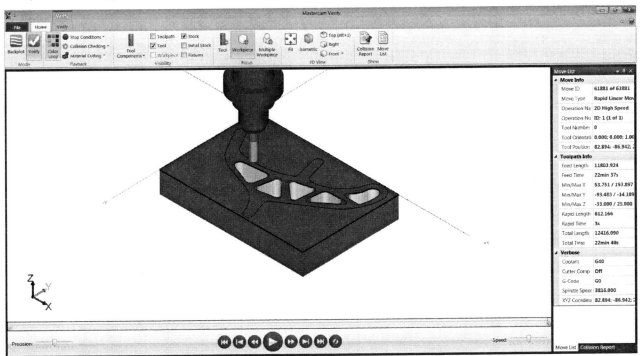

- To go back to Mastercam window, minimize **Verify** window as shown.

STEP 11: COPY THE TOOLPATH

In this step you will learn how to copy a toolpath.

* In the **Toolpaths Operations Manager**, make sure that the toolpath is selected (signified by the green check mark) as shown in <u>Figure: 11.0.1</u>.

Figure: 11.0.1

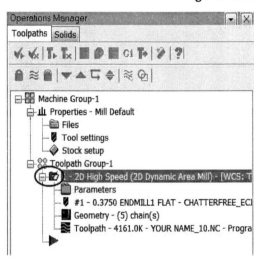

* Right click on the folder and hold the right mouse button down and drag the operations to a point below the insert arrow as shown in <u>Figure: 11.0.2</u>.

Figure: 11.0.2

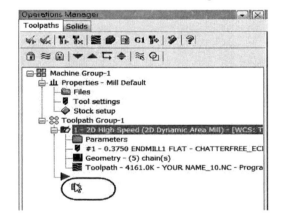

◆ Release the right mouse button and select the option **Copy After** as shown in <u>Figure: 11.0.3</u>.

Figure: 11.0.3

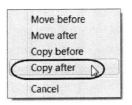

◆ Make sure that the insert arrow is below the last toolpath as shown in <u>Figure: 11.0.4</u>.

Figure: 11.0.4

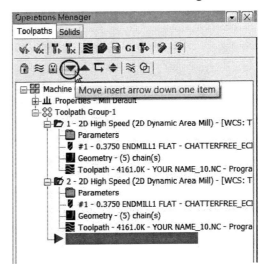

◆ Otherwise pick the **Move insert arrow down one item** icon to move the insert arrow down below the last operation.

STEP 12: DYNAMIC REST MILL

In this step you will delete one of the chains that was completely machined in the previous operation and does not require a rest mill operation. Then, you will change the toolpath type and the parameters to generate a **2D Dynamic Rest Mill** toolpath. The **Dynamic Rest Mill** toolpath machines the areas inside of the pockets that were not machined previously due to the size of the tool.

Toolpath preview:

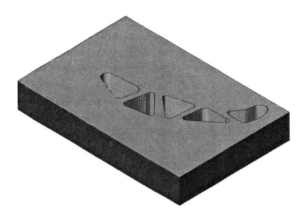

12.1 Delete One Chain from the Second Toolpath

* Select Geometry in Operation #2 as shown in Figure: 12.1.1.

Figure: 12.1.1

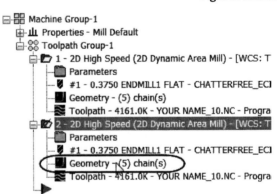

Mill Level 1 Training Tutorial

Mastercam. **X**⁷

• From **Chain Options** click on the **Select** button as shown in <u>Figure: 12.1.2</u>.

Figure: 12.1.2

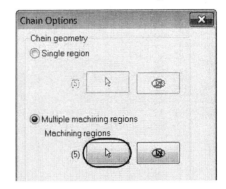

• In the **Chain Manager**, click on **Chain 1**.

> **NOTE:** The far left chain should be highlighted. Otherwise select the next chains until the far left chain is highlighted.

• Right mouse click on the chain and select Delete chain as shown <u>Figure: 12.1.3</u>.

Figure: 12.1.3

• Select the **OK** button twice to exit.

12.2 Change the Toolpath Parameters to Generate a Rest Mill Operation

♦ Select **Parameters** in Operation #2 as shown in <u>Figure: 12.2.1</u>.

Figure: 12.2.1

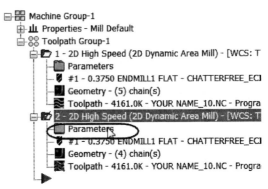

♦ In the **Toolpath Type** page, select **Dynamic Rest Mill.**

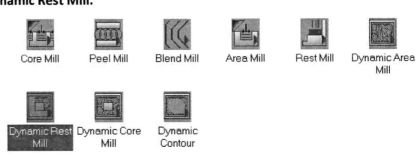

12.3 Select a 1/8" Flat Endmill from the Library and set the Tool Parameters

♦ Select **Tool** from the **Tree view list.**

♦ Click on the **Select library tool** button. Select library tool...
♦ Select the **New library** button as shown.

♦ Select the **MILL_INCH.TOOLS-7** from the list as shown.
♦ Open the library.
♦ Select the **Filter** button as shown.

♦ Select the **None** button and then under **Tool Types** choose the **Flat Endmill** icon.

◆ Under tool diameter pick **Equal** and input a value **0.125** as shown in <u>Figure: 12.3.1</u>.

Figure: 12.3.1

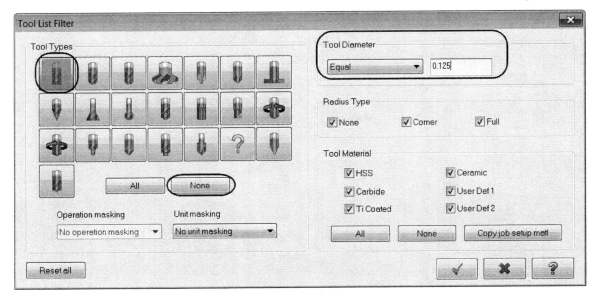

◆ Select the **OK** button to exit the **Tool List Filter.**
◆ In the **Tool Selection** dialog box you should only see the **1/8" Flat Endmill**.

#	Assembly Name	Tool Name	Holder Name	Dia.	Cor. rad.	Length	# Flutes	Type	Rad. Type
232	–	1/8 FLAT	–	0...	0.0	0.375	4	En...	None

◆ Select the tool in the **Tool Selection** page and then select the **OK** button to exit.

◆ Make all the necessary changes as shown in Figure: 12.3.2.

Figure: 12.3.2

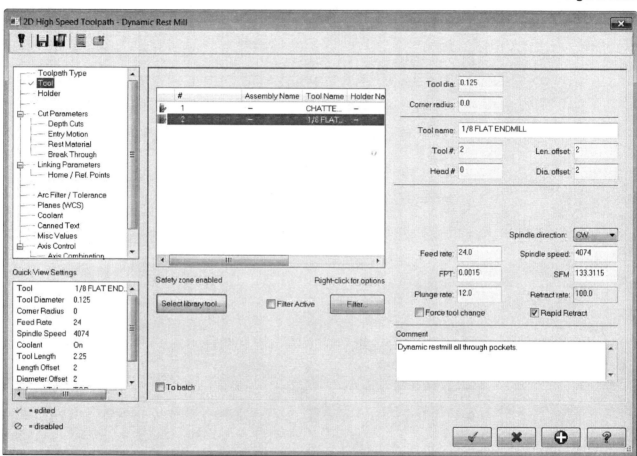

12.4 Cut Parameters

◆ From the **Tree view list**, select **Cut Parameters** and make sure that the parameters are matching <u>Figure: 12.4.1</u>.

Figure: 12.4.1

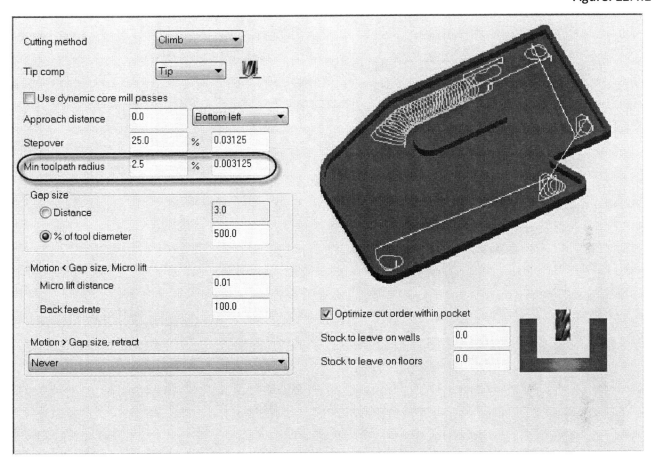

12.5 Depth Cuts

- From the **Tree view list,** select **Depth Cuts**.
- Change the **Max rough step** as shown in Figure: 12.5.1.

Figure: 12.5.1

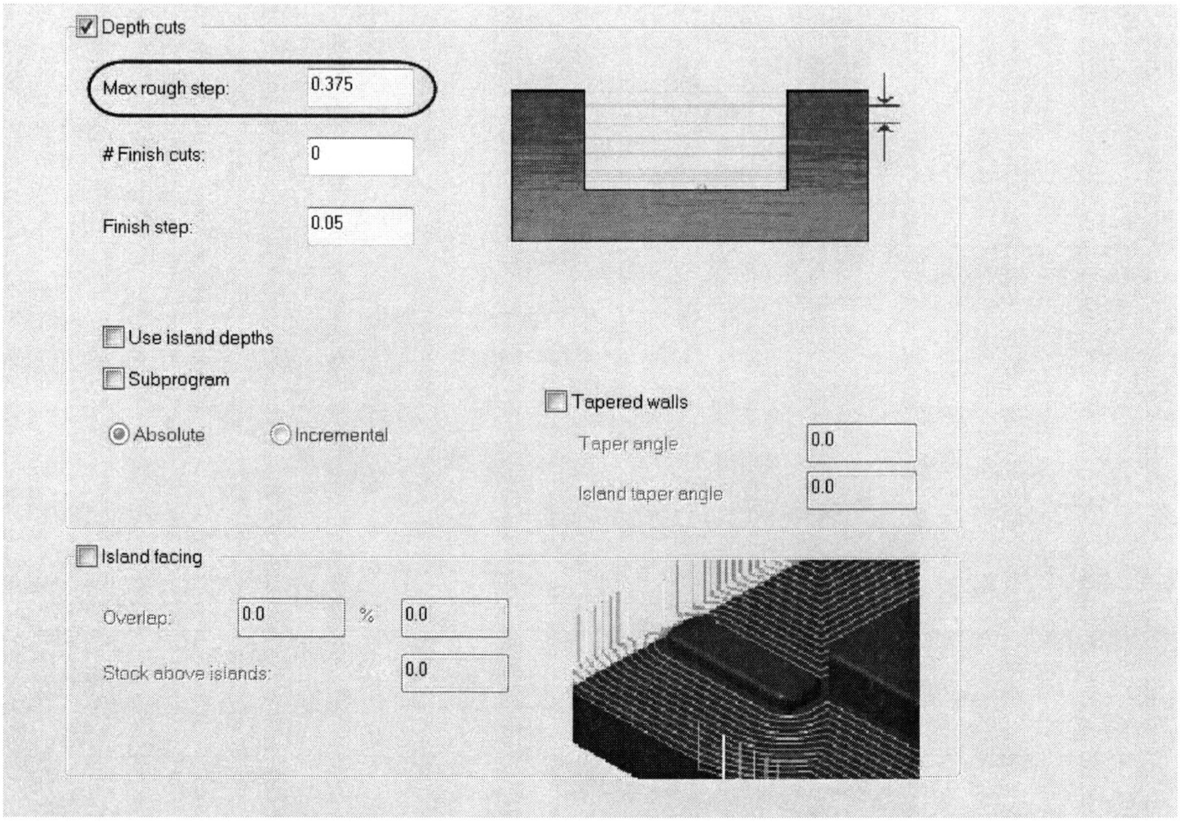

☑ Depth cuts

Max rough step:	0.375
# Finish cuts:	0
Finish step:	0.05

☐ Use island depths
☐ Subprogram

◉ Absolute   ○ Incremental

☐ Tapered walls

Taper angle   0.0

Island taper angle   0.0

☐ Island facing

Overlap: 0.0   %   0.0

Stock above islands: 0.0

12.6 Rest Material

This page defines how Mastercam calculates the stock model for a 2D high speed rest mill or a dynamic rest mill toolpath. You can choose to calculate the stock remaining from one or more source operations or based off of the roughing tool.

* From the **Tree view list,** select **Rest Material**.
* Under the option **Compute remaining stock from** enable the option **All previous operations** and enable **Use remaining stock as computed** as shown in Figure: 12.6.1.

Figure: 12.6.1

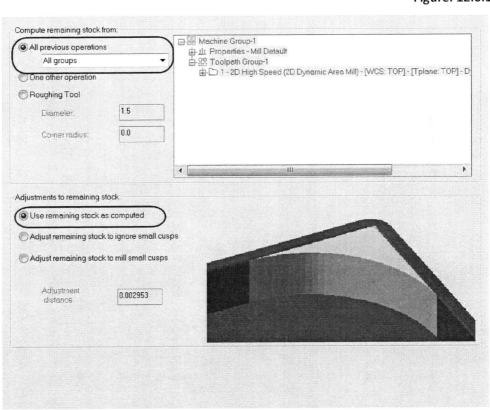

All previous operations calculates the remaining stock using all operations in the Toolpath Manager.

One other operations calculates the remaining stock from a single operation.

Roughing tool calculates the remaining stock based on the diameter and corner radius of a tool.

Use remaining stock as computed makes no adjustments to the stock model as calculated.

Adjust remaining stock to ignore small cusps use this setting to set the adjustment distance to reduce the stock model. Mastercam outputs cuts that engage large amounts of material.

Adjust remaining stock to mill small cusps use this setting to set the adjustment distance to expand the stock model.

• Choose the **OK** button to generate the toolpath.

> **NOTE:** Because the toolpath was copied, all the parameters were copied with it therefore, you do not have to change any other parameters.

• Choose the **Regenerate all dirty operations** button.

12.7 Backplot the toolpath

• Once the operation has been regenerated, **Backplot** the toolpath as shown on page 845.

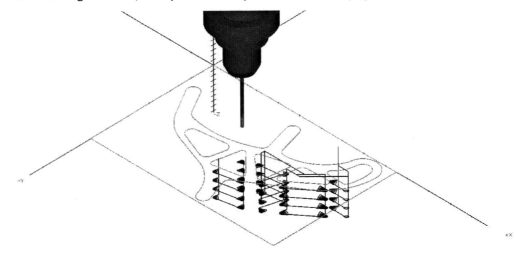

• To go back to Mastercam window, minimize **Backplot** window as shown.

12.8 Verify the toolpaths

• Select both operations by clicking on the **Select all operations** icon.

◆ Click on the **Verify selected operations** icon.

◆ **Verify** the toolpaths as shown on page 846.

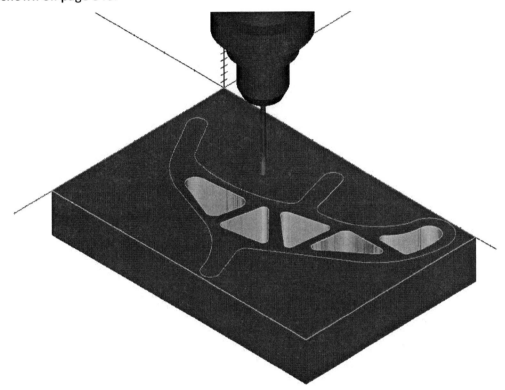

TOOLPATH CREATION -SETUP 2

> **NOTE:** The part is now positioned on a fixture so we can machine the material away from the part.

SETUP SHEET:

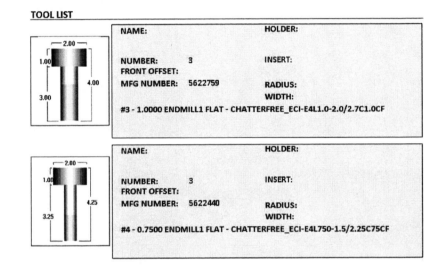

TOOL LIST

NAME:	HOLDER:
NUMBER: 3	INSERT:
FRONT OFFSET:	
MFG NUMBER: 5622759	RADIUS:
	WIDTH:

#3 - 1.0000 ENDMILL1 FLAT - CHATTERFREE_ECI-E4L1.0-2.0/2.7C1.0CF

NAME:	HOLDER:
NUMBER: 3	INSERT:
FRONT OFFSET:	
MFG NUMBER: 5622440	RADIUS:
	WIDTH:

#4 - 0.7500 ENDMILL1 FLAT - CHATTERFREE_ECI-E4L750-1.5/2.25C75CF

STEP 13: CREATING AND RENAMING TOOLPATH GROUPS

To machine the part in different setups, we will need to have separate programs. To be able to post the operations separate of each setup, we will create them under different toolpath groups with different NC names.

13.1 Rename the Current Toolpath Group - 1 and NC File

◆ Click two times on the **Toolpath Group - 1** to highlight it and rename it "Setup #1" as shown in Figure: 13.1.1.

Figure: 13.1.1

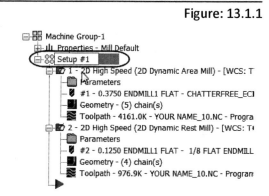

◆ Right mouse click on the Toolpath group (Setup #1) and select **Edit selected operations** and then, select **Change NC file name** as shown in Figure: 13.1.2.

Figure: 13.1.2

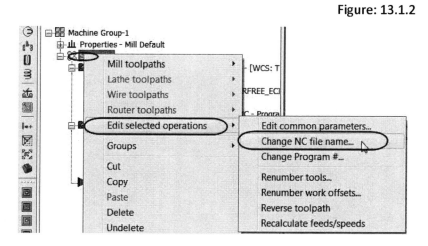

• Enter the new **NC name: Setup #1**.

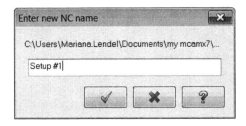

• Select the **OK** button to accept the new **NC name**.

13.2 Create a new Toolpath Group

• Right mouse click on the **Machine Group -1**.
• Select **Groups** and then **New Toolpath group** as shown Figure: 13.2.1.

Figure: 13.2.1

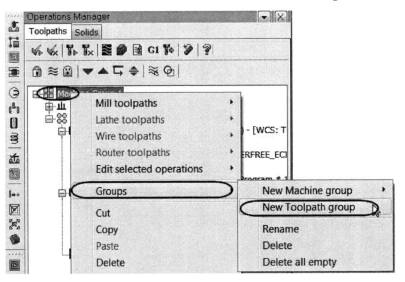

◆ Rename the toolpath group "**Setup #2**" as shown in <u>Figure: 13.2.2</u>.

Figure: 13.2.2

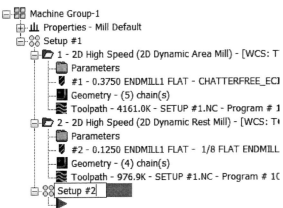

◆ If needed, select the **Move insert arrow down one item** icon ⬇ from the **Operations Manager** until the arrow is at the bottom of this list, as shown in <u>Figure: 13.2.2</u>.

STEP 14: 2D HIGH SPEED DYNAMIC CORE MILL

Generates the free-flowing motion needed to machine features, such as standing bosses and cores, in a single operation.

Toolpath Preview:

14.1 Chain Selection

Toolpaths

* **2D High Speed.**

* 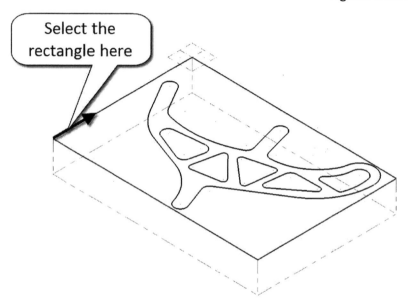 **Dynamic Core.**

* Leave the default setting in the **Chaining** dialog box and pick the first chain on the rectangle as shown in <u>Figure: 14.1.1</u>. This chain represents the stock boundary.

Figure: 14.1.1

Select the rectangle here

♦ Then choose the outside edge of the part as shown in <u>Figure: 14.1.2</u>. This chain represents the profile which we want to machine to.

Figure: 14.1.2

Select the chain here

♦ Select the **OK** button to exit the **Chaining** dialog box.

♦ Select the **OK** button to exit the **Chain Options** dialog box.

♦ In the **Toolpath Type** page, the **Dynamic Core Mill** is already selected.

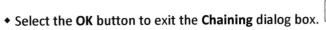

Core Mill   Peel Mill   Blend Mill   Area Mill   Rest Mill   Dynamic Area Mill

Dynamic Rest Mill   Dynamic Core Mill   Dynamic Contour

14.2 Select a ChatterFree 1"Endmill from the Library and set the Tool Parameters

♦ Select **Tool** from the **Tree view list**.

♦ Click on the **Select library tool** button. Select library tool...

♦ Select the **New library** button as shown.

Tool Selection – C:\users\public\documents\shared mcamx7\Mill\Tools\Mill_Inch.tools-7

C:\users\public\docum...\Mill_Inch.tools-7

• Select the **ISCAR HEM - IN.TOOLDB** from the list as shown.

Name	Date modified	Type	Size
BIG_Inch.TOOLS-7	22/10/2012 11:37 ...	MastercamX7 Tool...	5,080 KB
BIG_MM.TOOLS-7	22/10/2012 11:37 ...	MastercamX7 Tool...	3,009 KB
BIGMM_INCH.TOOLS-7	22/10/2012 11:37 ...	MastercamX7 Tool...	5,371 KB
CBore library-Inch.TOOLS-7	22/10/2012 11:37 ...	MastercamX7 Tool...	314 KB
CBore library-metric.TOOLS-7	22/10/2012 11:37 ...	MastercamX7 Tool...	314 KB
DM-ALUM.TOOLS-7	22/10/2012 11:37 ...	MastercamX7 Tool...	1,069 KB
DM-SS.TOOLS-7	22/10/2012 11:37 ...	MastercamX7 Tool...	954 KB
HOLDERS.TOOLDB	22/10/2012 11:37 ...	TOOLDB File	1,232 KB
ISCAR HEM -IN.TOOLDB	22/10/2012 11:37 ...	TOOLDB File	217 KB
ISCAR HEM -MM.tooldb	22/10/2012 11:37 ...	TOOLDB File	435 KB
METRICST52.TOOLS-7	22/10/2012 11:37	MastercamX7 Tool	844 KB

• Open the library.
• Select the **Filter** button as shown.

• Select the **None** button and then under **Tool Types** choose the **Flat Endmill** icon.

◆ Under tool diameter pick **Equal** and input a value **1.0** as shown in <u>Figure: 14.2.1</u>.

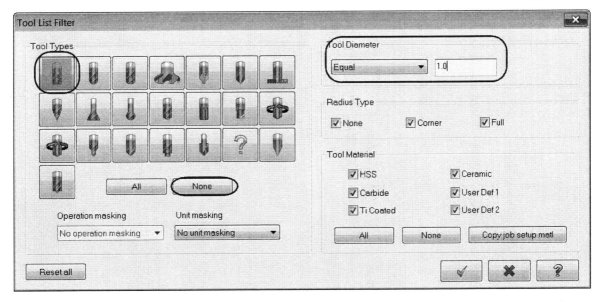

◆ Select the **OK** button to exit the **Tool List Filter**.
◆ In the **Tool Selection** dialog box you should only see two **ChatterFree 1" Endmill**.

#	Assembly Name	Tool Name	Holder Name	Dia.	Cor. rad.	Length	# Flutes	Type	Rad. Type
11	–	CHATTE...	–	1.0	0.0	2.0	4	En...	None
12	–	CHATTE...	–	1.0	0.0	2.0	4	En...	None

◆ Select the first **ChatterFree 1" Endmill** in the **Tool Selection** page and then select the **OK** button to exit.

* Enable **Iscar HEM** and change the **HEM Factor** and make all the necessary changes as shown in <u>Figure: 14.2.2</u>.

Figure: 14.2.2

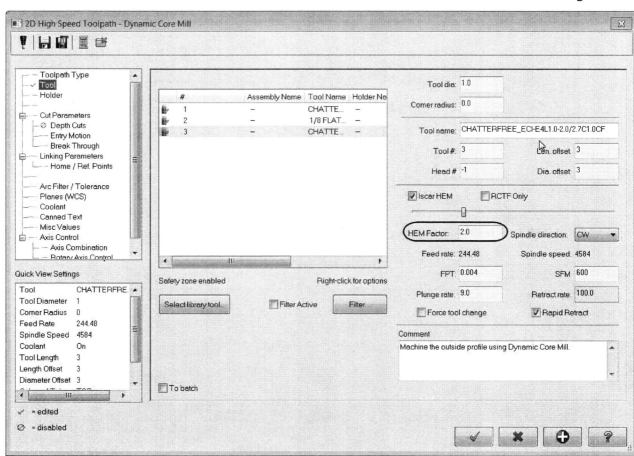

14.3 Cut Parameters

• Input an **Approach distance** of **0.5** and a **Stock to leave on walls** value of **0.02** as shown in <u>Figure: 14.3.1</u>.

Figure: 14.3.1

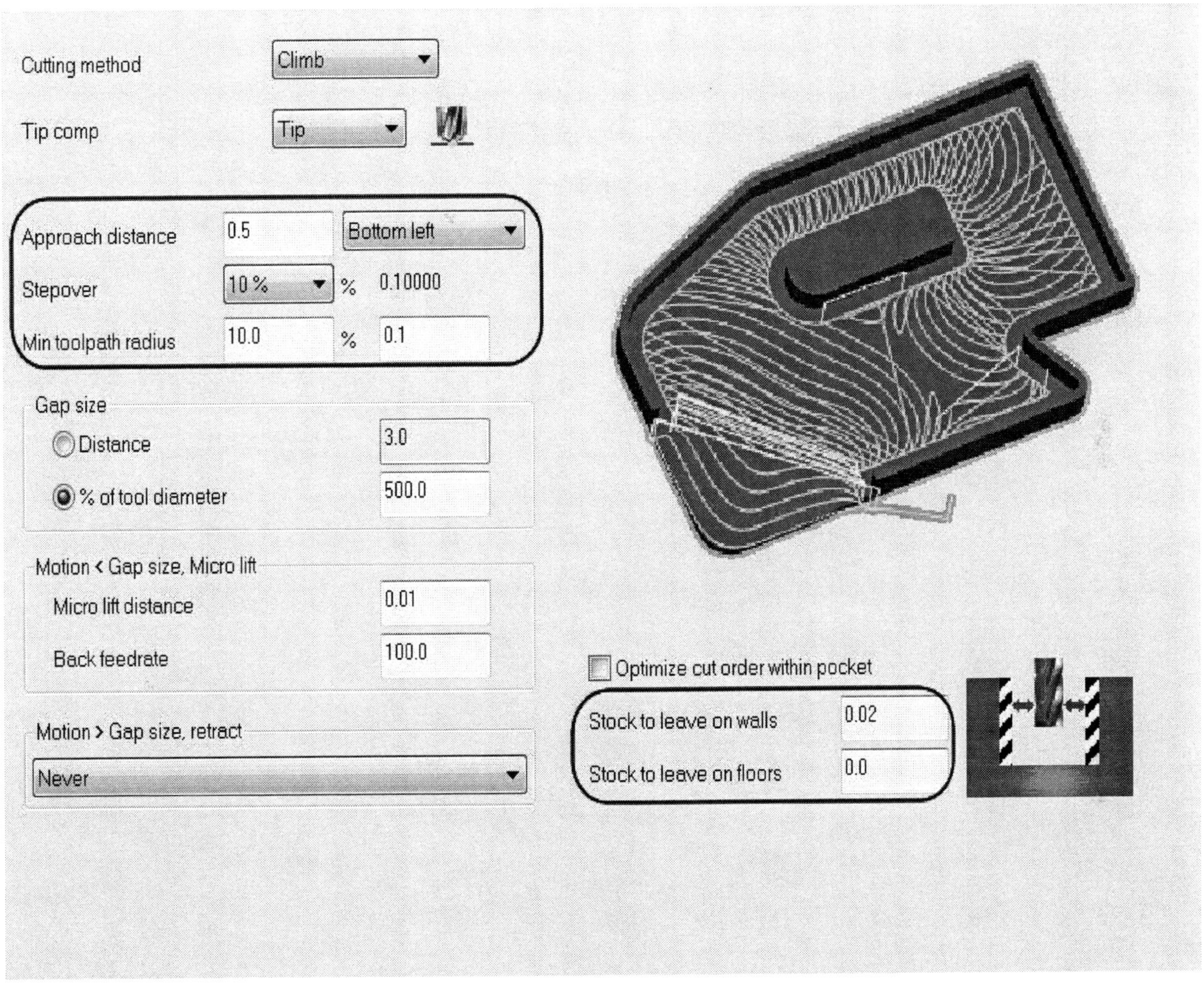

Cutting method	Climb
Tip comp	Tip
Approach distance	0.5 — Bottom left
Stepover	10 % — % 0.10000
Min toolpath radius	10.0 — % 0.1

Gap size
- ○ Distance — 3.0
- ● % of tool diameter — 500.0

Motion < Gap size, Micro lift
- Micro lift distance — 0.01
- Back feedrate — 100.0

Motion > Gap size, retract
- Never

☐ Optimize cut order within pocket

Stock to leave on walls	0.02
Stock to leave on floors	0.0

14.4 Depth Cuts

- Disable **Depth cuts** as shown in <u>Figure: 14.4.1</u>.

Figure: 14.4.1

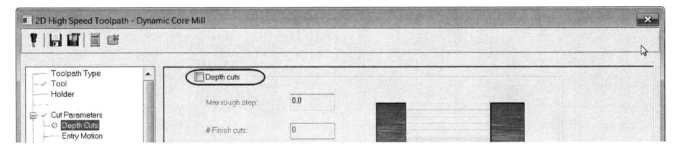

14.5 Entry Motion

- Change the **Entry method** to **Helix only** and leave the default **Helix radius** as shown in <u>Figure: 14.5.1</u>.

Figure: 14.5.1

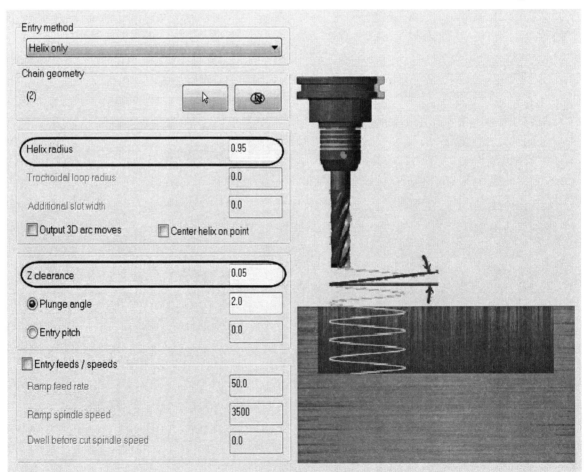

14.6 Break Through

• Enable **Break through** and set the **Break though amount** to **0.1** as shown in <u>Figure: 14.6.1</u>.

Figure: 14.6.1

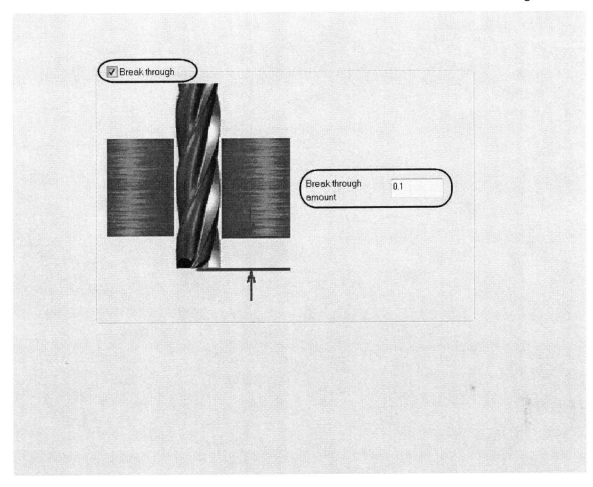

14.7 Linking Parameters

◆ Set the **Depth** to **-1.25** as shown in <u>Figure: 14.7.1</u>.

Figure: 14.7.1

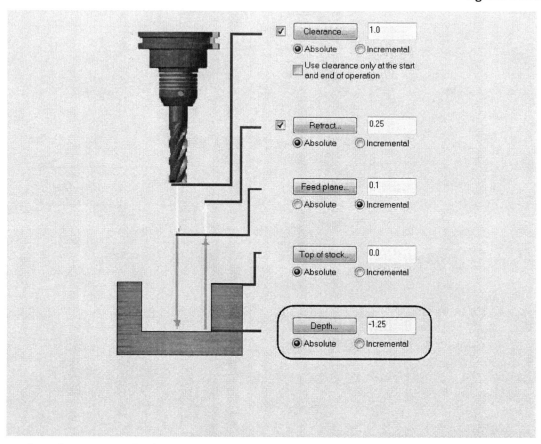

◆ Once the parameters have been entered select the **OK** button to generate the **Dynamic Core Mill** toolpath.

14.8 Backplot the toolpath

♦ To Backplot the toolpath see page 845.

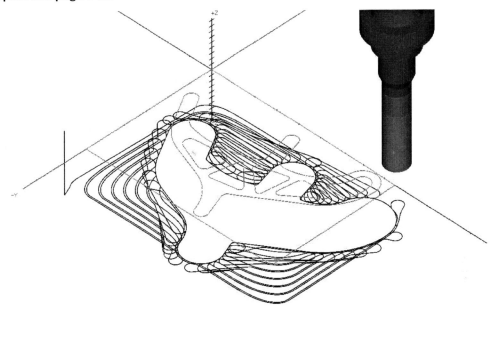

♦ To go back to Mastercam window, minimize **Verify** window as shown.

14.9 Verify the toolpaths

♦ Ensure all operations are selected, if they are not use the button **Select all operations** in the **Operations**

  Manager.

♦ Click on the Verify selected operations icon.

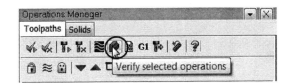

- To **Verify** the toolpath see page 846 to review the procedures.

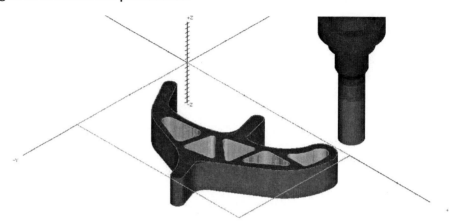

STEP 15: 2D HIGH SPEED DYNAMIC CONTOUR

Uses an intelligent efficient high speed contouring strategy to remove material along walls. This toolpath also supports multi-passes and can optionally include finishing passes.

Toolpath Preview:

15.1 Chain Selection

Toolpaths
- **2D High Speed.**

- ▣ **Dynamic Contour.**

• Leave the default settings in the chaining dialog box and pick the part as shown in <u>Figure: 15.1.1</u>.

Figure: 15.1.1

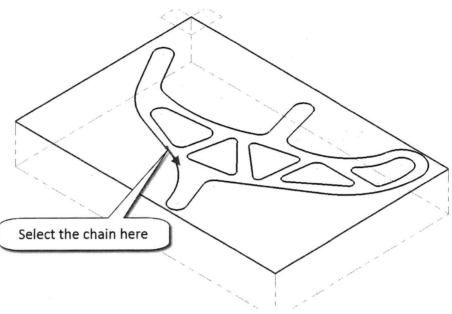

Select the chain here

• Select the **OK** button to exit the **Chaining** dialog box.

• Select the **OK** button to exit the **Chain Options** dialog box.
• In the **Toolpath Type** page, select **Dynamic Contour.**

Core Mill   Peel Mill   Blend Mill   Area Mill   Rest Mill   Dynamic Area Mill

Dynamic Rest Mill   Dynamic Core Mill   Dynamic Contour

15.2 Select a ChatterFree 3/4" Endmill from the Library and set the Tool Parameters

• Select **Tool** from the **Tree view list**.

• Click on the **Select library tool** button. Select library tool...
• Select the **Filter** button as shown.

• Select the **None** button and then under **Tool Types** choose the **Flat Endmill** icon.

- Under tool diameter pick **Equal** and input a value of **0.75** as shown in <u>Figure: 15.2.1</u>.

Figure: 15.2.1

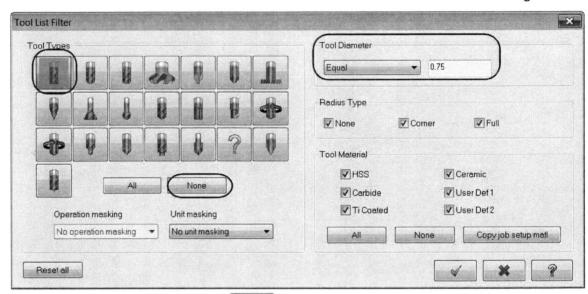

- Select the **OK** button to exit the **Tool List Filter.**

- In the **Tool Selection** dialog box you should only see **ChatterFree 3/4" Endmills**.

#	Assembly Name	Tool Name	Holder Name	Dia.	Cor. rad.	Length	# Flutes	Type	Rad. Type
24	–	CHATTE...	–	0.75	0.0	1.5	4	En...	None
25	–	CHATTE...	–	0.75	0.0	1.5	4	En...	None
35	–	CHATTE...	–	0.75	0.0	1.87	5	En...	None
36	–	CHATTE...	–	0.75	0.0	1.87	5	En...	None

- Select the first one in the **Tool Selection** page and select the **OK** button to exit.
- Make all the necessary changes as shown in Figure: 15.2.2.

Figure: 15.2.2

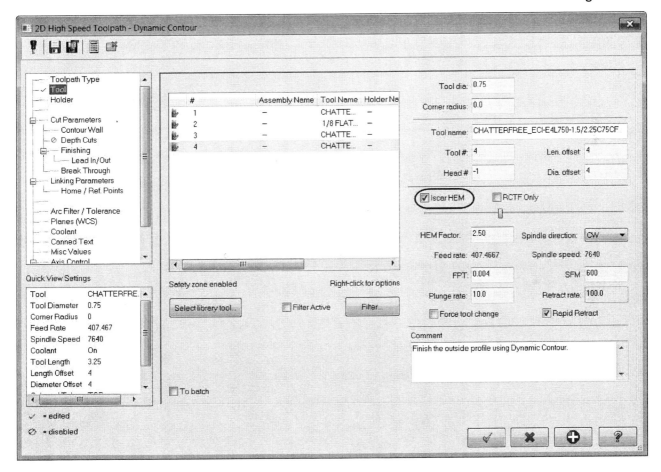

- From the **Tree view list** select the **Cut Parameters** page.
- Make sure that the **Compensation direction** is set to **Right** as shown in Figure: 15.2.3.

Figure: 15.2.3

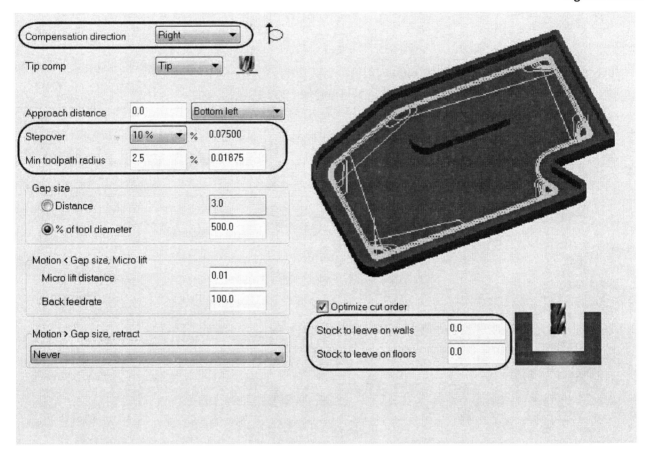

Mastercam X[7]

15.3 Contour Wall

- This page defines the stock thickness of the stock to be machined.
- **Radius of tool that shaped the stock** enter **0.5.**
- **Toolpath radius that shaped the stock** input **0.025.**
- **Stock thickness** set to **0.02** as shown in Figure: 15.3.1.

Figure: 15.3.1

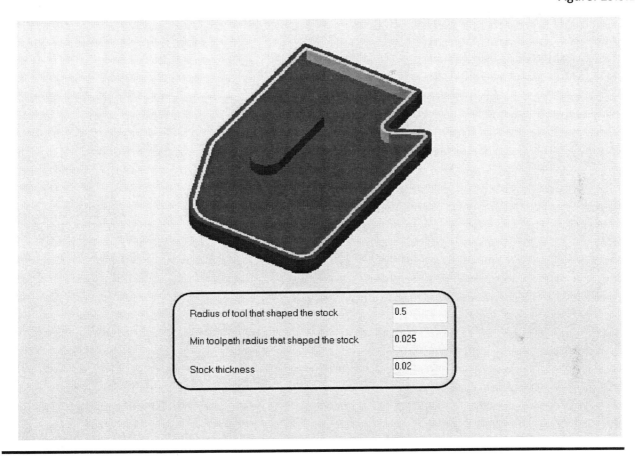

Radius of tool that shaped the stock	0.5
Min toolpath radius that shaped the stock	0.025
Stock thickness	0.02

Radius of tool that shaped the stock if the contour stock was already cut by another toolpath enter the radius of the tool used in the toolpath.

Toolpath radius that shaped the stock if the contour stock was already cut by another toolpath, enter the toolpath radius that was used to smooth out any sharp motion in the previous toolpath.

Stock thickness enter the thickness of the stock in XY for the toolpath to remove. Mastercam calculates the stock to remove along the contour wall using the stock thickness and if provided the radius of the tool that shaped the stock and the toolpath radius that shaped the stock.

15.4 Depth Cuts

* Disable **Depth cuts** as shown in <u>Figure: 15.4.1</u>. We want the tool to use the entire flute length to cut the side of the part.

Figure: 15.4.1

2D High Speed Toolpath - Dynamic Contour

Toolpath Type
Tool

☐ Depth cuts

15.5 Finishing

This page will add high speed finishing passes along the contour walls.

* Enable **Finish pass**.
* **Number of passes** set to **1** and enter a **Spacing** of **0.01**.
* Enable the option to **Machine finish passes only at final depth** as shown in <u>Figure: 15.5.1</u>.

Figure: 15.5.1

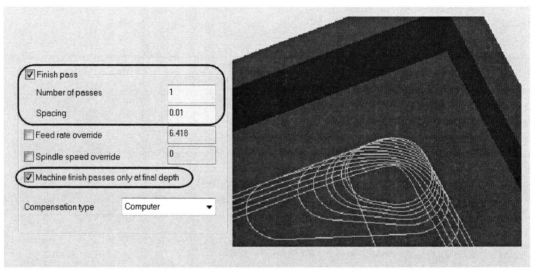

Number of passes sets the number of finish passes for the toolpath.

Spacing enter the amount of stock to remove with each cut.

Machine finish passes only at final depth only performs the finish passes at the final cutting depth.

Keep tool down determines whether or not to retract the tool between depth cuts/multi-passes.

15.6 Lead In/Out

◆ Input a **Sweep** angle of **90** degrees as shown in <u>Figure: 15.6.1</u>.

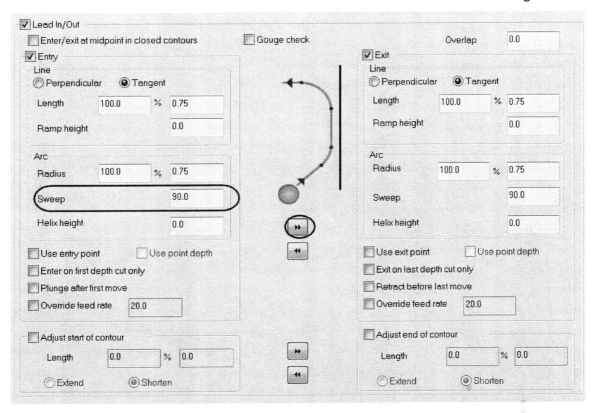

15.7 Break Through

♦ Ensure **Break through** is enabled and **0.1** is entered as a **Break through amount** as shown in Figure: 15.7.1.

Figure: 15.7.1

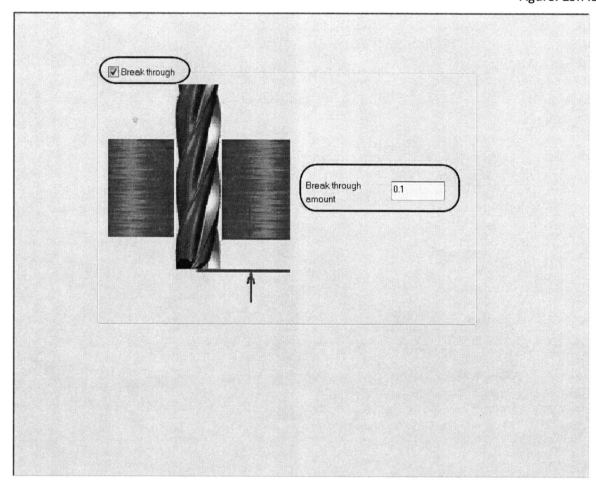

15.8 Linking Parameters

♦ Enter a **Depth** of **-1.25"** as shown in <u>Figure: 15.8.1</u>.

Figure: 15.8.1

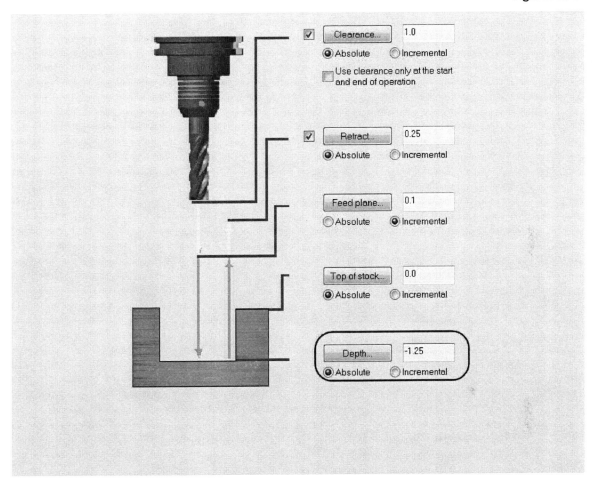

♦ Once the parameters have been entered select the **OK** button to generate the **Dynamic Contour Mill** toolpath.

15.9 Backplot the toolpath

♦ To Backplot the toolpath see page 845.

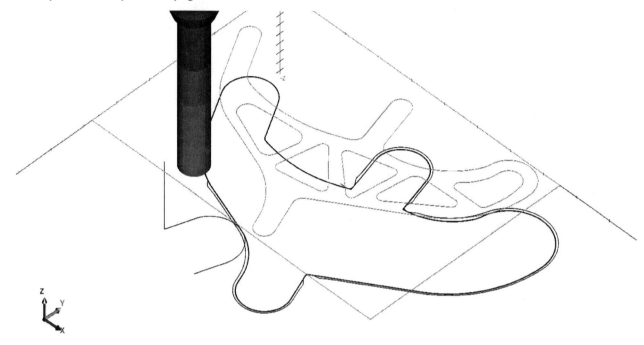

♦ To go back to Mastercam window, minimize **Verify** window as shown.

15.10 Verify the toolpaths

♦ Ensure all operations are selected, if they are not use the button **Select all operations** in the **Operations Manager.**

♦ Click on the **Verify selected operations** icon.

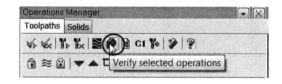

Mastercam. X⁷

◆ To **Verify** the toolpath see page 846 to review the procedures.

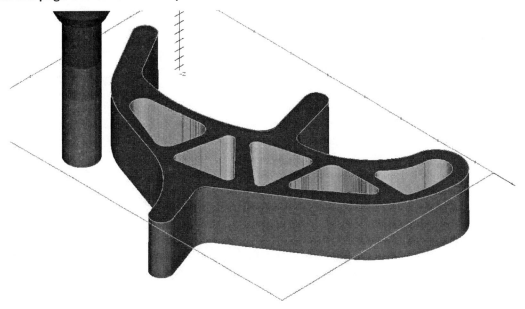

◆ To exit **Verify** click on the **Close** icon.

STEP 16: RENAME THE NC FILE

The 2D High Speed Toolpaths in "Setup #2" kept the NC name from Setup #1. We need to rename this operation so it will create a separate program for this setup.

* Select "**Setup #2**".
* Right click on the group (make sure all the operations in setup #2 are selected), choose the option **Edit selected operations** and then pick **Change NC file name** as shown in <u>Figure: 16.0.1</u>.

Figure: 16.0.1

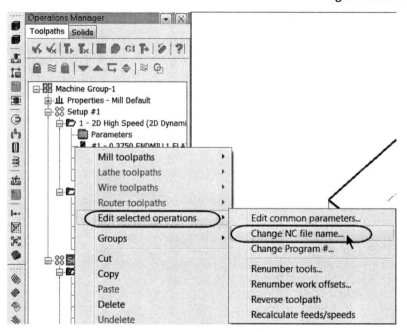

* When the **Enter new NC name** dialog box appears select **"Setup #2"** as shown in <u>Figure: 16.0.2</u>.

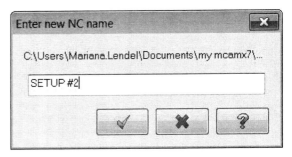

* Select the **OK** button to apply the changed NC name to all the operations in the second setup.
* The result you should see is **Setup #2.NC** in any of the operations in the second setup as shown in <u>Figure: 16.0.3</u>.

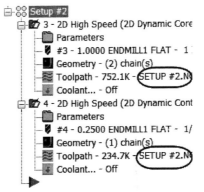

STEP 17: POST THE FILE

- Ensure all operations are selected, if they are not use the button **Select all operations** in the **Operations Manager.**

- Select the **Post selected operations** button from the **Operations Manager.** G1
- In the **Post processing** window make the necessary changes as shown in <u>Figure: 17.0.1</u>.

Figure: 17.0.1

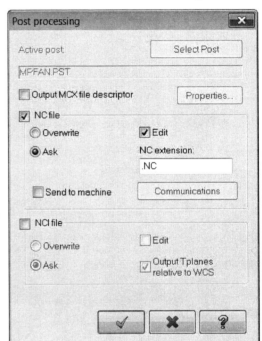

NC File enabled allows you to keep the NC file and to assign the same name as the MCX file.

Edit enabled allows you to automatically launch the default editor.

- Select the **OK** button to continue.
- Save **SETUP #1.NC** file.
- Save **SETUP #2.NC** file.

◆ A window with the NC programs will appear as shown in <u>Figure: 17.0.2</u>.

Figure: 17.0.2

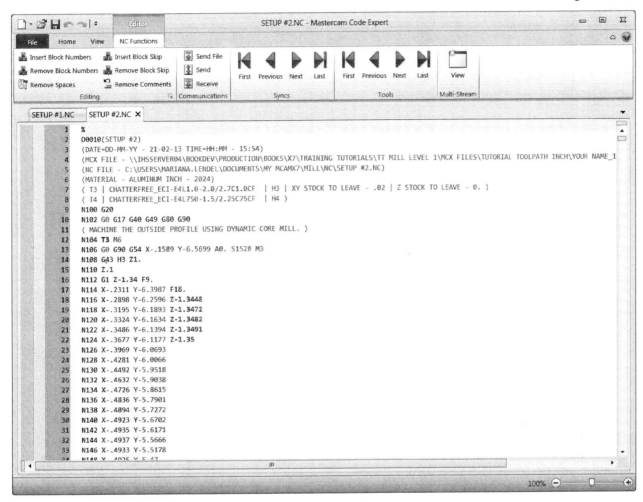

◆ Select the red "X" box at the upper right corner to exit the editor.

STEP 18: SAVE THE UPDATED MCX FILE

CREATE THE TOOLPATHS FOR TUTORIAL #10 EXERCISE

Create the Toolpaths for Tutorial #10 Exercise as per the instructions below.

* Download the part from www.emastercam.com.
* Open the part into Mastercam.
* Setup the **Tool Settings** and **Stock Setup**.

Create a 2D High Speed Core Mill toolpath.
* Use a **ChatterFree 1" Endmill**.
* Enable **Iscar HEM**.
* Enable **Min toolpath radius** and leave the default values.
* Ensure depth cuts are selected and input an appropriate depth cut.
* Select an **Entry method** and setup the method of choice.
* Set the **Linking Parameters**.

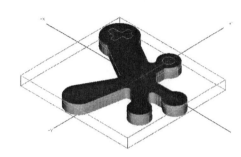

Create a 2D High Speed Dynamic Contour toolpath.
* Select a **1/4" Flat Endmill** from the library.
* On the **Contour Wall** page input the values used to create the previous toolpath.
* Ensure **Depth cuts** are selected and input an appropriate depth cut.
* Enable **Finish passes** and input the appropriate values.
* Enable **Break Through**.
* Set the **Linking Parameters**.

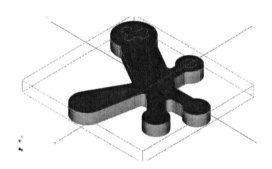

Create two separate 2D High Speed Core Mill toolpath to remove the material around the islands.
* Use a **ChatterFree 1/2" Endmill**.
* Enable **Iscar HEM**.
* Enable **Min toolpath radius** and leave the default values.
* Disable **Depth cuts**.
* Select an **Entry method** and setup the method of choice.
* Set the **Linking Parameters**.

Create another 2D High Speed Core Mill toolpath to remove the center of the part.
- Select the outer profile of the part and then choose the islands.
- Use the **ChatterFree 1/2" Endmill.**
- Enable **Iscar HEM.**
- Enable **Min toolpath radius** and leave the default values.
- Disable **Depth cuts.**
- Select an **Entry method** and setup the method of choice.
- Set the **Linking Parameters.**

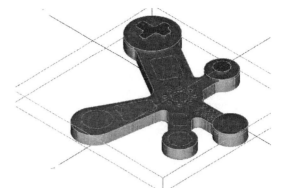

Create a Circle Mill toolpath to remove the material on top of the islands.
- Select the tops of the islands.
- Use the **1/2"Flat Endmill.**
- Enable **Roughing.**
- Enable **High Speed Entry** and set an angle of 45 degrees.
- Disable **Depth cuts.**
- Set the **Linking Parameters.**

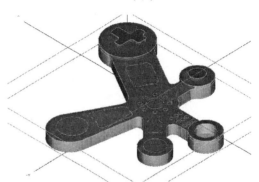

Copy the circle mill toolpath below.
- Delete the chains and reselect all the holes at their bottom.
- Enable **Depth Cuts** and input an appropriate value.
- Set the **Depth** to **incremental** on the **Linking Parameters** page.

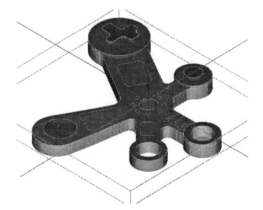

Create multiple 2D High Speed Dynamic Area Mill Toolpath to machine the pockets.
- Select the bottom of the pockets.
- Use the **ChatterFree 1/4" Endmill.**
- Enable **Iscar HEM.**
- Enable **Depth cuts** and set an appropriate **Max rough step.**
- Set the **Linking parameter** to the proper depth.

Spot drill and drill the 3/8" diameter holes.

* Use **Mask on arc** to select the holes.
* Choose a **1/2" Spot Drill**.
* Enter the depth including a **0.05** chamfer on the finished holes.
* Copy the spot drill toolpath and change the following parameters to drill the holes.
* Use a **3/8" Drill**.
* Change the cycle to a **Peck Drill cycle**.
* Input a **Depth** to drill to the bottom of the part.
* Enable **Tip Comp** to ensure the tool drills through.

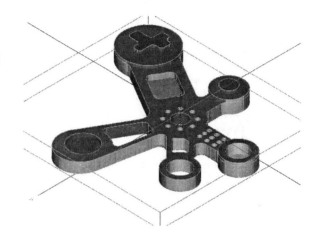

NOTES:

TUTORIAL #10 QUIZ

◆ What is the advantage of the 2D High Speed Dynamic Area Mill Toolpath?

◆ What does a 2D High Speed Core Mill toolpath machine?

◆ Define a 2D High Speed Dynamic Contour toolpath.

CREATING/EDITING TOOLS

Objectives:

✓ The Student will learn how to create and modify tools.

CREATING AND EDITING A MILL TOOL LIBRARY

NOTE: The purpose of tool libraries is to hold the tool data. The libraries can be edited or added to by following the directions below. Each time the **Tool Type** or **Cutter diameter** is changed in the **Toolpath parameters**, the tool library recalculates the feed rate and spindle speed. The following menu selections will allow you to create a new tool.

CREATING A NEW TOOL

Machine type
* **Mill.**
* **Default .**

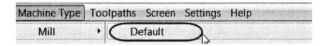

Option 1: Create a new tool using the Tool Manager

Toolpaths

* ﹗ **Tool Manager.**
* **Right click** in the tool display area.
* Select **Create new tool** as shown.

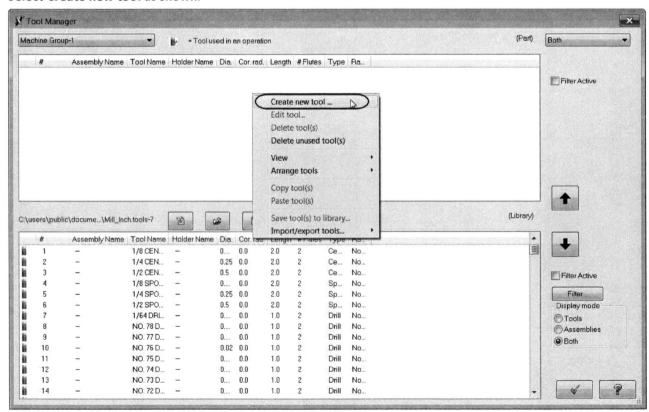

Option 2: Create a new tool inside of the Toolpath Parameters

Toolpaths

- 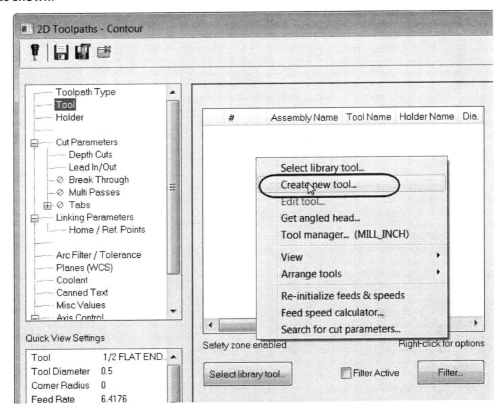 **Contour.**
- Chain the contour.
- From the **Tree view list,** select **Tool.**
- **Right-click in** the tool display area.
- Select **Create new tool** as shown.

1. What type of tool would you like to create?

The **Create New Tool** dialog box displays all the default tool type options in Mastercam.

• The following screen will appear as shown.

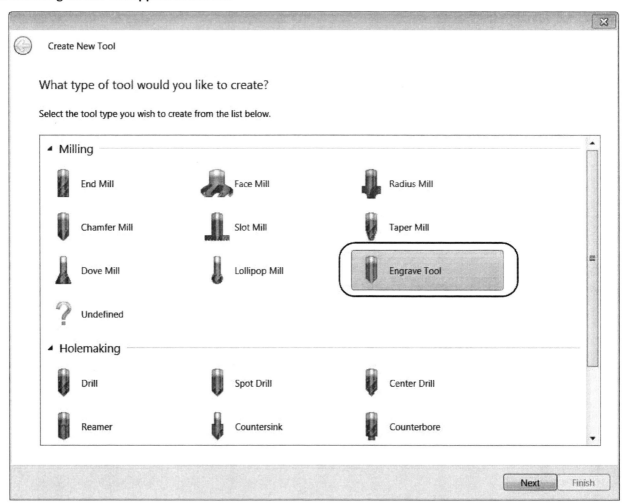

• Choose the tool type you wish to modify and then select **Next** button.

2. *Define geometric tool parameters.*

Define geometric tool parameters lets you enter new parameters or edit current parameters of Mill tools. A description of each parameter in the **Define geometric tool parameters** is listed below.

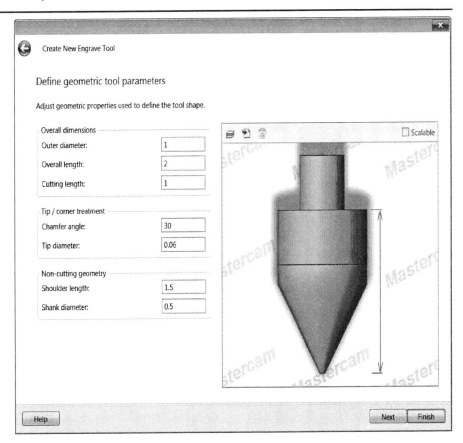

> **NOTE:** The fields on the tabs change depending on the type of tool you are creating.

Overall Dimensions

Cutting Diameter - sets the diameter of the tool.

Overall Length - sets the length of the tool.

Cutting Length - sets the length from the top of the flutes to the tip of the tool.

Tip/CornerTreatment

Corner Type- allows you to choose between None, Chamfer, Corner radius and Full radius.

Radius - sets the tool tip's corner radius.

Chamfer Distance - sets the tool chamfer distance.

Non-Cutting Geometry

Shoulder Length - sets the distance from the top of the shoulder to the tip of the tool.

Shank Diameter - sets the diameter of the tool shank.

Taper Angle - measures the angle from the center line of the tool to the outer angle of the tool.

Taper Length - sets the length of the taper as the distance from the top of the shoulder to the bottom of the shank.

• Set the dimension values and then select **Next** button.

3. Finalize miscellaneous properties

This area allows you to type information such as Name, Manufacturer Name and Manufacture's tool code. It also allows you to enter the tool offset numbers, the feeds and speeds, the material, coolant settingsand other settings.

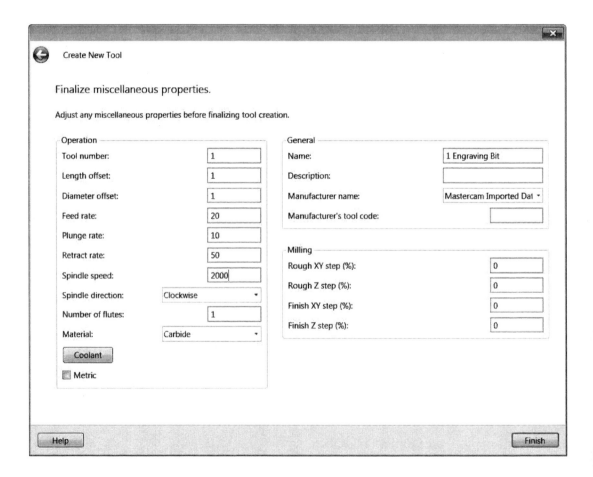

Operation

Tool Number - sets the default tool assembly number.

Length Offset - sets the number that corresponds to a register in the machine that compensates for the tool length.

Diameter Offset - sets the number that corresponds to a register in the machine that offset the diameter.

Feed Rate - sets the default feed rate.

Plunge Rate - sets the default plunge rate.

Retract Rate - sets the default retract rate.

Spindle Speed - sets the spindle speed in RPM.

Spindle Direction - allows you to choose the spindle direction between Clockwise, Counterclockwise and Static.

Number of flutes - specifies the number of flutes on the tool which is used to calculate the feed rate.

Material - displays the tool material.

Coolant - allows you to set the canned text coolant options.

Metric - allows you to enable metric tools.

General

Name - allows you to type the name of the tool.

Description - displays additional info.

Manufacturer name - allows you to type the name of the Manufacturer.

Manufacturer's tool code - allows you to type the tool code.

Milling

Rough XY step (%)- allows you to set the size of a roughing step in the X and Y axes for the tool. The system measures this distance as a percentage of the tool diameter.

Rough Z step (%) - allows you to set the size of a roughing step in the Z axis for the tool. The system measures this distance as a percentage of the tool diameter.

Finish XY step (%)- allows you to set the size of a finish step in the X and Y axes for the tool. The system measures this distance as a percentage of the tool diameter.

Finish Z step (%) - allows you to set the size of a f step in the Z axis forinish the tool. The system measures this distance as a percentage of the tool diameter.

EDITING AN EXISTING TOOL

Option 1: Edit an existing tool using the Tool Manager

Toolpath

♦ 🛠 **Tool Manager.**
♦ **Right click** on the existing tool.
♦ Select **Edit tool** as shown.

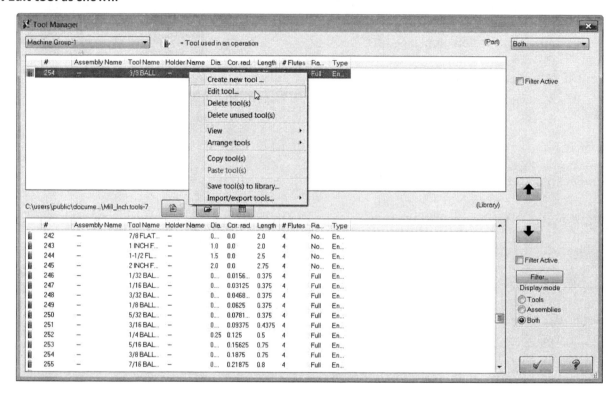

Mill Level 1 Training Tutorial *Mastercam. X*⁷

Option 2: Editing an existing tool inside of the toolpath parameters

• In Toolpath parameters dialog box, right click on the existing tool and then select **Edit tool** as shown.

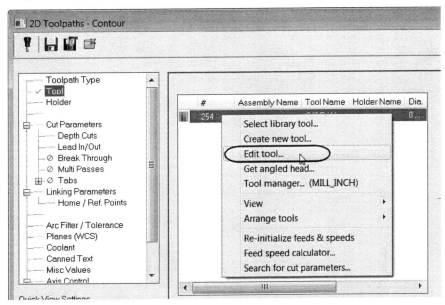

• Make the changes and then select the **Save to library** button to save the tool with the new changes.

Mastercam. X⁷

QUIZ ANSWERS

Objectives:

✓ The answers to the 10 Tutorial quizzes.

MILL LEVEL 1 TUTORIAL QUIZ ANSWERS

Tutorial 1 Answers

- What is a Contour Toolpath used for?
- Contour toolpaths remove the material along a path defined by a chain of curves. Contour toolpaths only follow a chain; they do not clean out an enclosed area.

- What does Backplot do?
- **Backplotting** shows the path the tools take to cut the part. This display lets you spot errors in the program before you machine the part. As you backplot toolpaths, Mastercam displays the current X, Y, and Z coordinates in the lower left corner of the screen.

- When would you use Multi Passes?
- **Multi Passes** lets you define multiple cutting passes. The tool approaches the part geometry at the cutting depth in steps instead of cutting right to the part geometry.

- When would you use the drill cycle Peck Drill?
- **Peck Drill** retracts fully out of the drill hole to remove material chips. Often used with chips that are hard to remove.

Tutorial 2 Answers

- What is a Facing Toolpath used for?
- **Facing toolpath** quickly removes material from the top of the part to create an even surface for future operations.

- What does a Pocket Toolpath allow you to do?
- **Pocket toolpaths** remove the material from an enclosed boundary.

- What is the difference between Climb and Conventional cutting?
- **Climb** cuts with the tool rotating in the opposite direction of the tool motion. **Conventional** cuts with the tool rotating in the same direction as the tool motion.

- What does verify allow you to do?
- **Verify** allows you to use a solid model to simulate the machining of a part. The model created by verification represents the surface finish, and shows collisions, if any exist.

Tutorial # 3 Answers

◆ What does Slot mill toolpath do?

◆ **Slot Mill** toolpath allows Mastercam to efficiently machine obround slots. These are slots that consist of 2 straight lines and two 180-degree arcs at the ends.

◆ What does 2D HS Dynamic Core mill do?

◆ **2D HS Dynamic Core** machines, utilizing the entire flute length of their cutting tools, open pocket shapes or standing core shapes using the outmost chain as the stock boundary. The tool moves freely outside of this area; the inner chain defines the limit of the toolpath.

◆ What does 2D HS Dynamic Contour mill do?

◆ **2D HS Dynamic Contour** toolpath utilizes the entire flute length of the cutting tools and is used to mill material off walls. It does support both closed or open chains.

◆ What is the process used to be able to post different operations as different programs?

◆ Create a new toolpath group and then rename it.

Tutorial # 4 Answers

◆ What does Core Mill require and what do those requirements do?

◆ **Core Mill** requires two chains. An outside chain defining the stock boundary, allowing the toolpath to move freely outside this area. An inner chain defines the limit of the toolpath.

◆ What does smoothing do?

◆ **Smoothing** replaces sharp corners with arcs for faster and smoother transitions in tool direction.

◆ What does pocket remachining do?

◆ Calculates areas where the pocket roughing tool could not machine the stock and creates a remachining pocket toolpath to clear the remaining material.

Tutorial # 5 Answers

◆ Define a dynamic toolpath?

◆ **2D High Speed Dynamic Mill** utilizes the entire flute length of their cutting tools to produce the smoothest, most efficient tool motion for high speed pocketing and core milling. The toolpath supports a custom entry method and many others. Micro lifts further refine the dynamic milling motion and avoid excessive heat build up. Custom feeds and speeds optimize and generate safe tool motion.

◆ What does a **Dwell before cut spindle speed** do?

◆ Adds a dwell after the entry ramp into the cut. This pause allows the spindle to ramp up to the desired spindle speed before starting the cutting passes.

- ◆ What does a transform toolpath operation do?
- ◆ It allows you to run the same toolpath in different locations. You can transform a single toolpath or several at a time.

Tutorial # 6 Answers

- ◆ What does the Translate join command do?
- ◆ **Translate Join** transforms a copy of the selected entities to a new position in the graphics window and maintains the position of the original entities. Mastercam creates lines or arcs to connect the endpoints of the original entities to the endpoints of the transformed entities.

- ◆ What does a 2D High Speed Rest Mill Toolpath do?
- ◆ 2D High Speed Rest Mill toolpath targets material left behind by previous toolpaths.

- ◆ What is the use of WCS in Mastercam?
- ◆ This tells Mastercam how your part is position or orientated in the machine.

- ◆ After creating a new toolpath group why do you rename the NC file?
- ◆ To create two separate programs.

Tutorial # 7 Answers

- ◆ What is the advantage of Dynamic Mill?
- ◆ **2D High Speed Dynamic Mill** utilizes the entire flute length of their cutting tools to produce the smoothest, most efficient tool motion for high speed pocketing and core milling. The toolpath supports a custom entry method and many others. Micro lifts further refine the dynamic milling motion and avoid excessive heat build up. Custom feeds and speeds optimize and generate safe tool motion.

- ◆ What features does Core Mill Machine?
- ◆ **2D High Speed Core Mill** toolpath generates the free flowing motion needed to machine features such as standing bosses and cores in a single operation.

- ◆ What entities need to be chained to utilize Core Milling?
- ◆ We need to chain the outer boundary of the part to define the stock and then machine the inner boundary which will be defined as an island and will not be machined.

- ◆ How does a Blend Mill toolpath work?
- ◆ **2D High Speed Blend Mill** toolpath morph smoothly between two open chains.

Tutorial # 8 Answers

- ◆ What does FBM Drill do?

- **FBM Drill** automatically detects holes in a solid based on your specific criteria and to generate a complete series of drilling and chamfering. FBM drill also generates circle mill or helix bore operations for large-hole features when you activate these settings.

• What is the purpose of Predrilling?
• The purpose of predrilling Pre-drilling is to drill holes prior to tapping, reaming, or boring them.

• What does Hole Mapping do?
• A **hole mapping** file contains data that assigns a specific tool to a hole feature. When hole mapping is enabled, FBM drill scans the current hole mapping file during feature detection. If a detected hole matches the file diameter and hole type, FBM assigns the specific tool to this hole. This assignment overrides all tool page settings.

• What does Circle Milling allow you to do?
• Adding **circle mill** or **helix bore** toolpaths to your FBM drill operation lets Mastercam switch from drilling to milling when machining holes that are significantly larger than drills, or require flat bottoms.

Tutorial # 9 Answers

• What does FBM Mill allow you to do?
• With a single operation Mastercam analyzes a solid part detects all machining features in a specified plane and automatically generates all of the 2D milling toolpaths necessary to completely machine the selected features.

• What does automatic tool selection do?
• **Automatic tool selection** chooses the tools used to cut the part when use tool library or create as needed are selected.

• What does % Long tool do in the roughing and restmill parameters?
• **% Long Tool** reduces the amount of material removed in the Z axis based on the tool diameter and depth the tool is going.

• What does Hole Milling allow you to do?
• **Hole milling** lets you machine round features using circle mill or helix bore toolpaths.

Tutorial # 10 Answers

• What is the advantage of the 2D High Speed Dynamic Area Mill Toolpath?
• This toolpath is used to machine pockets using a smooth clean motion. Helical entries and tangent stepovers create efficient motion for your machine tools. Cut parameters let you control corner rounding to create the bets toolpath, avoiding sharp corners or direction changes.

• What does a 2D High Speed Core Mill toolpath machine?
• Machines features, such as standing bosses and cores.

• Define a 2D High Speed Dynamic Contour toolpath.
• Uses an intelligent efficient high speed contouring strategy to remove material along walls. This toolpath also supports multi-passes and can optionally include finishing passes.

Mill Level 1 Training Tutorial

Mastercam. X⁷

Symbols

Numerics

A

B

C

D

E

F

G

H

Mill Level 1 Training Tutorial

Mastercam. X⁷